Ronald Bockius (ed.)

Between the Seas

RGZM – TAGUNGEN

Band 3

Römisch-Germanisches Zentralmuseum
Forschungsinstitut für
Vor- und Frühgeschichte

R G Z M

Römisch-Germanisches Zentralmuseum
Forschungsinstitut für Vor- und Frühgeschichte

Ronald Bockius (ed.)

BETWEEN THE SEAS

TRANSFER AND EXCHANGE IN NAUTICAL TECHNOLOGY

PROCEEDINGS OF THE ELEVENTH INTERNATIONAL SYMPOSIUM
ON BOAT AND SHIP ARCHAEOLOGY
MAINZ 2006

ISBSA 11

Hosted by
Römisch-Germanisches Zentralmuseum,
Forschungsbereich Antike Schiffahrt, Mainz

With support from
Gesellschaft der Freunde des
Römisch-Germanischen Zentralmuseums

Verlag des Römisch-Germanischen Zentralmuseums   Mainz 2009

Redaktion: Ronald Bockius, Martin Schönfelder (RGZM);
Antony Brown
Satz: Manfred Albert (RGZM); Michael Braun (Datenshop
Wiesbaden)
Bildbearbeitung: Manfred Albert; Katja Hölzl;
Ulrike Kessel (RGZM)
Umschlaggestaltung: Reinhard Köster (RGZM)

Bibliografische Information
der Deutschen Nationalbibliothek

Die Deutsche Nationalbibliothek verzeichnet diese Publikation in
der Deutschen Nationalbibliografie; detaillierte bibliografische
Daten sind im Internet über **http://dnb.d-nb.de** abrufbar.

ISBN 978-3-88467-142-9
ISSN 1862-4812

Herstellung: Druck- und Verlagsservice Volz, Budenheim
Printed in Germany.

Published in honour of Ole Crumlin-Pedersen

CONTENTS

SHIP CONSTRUCTION

PLATES 1-6

PREFACE

The 11th meeting of the International Symposium on Boat and Ship Archaeology took place in Mainz from the 25th to 29th of September 2006. Hosted by the research branch for Ancient Navigation of the Römisch-Germanisches Zentralmuseum (RGZM), some 120 scholars, students and interested guests attended the conference, which for the first time in its history was held at a continental inland location far away from the sea. The participants, 25% of which came from southern Europe, the Near East and overseas joined this meeting to contribute in different ways to the theme »Between the Seas – Transfer and Exchange in Nautical Technology«. Interrupted by a one day long ship excursion passing through the romantic Middle Rhine valley, more than 50 papers were given, and a smaller number of poster presentations were displayed in the rooms of the baroque style palace of the local electoral bishops. The participants came together at reception and evening events hosted in the Museum of Ancient Navigation in front of scenes of late Roman Mainz wrecks and their full-scale replicas displayed there, side by side with ship models and ancient monuments related to Roman shipping and navy activities.

The congress was organized by the Museum of Ancient Navigation (Museum für Antike Schiffahrt). This is a rather young institution, established by the Römisch-Germanisches Zentralmuseum in 1994, initially to take care of conservation, analysis and display of the Mainz ship finds; secondly, as a permanent scientific commission to carry out research in the fields of ancient shipbuilding and navigation in concert with Old World archaeology. Due to the small number of scholarly and technical personnel, preparation and realization of ISBSA 11 needed the assistance of the general institute RGZM, along with its administrative, technical and editorial facilities. The fact that the local organization team was rather short-handed, meant that the steering committee consisting of former IBSA hosts lent support, assistance and considerable experience in organizing the conference.

Due to the fact that during the vote for the host of the 11th meeting in 2003, Mainz seemed to many people to be a curious place to conduct a congress on boat and ship archaeology, the steering committee kept a strict eye on all on-going activities, but nevertheless bearing in mind the topical conditions and options. The ideas on a conference theme related to the meeting place and its possible attractions were discussed very carefully. It was agreed to focus such aspects, which are also reflected by the scholarly interest of the Mainz institute and its exhibition: on the one hand, problems of development, transfer, alterations and exchange of shipbuilding in the sense of skill, technical capabilities and ship architecture, not at least the interaction of human mobility, culture and tradition as a pioneer of progress; on the other hand, special interest should to be paid to inland navigation, river vessels and their classification, inland waterways and waterfront structures as well, on which the location of the conference could paint a vivid picture. To link inland navigation with seafaring and to present a platform for subjects frequently discussed at ISBSA, the Mainz meeting was considered to respect a wider perspective, not least to include newly discovered material.

Papers given over seven sessions in 2006, are published in this volume together with a selection of articles based on poster presentations. Some articles considerably exceed the size standard defined by the ISBSA publication guidelines. The editor decided also to accept longer papers where they were particularly pertinent to the subject; in certain cases he inspired authors to enlarge their manuscripts availing a better understanding of the topic.

The symposium was funded largely by the fees of the participants and a grant received from the Gesellschaft der Freunde des Römisch-Germanischen Zentralmuseums, to which the organizers are much indebted. From the same society another generous grant was most gratefully received to print this volume. Last but not least, we are obliged to the organising committee and advisory panel established by previous ISBSA secretaries, colleagues and friends, Patrice Pomey (Tatihou 1994), Jerzy Litwin (Gdańsk 1997), Carlo Beltrame (Venice 2000), Fred Hocker and Anton Englert (Roskilde 2003) for their abundant assistance. Particular gratitude is due to Anton Englert and Else Snitker who may be mentioned instead of all those being busy behind the scene. They acted as the very lives and souls of the enterprise; both more than once catched the helm to steer the boat into calm waters.

Mainz, August 2007
Ronald Bockius

JERZY LITWIN

TRIBUTE TO A FOUNDING MEMBER OF THE INTERNATIONAL SYMPOSIA ON BOAT AND SHIP ARCHAEOLOGY

The person of Ole Crumlin-Pedersen turned up quite early in my professional life, during my studies at the Faculty of Naval Architecture of the Technical University of Gdańsk. As a student and enthusiastic modeller I had agreed to the proposition on the part of the then director of the Maritime Museum in Gdańsk, Przemysław Smolarek, that in my spare time I would begin making reconstruction models of medieval ships for the museum. Smolarek also suggested that I should approach Ole Crumlin-Pedersen for advice regarding the interpretation of the appearance of the hull shapes of medieval ships like the cog and holk. I discovered then somewhere around 1966 that the Danish expert was a naval architect by profession and that he could be a role model for me. At that time I had not yet thought about taking up a post at the museum after graduation; I treated the building of model ships and my attempts at reconstructing medieval vessels as an interesting hobby which also brought in a bit of pocket money. Nonetheless, the detailed response I received from Ole Crumlin-Pedersen deepened my interest in medieval shipbuilding technology. I should mention at this juncture that Smolarek, already then friends with Ole Crumlin-Pedersen and other Scandinavian researchers, was interested in the boatbuilding of the Viking Age, and was undertaking his own studies of Slavic boatbuilding in that period, i.e. from the 8th to 13th centuries.

In 1965 Ole Crumlin-Pedersen paid a visit to Gdańsk, and during an official meeting with Polish archaeologists, he stated that, in their construction technique, none of the wrecks of early-medieval boats found up to that time in Pomerania resembled boats built in Scandinavia. Moreover, he called for the immediate publication of the ship-finds that had accumulated in Poland since 1945. This first, officially expressed opinion from an already then acknowledged expert on historical shipbuilding lent very considerable support to the views and interpretations regarding the Pomeranian wrecks, which Przemysław Smolarek was to present in condensed form at a somewhat later date (Smolarek 1969).

It was in 1975, then already as an employee of the Polish Maritime Museum, that on a brief visit to Denmark I was able to meet Ole Crumlin-Pedersen, director of the Viking Ship Museum at Roskilde, for the first time. This was an unforgettable meeting, standing as I was eye to eye and without prior announcement with this outstanding specialist. He received me with that kind, friendly smile that so often graces his face. I visited the Museum, where work was in progress to reconstruct the wrecks of the Skuldelev ships. I left Roskilde with the conviction that I had done the right thing in taking up work at the Maritime Museum in Gdańsk, and Ole Crumlin-Pedersen did indeed become my role model.

For the benefit of my younger colleagues who read these words, I would like now to recount some of the more important aspects of the professional activities of our esteemed teacher and colleague, with which I am acquainted. The beginnings of Ole Crumlin-Pedersen's professional career hark back to the second half of the 1950s, when he, as a student of naval architecture with a strong personal interest in maritime archaeology, met up with the curator of the medieval department of the National Museum in Copenhagen, Olaf Olsen. Despite the difference in their ages and professional experience, the two men started working together in 1957, when Ole Crumlin-Pedersen became Olsen's assistant in a project aimed at the recovery of Viking ships that had been sunk in order to block a narrow strait of the Roskilde Fjord near the village of Skuldelev. The significance of the work that ought to be undertaken around the coasts of Denmark was made clear by the two researchers in an article on underwater archaeology contained in a National Museum publication of 1959; they defined the significance of this field of research for science and the conditions for its development (Olsen & Crumlin-Pedersen 1959). They also emphasised the need to seek new research techniques based on a firm scientific foundation, adding that the exploration site at Skuldelev would be an excellent place for trying out such new methods. On 1st February 1962, having completed his studies of naval architecture as well as his national service, Ole Crumlin-Pedersen took up a position at the National Museum as a specialist in shipbuilding and maritime history, becoming the first employee of the young Institute of Maritime Archaeology. Not long afterwards, the site of the Skuldelev wrecks was surrounded by a sheet pile wall and work started that was to be of capital importance for maritime archaeological research in Denmark. Modern research methodologies and technical approaches were used there, as and at that time the wet and dry exploration of artefacts was something new. Stereogrammetric photography was used for the first time in Denmark to record the various fragments of the hulls *in situ*, after which each fragment was carefully raised. In this way thousands of plastic sacks were filled, in which the recovered artefacts were protected from the atmosphere. A further novelty was that the excavation site was made accessible to the public – some thirty thousand people visited the site at that time, and a special ferry service was run to bring them there. At the same time as the artefacts were being recovered from the site, discussions were being held regarding where they were to be put on display, in other words, where the future museum was to be situated. The Roskilde municipal authorities became involved in these discussions and offered far-reaching assistance and several possible locations for the museum. In the end, the Strandengen beach at Roskilde was chosen, and construction work began there on 26th September 1966. The work was completed on 1st March 1968, and the museum was officially inaugurated on 20th June 1969 in the presence of King Frederik IX. Ole Crumlin-Pedersen was appointed director of the museum.

In May 1963, one year after the founding of the National Museum's Institute of Maritime Archaeology, the Danish authorities decided that the National Museum in Copenhagen would specialise in underwater archaeological explorations and issued an act concerning the protection of historical wrecks. It contained the important criterion that a wreck was to be regarded as historical if at least 150 years had elapsed since the vessel in question had sunk. This meant that any wreck at least 150 years old became the unconditional property of the State. This time criterion was later revised to the period of 100 years, counting from the loss of the vessel.

From 1969 to 1983 the National Museum's Institute of Maritime Archaeology and the Viking Ship Museum were led in personal union by Ole Crumlin-Pedersen in Roskilde. The Institute of Maritime Archaeology grew with the employment of such specialists as a boatbuilder with diving qualifications, a conservator of monuments, a shipbuilding engineer and an archaeologist. Soon, too, the Viking Ship Museum and the Institute of Maritime Archaeology became the object of study visits by experts from many countries. One such visit was by Basil Greenhill, the Director of the National Maritime Museum in London. On becoming acquainted with Ole Crumlin-Pedersen's work, he inaugurated a Department of the Archaeology of the Ship in his museum in 1973. Sean McGrail was appointed Head of this Department, and by bringing in many outstanding specialists to his team, soon turned this research institute into one of the leaders in its field. In cooperation with Ole Crumlin-Pedersen he organised in London the first International Symposium of Boat and Ship Archaeology in 1976. Since that time, such symposia have been held every three years at various archaeological and historical centres in Europe.

Initially, attempts were made to place the first ISBSAs within the more formal framework of an international association with an elected administration. Nothing came of these attempts, however, and every next symposium was convened quite spontaneously. Only a steering committee consisting of the organisers of the three previous symposia was elected, with the participant who had served longest on the committee being replaced by a new one. I know from my own experience that the organiser of the next symposium could always count on the assistance and invaluable advice of Ole Crumlin-Pedersen, Sean McGrail and other specialists. I have to admit that this democratic system of convening symposia works admirably, and as I have noticed, is free from personal or national conflicts. Moreover, the organisers always take pains to enable researchers from less affluent countries to attend the conferences. Formerly, such people came from the ex-communist states, now they hail from the developing countries. I was one of those who received such generosity in the past, and I would like once again to say »Thank You« to all those who made it possible for me and others like me to attend the symposia in years gone by.

In 1983 Ole Crumlin-Pedersen decided to focus on running the Institute of Maritime Archaeology, as a result of which he handed over the duties of director of the Viking Ship Museum to the prehistoric archaeologist Jan Skamby Madsen. Soon afterwards, on the initiative of Ole Crumlin-Pedersen, a national inter-institutional maritime archeological reference group (MARE) was formed with the task to promote maritime archaeology in Denmark. A year later, this activity received formal blessing from the authorities, and the University of Copenhagen opened a course of studies in Maritime Archaeology. From the group's inception, Ole Crumlin-Pedersen, coordinated its scientific activities. His experience as a team leader enabled him to take his research activities in new directions, such as the relations between ship and port, and the development of towns and their hinterland, as a result of which a new subject – »the maritime cultural landscape« – became an important field of further research. Independently of this, the Viking Ship Museum undertook »experimental archaeology« by building of sailing reconstructions of the boats whose wrecks were discovered at Skuldelev. The reconstructed craft were used in all sorts of tests and scientific studies. The museum's new director also initiated a programme for the building of folk boats from different countries of the world, which were to be constructed publicly at Roskilde by authentic »native« boatbuilders; this became a great attraction for the Museum's visitors. Moreover, a series of important publications ensued from the documentation of these reconstructions.

In 1984 responsibility for historical wrecks and underwater monuments in Denmark was divided between the Ministry for Cultural Matters and the Ministry for Environment. It was decided that documentation, invigilation, protection and conservation *in-situ* would be the task of the Ministry for the Environment, whereas the recovery and the conservation of artefacts raised from the sea bed would be carried out under the supervision of the Conservator General and the historical museums.

By the end of the 1980s the Viking Ship Museum and Institute of Maritime Archaeology had achieved universal renown and were regarded as one of the leading institutions of its kind in the world. That is why the participants of the 5th ISBSA in Porto greeted the invitation to the 6th symposium at Roskilde with enthusiasm. The 6th ISBSA took place in September 1991, and a record number of over 200 people took part in the conference.

In 1993 Ole Crumlin-Pedersen passed the directorship of the Institute of Maritime Archaeology on to Flemming Rieck, and himself took on the management of the Centre for Maritime Archaeology in Roskilde, formed thanks to the efforts of the Institute and Viking Ship Museum and a special five-year subsidy from the Danish National Research Foundation.

The work carried out at the new centre was documented in an English-language »Maritime Archaeology Newsletter from Roskilde«, published twice yearly since December 1993, whose scientific editor was Ole Crumlin-Pedersen. He was able to invite a sizeable group of young researchers to work at the centre who, under the watchful eye of their master, achieved a high standard of professionalism; the results of their studies are documented in numerous publications. In secret, Ole Crumlin-Pedersen's staff prepared a special volume – »Shipshape« – published in 1995, to mark his 60th birthday. This scientifically valuable edition contains articles by 30 authors from Scandinavia and elsewhere (Olsen *et al.* (eds) 1995).

In spite of his numerous duties at the Centre for Maritime Archaeology, Ole Crumlin-Pedersen continued to support the work of the Viking Ship Museum with his advice, and played a part in its plans for extension. These began to materialise in 1994, when on the 25th anniversary of the Museum's inauguration, it received planning permission to extend and the promise of an appropriate subsidy. Construction plans were quickly produced, the intention being to create a museum harbour where the sizeable flotilla of reconstructed Viking ships and other historical vessels could be moored. However, by spring 1997 six wrecks of 11th to 14th century craft had been discovered during the construction work, and in the autumn of the same year a further three sets of boat remains were identified. Such an abundance of historical wrecks had not been expected, even though the discovery of some artefacts was inevitable, given the fact that the shore of the fjord in this part of the town had been a harbour back in the Middle Ages. So it was that the museum's extension erected for five ship-finds brought the discovery of a further nine! I should add that during the centre's lifetime further wrecks were found in the rest of Denmark, the exploration of which could be undertaken by the centre's and institute's scientific staff, as was the case in Copenhagen, where in 1996 to 1997 eight wrecks of the early modern period were discovered on land formerly occupied by the Burmeister & Wain shipyard. The extension to the Viking Ship Museum was completed in 1997 and was officially inaugurated by Queen Margrethe on 7th June of that year.

In January 1998 the Danish National Research Foundation approved a further five-year subsidy for the centre. Thus, this scientific institution received the opportunity for further development. On 15th November 2001, the University of Copenhagen conferred an honorary doctorate on Ole Crumlin-Pedersen for his pioneering scholarly effort in the field of maritime archaeology.

In recognition of the maritime archaeological achievements at the centre, the institute and the museum in Roskilde, a substantial majority of the participants of the 9th ISBSA in Venice in 2000 decided to accept an invitation to hold the 10th symposium there in 2003. Perhaps its organisers were counting on the Danish National Research Foundation extending the centre's lifetime – but it was not to be. The Centre for Maritime Archaeology of the National Museum of Denmark in Roskilde was forced to cease its activities after ten years of intensive research. This decision affected not only the Danish researchers, along with their indefatigable leader, Ole Crumlin-Pedersen, but also the whole international community of maritime archaeologists, who received from Roskilde professional assistance, the means to improve their qualifications and inspiration for further work, not to mention newcomers to the field, who could always count on getting a research grant there and excellent facilities for their research work. The closure after ten years of the research centre in Roskilde, and also the earlier dissolution of the Archaeological Centre at the National Maritime Museum in London, which incidentally had also functioned for ten years, dealt a severe blow to researchers not just in Denmark and Britain, but to the entire international community of maritime archaeologists. But there was no stagnation, let alone a collapse, of interest in the aftermath of these closures. Quite the reverse: the need for this kind of scientific work is increasing all the time, as is the number of people around the world who are interested in diving and in underwater archaeology. So we shall continue to discuss the results of our work with Ole Crumlin-Pedersen and his numerous students in Denmark and various other parts of the world, and whenever possible pay a visit to the Viking Ship Museum in Roskilde, where maritime archaeology has found a permanent base.

REFERENCES

Olsen, O. & Crumlin-Pedersen, O. 1959: Arkæologi under vandet. Vikingeskibene ved Skuldelev i Roskilde Fjord. *Nationalmuseets Arbejdsmark* 1959, 5-20.

Olsen, O., Skamby Madsen, J. & Rieck, F. (eds) 1995: *Shipshape.*

Essays for Ole Crumlin-Pedersen. On the occasion of his 60th anniversary, February 24th 1995. Roskilde.

Smolarek, P. 1969: *Studia nad szkutnictwem pomorza gdańskiego X-XIII wieku*. Prace Muzeum Morskiego w Gdansku 3. Gdańsk.

HISTORY OF ISBSA

The first International Symposium on Boat and Ship Archaeology (ISBSA) was organized on the suggestion of E. V. Wright by the National Maritime Museum in Greenwich, England, in 1976. The purpose was to »bring together all those involved in the study of the form, structure, function, and operational performance of ancient boats«.

Under the direction of Seán McGrail, the chairman of the organising committee, the first symposium examined the methodological problems of studying boat remains. Many of the topics addressed at that initial meeting, such as experimental archaeology and ethnography, have remained core elements in the programmes of subsequent conferences.

The themes of meetings have varied, although the subject matter until 2000 was primarily focused on northern Europe. Held every three years since 1976, the conferences have been hosted by a different institution, and all the proceedings have been published. These volumes have become not only sources of much useful information for scholars of the history of shipbuilding, but also a snapshot history of the field of maritime archaeology in Europe over almost three decades.

PREVIOUS ISBSA MEETINGS

1976 (1st) Greenwich, England, UK: S. McGrail (ed.), Sources and Techniques in Boat Archaeology. British Archaeological Reports, Suppl. Series 29, 1977.

1979 (2nd) Bremerhaven, Germany: S. McGrail (ed.), The Archaeology of Medieval Ships and Harbours in Northern Europe. British Archaeological Reports, Internat. Series 66, 1979.

1982 (3rd) Stockholm, Sweden: C.O. Cederlund (ed.), Postmedieval Boat and Ship Archaeology. British Archaeological Reports, Internat. Series 256, 1985.

1985 (4th) Porto, Portugal: L.O. Filgueiras (ed.), Local Boats. British Archaeological Reports, Internat. Series 438, 1988.

1988 (5th) Amsterdam, Netherlands: R. Reinders and K. Paul (eds), Carvel Construction Technique. Oxbow Monograph 12, 1991.

1991 (6th) Roskilde, Denmark: Chr. Westerdahl (ed.), Crossroads in Ancient Shipbuilding. Oxbow Monograph 40, 1994.

1994 (7th) Tatihou, France: P. Pomey and É. Rieth (eds), Construction navale maritime et fluviale. Archaeonautica 14, 1998.

1997 (8th) Gdańsk, Poland: J. Litwin (ed.), Down the River to the Sea. Polish National Maritime Museum, 2000.

2000 (9th) Venice, Italy: C. Beltrame (ed.), Boats, Ships and Shipyards. Oxbow Books, 2003.

2003 (10th) Roskilde, Denmark: L. Blue, A. Englert and F. Hocker (eds), Connected by the Sea. Oxbow Books, 2006.

2006 (11th) Mainz, Germany: R. Bockius (ed.), Between the Seas. This volume.

2009 (12th) Istanbul, Turkey

LIST OF CONTRIBUTORS

Paul L. C. Adam (late)
2, Chemin du Maine
F - 17800 Pérignac
paadam@frea.fr

Béat Arnold
LATÉNIUM
Parc et Musée d'Archéologie Neuchâtel
Espace Paul Vouga
CH - 2068 Hauterive
oman@ne.ch

John Atkin
Institut Ausonius
Maison de l'Archéologie
Université Michel de Montaigne
19, avenue Prince Noir
F - 33750 Camarsac
jatkin1588@aol.com

Jens Auer
Toftsvej 30, 2 TH
DK - 6700 Esbjerg
jensauer@gmail.com

Lawrence E. Babits
Program in Maritime Studies
USA - Greenville 27858-4353
North Carolina
babitsl@ecu.edu

Rex Bangerter
13 Larchfield
IRL - Kilkenny

Ofra Barkai
Leon Recanati Institute
for Maritime Studies
University of Haifa
IL - 31905 Haifa
ofi.barkai@gmail.com

Tomasz Bednarz
Centralne Muzeum Morskie
ul. Ołowianka 9-13
PL - 80-751 Gdańsk
t.bednarz@cmm.pl

Mike Belasus
Römisch-Germanische Kommission
c/o Landesamt für Kultur
und Denkmalpflege
Domhof 4-5
D - 19055 Schwerin
belasus@rgk.dainst.de

Carlo Beltrame
Dipartimento di Scienze dell'Antichità
e del Vicino Oriente
Università Ca'Foscari Venezia
Dorsoduro 3484/D
I - 30123 Venezia
beltrame@unive.it

Swarup Bhattacharyya
180 Bhag Bazaar Street
IND - 700 003 Calcutta
saranga_nao@yahoo.com

Jan Bill
Kulturhistorisk Museum
Universitetet i Oslo
Postboks 6762 St. Olavs plass
N - 0130 Oslo
jan.bill@khm.uio.no

Paul Bloesch
Schalerstraße 1
CH - 4054 Basel
bloesch.bs@bluewin.ch

Lucy Blue
Centre for Maritime Archaeology
University of Southampton
Avenue Campus, Highfield
GB - Southampton SO17 1BJ
l.blue@soton.ac.uk

Ronald Bockius
Forschungsbereich Antike Schiffahrt
Römisch-Germanisches Zentralmuseum
Neutorstraße 2b
D - 55116 Mainz
bockius@mufas.de

Giulia Boetto
Centre Camille Jullian (UMR 6573)
Aix-Marseille Université – CNRS
Maison Méditerranéenne
des Sciences de l'Homme
5, rue du Château de l'Horloge BP 647
F - 13094 Aix-en-Provence
boetto23@mmsh.univ-aix.fr

Bart Boon
Bart Boon Research and Consultancy
Kolonel Clarklaan 10
NL - 2111 XB Aerdenhout
bart.boon@hccnet.nl

Hanneke Boon
James Wharram Designs
Greenbank Road, Devoran
GB - Truro TR3 6PJ
hboon@btconnect.com

Lena Lisdotter Börjesson
Fosen Folkehögskole
N - 7100 Rissa
lenalisdotter@hotmail.com

Alessio Canalini
Via Guido d'Arezzo 11
I - 61100 Pesaro
acunamatata90@hotmail.com

Ole Crumlin-Pedersen
Vikingeskibsmuseet
Vindeboder 12
DK - 4000 Roskilde
crumlin@c.dk

Deborah Cvikel
Leon Recanati Institute
for Maritime Studies
University of Haifa
IL - 31905 Haifa
dcvikel@research.haifa.ac.il

Aoife Daly
Center for Maritime
og Regionale Studier
Syddansk Universitet
Fuglsang Alle 111
DK - 2700 Brønshøj
dendro@dendro.dk

Robert Domżal
Centralne Muzeum Morskie
ul. Ołowianka 9-13
PL - 80-751 Gdańsk
r.domzal@cmm.pl

Anton Englert
Vikingeskibsmuseet
Vindeboder 12
DK - 4000 Roskilde
ae@vikingeskibsmuseet.dk

Thomas Förster
Deutsches Meeresmuseum
Katharinenberg 14-20
D - 18439 Stralsund
t.foerster@imail.de

Damian Goodburn
Museum of London – Specialist Services
Mortimer Wheeler House
46 Eagle Wharf Road
GB - London N1 7ED
damian.goodburn@googlemail.com

Daniela Gräf
Schierker Straße 20
D - 12051 Berlin
danielagraef@genion.de

Frédéric Guibal
Institut Méditerranéen d'Ecologie
et de Paléoécologie
CNRS, UMR 6116
Universités d'Aix-Marseille I et III
Avenue Louis Philibert BP 80
F - 13545 Aix-en-Provence
frederic.guibal@univ-cezanne.fr

Marc Guyon
Institut National des Recherches
Archéologiques Préventive
12, rue Louis Maggiorini
F - 69 500 Bron
marc.guyon2@wanadoo.fr

Fred Hocker
Vasamuseet
Box 27131
S - 102 52 Stockholm
fred.hocker@smm.se

Olaf Höckmann
Taunusstraße 39
D - 55118 Mainz
u.hoeck@t-online.de

Karin Hornig
Jacob-Burckhardt-Straße 5
D - 79098 Freiburg
karin.hornig@archaeologie.
uni-freiburg.de

Kate Hunter
The Newport Ship Unit
22, Maesglas Industrial Estate
GB - Newport NP20 2NN
kate.hunter@newport.gov.uk

George Indruszewski
ENSPAC-RUC Universitet
P.O. Box 260
DK - 4000 Roskilde
georgin@ruc.dk

Hanus Jensen
Vikingeskibsmuseet
Vindeboder 12
DK - 4000 Roskilde
hj@vikingeskibsmuseet.dk

Yaakov Kahanov
Leon Recanati Institute for Maritime
Studies
University of Haifa
IL - 31905 Haifa
yak@research.haifa.ac.il

Inese Karklina
Latvijas Universitate
Kundzinsala 13, Linija 9-2
LV - 1005 Riga
inesekarklina@inbox.lv

Peter Kaute
Landesamt für Kultur
und Denkmalpflege
Dezernat Bodendenkmalpflege
Domhof 4/5
D - 19055 Schwerin
stadtarchaeologie@archaeologie-mv.de

Stefanie Klooß
Institut für Ur- und Frühgeschichte
Christian-Albrechts-Universität Kiel
Johanna-Mestorf-Straße 2-4
D - 24118 Kiel
stefanie.klooss@gmx.de

Ufuk Kokaba
İstanbul Üniversitesi
Edebiyat Fakültesi
Taşınabilir Kültür Varlıklarını Koruma
ve Onarım Bölümü
Ordu Caddesi
TR - 34459 Laleli-Istanbul
ufukk@istanbul.edu.tr

Rosemarie Leineweber
Landesamt für Denkmalpflege
und Archäologie Sachsen-Anhalt
Richard-Wagner-Straße 9
D - 06114 Halle (Saale)
rleineweber@lda.mk.sachsen-anhalt.de

Christian Lemée
Bakkedraget 69
DK - 4000 Roskilde
christianlemee@hotmail.com

Jerzy Litwin
Centralne Muzeum Morskie
ul. Ołowianka 9-13
PL - 80-751 Gdańsk
j.litwin@cmm.pl

Luc Long
Département des Recherches
Archéologiques Subaquatiques
et Sous-Marines
Fort St-Jean
F - 13235 Marseille
luc.long@culture.gouv.fr

Harald Lübke
Schleswig-Holstein State Museums
Foundation Schloß Gottorf
Centre for Baltic and
Scandinavian Archaeology
Schloßinsel
D - 24837 Schleswig
harald.luebke@imail.de

Francis Mallon
Sandford Close Apartments
Apartment 2, House 2
Sandford Close, Ranelagh
IRL - Dublin

José Manuel Matés Luque
Agirre Lehendakari 21
Esc1 5 IZDA
E - 48970 Basauri Bizkaia
j.luque@euskalnet.net

Sabrina Marlier
Centre Camille Jullian
CNRS, UMR 6573
Université de Provence
5, rue du Château de l'Horloge BP 647
F - 13094 Aix-en-Provence
marlier@mmsh.univ-aix.fr

Hadas Mor
Leon Recanati Institute
for Maritime Studies
University of Haifa
IL - 31905 Haifa
dasinka1@gmail.com

Seán McGrail
Centre for Maritime Archaeology
University of Southampton
GB - Southampton SO17 1BF

Nigel Nayling
Department of Archaeology
and Anthropology
University of Wales
GB - Lampeter SA48 7ED
n.nayling@lamp.ac.uk

Waldemar Ossowski
Centralne Muzeum Morskie
ul. Ołowianka 9-13
PL - 80-751 Gdańsk
w.ossowski@cmm.pl

Colin Palmer
Centre for Maritime Archaeology
University of Southampton
Avenue Campus, Highfield
GB - Southampton SO17 1BJ
c.palmer@soton.ac.uk

Henrik Pohl
Gaisbergstraße 38c
A - 5020 Salzburg
henrik.pohl@gmx.de

Patrice Pomey
Centre Camille Jullian
CNRS, UMR 6573
Université de Provence
5, rue du Château de l'Horloge BP 647
F - 13094 Aix-en-Provence
pomey@mmsh.univ-aix.fr

Iwona Pomian
Centralne Muzeum Morskie
ul. Ołowianka 9-13
PL - 80-751 Gdańsk
i.pomian@cmm.pl

Cemal Pulak
Nautical Archaeology Program
Department of Anthropology
Texas A&M University
USA - College Station,
Texas 77843-4352
pulak@tamu.edu

Irena Radić Rossi
Hrvatski restauratorski zavod Odjel
za podvodnu arheologiju u Zagrebu
Cvijte Zuzoric 43
HR - 1000 Zagreb
iradic@h-r-z.hr

H. Reinder Reinders
Groningen Institute of Archaeology
Poststraat 6
NL - 9712 AD Groningen
h.r.reinders@rug.nl

Éric Rieth
CNRS (LAMOP, UMR 8589)
Musée Nationale de la Marine
Palais de Chaillot
F - 75116 Paris
e.rieth.cnrs@libertysurf.fr

Eelco van Riethbergen
Spaarnwater
Kempstraat 11
NL - 2023 ER Haarlem
spaarnwater@xs4all.nl

Michel Rival
Centre Camille Jullian
CNRS, UMR 6573
Université de Provence
5, rue du Château de l'Horloge BP 647
F - 13094 Aix-en-Provence
michel-rival@orange.fr

Jason Rogers
Department of Archaeology
University of Exeter
7009 Madelynne Way
USA - Anchorage, Alaska 99504
jsr201@exeter.ac.uk

Corinne Rousse
École Française de Rome
Piazza Farnese 67
I - 00186 Roma
corinne-rousse@club-internet.fr

Giannina Schindler
Landesamt für Kultur und
Denkmalpflege
Dezernat Bodendenkmalpflege
Domhof 4/5
D - 19055 Schwerin
stadtarchaeologie@archaeologie-mv.de

Patricia Sibella
Institut Ausonius – Maison de
l'Archéologie
Université Michel de Montaigne
11, rue Turenne
F - 33000 Bordeaux
psibella@hotmail.com

Petr Sorokin
Institute of the History of Material
Culture
Russian Academy of Science
Dvorzovaya nab. 18
RU - St. Petersburg
petrsorokin@yandex.ru

Maik-Jens Springmann
Historisches Institut
Ernst-Moritz-Arndt-Universität
Domstraße 9a
D - 17487 Greifswald
archsa@gmx.de

Błażej Stanisławski
Institute of Archaeology and Ethnology
Polish Academy of Sciences
ul. Zamkova 16
PL - 72-510 Wolin
st-wski@wp.pl

John Starkie
3 Colebrook Place
Guildford Road, Ottershaw
GB - Chertsey KT16 1OQ
john.starkie@mouchelparkman.com

Wilfried Stecher
Im Winkel 8
D - 21717 Fredenbeck
seeteufel04@aol.com

Morten Sylvester
Norges teknisk-naturvitenskapelige uni-
versitet Vitenskapsmuseet
Seksjon for arkeologi og kulturhist.
N - 7491 Trondheim
morten.sylvester@vm.ntnu.no

Katrin Thier
Oxford English Dictionary
Oxford University Press
Great Clarendon Street
GB - Oxford OX2 6DP
katrin.thier@oup.com

Darina L. Tully
Saor Ollscoil na Èireann
1 Mayville Terrace
Leslie Avenue
IRL - Dalkey, Dublin
darinat1588@eircom.net

Aleydis Van de Moortel
Department of Classics
1101 McClung Tower
University of Tennessee
USA - Knoxville, Tennessee 37996-0413
avdm@utk.edu

Robert Van de Noort
Department of Archaeology
University of Exeter
Laver Building, North Park Road
GB - Exeter EX4 4QE
r.van-de-noort@ex.ac.uk

Cheryl Ward
Director, Center for Archaeology
and Anthropology
Coastal Carolina University
P.O. Box 261954
Conway, SC 29528
cward@coastal.edu

James Wharram
James Wharram Designs
Greenbank Road, Devoran
GB - Truro TR3 6PJ
hboon@btconnect.com

Timm Weski
Bayerisches Landesamt
für Denkmalpflege
Hofgraben 4
D - 80538 München
timm.weski@blfd.bayern.de

Julian Whitewright
Archaeology Department
University of Southampton
Avenue Campus, Highfield
GB - Southampton SO17 1BF
r.j.whitewright@soton.ac.uk

Chiara Zazzaro
Università degli Studi
di Napoli »L'Orientale«
Piazza Nicola Amore 2
I - 80138 Napoli
c.zazzaro@exeter.ac.uk

ABBREVIATIONS

Biblography according to ISBSA guidelines

Acta Arch.	*Acta Archaeologica* (København)
Arch. Korrbl.	*Archäologisches Korrespondenzblatt* (Mainz)
Arisholm *et al.*, Klink og seil	T. Arisholm, K. Paaske & T. L. Wahl (eds), *Klink og seil. Festskrift til Arne Emil Christensen*. Oslo 2006
BAR	British Archaeological Reports
Brandt & Kühn, Haithabu	K. Brandt & H. J. Kühn (eds), *Der Prahm aus dem Hafen von Haithabu. Beiträge zu antiken und mittelalterlichen Flachbodenschiffen*. Schriften des Archäologischen Landesmuseums. Ergänzungsreihe 2. Neumünster 2004
CBA, Res. Report	Council for British Archaeology, Research Report
IJNA	*International Journal of Nautical Archaeology*
INA	Institute of Nautical Archaeology (College Station/Texas)
ISBSA 3	C.O. Cederlund (ed.), *Postmedieval Boat and Ship Archaeology. Papers based on those presented to an International Symposium on Boat and Ship Archaeology in Stockholm in 1982*. BAR, Internat. Series, no. 256. Oxford 1985
ISBSA 5	H. R. Reinders & K. Paul (eds), *Carvel Construction Technique. Skeleton-first, Shell-first*. Fifth International Symposium on Boat and Ship Archaeology, Amsterdam 1988. Oxbow Monograph 12. Oxford 1991
ISBSA 6	Ch. Westerdahl (ed.), *Crossroads in Ancient Shipbuilding. Proceedings of the Sixth International Symposium on Boat and Ship Archaeology*, Roskilde, 1991. Oxbow Monograph 40. Oxford 1994
ISBSA 7	P. Pomey & E. Rieth (eds), *Construction navale maritime et fluviale. Appproches archéologique, historique et ethnologique. Actes du 7e International Symposium on Boat and Ship Archaeology*, Tatihou 1994. Archaeonautica, no.14. Paris 1998
ISBSA 8	J. Litwin (ed.), *Down the river to the sea. Proceedings of the Eighth International Symposium on Boat and Ship Archaeology*, Gdańsk 1997. Gdańsk 2000
ISBSA 9	C. Beltrame (ed.), *Boats, Ships and Shipyards. Proceedings of the Ninth International Symposium on Boat and Ship Archaeology*, Venice 2000. Oxbow Books. Oxford 2003
ISBSA 10	L. Blue, F. Hocker & A. Englert (eds), *Connected by the Sea. Proceedings of the 10th International Symposium on Boat and Ship Archaeology*, Roskilde 2003. Oxbow Books. Oxford 2006
Jahrb. BMV	*Bodendenkmalpflege in Mecklenburg-Vorpommern, Jahrbuch*

Jahrb. RGZM	*Jahrbuch des Römisch-Germanischen Zentralmuseums Mainz*
MAN Roskilde	*Maritime Archaeology Newsletter from Roskilde, Denmark*
MM	*The Mariner's Mirror*
NAU	*NAU-Nachrichtenblatt Arbeitskreis Unterwasserarchäologie*
PPS	*Proceedings of the Prehistoric Society*
TROPIS II	H. Tzalas (ed.), *TROPIS II. 2nd International Symposium on Ship Construction in Antiquity, Delphi 1987, Proceedings.* Athens 1990
TROPIS IV	H. Tzalas (ed.), *TROPIS IV. 4th International Symposium on Ship Construction in Antiquity, Athens 1991, Proceedings.* Athens 1996
TROPIS V	H. Tzalas (ed.), *TROPIS V. 5th International Symposium on Ship Construction in Antiquity, Pylos 1993, Proceedings.* Athens 1999
TROPIS VI	H. Tzalas (ed.), *TROPIS VI. 6th International Symposium on Ship Construction in Antiquity, Lamia 1996, Proceedings.* Athens 2001
TROPIS VII	H. Tzalas (ed.), *TROPIS VII. 7th International Symposium on Ship Construction in Antiquity, Pylos 1999, Proceedings.* Athens 2002
TROPIS VIII	H. Tzalas (ed.), *TROPIS VIII. 8th International Symposium on Ship Construction in Antiquity, Hydra 2002, Proceedings*
TROPIS IX	H. Tzalas (ed.), *TROPIS IX. 9th International Symposium on Ship Construction in Antiquity, Agia Napa 2005, Proceedings*

NEWS FROM THE MEDITERRANEAN

CHIARA ZAZZARO

NAUTICAL EVIDENCE FROM THE PHARAONIC SITE OF MARSA/WADI GAWASIS

REPORT ON TWO PARTS OF A STEERING OAR/RUDDER

The site of Marsa/Wadi Gawasis is located 23 km S. of the modern Port of Safaga on the Red Sea (Egypt). The first excavations were conducted by Professor Abdel Monem Abdel Haleem Sayed in 1976-1977. On the basis of textual evidence, he identified Marsa/Wadi Gawasis as the Middle Kingdom Pharaonic port of *Saww*, used in seafaring expeditions to the Land of Punt, located somewhere in the S. Red Sea region (Sayed 1977; 1980; 1983).

Since December 2001 the site has been jointly excavated by the University of Naples »L'Orientale« and Boston University (cf. Bard & Fattovich 2007; Fattovich *et al.* 2002; 2003; 2005; Fattovich, Bard *et al.* 2004; 2005; 2006), and a variety of new evidence has been discovered related to the maritime activities in the area. Ceremonial monuments along the top of the E. terrace, in the *marsa*, originally also functioned as landmarks for vessels approaching from the sea, as suggested by Honor Frost (1996: 876).

Recent excavation has revealed a possible landing place at the base of the S.E. slope, indicated by an anchor with clear signs of wear found lying on an ancient playa. In the W. sector of the site, six caves carved into the wall terrace were discovered beneath a thick sand deposit. The excavation of one of these caves (Cave 2) revealed it was used for food processing, as well as to store and dismantle ship timbers. Nautical evidence mainly found in this area consists of ship timbers, stone anchors and cordage. In Cave 2 ship timbers and anchors were often re-used in the cave structure itself. Specifically, ship timbers were re-employed, during different occupation phases, as threshold, ramp or walkway, and in the wall structure (Fattovich, Bard *et al.* 2005; 2006).

About 25 stone anchors discovered at Marsa/Wadi Gawasis represent the largest collection of ancient Egyptian anchors from the Pharaonic period. Each characterized by an upper hole and a groove for the rope, several examples also show L-shaped basal holes and dovetail mortises. While the upper hole and the L-shaped basal hole were used to remove the anchors from the sea bottom, the dovetail mortises seem to be secondary features, carved in order to adapt the stone anchors for re-use in the cave structure. Stone anchors recycled as constructional elements after the naval expeditions, reflect the seasonal and provisional nature of the site occupation (Zazzaro & Abd El-Maguid 2006: 139-162).

Numerous rope fragments, and approximately 30 bundles of rope stored within Cave 5, might also have been part of ship equipment employed for seafaring expeditions. The cordage is characterized by three twisted yarns of average 3.5 cm in diameter (Fattovich, Bard *et al.* 2006).

During the 2004-2005 excavation season, also two parts of a steering oar/rudder blade[1] were found covered by windblown sand at the entrance to Cave 2, facing each other. The associated pottery dates to the early New Kingdom[2] (ca. 1550 to 1400 B.C.), a period that corresponds to the site's final occupation phase (Fattovich, Bard *et al.* 2005). While the two blade elements were immediately recognized as parts of an ancient Egyptian steering device, the original aspect of the complete steering oar/rudder was more difficult to determine since it was found dismantled and incomplete. Furthermore, the fragments are not identical in shape and dimensions, as might have been expected, and they seem to have been modified and re-employed at least once. Nevertheless, it seems the two blade elements were part of the same steering

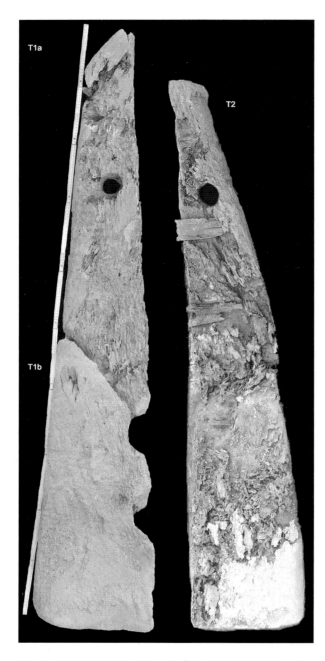

Fig. 1 Marsa/Wadi Gawasis. – T1 face A (left) and T2 face A (right) (Photo Chiara Zazzaro).

oar/rudder blade, based on their position as found and their archaeological context: they were dismantled and abandoned in the cave's entrance at the end of the last occupation phase.

This paper presents a preliminary attempt to reconstruct the original rudder, providing a technical description of the blade parts, and pointing to some archaeological and iconographical comparisons.

DESCRIPTION

It was possible to carefully record the two parts of a blade on each side (**Fig. 1**) except for face B of element T2, and all portions that were in fragile condition. Further information is expected during the forthcoming restoration.

Both timbers are almost triangular in shape, with rounded external edges and rounded angles, and a slight groove on the top. Elements T2 and T1a are made of *Acacia nilotica*[3]. T1a, face A, has a fragile consistency and its surface has been damaged by insect activity, whilst the opposite surface on face C is much better preserved. T2 is poorly preserved, and the lower part has been completely eroded by shipworms. Element T1b is made of *Faidherbia albida* (Ana tree), an indigenous as well as sub-Saharan species. T1b, face A, displays heavy salt encrustation due to the long deposition in the archaeological stratum. The opposite surface on face C is much better preserved.

T1, segments T1a and T1b

A scarf joins T1a and T1b (**Fig. 2**). T1b was made of a wood species different from T1a and T2. It might be a later substitution, as this part is much better preserved than T2's lower part. Indeed, the lower parts of the blades were most susceptible to damage, as they would have been immersed in the sea for a long time. The maximum dimensions of T1 as complete (T1a and T1b) are: max. length 200 cm, max. width 40 cm, min. width 15 cm, max. thickness 12 cm. The fastening system consists of six mortises, cut within the T1 edge, with five partly preserved tenons still *in situ*, and two partly preserved mortises cut perpendicularly

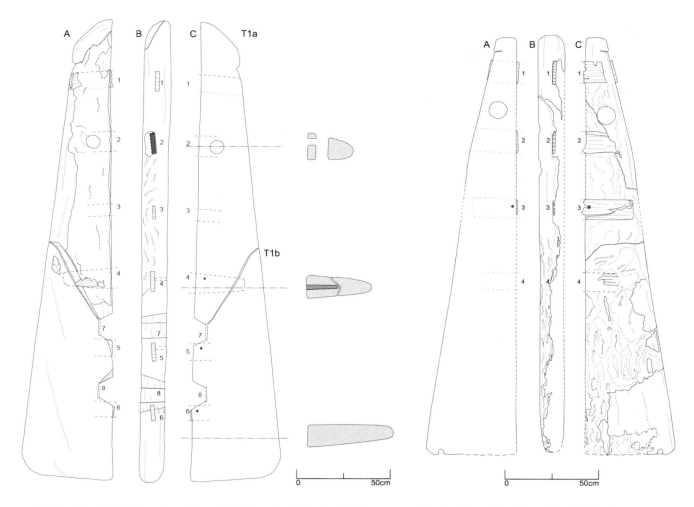

Fig. 2 Marsa/Wadi Gawasis. – T1a and T1b (Drawing Cinzia Perlingieri, Chiara Zazzaro).

Fig. 3 Marsa/Wadi Gawasis. – T2 (Drawing Cinzia Perlingieri, Chiara Zazzaro).

to the T1b faces. Dimensions of mortises nos 1, 2, 3 and 4 are: max. length 18.5 cm, max. width 9 cm, max. thickness 3 cm. Mortise-and-tenon joints 5 and 6 are partly interrupted by two trapezoidal cuts. Mortise 4 was cut into T1a and continued into T1b, displaying chisel marks in the cavity. Tenons in mortises 4, 5 and 6 are fixed with perpendicular pegs. The latter, 1 cm in diameter, are visible on face C, but do not appear on face A.

Tenons visible from edge B (nos 1, 3, 5 and 6) show tool marks indicating they were cut during dismantling. Remains of two more mortises (nos 7 and 8) are located between mortises 5 and 6, in correspondence of the two cuts; they are cut perpendicularly through the two faces of T1b (**Fig. 4**). Traces of copper still visible in these mortises might be caused by copper strips, which were removed by the two trapezoidal cuts, during the dismantling of the rudder, probably to reutilize the copper fittings. Mortise 8 contains some rope remains. The author suggests thin copper strips passed through the mortise adhering along one side of the cavity, and the remaining part of the mortise was filled by rope[4].

The scarf joining T1a and T1b is cut at an angle of 140°, whereby T1a's lower end and T1b's upper end are diagonally cut. A hole, 6 cm in diameter, through which rope would have passed, is perpendicularly carved into the upper part of the blade. Probably, the hole was carved where originally a mortise-and-tenon joint (no. 2) existed.

Fig. 4   Marsa/Wadi Gawasis. – T1b, face C, details of mortises 7 and 8 (Photo Chiara Zazzaro).

T2

The maximum dimensions of T2 are (**Fig. 3**): max. length 180 cm, max. width 35 cm, max. thickness 12 cm. The fastening system consists of four fragmentary mortises with three partly preserved tenons. Originally two more mortises may have existed in the lower part of T2, where information has been lost due to significant shipworm and insect damage. The maximum dimensions of the mortises are: max. length 18.2 cm, max. width 7.1 cm. Because of erosion across the entire surface of face B, the thickness of the mortises were not measurable. Mortise 3 reveals a peg perpendicularly fixed through a tenon, also visible on the opposite face (C).

A hole through which rope would have passed, measuring 7.5 cm in diameter, is carved into the upper part of the blade. It is suggested the lower part of T2 originally featured a similar system of joinery as T1, with mortises perpendicular to face A and C, since the damaged surface of T2 includes copper and rope fragments.

COMPARISONS AND INTERPRETATION

The mortise-and-tenon fastening system of artefacts T1 and T2 obviously was designed to connect each element to a central loom. A similar system is attested by the steering oars from the Dahshur boats dating to the reign of Senwosret III (1870 to 1831 B.C.) (Creasman 2005: 109, fig. 51; Ward 2000: 96). Hence, the original steering device from Wadi Gawasis was composed of two blade segments and a central loom (which is missing), dismantled by cutting the tenons.

The original fastening also included the use of copper strips, since copper traces are still visible in the two cuts along the edge of T1 and in the lower part of T2. The copper strips may have been used to protect or reinforce the mortise-and-tenon joints, or to fasten the blade elements to each other and to the loom. The strips were probably removed with parts of the timber during the dismantling of the ship (cf. the two trapezoidally cuts on T1). Dark bands on steering oars and quarter rudders visible in representations of ancient Egyptian ships, were interpreted as evidence of metal bands already by Reisner and Boureaux (cf. Boureaux 1925: 341-345; Reisner 1913: pl.12-13, 4801, 4820, 4825, 4844). Estimating the tentative reconstruction, the author also notes the two holes are roughly symmetrical to each other, and the mortise-and-tenon joints alternate between the two blade fragments, a system that might have improved the resistance of the steering oar/rudder as a whole. The circular holes in the two Gawasis timbers provide channels for rope to secure the (side?) rudder to the hull, as either found on the steering oars from the Dashur boats (Ward 2000: 96) and in several representations of ancient Egyptian ships and boats (Faulkner 1940: 7).

The triangular shape of the Marsa/Wadi Gawasis steering oar/rudder matches those shown in ship representations of the Second Intermediate Period to New Kingdom. Comparable examples include the triangular quarter rudders of the gold boat model from the Theban tomb of Ahhotep (ca. 1535-1525 B.C.) now in the Cairo Museum (JE 4681, JE 4669), boat models from Tutankhamen's tomb (1336-1327 B.C.) (cf. Jones 1990), and relief depictions at Ramses III's temple at Medinet Habu (1184-1153 B.C.), illustrating the naval battle against the Sea Peoples. The shape of the top of the blade also coincides with New Kingdom iconography such as the obelisk barge of Hatshepsut (1473-1458 B.C.) and the ships of the relief imaging queen Hatshepsut's expedition to Punt (Naville 1907-1913, pl. 72-75).

Although we do not know in detail the use of the Gawasis steering oar/rudder blade, it can provide us with information about ship dimensions. According to ancient Egyptian representations, and compared with the steering oars of the Dahshur boats, the proportion of the steering oar/rudder blade to the hull is frequently 1-8 to 1-9. Therefore, the dimension of the Marsa/Wadi Gawasis blade suggest a ship of about 14 to 18 m length, which seems appropriate for a vessel sailing on the Red Sea. Fleets sailing to Punt apparently included ships of different sizes, as is attested not only by Hatshepsut's relief (Naville 1907-1913, pl. 72-75), but also by the Papyrus Harris, which records Ramses III's expedition to Punt (Bongrani 1997: 46).

Queen Hatshepsut's expedition is the only one known that coincides with the probable date of the Marsa/Wadi Gawasis finds under discussion. However, there may have been other seafaring expeditions to Punt in the early New Kingdom that are unknown because no records of them have survived. Nevertheless, the discussed timbers testify to the final return trip of a Pharaonic ship on the Red Sea to Marsa Gawasis.

ACKNOWLEDGEMENTS

The author wishes to express her gratitude to Rodolfo Fattovich and Kathryn A. Bard, directors of the UNO-BU excavation project at Marsa/Wadi Gawasis, and to all participants of the project who, in different ways, assisted her to complete this study: Cheryl Ward, nautical archaeologist; Rosanna Pirelli, egyptologist; Cinzia Perlingieri, ceramologist; Andrea Manzo, archaeologist; Mohamed M. Abd El-Maguid, nautical archaeologist and Claire Calcagno, maritime archaeologist.

This paper is based on work carried out at the Marsa/Wadi Gawasis site from December 2004 to January 2005, and at the Qift Magazine, Qift, in January 2006 and January 2007. Excavation and work at the magazine were conducted with the permission and assistance of the Supreme Council of Antiquities, Cairo. The author is grateful to SCA Inspectors Mr. Elal Mahmud Ahmed and Mr. Mohamed Rayan, Quseir Inspectorate, Quseir, and to all the staff of the Qift Magazine for their kind support and help.

The UNO-BU excavation project has been conducted with grants from the UNO, IsIAO, Ministry of Foreign Affairs (Rome), and generous contributions by Mr. Wallace Sellers, Lahaska, PA (USA), and the Glen Dash Charitable Foundation, Woodstock, CT (USA).

NOTES

1) The author decided to use the term »steering oar/rudder« since it cannot be specified whether the two elements of blade were originally part of a steering oar or a quarter rudder, which are both of them typical of ancient Egyptian boats and ships.

2) This paper follows the basic chronology set in the *Oxford History of Ancient Egypt* (Shaw 2000).

3) Wood analysis of ship timbers was carried out by Rainer Gerisch; cf. Fattovich, Bard *et al.* 2005.

4) The copper traces on the T1b edge, associated with the mortise and the rope remains suggest comparisons with evidence of similar and better preserved fastenings visible on other timbers from Marsa/Wadi Gawasis, which were discovered during the 2006/2007 field season, currently under study.

REFERENCES

Bard, K. A. & Fattovich, R. (eds), 2007, *Harbor of the Pharaohs to the Land of Punt. Archaeological Investigations at Mersa/Wadi Gawasis, Egypt, 2001-2005*. Università degli Studi di Napoli »l'Orienatale«. Napoli.

Bard, K. A., Fattovich, R., Arpin, T., Childs, S. T., Lim, C. S., Perlingieri, C., Pirelli, R. & Zazzaro, C., 2005, *Recent Excavations at the Pharaonic Port of Mersa Gawasis on the Red Sea, 2004-2005 Field Season* (www.archeogate.com).

Bard, K. A., Fattovich, R., Arpin, T., Childs, S. T., Mahmoud, A. M., Manzo, A., Perlingieri, C. & Zazzaro, C., 2004, *Mersa Gawasis (Red Sea, Egypt): UNO/IsIAO and BU 2003-2004 Field Season* (www.archeogate.com).

Bard, K. A., Fattovich, R., Koch, M., Mahmud, M. A., Manzo, A. & Perlingieri, C., 2001, The Wadi Gawasis/Wadi Gasus, Egypt: A Preliminary Assessment. www.archaeogate.org/egittologia/article/43/1/the-wadi-gawasiswadi-gasus-egypt-a-preliminary-assessme.html [01.09.2009].

Bongrani, L., 1997, The Punt Expedition of Ramses IIIrd: Considerations on the Report from the Papyrus Harris I. In: I. Brancoli, E. Ciampini, A. Roccati & L. Sist (eds), *L'Impero Ramesside*, 45-59. Università di Roma »La Sapienza«. Roma.

Boureaux, C., 1924-1925, *Étude de nautique égyptienne: l'art de la navigation en Egypte jusqu'à la fin de l'ancien empire*. Mémoires de l'Institut Français d'Archéologie Orientale du Caire, 50. Cairo.

Creasman P. P., 2005, *The Cairo Dahshur Boats*. Unpublished, MA Thesis Submitted to the Office of Graduate Studies of Texas A&M University.

Fattovich, R. & Bard, K. A., 2006, Joint Archaeological Expedition at Mersa/Wadi Gawasis (Red Sea, Egypt) of the University of Naples »l'Orientale« (Naples, Italy), Istituto Italiano per l'Africa e l'Oriente (Rome, Italy), and Boston University (Boston, USA) – 2005-2006 Field Season. www.archaeogate.org/egittologia/article/441/1/joint-archaeological-expedition-at-mersawadi-gawasis-re.html [01.09.2009].

Fattovich, R., Mahmoud, A. M., Manzo, A., Perlingieri, C. & Zazzaro, C., 2005, Archaeological Investigations at the Wadi Gawasis, Egypt, 2001-2002: A Preliminary Report. *Annales du Service des Antiquités de l'Égypte*, 79, 61-84.

Fattovich, R., Mahmoud, A. M., Manzo, A., Perlingieri, C., Pirelli, R. & Zazzaro, C., 2003, Archaeological Investigations at Wadi Gawasis (Red Sea, Egypt) of the Italian Institute for Africa and the Orient (Rome) and »L'Orientale« (Naples): December 2002-January 2003 Field Season. www.archaeogate.org/egittologia/article/11/5/archaeological-investigation-at-wadi-gawasis-red-sea-eg.html [01.09.2009].

Frost, H. 1996, Ports, Cairns and Anchors. A Pharonic Outlet on the Red Sea. Topoi, 6.2, 869-890.

Naville, E., 1907-1913, *The Temple of Deir el Bahari III*. Egypt Exploration Society. London.

Reisner, G. A., 1913, *Catalogue général des Antiquités égyptiennes du Musée du Caire, Models of Ships and Boats*. Institut Française d'Archéologie Orientale. Cairo.

Sayed, A. M., 1977, *Discovery of the Site of the 12th Dynasty Port at Wadi Gawasis on the Red Sea Shore*. Revue d'Égyptologie, 29, 140-178.

1980, Observations on Recent Discoveries at Wadi Gawasis. *Journal of Egyptian Archaeology*, 66, 154-157.

1983, New Light on the Recently Discovered Port on the Red Sea Shore. *Chronique d'Égypte*, 58, 23-37.

Shaw, I. (ed.), 2000, *The Oxford History of Ancient Egypt*. Oxford.

Ward, C., 2000, *Sacred and Secular. Ancient Egyptian Ships and Boats*. Archaeological. Boston.

2006, Seafaring in Ancient Egypt. In: Essam el-Saeed, El-Sayed Mahfuz & Abdel Monem Megahed (eds), *Festschrift Volume presented to Prof. Abdel Monem AbdelHaleem Sayed*. Alexandria, 199-228.

Zazzaro, C. & Abd El-Maguid, M. M., 2006, Ancient Egyptian Anchors: New Results from Wadi Gawasis. In: Essam el-Saeed, El-Sayed Mahfuz & Abdel Monem Megahed (eds), *Festschrift Volume presented to Prof. Abdel Monem AbdelHaleem Sayed*. Alexandria, 139-162.

CHERYL WARD

EVIDENCE FOR ANCIENT EGYPTIAN SEAFARING

The origins of seafaring in Egypt are poorly defined, but probably date to at least the mid-4th millennium B.C. when a steadily increasing number of burials with grave goods from Nile Valley sites include Red Sea shells. At the same time, models, images, and, by the early First Dynasty (ca. 3000 B.C.), planked wooden boats (Ward 2006) at Nile sites show a steady development of boatbuilding technology concurrently with evidence for trade with the Levant, Northern Mesopotamia, and Punt in the Red Sea.

Mediterranean seafaring by Egyptians is supported by indirect evidence such as a stone vase fragment bearing the name of the Second Dynasty ruler Khasekemwy (died 2686 B.C.) (Dunand 1937: no. 1115) and regular contact with the Levant, especially Byblos, from the early third millennium (Ward 1963). The late 5th Dynasty Palermo stone mentions 40 ships, loaded with cedar, brought to Egypt during the 4th Dynasty reign of Snefru (2613-2589 B.C.) and used to build river ships of 100 cubits. Egypt's traditional source of cedar was Lebanon, and its use for the two disassembled ships of Khufu (2551-2528 B.C.) beside the Great Pyramid at Giza provides physical evidence for such trade. A gold Egyptian axe head found in Lebanon is inscribed »the boat crew Pacified-is-the-Two-Falcons-of-Gold port gang«, and it is linked either to Khufu or to the 5th Dynasty king Sahure (2458-2446 B.C.) as both kings used the epithet *Two Falcons of Gold*.

A Mediterranean context for illustrations on Sahure's causeway of 12 ships with fine details of rigging, construction, and passengers indicates a broad familiarity with ocean travel along established routes by the mid-3rd millennium, a practice often discounted by modern scholars because the Egyptians did not mention sea travel frequently in monumental inscriptions. The Palermo stone also describes an expedition to Punt by Sahure, and recent excavations by the Supreme Council of Antiquities of Egypt at his Abusir mortuary temple revealed new decorated fragments of an incense tree, either frankincense or myrrh, and discribed a trip to Punt along the Red Sea in context with primates, dogs, and inhabitants of Punt. Sahure's expedition took place in his 13th regnal year (ca. 2443 B.C.) and returned from Punt with incense trees and 80,000 measures of incense, a capacity suggestive of relatively large ships operated by crews with experience and success in navigating the reef-lined shores of the Red Sea. These ships were called *h'w* or *kbn.t* ships for another 2,000 years, and recent discoveries at Wadi Gawasis on Egypt's Red Sea coast support the argument that the term refers to the source of the wood used to build seagoing vessels, cedars from the Levant.

SHIP TIMBERS FROM EXCAVATIONS AT WADI GAWASIS

Excavations at Wadi Gawasis have produced direct evidence of pharaonic seafaring in Egyptian ships. The site, first excavated by Abdel Monem el Sayed (1977, 1978, 1983), was a staging area for sea voyages as indicated by a number of inscriptions honoring the officials and kings who organized the trips to Punt. Once located on the fringes of a lagoon linked to the sea, recent excavations have identified a number of deep rooms carved into the fossil coral terrace and utility, habitation, and ritual areas (Fattovich, Bard *et al.* 2005; 2006; Zazzaro this volume pp. 3-8). In addition to written evidence and other finds at the site, exten-

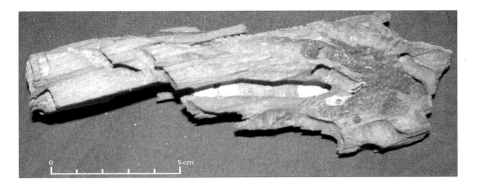

Fig. 1   The shells and tunnels of marine molluscs offer silent testimony to extended sea voyages by the ancient Egyptians (Photo C. Ward).

sive damage to planks and fastenings by the shipworm, or marine borer, furnishes irrefutable evidence of seafaring.

Twenty-two other ancient Egyptian watercraft built for use on the Nile date from about 3000 to about 500 B.C. (Ward 2004). As Egyptian construction techniques used to build these riverine vessels differ significantly from those of later Mediterranean seagoing craft, many scholars assumed that Egyptian ships would more closely reflect Mediterranean-type construction. Discoveries at Gawasis prove that Egyptian design and construction techniques relying on unpegged, deep mortise-and-tenon joints were successful both on the Nile and at sea.

Most timbers found at Gawasis in 2004-2005 and those excavated in 2005-2006 were in contexts indicative of discard or reuse and recycling in ramps, entrances, and walkways. Many planks were significantly reduced in size or reworked. In addition to 53 individually documented ship components, archaeologists also recovered at least a thousand wood debris fragments related to the dismantling of ships in concert with an aggressive hull cleaning and rot-removal process. Much of the wood debris shows damage from shipworm infestation (**Fig. 1**).

Hull components

This paper presents a preliminary evaluation of artifacts studied in January 2006 at Gawasis. Finds related to ship structure were grouped into four types with a fifth group of auxiliary equipment. The brief descriptions offered here are intended to be representative of the timber types. Wood identification was made by Rainer Gerisch.

The only transverse structural member (Type 1) is a complete cedar, deck-level beam (**Fig. 2**) placed upside down and re-used as an architectural element to stabilize sediments around the cave entrances. Rounded on its lower surface, beam T32 has ledges to receive deck planking on its upper face to either side of a central pedestal. Square holes in its curved ends permitted the beam to be fastened to hull planks. The beam's basic design and shape resemble beams on Dahshur boats, although it is proportionally deeper and rounded rather than squared on its lower surface.

Overall shape similar to plank shapes from other Egyptian watercraft, comparable dimensions, and damage from marine molluscs are the characteristics of 16 timbers classified as hull planks (Type 2). Planks rely on wood-to-wood fastenings except in a single instance on T34. The 11 sampled Type 2 planks are cedar, including T34, a knife-shaped plank (293 by 46 by 15 cm) like some in the Khufu and Dahshur hulls and

Lisht timber assemblage (**Fig. 3a**). Other timbers were identified as hull planks if 6.5 cm thick or thicker and had paired, un-pegged deep mortise-and-tenon joints and evidence of shipworm damage, usually on one wide face and adjacent edges. As in isolated fastenings on the Dahshur boat in Pittsburgh (Ward 2000) and a hull timber from Lisht (Haldane 1992), one of the 25 mortise-and-tenon joints on T34 has a peg that passes from the outside of the timber into the tenon, probably to fix a loose fastening in place. Like the lowest strakes in the Khufu ship, the tip of the plank is connected to the timber beneath it with a ligature channel cut into a recess on the exterior surface (**Fig. 3b**); the ligature consists of four copper strips 2 cm wide.

Type 3 planks are identified as deck planks because of their similarity in proportion and shape to deck planks from the Dahshur boats. The 7, possibly 9, short lengths of planking (75 to 90 cm) have chamfered ends on one wide face, widths up to 35 cm, and thickness of less than 5 cm (**Fig. 4**). Gawasis deck planks are better finished, slightly larger in scale than most Dahshur deck planks, which are 52 to 68 cm long, up to 29 cm wide and 3.5 cm thick, and at 10 cm, the angled portion of the lower face is longer than most chamfered ends of the Dahshur deck planks (4 to 9 cm).

Most Type 3 examples that were identified are cedar; some are sycamore fig (*Ficus sycomorus*). Many of these planks have traces of white plaster on at least one wide face; several showed signs of marine borer infestation. Numerous and deep adze marks and red paint over the damaged areas suggest these areas had been marked out for rot removal but turned out to be more damaged than expected and the planks were recycled as walkway components or wedged beneath larger planks on entrance walls to compensate for plank curvature. One example (T13, of sycamore) has a series of incised marks in the centre of its lower face; another (T25) was originally a hull plank (Type 2) and was reshaped with chamfered ends before being recycled in a ramp leading to Cave 3's entrance.

Each Type 4 plank studied was reused in ramps leading into the entrances to Cave 3 and Cave 4.

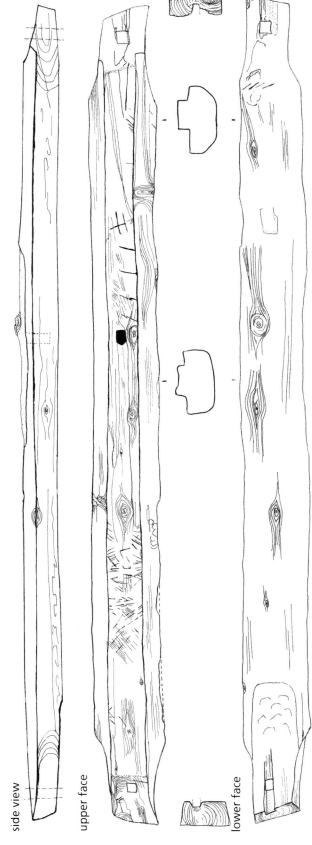

side view　upper face　lower face

Fig. 2 A complete beam (T32) provides information about the transverse reinforcement of seagoing ships. The centre of the beam is worn down by foot traffic, and tool marks on its upper face suggest its reuse as a work surface (Drawing C. Ward).

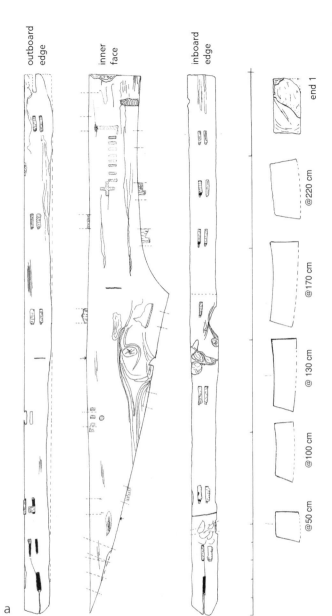

Fig. 3 **a** A complete hull plank permits comparison with those from river-going craft. Plank T34 is nearly 3 m long (Drawing C. Ward). – **b** Four thin, copper strips 2 cm wide are threaded through T34 near its tip. A recess on the lower face protected the strips from abrasion and the strips exit a narrow mortise on the inner face (Photo C. Ward).

These planks (2.5 to 3.5 cm thick) are thinner than planks in the hull of any pharaonic watercraft. They are joined to one another with both mortise-and-tenon fastenings and ligatures (**Fig. 5**). Mortises are only 7 cm deep with a maximum tenon length of 14 cm. Ligatures consist of 1 to 1.5 cm-diameter holes that pass through the plank's wide faces and are associated with shallow grooves about 4 to 5 cm long and 4 mm deep that extend to the plank edge on the inner surface only. No lashing was visible in any of the grooves or holes although excavators found twisted copper strips 2 cm wide in association with the outer face of several planks of this type. No evidence for marine molluscs is recorded for any Type 4 plank although at least three have a black coating along plank seams on the outer face that probably represents a water-proofing agent. All identified members of this class are of Egyptian wood types (acacia and sycamore) and are in good to incoherent condition.

The auxiliary group (Type 5) is comprised of maritime equipment that was not part of a ship's hull, that is, blades from a quarter rudder recovered in 2004-2005 (T1 and T2), a 1.89 m long crutch or stanchion

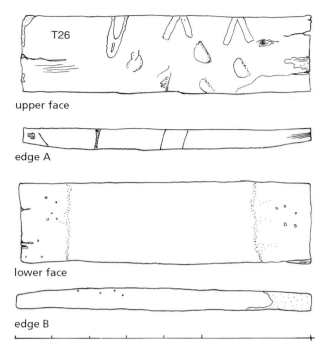

Fig. 4 Deck planks range from 76 to 88 cm in length and are 6 cm thick. This example has deep adze gouges and traces of red paint on its upper surface (Drawing C. Ward).

(*Acacia nilotica*), and some small pieces including three from projecting knobs that may be oarlocks or pins. Half-round and round-sectioned fragments were also recorded and may represent the remains of oar looms, poles, spars, or battens.

Wood debris and discarded fastenings were separated from bits of branches, twigs, charcoal, boxes, and furniture remains. While many fragments were so eroded that features were indistinguishable, others retained tool marks, fasteners, and properties that provide at least an outline of their use history. For example, a 4 cm-thick acacia plank fragment with a faceted dowel (T50) and faceted dowel W67 (14.2 by 1.2 cm) were not part of the hull itself, but illustrate the use of common carpentry techniques to join wood. Similarly, pegs in fragments of thin planks and wooden boxes resemble loose pegs found in association with ship debris, but are rarely seen in the remains of hull planks. Fastenings incorporate useful information about construction techniques, even without an entire vessel to study. In the case of the Mersa/Wadi Gawasis planks, this category includes free tenons of several sizes in planks and in upper levels of sediments both inside and outside caves; mortises and holes cut into planks for wood-to-wood fastenings; holes drilled for ligatures and lashing channels; pegs and dowels; and copper strips.

Analysis and comparison to other finds

Shipbreaking is the primary activity documented in areas directly outside the carved rooms at Gawasis. In the entrance areas of Caves 2 and 3, work areas identifiable by extensive deposits of chipped and ship-worm-infested wood fragments, and fastenings cut and broken with tools, testify to the trimming and reworking of planks. Examination of wood debris indicates large-scale removal of damaged wood from ships built of planks like those recorded in 2005-2006. Inscriptions show that the ships were supplied from the Nile and travelled to Punt (Fattovich & Bard 2006).

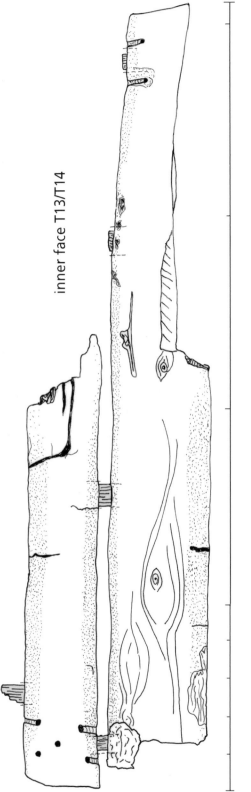

inner face T13/T14

Fig. 5 Planks of Type 4 include a combination of fastening types and evidence for a pitch-like waterproofing on the inner face along seam lines (Drawing C. Ward).

Once ships returned from Punt and were pulled onto shore at Gawasis, shipwrights inspected the hulls, marking unsatisfactory timbers with red paint. Workers removed planks from the hulls by prying seams apart and sawing or chiselling through tenons, and others most likely followed behind them and pulled planks off the ship from the outside. Once timbers were broken off the ships outside the carved rooms, men carried them inside. They walked over ramps reinforced with mud-bricks and planks and across walkways made of short and cut-up planks about 80 to 100 cm long from the entrance across the lower levels of Cave 2 into a 19 by 4 m working space. There, workers cleaned and prepared individual planks, some of which may have been returned to shipyards on the Nile, while others were recycled in architectural features on the site. Some planks were stored or discarded in the cave rooms, and some were even used as fuel, as indicated by charcoal samples Rainer Gerisch identified as non-native species *Cedrus libani*, *Pinus* sp., *Quercus* sp., and even Egyptian ebony.

While the Gawasis excavations took place, other archaeologists working further N. on Egypt's Red Sea coast also discovered what seem to be ship timbers stored in galleries near mines at Ayn Sokhna near Suez (el-Raziq *et al.* 2006). There, a number of timbers 10 cm thick and up to 23 cm wide with both mortise-and-tenon fastenings and lashing channels like those on the Khufu ships were recorded by Patrice Pomey. These recent finds provide reinforcement for the perception of the Egyptians as seafarers.

As in Egypt, recent discoveries on land in Oman and Kuwait provide proof of Persian Gulf seafaring in conditions comparable to those in the Red Sea as early as the mid-6th millennium B.C. (Lawler 2002). Robert Carter (2006) excavated fragments of bitumen impressed with reeds and cordage on one side and barnacles on the other at As-Sabiyah, Kuwait. The fragments resemble mid-3rd millennium B.C. bitumen fragments from Ra's al-Junayz, Oman, which also include evidence of wood planks, lashed through rectangular channels subsequently plugged with wood (Cleziou & Tosi 1994). The ability to waterproof boats with bitumen provided a tremendous advantage to early seafarers in the Persian Gulf and Indian Ocean and bitumen's value as a recyclable material is demonstrated by the caches.

Nothing like bitumen coatings for reed boats has been discovered in ancient Egypt, and underwater surveys have provided little information about pre-medieval seafaring (Haldane1996), but ancient Egypt shares two significant features with cultures of the ancient Indian Ocean. Both groups recycled materials that demanded significant amounts of labour to obtain (wood and bitumen, respectively) and successfully established an elaborate bureaucratic infrastructure that supported the shipbuilding industry. J. Zarins has recently opened an entirely new and rich source of information in cuneiform tablets detailing the assignment of personnel and materials to a boatyard on the Persian Gulf. Similar documents for a royal dockyard at Abydos (ancient This) offer insight into an institution founded by the Second Dynasty (Simpson 1965).

CONCLUSIONS

Documented constancy in Egyptian hull construction techniques is visible in the rejection of locked (pegged) mortise-and-tenon joints and in the very dimensions of fastenings between planks. By relying on paired, deep mortise-and-tenon joints left unpegged, Egypt's shipwrights continued a tradition that allowed watercraft to be more easily disassembled and reassembled, transported, and recycled. The ability to transfer boats across the desert from the Nile River to the Red Sea is likely one of the most important reasons boats were designed for disassembly, and the construction of all of Egypt's hulls reflects that design practice.

Like other unique artifacts discovered by archaeologists working at Gawasis, the ship timbers and remains contribute to a broader understanding not only of the role of shipbuilding technology and achievement, but also of the vast administrative and bureaucratic nature of ancient Egyptian contacts with the world beyond Egypt's borders.

ACKNOWLEDGEMENTS

The author is grateful to Kathryn Bard and Rodolfo Fattovich for permission to study this material. She also thanks Chiara Zazzaro, Rainer Gerisch, Mohamed abd el-Maguid and other members of the excavation team at Mersa/Wadi Gawasis for sharing their expertise and knowledge with her.

REFERENCES

Carter, R., 2006, Boat remains and maritime trade in the Persian Gulf during the sixth and fifth millennia BC. *Antiquity*, 80, 52-63.

Cleziou, S. & Tosi, M., 1994, Black boats of Magan: Some thoughts on Bronze Age water transport in Oman and beyond from the impressed bitumen slabs of Ra's al Junayz. In: A. Parpola & P. Koskikallio (eds), *South Asian Archaeology, 1993.* Annales Academiae Scientiarum Fennicae, vol. B, no. 271. Helsinki, 745-761.

Dunand, M., 1937, *Fouilles de Byblos 1926-1932*, vol. 1. Paris.

el-Raziq, M. A., Castel, G. & Tallet, P., 2006, Ayn Souknah et la Mer Rouge. *Egypte, Afrique et Oriente*, 42, 3-6.

Fattovich, R. & Bard, K., with contributions by T. Arpin, A. Carannante, S. T. Child, G. Dash, R. Gerisch, E. Mahfouz, A. Manzo, G. Morganti, C. Pepe, C. Perlingieri, R. Pirelli, B. Vining, C. Ward & C. Zazzaro, 2006, *Joint Archaeological Expedition at Mersa/Wadi Gawasis, (Red Sea, Egypt), of the University of Naples »l'Orientale« (Naples, Italy), and Boston University (Boston, USA) 2005-2006 Field Season.* www.archaeogate.org/egittologia/article/339/1/recent-excavations-at-the-pharaonic-port-of-mersa gawas.html (01.09.2009).

Fattovich, R. & Bard, K., with contributions by T. Arpin, S. T. Child, C. S. Lim, C. Perlingieri, R. Pirelli & C. Zazzaro, 2005, *Recent Excavations at the Pharaonic Port of Mersa Gawasis on the Red Sea, 2004-2005 Field Season.* www.archaeogate.org/egittolo

gia/article/441/1/joint-archaeological-expedition-at-mersawadi
gawasis-re.html (01.09.2009).

Haldane, C. [Ward], 1992, The Lisht Timbers: A Report on their Significance, Appendix. In: D. Arnold, *The Pyramid Complex of Senwosret, vol. I*. New York, 102-112 pl. 115-133.

1996. Archaeology in the Red Sea. *Topoi*, 6, 853-68.

Lawler, A., 2002, Report of oldest boat hints at early trade routes. *Science*, 296, 1791-1792.

Sayed, A. M., 1978, The Recently Discovered Port on the Red Sea Shore. *Journal of Egyptian Archaeology*, 64, 69-71.

1980, Observations on recent discoveries at Wadi Gawasis. *Journal of Egyptian Archaeology*, 66, 154-171.

1983, New Light on the Recently Discovered Port on the Red Sea Shore. *Chronique d'Egypte*, 48, 23-37.

Simpson, W. K., 1965, *Papyrus Reisner*, vol. 2. Boston.

Ward, C. A., 2000, *Sacred and Secular: Ancient Egyptian Ships and Boats*. Boston.

2004, Boatbuilding in Ancient Egypt. In: F. Hocker & C. Ward (eds), *The Philosophy of Shipbuilding*. College Station/Texas, 13-24.

2006, Boat-building and its social context in early Egypt: Interpretations from the First Dynasty boat-grave cemetery at Abydos. *Antiquity*, 80,118-129.

Ward, W. A., 1963, Egypt and the East Mediterranean from Predynastic Times to the End of the Old Kingdom. *Journal of the Economic and Social History of the Orient*, 6.1,1-57.

YAACOV KAHANOV · HADAS MOR

DOR 2001/1: UPDATED INFORMATION
AND THE RETRIEVAL OF A SECTION OF THE SHIPWRECK

Dor 2001/1 was first presented at the 10th ISBSA meeting at Roskilde in 2003 (Kahanov & Mor 2006) and at the 9th International Symposium on Ship Construction in Antiquity at Agia Napa in 2005 (Mor in press). A preliminary report was published in 2006 (Mor & Kahanov 2006). The vessel identified as a coaster carrying building stones, was wrecked in Dor/Tantura lagoon (Israel) in the mid-1st millennium A.D. (**Fig 1**). The shipwreck was about 70 m offshore, adjacent to the lagoon's navigation channel, at a water depth of 1 m, and buried under 1.8 m of sand. The archaeological find spread over 11.5 by 4.5 m, and the estimated dimensions of the original ship were 17 by 6 m.

In the ISBSA Roskilde meeting it was suggested that the ship was built based on frames without edge-joints, and was thus one of the earliest frame-based hulls in the Mediterranean. This conclusion was questioned, mainly as a result of the experience of the Institute of Nautical Archaeology (INA) of the Bozburun shipwreck (Harpster 2004: 88-90). It was felt that such significant information should not be based merely on underwater observation, but rather by working in laboratory conditions on land. This suggestion was seriously considered, and implemented in the fourth excavation season in 2005. The preliminary results are presented below.

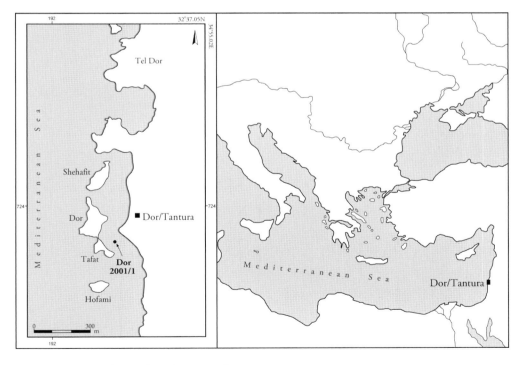

Fig. 1 Dor/Tantura lagoon (Drawing S. Haad).

THE HULL REMAINS

The hull remains included sections of the keel, false keel, 42 frames (floor timbers, half-frames, and futtocks), 29 strakes, including a chine strake and two wales, 21 ceiling strakes, among them two foot-wales and a clamp, a central longitudinal timber, two central stringers, and a mast step sister (**Fig 2**; Dor 2001/1, top view).

Keel, false keel

The keel, of *Cupressus sempervirens*[1], survived for almost 8 m, with one scarf about midships, and another scarf closer to the N. W. end. It was 11 cm sided and 14.5 cm moulded. There was no rabbet or chamfer for the garboards, which butted the keel from the sides, but were not connected to it. The seams between the garboards and the keel were caulked, as were all the other seams. There were remains of frame nails in the upper surface of the keel at almost all frame stations. The false keel was of hard wood, *Quercus coccifera*, and was 11 to 13 cm wide and 5 to 9 cm thick. It was fixed to the keel by iron nails driven through pre-drilled holes at intervals of 20 to 30 cm.

Endpost

An endpost of *Ulmus campestris* was found at the N. W. end. Its scarf with the keel was not observed underwater, but was later discovered in the timbers retrieved and conveyed to the laboratory, and is currently under study. The endpost survived to a length of 3.3 m, and was maximum 10 cm sided and 20 cm moulded. It had a rabbet 9 cm beneath its upper surface, to which the planks on both sides were fixed with iron nails. The gaps were filled with caulking material.

Frames

Of the 44 frame stations identified in the wreck, 42 wholly or partly survived. Framing timbers were generally 10 cm sided by 10 cm moulded, with average room and space of 24 cm. The framing pattern at the midship section of the shipwreck was of alternating floor timbers and pairs of half-frames. At the N. W. end there were full frames. Floor timbers spanned the bottom to the turn of the bilge.
Futtocks at the end of the floor timbers continued upward along the side, a few shaping the turn of the bilge. Some futtocks had diagonal butt scarfs in the vertical plane, some were laid from the side, others just touched the floor timbers. However, except for one case, no nails were found connecting futtocks and floor timbers.
Pairs of half-frames were scarfed near the keel. If the scarf was exactly above the keel both parts were nailed to it. Half-frames were made of naturally-curved single timbers, which formed and maintained the turn of the bilge. This vulnerable area was additionally reinforced longitudinally by a foot-wale and chine strake. The floor timbers and half-frames were not notched for fitting onto the keel, but were fastened to it by iron nails. The nails were tapered, with a rectangular cross-section averaging 12 by 12 mm.
The frames amidships had flat, almost horizontal, undersides, and sharp turns at the bilge, creating a hard chine, with the angle of deadrise increasing towards the bow and stern. The frames generally had two limber-holes, one on either side of the keel, above the garboards. A few additional limber holes were found, but these were not located in any specific pattern.

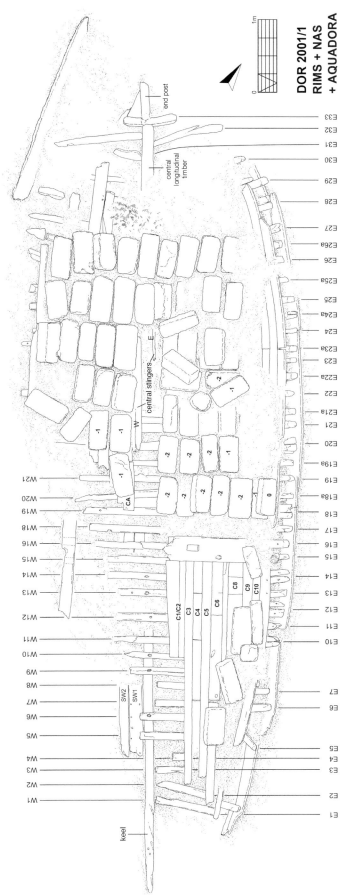

Fig. 2 Dor 2001/1. – Top view (Drawing C. Brandon, updated by S. Haad).

The frames were made of seven different tree species: *Fagus orientali, Pinus brutia, Quercus cerris, Quercus coccifera, Ulmus campestris, Ziziphus spina-christi* and *Tamarix X5*. The origin of the first five was W. Turkey, where they can all be found in the same area. The last two do not grow in W. Turkey, but are local to the wreck-site. They were only found in the N.W. end of the hull. Thus, it seems that these were installed locally, maybe as a repair.

Planking

Sections of 29 strakes survived, the majority of *Cupressus sempervirens*: nine on the S.W. side of the hull, and 20 on the N.E. side. They were all attached to the frames by iron nails with a square cross-section of 6 mm, which narrowed down to a 4 mm section where they entered the frames. The garboards butted the keel, but were not connected to it. Planks were 10 to 17 cm wide and 2.5 to 3 cm thick.
The chine strake and wales were half-logs. The chine strake was 15 cm wide and 9.5 cm maximum thickness. The wales were about 20 cm wide and 10 cm maximum thickness. Planks were butt-joined at frame stations. Caulking was evident in the seams.

Central longitudinal timber

A central longitudinal timber of *Quercus cerris* was found intact at the N.W. end of the hull. It was 2.5 m long, 15 cm sided by 18 cm moulded, with notches in its lower surface, into which the frames fitted. It was attached to the keel and frames by five long iron nails. It appears that the whole timber survived, so that it could not have been a section of a keelson.

Central stringers and mast step sister

Sections of two half-log central stringers were found. They averaged 11 cm wide and 7 cm thick. The space between them was probably partly occupied by the missing mast step. A timber, 122 cm long, 35 cm wide and 7 cm thick, lying at 90° to the hull's longitudinal axis, was perhaps one of the mast step sisters or a crutch.

Ceiling

Twenty-one ceiling strakes of *Pinus brutia* survived. They generally alternated: a long plank nailed to the frames beneath, and several short planks not attached to the frames. With a few exceptions (foot-wales and the clamp) they were slightly thinner than the hull planks: 1.8 to 2.9 cm thick, with widths varying between 6 and 28 cm and lengths between 60 cm and 8.5 m.

THE CARGO

Building stones

About 96 stones were found *in situ* (**Fig. 2**), apparently the main cargo of the ship. The stones were voussoirs of an arch, with average dimensions of 57 by 28 by 18 cm, weighing about 60 kg each. They were stacked in two layers of three to seven adjacent rows on the ceiling planking. After documentation they were removed and placed in a specially dug trench near the hull remains.

Fig. 3   Dor 2001/1. – The cut-out section (Photo D. Gary).

Ceramics

The site was rich in Byzantine shards, which were found mostly above the wreck, some above and between the stones, and very few within the hull. Most of these were severely damaged, although it may be possible to restore some of them partially. They were mostly the remains of »Yassi Ada amphoras«, »Gaza Ware« and »Byzantine cooking pots«, which span a period between the end of the 4th and the beginning of the 7th c. A.D.

Due to the nature of the lagoon, where the heavy winter storms move pottery and stones very easily, none of the ceramics finds can be reliably confirmed as belonging to the ship, and *in situ* (Royal & Kahanov 2005: 309). Finds from the inside of the hull are of the same pottery types, but they are very few, and are mixed with Late Roman, Hellenistic and Persian ware. Furthermore, currently, all the pottery finds, and their relation to the ship, are suspect, but a thorough comparative study is in progress.

Dating

This shipwreck has very significant implications for the evolution of ship construction in late antiquity; therefore special care is being taken in its dating. Because of the problematic pottery context, the dating has so far been based on ^{14}C tests. Traditional methods and AMS radiocarbon tests of short-lived organic material gave a date between A.D. 420 and 540[2]. Dendrochronology tests are now being conducted. If successful, the dating information will be invaluable.

HULL CONSTRUCTION

The hull remains, construction sequence, attachment methods, plank scarfs and seam caulking, and the total absence of planking edge joints or any other features characteristic of shell-first construction, lead to the conclusion that the ship was built based on frames. Thus it is one of the first wrecks found so far in the Mediterranean, which demonstrates the complete transition from the earlier shell-first to the later frame-first construction.

THE SECTION

A section of the hull about 2 m long was sawn out for examination in the laboratory at the University of Haifa (**Fig. 3**). The smallest section possible, which would provide significant information and cause minimum damage to the archaeological find, was taken. This action was decided upon after serious consideration, and after consulting the Israel Antiquities Authority. It included sections of the keel, false keel, central longitudinal timber, stringers, frames, planks up to the second wale (strake no. 20), and ceiling planks. The timbers were transferred from the site in stainless steel trays to a holding tank on shore (**Fig. 4**), and then to the conservation facilities of the Recanati Institute at the University of Haifa. They are being desalinated with tap water as the first stage of conservation, at the same time being examined in detail and recorded by drawings and photographs.

Fig. 4   Dor 2001/1. – Bringing the keel section to shore (Photo D. Gary).

PRELIMINARY RESULTS

Preliminary results clearly indicate that the section retrieved was built based on frames. Planks, 2.5 to 3 cm thick, were nailed to frames with 6 mm^2 iron nails. The garboards were not connected to the keel, and planks were butt-joined at frame stations. The seams were caulked, and as yet no planking edge joints have been found.

The research has revealed more significant information related to the hull construction. Although this hull was based on frames, a few frames were not nailed to the keel. Several futtocks were not scarfed to floor timbers, rather just touching the frames below, without nailing. Planks were nailed to them from the outside. One frame was connected to the keel with a nail driven from the underside. Perhaps the terminology suggested by Seán McGrail: »framing first«, rather than »frame first«, applies here (McGrail, this volume).

The scarf between the keel and the gripe was identified (**Fig. 5**). It was about 35 cm long and maximum 18 cm moulded. In addition to four nails that reinforced the scarf, it was apparently further strengthened by two boards, which did not survive, one on each side of the scarf.

This wreck raises the question whether the existence of a keelson is essential in defining a frame-based hull. Although it does not have a keelson, but rather a short central longitudinal timber, this hull is clearly built on frames. It seems that other elements, such as the keel and false keel, chine strake, wales, stringers, long

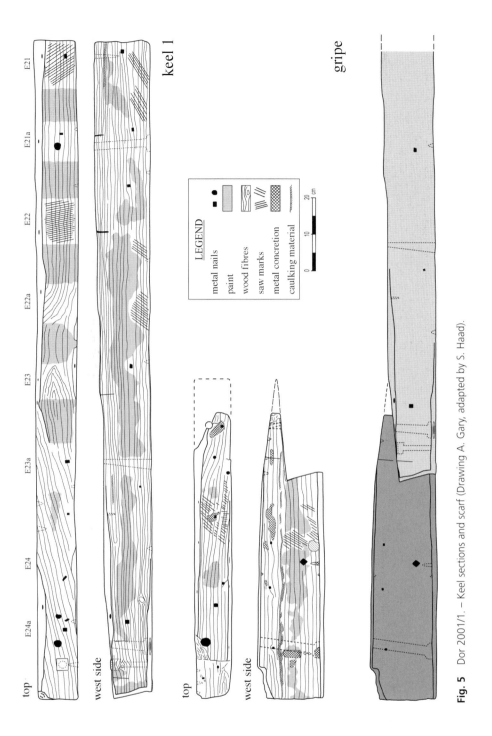

Fig. 5 Dor 2001/1. – Keel sections and scarf (Drawing A. Gary, adapted by S. Haad).

ceiling planks nailed to frames, foot-wales, a clamp, and perhaps additional elements that did not survive, provided the longitudinal integrity of the hull.

CONCLUSIONS

It is clear that this hull was built on frames, although not all frames were nailed to the keel before planking, and not all futtocks were scarfed and nailed to floor timbers. Other features, such as frames nailed to the keel, planking nailed with small iron nails to the frames, garboards not connected to the keel, planks butt-joints at frame stations, seam caulking, and the total absence of planking edge joints or any other features characteristic of shell-first construction, confirm without doubt that the concept of the ship's hull and the construction sequence was based on frames. The function of the central longitudinal timber, the absence of a keelson, and their significance for the integrity of the hull, and the definition of skeleton, remain questions for further study.

It is planned to complete the research and documentation, conserve the wood, and reassemble the timbers in a museum. The controlled cutting out of a section of a wreck for research-purposes should perhaps be considered for future projects.

ACKNOWLEDGMENTS

Dor 2001/1 is a combined project of the Leon Recanati Institute for Maritime Studies at the University of Haifa, the Nautical Archaeology Society of Great Britain, and the Aquadora Diving Club. It was supported by Lord Jacobs, the Israel Science Foundation, the Hecht Foundation, and the University of Haifa, to whom we are grateful.

NOTES

1) Tree species analysis was carried out by Prof. N. Liphschitz of the Botanical Laboratories of the Institute of Archaeology, Tel Aviv University (Liphschitz 2002).

2) ^{14}C tests were made by Dr. E. Boaretto of the Weizmann Institute of Science, Israel, and by Dr. G. Bonani of the Institute of Particle Physics of the Swiss Federal Institute of Technology, Zürich.

REFERENCES

Harpster, B. M., 2004, Dowels as a Means of Edge-to-Edge Joinery in the 9th-century AD Vessel from Bozburun, Turkey. *IJNA*, 34.1, 88-94.

Kahanov, Y. & Mor, H., 2006, The Dor 2001/1 wreck, Dor/Tantura lagoon, Israel: Preliminary report. In: *ISBSA 10*, 84-88.

Liphschitz, N., 2002, *Byzantine Ship 2001/1 Dor lagoon, Dendro-archaeological Researches 352*, Archaeological Institute, Tel Aviv University (unpublished, in Hebrew).

Mor, H. & Kahanov, Y., 2006, The Dor 2001/1 Shipwreck, Israel – A Summary of the Excavation. *IJNA*, 35.2, 274-289.

Mor, H., in press, Dor 2001/1 Wreck-Hull Construction Report. In: *TROPIS IX*.

Royal, G. J. & Kahanov, Y., 2005, New Dating and Contextual Evidence for the Fragmentary Timber Remains Located in the Dor D Site, Israel. *IJNA*, 34, 2, 308-313.

OFRA BARKAI

THE TANTURA F SHIPWRECK

Tantura F was discovered in 1996 during a survey in Dor/Tantura Lagoon (Israel) by a combined expedition of the Institute of Nautical Archaeology at Texas A&M University (INA) and the Leon Recanati Institute for Maritime Studies at the University of Haifa (RIMS), headed by S. Wachsmann (Wachsmann *et al.* 1997: 7). The wreck was designated Trench 10 or Tantura 10, and now Tantura F.

In the 2004-2006 seasons the wreck was excavated by a combined expedition of the Leon Recanati Institute of Maritime Studies headed by Yaacov Kahanov and the Nautical Archaeology Society (NAS) of Great Britain headed by Chris Brandon, together with Kurt Raveh. A report has been published on the construction, and the findings are summarized below (Barkai & Kahanov, 2007). Based on ^{14}C tests, some by the AMS method on short-lived organic materials[1], the wreck was dated to the beginning of the 8th c. A.D., which is the local early Islamic Umayyad period.

THE HULL REMAINS

The wreck was found about 70 m offshore, a few metres N.W. of the lagoon's navigable channel, near Dor Island. It is in 85 cm of water, buried under an additional 1.5 m of sand mixed with shells and stones spread over an area of 12 by 3.5 m. The original ship is estimated to have been 15 m long.

The hull survived up to the turn of the bilge, and almost to the bow and the stern. Its remains comprise the complete keel, frames (floor timbers, futtocks and pairs of half-frames), sections of strakes from the port and starboard sides, stringers, the mast step assemblage, and central longitudinal timbers. There was no evidence of ceiling planking.

The keel was made of *Pinus brutia*[2]. Average dimensions were 9.5 cm sided and 16 cm moulded. There were no rabbets or chamfered edges for the garboards, but rabbets were identified at the ends of the keel. Remains of scarfs were found at the bow and stern ends. As yet, it is unclear exactly which components were scarfed: whether the keel to the stem, the stem to its extension, or something else. Another scarf was found

Fig. 1 Tantura F. – Half-frame scarf (Photo S. Breitstein).

Fig. 2 Tantura F. – Futtock (Photo S. Breitstein).

Fig. 3 Tantura F. – The mast step (Photo I. Grinberg).

in the keel between frames F7 and F8; its details are still hidden. The use of at least two scarfs and two different tree species in the keel may be a hint that it was difficult to obtain long timbers suitable for the keel. The distance between the garboards and the upper edge of the keel varied between 2 and 8 cm. The frames were notched accordingly.

All the original 36 frame stations were evident. Timbers of 31 frames were recovered, including floor timbers, pairs of half-frames, and futtocks. Frames were on the average 8 cm sided and 11 cm moulded, with room and space of 28 cm, and most were fixed to the keel with 20 mm iron nails. Generally, the framing pattern was of alternating floor timbers and half-frames, except under the mast step, where a series of floor timbers and futtocks only was identified. Half-frames were scarfed to each other side by side (**Fig. 1**), and connected to the keel by iron nails. They were not connected to each other.

Sections of 15 futtocks were recovered. They were round timbers, 13 cm diameter, 9 cm thick, unworked except for a flat face where they adjoined the floor timbers (**Fig. 2**). They were fixed to the floor timbers from the sides with iron nails only, randomly forward or aft of their associated floor timbers.

Planks were from 8 to 20 cm wide, with an average thickness of 25 mm. They were connected to the frames by 5 mm square iron nails, driven from the outside. One or two nails connected each plank to each frame, depending on plank width. No planking edge joints were found anywhere. Caulking was found between seams.

Six half-log stringers were found. Average dimensions were 15 cm wide by 6 cm thick. Two central stringers were connected to the top surfaces of the frames, with their flat surfaces upward, located on each side of the longitudinal axis of the ship, and spaced at about 5 cm. The other four stringers, two on each side, were nailed to some of the frames, but not to all, with their flat surfaces downward, matching the upper surfaces of the frames.

Two central longitudinal timbers were found at the bow and the stern. They were fixed to the frames from above and the sides with iron nails. They were notched underneath to match the frames. The timber at the bow was 14 cm sided, 12 cm moulded, and 200 cm long. The stern timber was 14 cm sided, 15.5 cm moulded, and 140 cm long. They were worked on all sides.

The mast step assemblage comprised the mast step itself and two lateral sisters (**Fig. 3**). Measurable dimensions of the mast step were length 145 cm, width 26 cm, and thickness 20 cm. There were two mortises in its upper surface (**Fig. 4**). The mast step was installed between the stringers, but not nailed to them.

SEQUENCE OF CONSTRUCTION

The general sequence of construction of the hull was apparently as follows: firstly keel and posts were joined together, then the frames were nailed to the keel and extended by futtocks. The connection be-

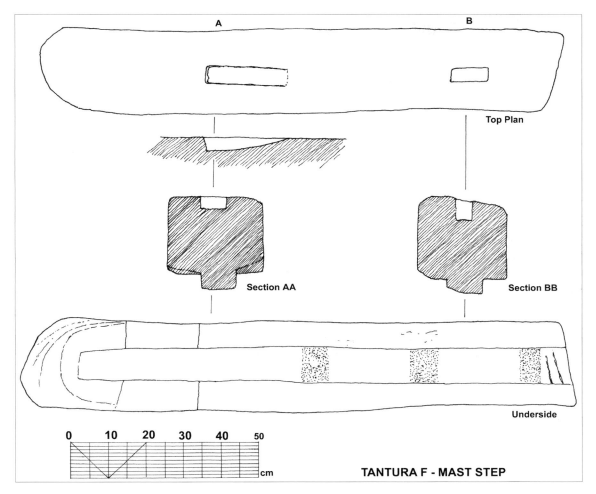

Fig. 4 Tantura F. – The mast step (Drawing C. Brandon).

tween the futtocks and the floor timbers was weak (only one nail, without a scarf), so it is likely that the frames had temporary supports during the construction. Then, planks were nailed to the frames, with butt scarfs at frame stations, and caulking was driven into the plank seams. The last step was the installation of all the internal components (central longitudinal timbers, central stringers, and the mast step assemblage above them). This conception of the hull was thus based on keel and frames, not on planks.

THE FINDS

Ceramics

The pottery assemblage included remains of about 30 ceramic vessels, including eight amphoras, two small jugs, and at least 20 storage jars. Most of these were found *in situ* in the bottom of the wreck near the mast step. A comparative typological analysis was made to confirm the date of the wreck. Petrography and chemical composition (mass spectrometry) analyses were made on representative samples to identify the provenance of the raw material.

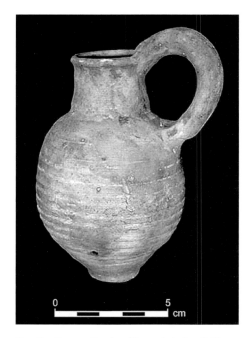

Fig. 5   Tantura F. – Amphora (Photo J. J. Gottlieb).

Fig. 6   Tantura F. – Jug (Photo J. J. Gottlieb).

Amphoras (Fig. 5)

Type: These are similar to the Late Roman 2C type, distributed throughout N. Africa, Italy and the Levant (Piéri 1998: 100). This type was found in the 7th c. Yassi Ada shipwreck (van Doorninck 1989: 11, fig. 1), Caesarea, Israel, Stratum 8, which is dated to the local early Islamic period (Arnon 2003: pl. 74.11), and Saraçhane in Istanbul, Turkey, mainly 7th c., perhaps also 8th c. (Hayes 1986: 3, fig. 23, type 29).

Petrography: The fabric of this amphora was highly calcareous. Inclusions were carbonate globules, quartz grains, quartzite and calcite. Petrography gives little information about the provenance.

Jugs (Fig. 6)

Type: A similar type to that found at Kellia, in the Nile Delta, dated to the end of the 7thc., after the Arab conquest (Bonnet & Cattin 1999: 236; 247, fig. 491).

Petrography: The fabric contains feldspar (*plagioclase*) and other minerals, such as pyroxene. The inclusions were coarse-grained components, poorly sorted rounded quartz. This juglet was probably made from Nile Delta mud[3].

Storage jars (Fig. 7)

Type: A similar type is recorded in Caesarea, Israel, Stratum 8 (Arnon 2003: 10 pl. 74), along the Israeli coast (Zemer 1977: 61-62 pl. 22), at Amman Citadel, Jordan (Sauer 1986: 48, fig. 2), in Pella, Jordan, from the collapse deposit of the A.D. 747 earthquake, and from the early 8th c. deposit – the earliest appearance at the site (Watson 1995: 3, fig. 9; Smith 1977: 295; 489, pl. 32), in Kellia in the Nile Delta (Types 187-190)

Fig. 7   Tantura F. – Storage jar (Photo J. J. Gottlieb).

from the 8th c. (Egloff 1977: 3 pl. 22) and in El-Ashmunein, Egypt: one context is dated to the 8th to 9th c. (Bailey 1998: 24 pl. 86), the second context to 675-750 (Bailey 1998: 25 pl. 133). Benghazi, specified by Riley as LRA5, dated it predominantly to the 7th to 8th c. (Riley 1979: 224, fig. 92; 358). The jars had resinous linings.

Petrography: The raw material appears to be Nile Delta silt. The inclusions were a coarse-grained component, well-rounded quartz, grain size 0.3 mm; rounded amphibole and pyroxene minerals, grain size 0.15 mm. Also, (very rare) elongated structures, possibly straw or halm, and particles (very rare), possibly remains of shells.

Comparative typological analysis of the pottery supports the 14C dating of the wood to the beginning of the 8th c. Petrography gives little information about the provenance of the amphoras, but indicates a Nile Delta origin for the jugs and the storage jars.

Organic materials

The frames and the amphoras resting on them were protected with matting made of *Phragmites communis*. Other organic remains were a bone needle, a rope, a wooden ring, a basket, fishbones, and food remains – carobs (**Fig. 8**) and olive pits (**Fig. 9**).

Fig. 8   Tantura F. – Carobs (Photo A. Yurman).   **Fig. 9**   Tantura F. – Olive pits (Photo O. Barkai).

The jars contained a residue of small fishbones, which could have been a fish product (fish sauce or salted fish). No oil or seasonings were identified. The fish was identified as Tilapia[4]. Hundreds of bones from all parts of the skeleton were found in each jar. There are many varieties of Tilapia, and it is not yet clear whether it is a local species or the Nile Tilapia (*Oreochromis niloticus*). The fish-bones and the needle hint that this may have been a fishing vessel.

CONCLUSIONS

The sequence of construction of the hull is frame-based. Its 8th c. dating is earlier than generally accepted for this technique.

The identification of the production centre of the ceramic ware indicates a passage from Egypt to Dor. The Tantura F, whether or not it was a fishing vessel, apparently plied the Levant coast and entered Dor/Tantura Lagoon intentionally. This is evidence of maritime connections, and more particularly, a sailing route between Egypt and Dor in the 8th c. It is significant evidence for the existence of a community at Dor/Tantura, and demonstrates that Dor lagoon served as an anchorage for coastal commerce during a period for which there are no historical sources (Dahl 1915: 90-123) or archaeological evidence (Stern 2000: 319).

ACKNOWLEDGMENTS

This research is supported by Lord Jacobs, the Israel Science Foundation, the Hecht Foundation, the Sir Maurice Hatter Fellowship for Maritime Studies, and the University of Haifa, to whom we are most grateful.

NOTES

1) AMS radiocarbon dating was carried out by G. Bonani of the Institute of Particle Physics, Zurich. Sample numbers are (all ETH numbers, uncalibrated): ETH-31266 (1340±45), 31267 (1255 ±45), 29800 (1360±40), 29801 (1280±40), 29802 (1300 ±40), 29803 (1340±40), 29804 (1320±40).

2) Tree species were identified by N. Liphschitz of Tel Aviv University.

3) Food remains were analysed by M. Kislev of Bar Ilan University.

4) Fish remains were analysed by I. Zoar, of the Recanati Institute for Maritime Studies at the University of Haifa.

REFERENCES

Arnon, Y., 2003, *Development and Continuity in the Early Islamic Pottery Types from the 7th Century to the 12th Century CE. The Caesarea Data as a Study Case*. PhD thesis, University of Haifa.

Baily, D. M., 1998, *Excavations at El Ashmunein V Pottery, Lamps and Glass of the Late Roman and Early Arab Period*. London.

Barkai, O. & Kahanov, Y., 2007, The Tantura F Shipwreck, Israel. *IJNA*, 36, 1, 21-31.

Bonnet, B. F. & Cattin, M. I., 1999, La Matériel Archéologique Catalogue Systématique du Materiel. In: P. Bridel (ed.), *Explorations aux Qoucour el-Izeila lors des campagnes 1981, 1982, 1984, 1985, 1986, 1989 et 1990*. Louvain-Leuven.

Dahl, G., 1915, The Material for the History of Dor. *Transactions of the Connecticut Academy of Arts & Sciences*, 20. New Haven/Connecticut.

Egloff, M., 1977, *Kellia III: La poterie copte*, vols. 1-2. Genève.

Hayes, J. W., 1992, *Excavation at Saraçhane in Istanbul: the Pottery*, vol. 2. Princeton/New Jersey.

Piéri, D., 1998, Les importations d'amphores orientales en Gaule meridionale durant l'antiquité tardive et le haut moyen age (IVe-VIIe siècles après J-C.). Typologie, chronologie et contenu, Société Française d'Étude de la Céramique Antique en Gaule. *Actes du Congrès d'Istres*. Marseille, 97-106.

Riley, J. A., 1979, The coarse pottery from Benghazi. In: J. A. Lloyd (ed.), *Excavations at Sidi Khrebish, Benghazi (Berenice) II*. Libya Antiqua, Suppl. 5. Tripoli, 91-497.

Sauer, J. A., 1986, Umayyad Pottery from Sites in Jordan. In: T. G. Lawrence & G. H. Larry (eds), *The Archaeology of Jordan and other studies*. Berrien Springs/Michigan, 301-330.

Smith, R. H., 1973, *Pella of the Decapolis I*. Wooster/Ohio.

Stern, E., 2000, *Dor-Ruler of the Seas*. Jerusalem.

van Doorninck, F. H. Jr., 1989, The Cargo Amphorae on the 7th Century Yassi Ada and the 11th Century Serçe Limanı Shipwrecks: Two Examples of a Reuse of Byzantine Amphorae as Transport Jars. In: V. Dèroche & J. M. Spieser (eds), *Recherches sur la Céramique Byzantine*. Bulletin de Correspondence Hellénique, Suppl. XVIII, 247-257.

2002, Byzantine Shipwrecks. In: A. E. Laiou (ed.), *The Economic History of Byzantium: From the Seventh through the Fifteenth Century*, vol. 2. Washington/DC, 899-905.

Wachsmann, S., Kahanov, Y. & Hall, J., 1997, The Tantura B Shipwreck: The 1996 INA/CMS Joint Expedition to Tantura Lagoon. *INA Quarterly*, 24, 4, 3-15.

Watson, P., 1995, Ceramic Evidence for Egyptian links with northern Jordan in the 6th-8th centuries. In: S. Bourke & J.-P. Descœudres (eds), *Trade, contact, and the movement of peoples in the eastern Mediterranean. Studies in Honor of J. Basil Hennessy*. Mediterranean Archaeology, Suppl. 3. Sydney, 303-320.

Zemer, A., 1977, *Storage Jars in Ancient Sea Trade*. Haifa.

DEBORAH CVIKEL

DOR 2002/2 SHIPWRECK: THE CONSTRUCTION
OF A LATE OTTOMAN PERIOD VESSEL

Dor-Tantura Lagoon is located on the Mediterranean coast of Israel, 30 km S. of Haifa. Several small islands create a natural shallow anchorage, which is safe in a calm sea. In early May 2002 a shipwreck was naturally exposed on the shoreline of Dor Lagoon, and was designated Dor 2002/2 (**Fig. 1**). Two underwater excavation seasons were conducted as a joint project under the direction of the Leon Recanati Institute for Maritime Studies of the University of Haifa, with the cooperation of the Nautical Archaeology Society of Great Britain, and the local Aqua Dora Diving Centre.

THE EXCAVATION

The remains were oriented E.-W., covered by sand and seashells, extending 4.7 m from N. to S. and 5.0 m from E. to W. A maximum depth of 1.5 m below sea level was reached during the excavation. The shallowness of the site was not an advantage: the power of the dredgers was reduced, divers could only balance themselves with difficulty, and even small waves disturbed the work. A metal frame was used as a reference grid for the measurements, drawings, and photographs, and, together with the sandbags, protected the archaeological find.

During the first excavation season, the starboard side of the hull of a vessel was uncovered. It was possible to identify hull components, such as keelson, stem, frames, and planks. The carpentry details showed that it was built to a high standard. Each of the wreck's components was measured at intervals of 20 cm, taking into account their state of preservation. The parts at the E. end were covered with sand, and were thus protected; whereas those at the W. end were exposed from time to time, and had deteriorated.

THE HULL REMAINS

Bow components

The wreck comprised two parts: the bow area, and a section of the starboard side (**Fig. 2**). All components of the bow were made of *Pinus brutia*, apart from the stem (W3.1) which was the only ship timber made of *Quercus coccifera* (Liphschitz 2002; 2003). The data regarding the bow components are presented in **Table 1**.

Two recesses of different depths and at a small angle were found in the keelson remains. The similarity in dimensions between the re-

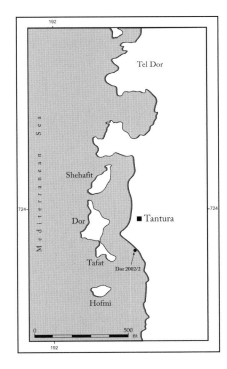

Fig. 1 Dor-Tantura Lagoon and the location of the Dor 2002/2 shipwreck (Drawing S. Haad).

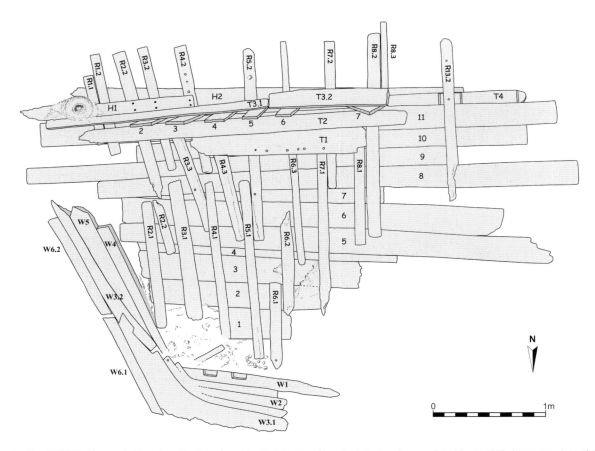

Fig. 2 Dor 2002/2 shipwreck (Drawing Ch. Brandon, Nautical Archaeology Society, London, updated by D. Cvikel & S. Haad, Haifa).

moulded (thickness, mm)			sided (width, mm)			surviving	designation	definition
ave.	max.	min.	ave.	max.	min.	length (cm)		
140	150	60	138	200	60	150	W1	Keelson
NA	255	NA	70	NA	NA	120	W2	Deadwood
198	300	50	100	110	90	210	W3.1	Stem
100	155	60	90	NA	NA	159	W3.2	Stem upper extension
NA	100	60	NA	260	NA	131	W4	Stemson
NA	160	NA	NA	NA	NA	142	W5	Apron
105	130	80	70	NA	NA	100	W6.1	False Stem
80	100	70	80	NA	NA	95	W6.2	False Stem

Table 1 Dor 2002/2. – The bow components.

cesses and the frames, and their proximity as found at the excavation site, suggest that the frames were set into the recesses in the keelson.

Frames

Eleven frames survived, each made of two or three components (**Figs 2-3**), connected by an oak treenail, and in some cases by additional iron nails. The frames were made of *Pinus brutia* and *Pinus nigra*, and were coated with pitch. Traces of tool marks were evident on the frames, mainly those of an adze and a saw.

Fig. 3 Dor 2002/2. – Frames looking E. (Photo G. Votruba, Leon Recanati Institute for Maritime Studies, Haifa).

The futtocks were apparently connected to the aft side of the floor timbers, facing the centre of the wreck. The lack of limber holes indicates that this was part of the side of a hull, not the bottom.

The shortest surviving frame timber measured 58 cm, and the longest 206 cm. Their sided and moulded dimensions were well preserved, ranging from 7 to 10 cm, average sided 9.4 cm and moulded 9.7 cm. Room and space, measured as close as possible to the keelson, was about 30 cm.

Hull planking

The 11 surviving hull planks were also made of *Pinus brutia*, and were covered with pitch (Nissenbaum, pers. comm., 2005). They were connected to the frames using square nails, two or three nails per plank, depending on the width of the plank. Two planks were very narrow, one being a repair patch and the other a drop-strake. The average width of the planks (excluding the two narrow ones) was 20.4 cm. Plank thickness varied between 2.0 cm and 3.8 cm, with an average of 2.8 cm.

Deck beams

Remnants of seven deck beams survived. Similarly to the hull planks, they were made of *Pinus brutia*, but were broken and rough to the touch. The average width of the deck beams was 17.5 cm, and average thickness was 3.1 cm. They were set across the ship at an angle of 63° to the side of the hull, which is a clue to the shape of the original hull in this area. This angle corresponds to the angle of the recesses in the keelson.

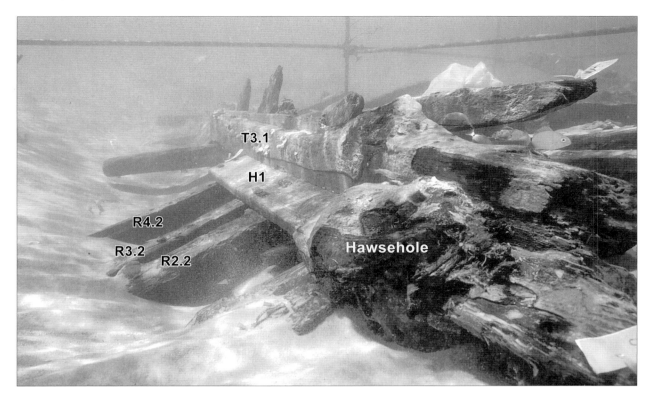

Fig. 4 Dor 2002/2. – Hawsehole looking W. (Photo I. Grinberg, Tel Aviv).

Attachments

Treenails and three types of iron nails were found in the wreck. The treenails were made of *Quercus coccifera* and were 20 mm in diameter. They were used to connect the parts of the frames. The first group of iron nails was used to connect the planks to the frames. They range between 6.1 to 7.2 mm in cross-section. Another group of iron nails was used to connect the frame components to each other. These were 9 to 10 mm in cross-section. The third group comprised evidence of iron bolts in the bow, where four holes were found in the keelson. Remnants of an iron bolt were found in one of the holes, 15 mm diameter, and 20 cm surviving length. It is likely that long bolts were driven through these holes, and used to connect the bow components: the keelson, deadwood and stem, to one another. If so, these bolts would have been at least 50 cm long.

Hawsehole

A hawse hole was found at the S. E. part of the wreck, covered with a heavy marine concretion (**Fig. 4**). It had a 30 cm outer concretion diameter, 10 cm thickness, with an inner diameter of 9 cm, and the diagonal length of the pipe was about 20 cm.

Organic traces

Traces of white paint were found on the S. part, where the frames were exposed above the deck line. Traces of green and yellow paint were found on the outer side of the hull. Analysis shows no evidence of a pigment binder in the paint. The paint medium was linseed oil and pine resin (Ribechini & Colombini 2003; 2004).

A piece of linen cloth was also found. The threads were Z2S, meaning that the Z-twist thread was made of two S-spun fibres. This type is not local, but is similar to the linen remains of French soldiers' uniforms found in excavations in Akko. The threads of the uniform cloth are single, Z-spun, and the thread used in sewing the buttons to the cloth is Z2S (Berman 1997: 97-98). The origin of the cloth has not been determined, but the Z-spin direction seems to indicate a western European origin.

THE AGE OF THE WRECK

Unlike many other shipwrecks, no finds were available for refining the dating of the wreck. Wood samples, recovered from different parts of the wreck, and one linen cloth sample, were sent for ^{14}C dating to the Institute of Particle Physics, Switzerland, and the Weizmann Institute of Science, Israel (Bonani 2002; 2006; Boaretto 2003). A weighted average of the calibrated ^{14}C results points to the year 1800. However, ^{14}C calibration for this period is problematic.

Additional information regarding the age of the wreck was obtained by comparison with another shipwreck from Dor-DW2. The ^{14}C dates of the two wrecks are similar. Moreover, clay tobacco pipes found in DW2 have been dated to not later than 1800 (Yovel, pers. comm., 2005). Also were metal finds analyzed for their characteristics and manufacturing processes, and were estimated to be 200 years old (Eisenberg, pers. comm., 2004).

In an effort to further investigate the dating, several samples were sent for dendrochonological analysis at the Cornell Tree-Ring Laboratory. At present, the samples available are few, and have only a limited number of tree-rings, thus no secure tree-ring dates have yet been established (Manning, pers. comm. 2006). It is hoped to pursue this research in the future with additional samples if possible.

Considering all the available data, the suggested date of Dor 2002/2 is 1800.

RECONSTRUCTION OF THE SHIP

On the grounds of the suggested dating, and after consulting experts from Israel and abroad, an attempt was made to reconstruct the dimensions of the original vessel by comparison with other Mediterranean wrecks of the same period. In addition, a 1:10 model of the archaeological timber remains was built. The model was useful in determining crucial details, such as the angle of the deck beams, the attachments of the frames within the keelson recesses, and their angles, and the position of the hawsehole (**Fig. 5**).

The origin of the wood was W. Turkey (Liphschitz 2002; 2003). Evidence of Greek construction tradition can be found in the angle of the stem, the deck beams, and in the recesses for the frames. According to historical sources, these neighbouring areas shared knowledge of ship construction techniques. Construction tradition was transferred by Greek shipwrights, who travelled between Turkish shipyards in the Aegean during the 16th to 18th c. (Damianidis 1989: 15). This information supports the possibility of Greek-oriented ship construction, but even so, it is impossible to determine whether it was the outcome of direct influence – the ship being built in a Greek shipyard or by Greek shipwrights, or indirect influence – the result of diffused ideas and techniques.

In view of all the available data, and presuming that the ship operated in the surroundings of Dor-Tantura lagoon where she was discovered, it is suggested that Dor 2002/2 shipwreck is the remnant of a small,

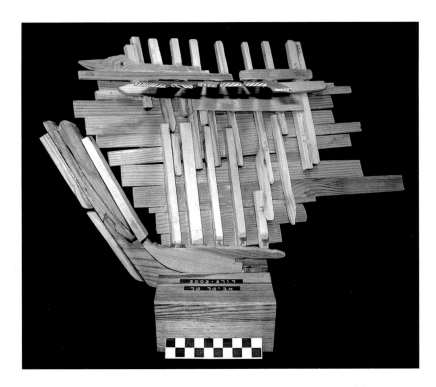

Fig. 5   Dor 2002/2 model (Photo J. J. Gottlieb, Leon Recanati Institute for Maritime Studies, Haifa).

high-quality, fast sailing vessel. The high standard of the carpentry details indicate a government or military vessel. The ship probably had one mast, and was 15 m long, with 4.5 m beam and 1.35 m draught, and had a displacement of about 35 tons. These suggested dimensions, together with the dimensions of the hawse-hole, were tested in the Shipping and Ports Administration, Ministry of Transport, compared with modern data for wind pressure of 6 Beaufort (American Bureau of Shipping, 1983). Once the Equipment Number of the ship was calculated as E.N. 52, it was determined that the suggested dimensions were reasonable, and that the original ship had to carry two anchors, 120 kg each (Livne, pers. comm., 2007; American Bureau of Shipping, 1983).

THE HISTORICAL BACKGROUND

At the beginning of 1799 Napoleon Bonaparte and his army advanced from Egypt towards what is now-adays Israel and Syria. On their way N. along the coast Bonaparte set up camp at Tantura. In early April 1799, Lambert, the French commander of Haifa, wrote in his memoirs that the port at Tantura was usable for boats and small ships of various types, but only in fair weather, for in a heavy sea, they might run aground or crash against the rocks (La Jonquière 1900: 379). About one month later, Rear-Admiral Perrée was ordered to send all his vessels to Tantura, and to use the two brigs anchored there in order to evacuate 400 wounded soldiers (Napoléon 1860: corr. 4126; La Jonquière 1900: 507-508). Since Perrée did not carry out this order (La Jonquière 1900: 510-511), local craft were used in order to evacuate some of the soldiers to Egypt.

SUMMARY

Dor 2002/2 is the remains of a small ship dated to about 1800. The wreck provides evidence of a 15 m-vessel built to a high standard and adds essential information to our knowledge of the construction of small vessels that plied the E. Mediterranean 200 years ago.

Napoleon Bonaparte and his army camped in Tantura in 1799, and used local craft. Combined with the fabric remains, a possible connection with these events seems probable. However, this cannot yet be proved definitely.

ACKNOWLEDGMENTS

This article is based on a MA thesis for the University of Haifa, entitled with »Archaeological Evidence in Tantura Lagoon and Historical Evidence of the Marine Aspect of Napoleon Bonaparte and his Army's Retreat from Acre«, supervised by Prof. Haim Goren and Dr. Yaacov Kahanov, to whom the author is indebted.

The research was supported by Lord Jacobs, the Sir Maurice Hatter Fellowship for Maritime Studies, the Fraenkel Fellowship Committee, the Israel Science Foundation, and the Hecht Foundation, to whom the author is also grateful.

The author would like to thank naval architect Henry Winters for volunteering his study of the wreck and for his advice and contribution; Dr. Eric Rieth for his insights and advice on the hull construction; Dr. Dan Livne, Chief Engineer of the Shipping and Ports Administration, Ministry of Transport, Israel, for his advice and contribution in the reconstruction of the ship's original dimensions; Mr. Avital Tal for building the model; and Mr. John Tresman for the English editing.

REFERENCES

American Bureau of Shipping, 1983, *Rules for Building and Classing Steel Vessels Under 61 Meters (200 Feet) in Length*, American Bureau of Shipping, Incorporated by Act of the Legislature of the State of New York 1862. New York.

Berman, A., 1997, Excavation of the Courthouse Site at Akko: A Siege-Trench of Bonaparte's Army in Areas TB and TC. *Atiqot*, 31, 91-103.

Boaretto, E., 2003, *Radiocarbon Dating*. Unpublished report. Weizmann Institute of Science, Rehovot.

Bonani, G., 2002, *AMS Radiocarbon Dating*. Unpublished report. Institute of Particle Physics, Zürich.

2006, *AMS Radiocarbon Dating*. Unpublished report. Institute of Particle Physics, Zürich.

Damianidis, K., 1989, *Vernacular Boats and Boatbuilding in Greece*. PhD thesis, University of St. Andrews, St. Andrews.

La Jonquière, C., 1900, *L'Expédition d'Egypte, 1798-1801*, IV. Paris.

Liphschitz, N., 2002, *Dor Lagoon Shipwreck 2002/2*. Unpublished Dendroarchaeological Report no. 353, The Archaeological Institute, Tel Aviv University.

2003, *Dor Lagoon Shipwreck 2002/2*. Unpublished Dendroarchaeological Report no. 361, The Archaeological Institute, Tel Aviv University.

Napoléon I, 1860, *Correspondance de Napoléon Ier*. Paris.

Ribechini, E. & Colombini, P., 2003, *Chemical Characterization of Natural Materials Employed to Finish Historic Wood Ships: Preliminary Results*. Unpublished. Università di Pisa.

2004, *Chemical Characterization of Natural Materials Employed to Finish Historic Wood Ships*. Unpublished. Università di Pisa.

ALESSIO CANALINI

THE LOGONOVO WRECK NEAR FERRARA

NEW EVIDENCES BY THE USE OF MODERN METHODOLOGY OF ARCHAEOLOGICAL RESEARCH

This paper deals with research carried out in the year 2004 (Canalini 2005) under the direction of C. Beltrame on the wreck of the Logonovo boat, discovered in 1959, together with other finds (an iron sword and a potsherd) at Comacchio, near Ferrara, during excavations of an artificial canal (**Fig. 1**).

FIRST OBSERVATIONS

My work had its starting point in the results of studies carries out on the boat by several scholars, such as Nereo Alfieri (Alfieri 1968: 206-207), the then Director of the Museum who carried out the complete salvage of the wreck, Marco Bonino (Bonino 1978: 15-18), for his contribution to the boat typology and Stella Patitucci Uggeri (Patitucci Uggeri 1979: 268-280) for his study on the finds recovered on the same site and specifically, an iron sword (**Fig. 2**) and a ceramic bowl. It was in fact Patitucci Uggeri who suggested that the above-cited finds should be associated with the wreck, attributing both to the 15th c. A.D.
It must be stated that this boat, having represented one of the very few archaeological witnesses attributed to the late medieval ages in the whole of the Mediterranean, has attracted for this very reason the interest of the most important historians of boatbuilding who have quoted it in their books of boatbuilding history (Steffy 1994; Ray Martin 2001).
The boat has a flat bottom, with the stempost that at the upper end tends to curve inwards, with a keel of equal thickness to the strakes, so as to suggest an apparently exclusive use in internal waters. From the bow towards the centre of the boat it is quite complete, whilst from the centre to stern it has been remounted in the 1960s with what remained of the original parts and integrated with new elements (Bonino 1985: 9-21). Its shape recalls the boat typology of the *trabaccoli* family (Marzari 1988).

METHODOLOGIES OF RESEARCH

Considering the Logonovo boat's importance, the author has chosen to use the modern methodology of archaeological research used in the French and American naval field. Thus it was necessary for his research to throw light on the following points: the real association between the finds – the sword and ceramic bowl – and the wreck; the real date of the wreck; the dynamics of the wrecking; the real boat typology of the wreck and its origins.

THE REAL ASSOCIATION BETWEEN THE FINDS

The organization carrying out the excavating work on the Logonovo Canal did not immediately report the finding at the moment it was made either to the police or to the Director of the National Archaeological

A

B

C

Fig. 1 Comacchio/Logonovo. – Discovery of the wreck during canal excavation.

Fig. 2 Comacchio/Logonovo. – Iron sword and hilt.

Museum of Ferrara (Alfieri 1959). This meant that it was impossible for Alfieri to carry out an adequate stratigraphic dig that would have guaranteed a real connection between the finds and the wreck and a correct georeference of the wreck itself. It was moreover impossible to carry out a salvage that was non-invasive and obtain full photographic documentation.

Consequently, these elements, which are lacking do not allow us to attribute with certainty the finds to the remains of the boat. However, thanks to further research carried out by experts, the ceramic bowl can be dated somewhere between the 16th c. and the beginning 17th c., and the sword from the

Fig. 3 Comacchio/Logonovo. – Documentation of the external planking.

end of the 15th c. to mid-17th c. Regarding the dating of the wreck, we have preferred to attempt other associations and study, which we will now illustrate to you.

DATING

The obtaining of as much data and as much information as possible regarding the dating of the Logonovo boat is strictly linked to a direct approach with the wreck, and one which was as analytic as possible. Being careful to distinguish the parts that were not correctly reconstructed during restoration (on the year 1960) from the original ones, every single external and internal element of the boat was catalogued, photographed, and documented (**Fig. 3**); a planigraphic and prospective relief of the whole the boat was produced (**Fig. 4**).

This procedure has allowed to identify a series of indicating signs. The draught notches on the stempost were made at distances that cannot be linked to the Venetian foot (1 venetian foot = 0.347735 m), a measure unit that was used along the Venetian and Dalmatian coast up to the end of the 18th c., but rather to the metric-decimal system adopted in Italy after its introduction by Napoleon at the beginning of the 19th c. (**Fig. 5**). Moreover, all the measurements of every element of the boat show the use of the metric-decimal system during the boat's construction (Kula 1987). This is the first element that demonstrates that the boat cannot have been built before the beginning of the 19th c.

The 14C AMS analyses (CEDAD), based on a wood sample taken from the inside of the stempost, indicate in effect the period, after which the boat was built and not a precise date, which is only guaranteed by a dendrochronological analysis. The period indicated by the 14C analyses places the wreck between a period going from 1440 A.D. to 1640 A.D., with a greater probability of being towards the end of the 16th c. and beginning of the 17th c. This would seem to take us away from the 19th c., but the sample taken from inside the stempost is probably part of the tree trunk's heartwood, from which the stempost was made. In this case it is quite difficult to try to hypothesize, which growth rings might still have existed when the tree was felled. The tree could have been at least 100 years old, in consideration of the fact that it is highly probable that the boat came from Istria, where by law, even under Napoleon, oaks – as in this case – could only be felled when they were more than 100 years old (Ivetić 2000: 136-147). Therefore at least another hundred years may be added to the results of the 14C, coming nearer to the 19th c.

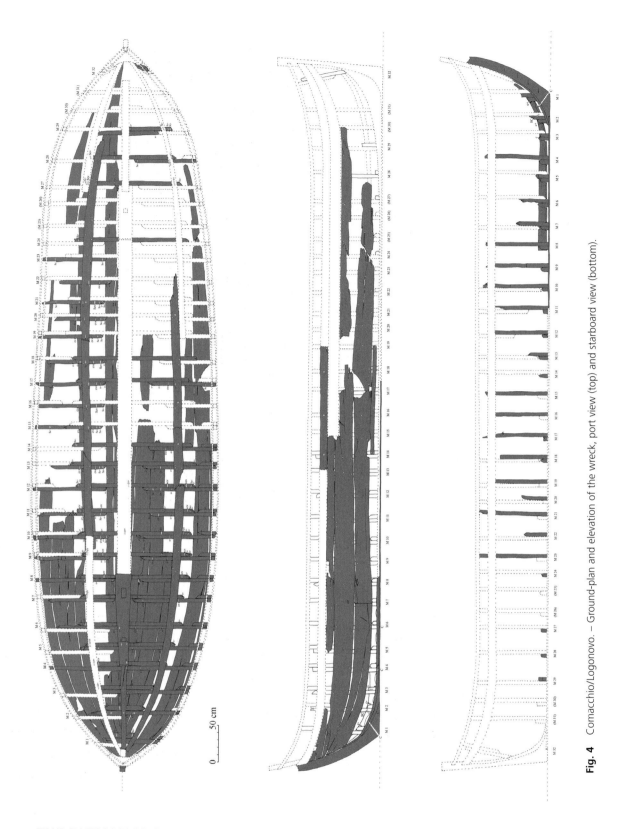

Fig. 4 Comacchio/Logonovo. – Ground-plan and elevation of the wreck, port view (top) and starboard view (bottom).

50 cm

0

THE DYNAMICS OF THE WRECKING

I thought it useful to reconstruct the stratigraphy of the subsurface at the site of the finding in order both to understand the formation dynamics of the wreck better and to verify further the date of the boat. Thanks to the results of a recent stratigraphy carried out at a distance of about 600 m S. W. of the

Fig. 5 Comacchio/Logonovo. – Distance between the draught marks on the stempost in decimal system.

place where the wreck was found, the soil at the depth, at which the wreck was found is sandy/muddy up to a depth of 15 m and then alternates between clay and grey sand up to a depth of 170 m. Thanks to the collaboration of Professor Bondesan, lecturer in geomorphology in he Department of Earth Sciences at the University of Ferrara, it was possible to compare the depth of the wreck with the data obtained in previous geomorphic studies. By assessing the coast advances over the centuries, examining the variation between the deposits and the removals of silt from rivers and finally assessing the anthropic factor in the morphological change of the wide surface of the Comacchio Lagoon (Bondesan 1986: 17-28; Cazzola 1987a; 1987b; 1989; 1990a; 1990b; 1995), it may be presumed that the dating of the wreck is near to the end of the 18th or the beginning of the 19th c. According to Alfieri's report (Alfieri 1959), in fact, the boat was 2.50 to 3 m below the ground level and below sea level at the moment of discovery, covered in sands and partly damaged by the mechanical digger: however, thanks to a recent interview with a witness of the facts, it was learned that the wreck was found at a depth that goes from just 1.50 to a maximum of 2 m in a sand dune that can be seen in one of the first aerial photographs taken in the year 1935 and from some photos taken during the excavation and salvage of the boat (**Figs 1-2; 6**). This testimonial also allows us to confirm two aspects: given the shallowness of the finding, the boat cannot be attributed to the 15th c.; moreover, in contrast to what scholars have claimed up to now, it is not a boat that sank but rather a boat that was beached and presumably abandoned and over-

Fig. 6 Morphological changes of the area from 1812 to 1935.

turned, that is with the keel pointing upwards. Some signs of rust would demonstrate this near the nails, which are evident on most of the outer surface of the boat. The rust has been formed by rain water, which by dripping for a long time over the boat's structure has created rivulets through the length of the boat with a very precise and constant flow due to the inclination, which the boat, which must have turned when it presumably laid on the side of a sand dune. Later the boat, after being left exposed to the sun and rain for some time, was overturned in the way that it was found and buried both by human activities in levelling the nearby ground in order to farm it, as well as the atmospheric elements, which changed the sand dunes. This may have occurred in a period of time that goes from the end of the Napoleonic Empire in 1813 to about the middle of the 19th c., a period when, as all the historical maps show (Bonasera 1963: 10-14), the first changes brought about by land owners cultivating the dunes began.

In support of the thesis of abandonment, in my opinion in non-submerged conditions, rather than a »ship wreck«, the almost complete lack of traces of *teredo navalis* is to be noted. The only identifiable trace is on the external surface of the boat near the so-called water-line and must certainly be attributed to the time when the boat was in use.

THE REAL BOAT TYPOLOGY OF THE WRECK AND ITS ORIGINS

The presumed length of the boat – including the non-original stern part – is about 10 m. Excluding this latter part, the actual size of the boat is about 5.08 m and the maximum width at the centre of the boat is

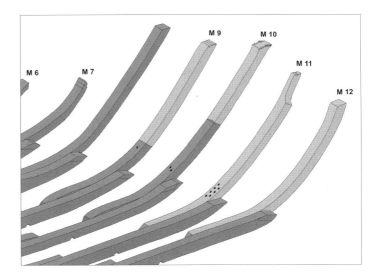

Fig. 7 Comacchio/Logonovo. – Sectional view of framing.

about 2.60 m wide: here the main section is rather rounded with the thickness of the external strakes the same as that of the keel; at the height of the bilge there is a gentle turn very similar to those found on »Trabaccoli«, large boats of the Adriatric sea that either transported goods or were used for fishing from the middle of the 18th to the middle of the 20th c. (Brizzi 1999; Marzari 1988).

The keel is not very different with regard to other strakes and on both sides it is 3.3 cm, thick compared to the 2.5 cm of the garboard; for this reason is highly suited to navigating in shallow waters. It is joined to the bow, the sternpost is missing, by a simple L-shaped join at the end of the stempost, simply blocked by a bolt, which runs from the outside to the inside. The wood used in the keel, as for the rest of the strake in the panelling and for the stempost, is oak – *Quercus robur* (dendrodata).

The stempost is made up of a single piece of wood that is 45 cm long, 120 cm high, between 12 and 16 cm thick and 6 cm wide. At the bottom it is flat, lining up with the keel, and as it rises it creates a turn of bilge of about 123° with a slight indentation towards the upper end: this is incomplete and with an obvious break: the stempost has a rabbet. On the right side of the stempost, draught notches are cut as stated previously.

The skeleton is made up of 28 frames of *Quercus robur*, each one made up of a floor timber in the centre that is joined by four to five iron nails and/or tree nails at both ends to a futtock, which in turn is joined at the outside edge to a frame timber on both sides. Starting from the bow as far as timber (M13), the structure is quite complete, then moving towards to the stern it gradually becomes more incomplete. The floor timbers of the frames are joined to the keel by bolts fixed from the outside to the inside: these are large iron nails about 30 cm long, about 1.5 cm in diameter and with a head width of about 3.5 cm.

Since there is only one part of the keel extending from the bow, it has not been possible to identify the complete numbers of bolt holes; moreover, during restoration work carried out after salvage, the frames that had come away were remounted without considering the original positions marked by the bolt holes present on the keel. It may be deduced that from M9 onwards the timbers were partly or completely re-positioned without assessing their original positions (**Fig. 7**). On several futtocks on the right side there are some cuts carried out by the carpenter with a U-pointed gouge: these most certainly were to indicate the correct positioning of the individual timbers, a fact that during restoration was not taken into consideration.

The counter-stem, 1.18 m long, is found inside the boat in correspondence to the stempost, with the same features as the wheel and placed above the first bow timbers.

brazzera

Fig. 8 The Brazzera type (Drawing A. Cherini).

trabaccolo

Fig. 9 Model of the Trabaccolo type built by R. Filippini, based on Patrignani 1987 (Photo R. Filippini).

The mast step is to be found straight after the end of the counter-stem, going towards the stern; like the counter-stem, it has slots and cuts in the edges, the former used to set the underlying frames, the latter facilitating the dripping of waters, funnelling them towards the limber hole. The mast step is 1.21m long, with a width between 22cm to 12cm, and 10cm thick. The two holes that hold the foot of the mast and the prop measure respectively: 7cm wide, 14cm long, 5cm thick and 7cm long and wide and 5cm thick.

The external planking is made up of planks of the same thickness that run longitudinally to the boat and which are fixed from the outside by nails next to the frames; the seams have been caulked with hemp and pitch, still present in some places. And finally the internal planking is made up of two strakes called foot whales positioned on both sides of the boat next to the joints between the floors and the futtock. They contribute towards strengthening the boat's sides.

The Logonovo boat reflects all in all the construction procedure of the skeleton first type. Due to its keel and its flat bottom with a very gentle and so clean turn of the bilge, we cannot hold that this boat comes from neighbouring territory to that, in which it was found (Bonino 1979: 216-237). Some interesting boats remain, which were used up to the last century and now abandoned for years at the Sicciole salt marshes in Istria (Bonin 1998: 331-334). Here not only did Napoleon attempt, and almost succeed, to revive together with the salt industry of Comacchio the prolific production of salt in order to create a monopoly from the port of Magnavacca – today Porto Garibaldi, but there was also a long period, starting in the 17th c., of continuous trading, often smuggling between the Istria and the Italian coasts (Veneto, Romagna, Marche and Puglia) of various goods: salt, salted fish, oil, wine, wood, Istrian stone etc. Such trading was carried out using medium and small boats such as »Brazzere« (**Fig. 8**) and »Pieleghi« which came from the families of Trabaccolo (**Fig. 9**), Polacche and Tartanoni. So during the Napoleonic Kingdom of Italy, too, of which Istria was part, this trading continued, as did the spread of the new Napoleonic political reforms, which included the use of decimal-metric measurements: such measurements began to be used not only in trade but also in boat-building (Apollonio 1998; Ivetić 2000). Hence it is possible that the Logonovo's boat, with its evident traces of such measurements, can be identified as one of the boat types above mentioned, and more probably a »Pielego« or a »Brazzera« which come from Istria. Both these boat types were able to sail with the mast towards the bow and with lateen sail, but there was also a version with two or three masts, both with lateen sail and lugsail.

CONCLUSIONS

In all probability, the Logonovo boat, according to the results, was built by an Istrian carpenter with local oak under Napoleonic domain, and was built to sail with one mast at the bow and with lateen sail, sailing in the Adriatic. Thanks to its shape it was able to enter the internal waters of the Comacchio lagoon, and was then inexplicably abandoned not far from the internal canal of the Vene del Bellocchio (Pezzoli 1987: 7-8) and forgotten under a sandy dune until its discovery in 1959.

ACKNOWLEDGEMENTS

For the xilotomic analyses the author thanks N. Martinelli (Dendrodata, Ricerche Datazioni Legno) Verona, Italy; for the ^{14}C AMS analyses L. Calcagnile (CEDAD Centro di Datazione e Diagnostica, Dipartimento di Ingegneria dell'Innovazione, Università degli Studi di Lecce, Italy); for the contribution of the ceramic bowl and the iron sword data we are indebted to S. Gelichi, Department of Sciences of Antiquity and the Middle East, Ca' Foscari University, Venice, Italy, and the arms scholar Mr. Rotasso, Belluno, Italy; and for the linguistic advice we are grateful to R. Coles, Facoltà di Scienze della Formazione, Università degli Studi di Urbino »Carlo Bo«, Italy and Fr. Falconi, research doctor in »Studi interculturali europei«.

REFERENCES

Alfieri, N., 1968, Tipi navali nel delta antico del Po. In: *Atti del Convegno Internazionale di Studi sulle Antichità di Classe, Ravenna 14-17 ottobre 1967*. Faenza, 206-207.

7 Settembre 1959, Protocollo n° 990 posizione S/3-B del Museo Archeologico Nazionale di Ferrara, alla Soprintendenza alle Antichità dell'Emilia e Romagna – Bologna. Ferrara.

Apollonio, A., 1998, *L'Istria veneta dal 1797 al 1813*. Gorizia.

Bonasera, F., 1963, La cartografia storica territoriale ferrarese (1571-1793). In: *La Pianura/Camera di commercio, industria, artigianato e agricoltura*, Ferrara, A. 1, no. 1, 10-14.

Bondesan, M., 1986, Lineamenti di geomorfologia del basso ferrarese. In: *La civiltà comacchiese e pomposiana, dalle origini preistoriche al tardo Medioevo. Atti del Convegno nazionale di studi storici, Comacchio, 17-19 maggio 1984*. Bologna, 17-28.

Bonin, F., 1998, Un breve cenno sulla marineria e sui tipi di imbarcazioni in uso nel litorale sloveno. In: M. Marzari (ed.), *Navi di legno – Evoluzione tecnica e sviluppo della cantieristica nel Mediterraneo dal XVI secolo a oggi*. Trieste, 331-334.

Bonino, M., 1978, Lateen-rigged medieval ships. New evidence from wrecks in the Po Delta (Italy) and notes on pictorial and other documents. *IJNA*, 7.1, 15-18.

1979, *Le barche del Po della valle e del mare in Mestieri della terra e delle acque*, vol. IV. Milano, 216-237.

1985, L'Arte di costruire. In: U. Spadoni (ed.), *Barche e gente dell'Adriatico*. Casalecchio di Reno, 9-21.

Brizzi, D., 1999, *Quando si navigava con i trabaccoli*. Rimini.

Canalini, A. (supervized by C. Beltrame), 2005, *Il relitto dell'imbarcazione di Logonovo di Ferrara*, Anno Accademico 2003-2004, Università Ca' Foscari Venezia – Facoltà di Lettere e Filosofia – Corso di Laurea in Conservazione dei Beni Culturali.

Cazzola, F., 1987a, La bonifica del Polesine di Ferrara dall'età estense al 1885. In: *La grande bonifica ferrarese, vol. 1: Vicende del comprensorio dall'età romana alla istituzione del consorzio (1883)*. Ferrara, 107-251.

1987b, Le bonifiche nella valle Padana: un profilo. *Rivista di Storia dell'Agricoltura*, no. 2, dicembre 1987. Firenze, 37-66.

1989, La terra costruita: Ferrara e la bonifica. In: A. M. Visser Travagli & G. Vighi (eds), *Terre ed acqua*: *le bonifiche ferraresi nel delta del Po. Ferrara, Castello Estense, 17 settembre 1989-18 marzo 1990*. Ferrara, 36-50.

1990a, La grande impresa: le bonifiche estensi. In: C. Bassi & A. M. Visser (eds), *L'ambiente come storia*: *il popolamento e il governo delle acque nei secoli*. Ferrara, 123-145.

1990b, Uomini, terra e acque: politica e cultura idraulica nel Polesine tra Quattrocento e Seicento. In: F. Cazzola & A. Olivieri (eds), *Atti del XIV Convegno di Studi Storici organizzato in collaborazione con l'Accademia dei Concordi, Rovigo, 19-20 novembre 1988*. Rovigo, 11-24.

1995, E la terra emerse dalle acque: le fasi storiche della grande bonificazione ferrarese. In: F. Cazzola, P. Luciani & G. Capuzzo (eds), *Dallo scolo naturale al sollevamento meccanico*. Ferrara.

Ivetić, E., 2000, *Oltremare*: *l'Istria nell'ultimo dominio Veneto*. Venezia, 136-147.

Kula, W., 1987, *Le misure e gli uomini dall'antichità a oggi*. Bari.

Marzari, M., 1988, *Trabaccoli e pieleghi nella marineria tradizionale dell'Adriatico*. Milano.

Patitucci Uggeri, S., 1979, Un contesto archeologico del XV secolo dall'area lagunare comacchiese. *Bollettino dei musei ferraresi*, 9-10, 1979-1980. Firenze, 268-280.

Patrignani, W., 1987, Il trabaccolo e la sua gente. Fano.

Pezzoli, S., 1987, *Una carta del Ferrarese del 1814*, ed. by S. Pezzoli & S. Venturi. Ferrara.

Ray Martin, L., 2001, *The art and archaeology of Venetian ships and boats*. College Station/Texas, London.

Steffy, J. R., 1994, *Wooden Ship Building and the Interpretation of Shipwrecks*. College Station/Texas.

NEWS FROM THE NORTHERN SEAS

MORTEN SYLVESTER

THE HAUGVIK BOAT – A PRE-ROMAN IRON AGE BOAT FIND FROM NORTHERN NORWAY

In research on prehistoric boats in Scandinavia, both boats and parts of boats found in bogs have always been an important resource. Some of the best known boat and ship finds were recovered from this type of context. Through the research project »Boats in Bogs«, under the auspices of *Vitenskapsmuseet*, the Museum of Natural History and Archaeology in Trondheim, 29 sites of boat finds in bogs have been documented in the Museum's district. One find from Haugvik in Sømna, Nordland, found in the 1920s and 1930s, was quite surprisingly dated to the transition period between the Bronze Age and Pre-Roman Iron Age (Sylvester 2006). New datings of boat parts found in 2006, however, show that the Haugvik boat find cannot be dated to the Bronze Age, but must be placed in the Pre Roman Iron Age, most likely the 1st or 2nd c. B.C. This makes the find one of the oldest in Norway, and it is one of very few traces of a plank-built boat from this period in Scandinavia.

HISTORY AND SITE OF THE FIND

The boat parts were found in a bog on the Haugvik farm in the municipality of Sømna in S. Helgeland, the region that comprises the southernmost part of the county of Nordland. Haugvik is located at latitude of 65° N., about 350 km (220 miles) N. of Trondheim (**Fig. 1**). The remains of the boat were found on at least two occasions by two different people. The first time, the remains emerged when a drainage ditch was dug through the bog in the 1920s. Apparently the finder did not tell anyone about the discovery, and we do not know how much of the boat was discovered. The second time that remains of the boat were found was when Ole Haugvik, the owner of the land, was cutting peat in the bog in 1931. He found the boat remains lying right on the gravel underneath the peat at a depth of about 0.7 to 0.8 m. Haugvik was asked to place the boat pieces in a dry place under the *stabbur* (storehouse on pillars), and he may also have rubbed a tar-like substance on the pieces.

In July 1941 – ten years after the find was made – the boat parts were examined by one of the museum's contact persons in the region. For reasons that were not specified, he gave permission for the best preserved part to be sawn into two pieces. Perhaps this was to make it easier to send to Trondheim. In 1942, the boat parts were sent to the Museum of Natural History and Archaeology in Trondheim. They were registered in the museum's

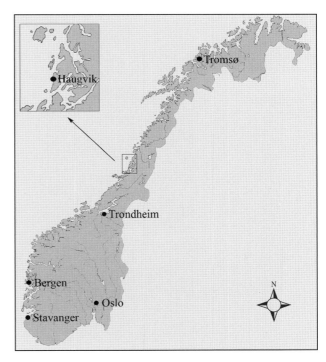

Fig. 1 Map of Norway showing the location of Haugvik.

Fig. 2 Coastal landscape at Haugvik. The site of the find, which is a bog today, was probably a bay in the Bronze Age. Then, as now, the coast was an archipelago with relatively calm and shallow water, sheltered from the open sea (Photo M. Sylvester).

accessions and incorporated in the collection. Correspondence between the museum in Trondheim and the contact person in the region resulted in a decision to conduct a small-scale investigation of the site in 1943, with a thorough survey of the peat pit. During the survey, several highly decayed parts of the boat found in the 1920s were rediscovered. These were also sent to the museum in Trondheim. The plan was to dig a few trenches in the area where Haugvik had found the boat remains, but one had to give up the project due to problems with water flowing in. Instead, a metal spike was used to probe for any remaining boat parts, but this proved fruitless. In the summer of 1944, Haugvik once again cut peat in a delimited area close to the site of the find, but he did not find any more of the boat.

In September 2006, the Museum of Natural History and Archaeology conducted an archaeological and paleobotanical survey of the site. The aim of the excavation was primarily to determine whether more pieces of the boat existed, and also to look for timber made from young wood, which could be used for new and more precise ^{14}C dating. Another intention has been to investigate the deposit and other circumstances of the site where the boat parts were found in the 1920s and 1930s. The highly decayed remains of a boat part with faint traces of a cleat were discovered, and a piece that probably comes from the boat's caprail. The boat parts were not lying *in situ*, but had been moved by Ole Haugvik in 1931. The wood was probably so poorly preserved even at that stage that he had not lifted it out of the bog.

The bog where the boat parts were found lies approximately 10 to 12 m above sea level and 300 m from the present shoreline. The area is a part of the wide strandflat, which comprises the W. part of Sømna (**Fig. 2**). There is information about shoreline displacement from a locality about 20 km E. of Haugvik (Drange 2003). It is possible to use a shoreline displacement curve for this locality as a basis for calculating an equivalent curve for Haugvik by taking account of the isobase direction and gradient. The calculations show that the sea level was about 8 m higher around the year 0, about 11.5 m higher in about 500 B.C. and about 15 m higher in about 1000 B.C. This means that the Haugvik find, which is dated to approximately 1st or 2nd c. B.C., must have lain near the shoreline when it was deposited or abandoned.

The paleobotanical analyses of a peat column removed from the dig in September 2006 are not yet complete, but preliminary analyses of diatoms in the gravel immediately below the peat nevertheless indicate that the boat find may have lain in open fresh water during the period before the peat began to grow. A sample of the peat from the base of the column has been ^{14}C dated to the period 20 B.C. to A.D. 40 (2005±25 BP; Tua-6271), and this dating must be regarded as a *terminus ante quem* for the dating of the boat find.

DESCRIPTION OF THE BOAT TIMBERS

Today, two boat components are preserved (**Figs 3-4**) with carved cleats (a-b) and (c), a worked board with treenails (d), four very decayed pieces, which may originate from the interior reinforcement of the Haugvik boat (e-h), and finally the decayed boat part with faint traces of a cleat, found in 2006 (i).

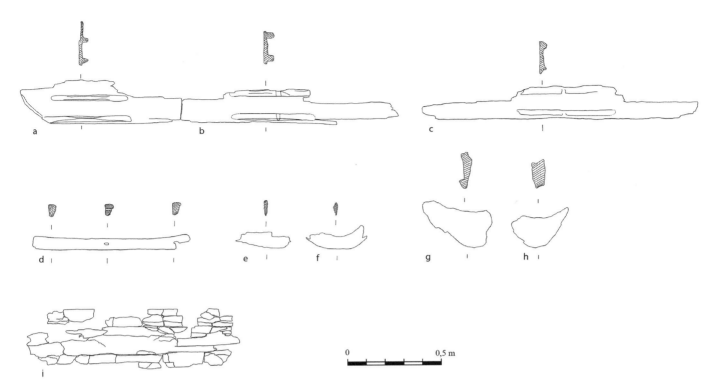

Fig. 3 Preserved boat timbers of the Haugvik find (Drawing M. Sylvester).

The boat part (a-b) of pine (*Pinus sylvestris*), which was sawn in two in 1941, is 205 cm long and 23 cm across the widest part (**Fig. 4**). The thickness varies between 1.5 and 1.8 cm. The diagonal bevelling seen on the left side of the piece is not part of its original shape; it is due to decomposition. On the inside of the timber, four cleats have been carved, divided into two rows. The distance between the row of cleats is 98 cm measured from hole to hole. The cleats are about 30 cm long, with a width of about 3 cm at the base, and a height of about 4 cm in the centre. The distance between the two cleats in each row is 11.5 to 13 cm. The holes in the cleats are triangular or trapezoid, with sides of about 2 cm. The holes are not drilled, but carved or chiselled out with a sharp tool, and traces of this process are visible on the inside of the holes. The carving of the holes seems remarkably fresh, and they seem to have no traces of wear. Tool marks can be seen on each side of the piece.

Piece (c), which is in far worse condition than (a-b), is also made of pine (*Pinus sylvestris*). It is 149 cm long and about 18 cm across the widest part. The thickness is the same as (a-b), about 1.5 to 1.8 cm. The remains of two cleats have been preserved.

The worked board (d) is also of pine (*Pinus sylvestris*), and a length of 84 cm has been preserved. The piece is 6 to 7 cm wide and about 5 cm thick. Although the board is badly decayed, it is possible to see that the cross section is an elongated rectangle. One of the faces is flat, and the other slants inward with faint traces of profiling. More or less at the centre and at one end, there are two rectangular nail holes of about 1 by 1.9 cm. The distance between the holes is 37 cm, and the two treenails that sat in the holes have been preserved. One nail is of pine (*Pinus sylvestris*), and the other is of goat willow (*Salix caprea*) or aspen (*Populus tremula*). This piece was found lying parallel to the two boat parts (a-b) and (c), and in the museum's accession catalogue it was interpreted as part of the boat's caprail. Arne Emil Christensen uses

Fig. 4   Haugvik. – Boat timber after being sawn in two pieces and before it was sent to the museum in Trondheim in 1941 (Photo P. E. Fredriksen).

the term *essinglist* (caprail) for this piece (Christensen 1988: 7). The interpretation seems reasonable, and the rail was probably nailed down with the flat side facing the inside or outside of the upper part of the boat's side.

The pieces (e-h) are so poorly preserved that it is difficult to draw any conclusions about their position and function in the boat. In the accession catalogue, it is speculated that two of the pieces originate from frames; these must be pieces (g) and (h). Christensen interprets these pieces as fragments of frames as well (Christensen 1988: 7).

The boat part (i) of pine (*Pinus sylvestris*), which was found in September 2006, is in about 50 fragments. The fragments have been assembled as far as possible by the museum's conservators. The total length is 114 cm and the piece is about 33 cm wide across the widest part. The thickness varies between 1.5 and 2.0 cm. On the inside, faint traces of a cleat are visible, and there are well preserved tool marks on both sides of the piece. A total of four fragments have an original faceted edge preserved, and it is likely that the whole piece comprises the fragmentary remains of the upper part of the boat's side.

TOOL MARKS

On the best preserved parts found in 1931, and also on the piece found in 2006, clear and fine tool marks are visible (**Fig. 5**). On the boat part (a-b), there are tool marks on both the outside and the inside, but they are clearest on the inside. The area around the cleats has been hewn using a tool with a blade of about 1.5 to 1.7 cm. The area between the two rows of cleats is finely carved using a tool with a blade of only 1 to 1.2 cm, and one can clearly see how the surface has been worked in a technique, in which one carving mark erases the previous one. The result of this technique is an even and smooth surface.

On the piece (i) found in autumn 2006, the tool marks on both the inside and the outside are remarkably well preserved. Silicon casts were taken of both the sides before PEG treatment and freeze drying, and later a more thorough analysis will be undertaken to investigate the tool marks and the woodworking tech-

Fig. 5 Haugvik. – **1** Traces left by a tool with a blade width of about 1.5 to 1.7 cm in the area between the cleats on (a). – **2** The outside of the boat part (i) with tool marks. – **3** 43 tool marks in an area of 10 by 10 cm on the outside of (i). – **4** Traces left by a tool with a blade width of about 1 to 1.2 cm on the inside of the boat part (a) (Photos M. Sylvester).

niques used on the Haugvik boat. Within future experimental archaeology, carving tests in pine with copies of Pre-Roman Iron Age tools will be carried out. At the current stage, the tool marks on the piece have been documented photographically, and it seems as though there may be traces of several phases in the boat building process, with the use of various types of tools and carving techniques. The number of tool marks within an area of 10 by 10 cm on the outside of the boat part is at least 43. The surface preparation of the outside of the boat thus required about 4500 »axe cuts« per square metre, which is an impressive number of work movements.

DATING OF THE HAUGVIK BOAT

As early as 1941, it had been established that the boat find from Haugvik must be prehistoric, and the find was compared with the Bårset boat and the Kvalsund ship from the late Iron Age/Viking period (Pedersen 2002: 9; Myhre 1980: 30).

Detlev Ellmers (1972: 333) argues that the Haugvik find must be dated to the Roman period or the Migration period. He bases this dating on a comparison with the cleats on the Nydam ship and the Halsnøy boat.

Today, the Nydam ship has been dendochronologically dated to cal. A.D. 310 to 320 (Rieck 2003: 304), and from the Halsnøy boat there is a ^{14}C dating that places the find in the period cal. A.D. 380 to 540 (Myhre 1980: 30).

Arne Emil Christensen also dates the Haugvik boat to the Iron Age based on comparison with the Nydam find, and he places the find in the period from the late Roman period to the Migration period (Christensen 1988: 7). In a more recent work, he confirms this dating, but he emphasizes that the double cleats are so far the only detail that can provide an indication of the date (Christensen in press).

Like the Halsnøy boat, the Nydam ship has double cleats. Ellmers (1972: 333) argues that the double cleats are a dating element; more recent vessels have only one cleat, and the older Hjortspring boat has three or more. The number of cleats is thus the principal argument in the typological dating of the Haugvik boat to the Roman period or the Migration period by both Ellmers and Christensen.

In connection with the new studies of the Haugvik find, four samples have been selected for ^{14}C dating. The first sample was taken from piece (h), which was dated to the period 840 to 540 cal. B.C. (2585±85BP; T-17519). Due to the great age of the sample, collated with typological dating, as well as the possibility that the sample had been polluted by a tar-like substance, a second dating was approved for validation. The new sample was drilled out of the back of one cleat on piece (b). The result of the sample is a dating to the period 780 to 420 cal. B.C. (2490±110BP; T-17519 I). As well as the dating of the pieces found in the 1920s and 1930s, samples of the uncontaminated pieces found in 2006 have also been taken. A sample has been taken from one of the fragments with a faceted edge on boat part (i) with the result 390 to 230 cal. B.C. (2245±25BP; TUa-6379), and one sample has been taken from what is probably part of the caprail, with the result 195 to 110 cal. B.C. (2120±25BP; TUa-6378). Since the boat find cannot be older than the most recent dating, the conclusion must be that the Haugvik boat dates back to about the 1st or 2nd c. B.C. This dating harmonizes well with the paleobotanical results, where the earliest peat is now dated to 20 B.C. to A.D. 40. The most probable explanation for the dating of the boat parts found in the 1920s and 1930s to the late Bronze Age or early Pre-Roman Iron Age is the contamination with a tar-like substance applied by Ole Haugvik in 1931, but other explanations cannot be excluded.

REMAINS OF A PLANK-BUILT BOAT?

Although not much of the Haugvik boat has been preserved, there is no doubt that the find with its early dating represents an important contribution to Scandinavian ship and boat archaeology; the boat find shows which technological standards existed and were applied in boat building during this period, from which we have so few finds. As mentioned, it was established early on that the Haugvik find was pre-historic, and the find was later interpreted as the remains of a plank-built boat with carved cleats, dating to the Roman Iron Age or the Migration period. The dating has now been pushed back to the Pre-Roman Iron Age, but is it still reasonable to interpret the find as the remains of a plank-built boat? No traces of joints have been preserved in the form of holes for sewing or nail holes along the edges. Naturally, this may simply be because the original edges were not preserved, but it could also indicate that they never existed – that the boat find is not the remains of a plank-built boat, but something else. Crumlin-Pedersen (pers. comm.) has argued that it is just as likely that the Haugvik find represents the remains of an expanded logboat. In his opinion, it is possible to document this nautical technology in Scandinavia back to at least the 1st c. A.D. (Crumlin-Pedersen 2006). However, the pattern of of annual growth rings shows that this cannot be the case. The growth rings, for example on the piece (a) (**Fig. 5, 4**), are nearly perpendicular to the cross section, indicating that the pieces were cut radially or tangentially from the pine log. If the Haugvik find was the remains of an expanded logboat, the pattern of the annual growth rings would be different, and the conclusion is therefore that the find represents the remains of a plank-built boat.

Both the dating and the construction details on the Haugvik boat make the Hjortspring boat from about the middle of the 4th c. B.C. (Crumlin-Pedersen & Trakadas 2003) the closest parallel find. Evidence that plank-built boats of the Hjortspring type existed so far N. is provided by the find of a thwart at Hampnäs in Västernorrland, Sweden (Jansson 1994; Holmqvist 1997); the thwart, which has been ^{14}C dated to the Pre-Roman Iron Age, is a clear parallel to the aft thwart in the Hjortspring boat.

Since so little of the Haugvik boat has been preserved, and several of the pieces are very poorly preserved, it is naturally not possible to draw detailed conclusions about the boat's full shape and size, but we can conclude that it was fully possible to build a wooden plank-built boat with a thin shell on the Norwegian coast in the Pre-Roman Iron Age. This may not come as a surprise, but the Haugvik boat is the first tangible archaeological evidence of this.

ACKNOWLEDGEMENTS

The author is grateful for the help received from Stein Johansen of the NTNU Library in Trondheim, who analysed the anatomy of the wood, and Lars Olsen, Geological Survey of Norway, who prepared estimates of the shoreline displacement for Haugvik. He is indebted to Ole Crumlin-Pedersen, Roskilde, for valuable comments on the author's Norwegian article about the Haugvik boat (Sylvester 2006), and to Arne Emil Christensen, Oslo for his comments along the way, for tightening the author's analyses and for placing an unpublished article at his disposal. Finally, deep gratitude is owed to Sigve and Ole Haugvik in Sømna for their kind welcome and permission to dig in the bog on their property.

REFERENCES

Christensen, A. E., 1988, Ferdselen til vanns – hva vet vi om båten i forhistorisk tid? *Spor – nytt fra fortiden,* 1988.1, 4-7.

in press, *Forfedrenes farkoster.* Oslo.

Crumlin-Pedersen, O., 2006, Den nordiske klinkbåds grundform – en totusindårig tradition og dens rødder. In: Arisholm *et al.,* *Klink og seil,* 33-56.

Crumlin-Pedersen, O. & Trakadas, A. (eds), 2003, *Hjortspring, a Pre-Roman Iron-Age Warship in Context.* Ships and Boats of the North, vol. 5. Roskilde

Drange, I., 2003, *Strandforskyvningsundersøkelser og kartlegging av tsunamisedimenter i Nordland.* Cand. Scient. oppgave, Universitetet i Bergen.

Elmers, D., 1972, *Frühmittelalterliche Handelsschiffahrt in Mittel- und Nordeuropa.* Offa-Bücher, no. 28. Neumünster.

Holmqvist, M., 1997, Hampnästoften. Sökandet fortsätter efter den »Norrländska Hjortspringbåten«. *Marinarkeologisk Tidskrift,* 1997, 13.

Jansson, S., 1994, A Hjortspring boat from northern Sweden? *MAN Roskilde,* 2, 16-17.

Myhre, B., 1980, Ny datering av våre eldste båter. *Arkeo,* arkeologiske meddelelser fra Historisk Museum, Universitetet i Bergen, 27-30.

Pedersen, W. M., 2002, *Bårsetbåten. En revurdering av rekonstruksjonen fra 1937.* Unpublished thesis in archaeology, Tromsø University.

Rieck, F., 2003, Skibene fra Nydam Mose. In: L. Jørgensen, B. Storgaard & L.G. Thomsen (eds), *Sejrens triumf – Norden i skyggen af det romerske Imperium.* København, 296-309.

Sylvester, M., 2006, Haugvikbåten fra Sømna – en plankebygd båt fra yngre bronsealder eller førromersk jernalder. *Viking, Tidskrift for Norsk Arkeologisk Selskap* 2006 (LXIX), 91-106.

LENA LISDOTTER BÖRJESSON

VIKING AGE NAVIGATION ON TRIAL –
ESTIMATES OF COURSE AND DISTANCE

A considerable part of the Viking Age voyages in the N. Atlantic had to be undertaken without sight of land. There is a discussion whether the navigators of that time made use of any navigational aids in addition to their own senses, good seamanship and knowledge of nature's signs. Among other objects, a kind of sun compass has been suggested as an answer to how they found their way across the N. Atlantic. It has also been argued for an extended terrestrial navigation by sailing from island to island, without the aid of any instruments at all. Inspired by this discussion, the author together with various Scandinavian crews carried out eight trial voyages.

TRIAL VOYAGES

The purpose of this explorative study was to learn about the difference in precision in navigation with a sun compass and a watch, compared with navigation without any instruments at all. Comparison of the average differences between estimated and actually sailed course and distance for a certain length of time, a leg, was chosen as method.

A total of 192 independent observations (with one exception, cf. below) were made under realistic conditions in the open sea. 114 of the observations, representing 1012 nautical miles, divided into four voyages (nos 1 to 4), were made with a sun compass and a watch as the only navigational aids. As distance is a result of the combined knowledge of speed and time, a watch was used to distinguish the distance estimating abilities of the crew. Another 78 observations were made during voyages nos 5 to 8, representing 790 nautical miles and made with no instruments at all. A general chart in small scale with erased position markers was used, though, during all trial voyages in order to communicate the estimated positions to the next helmsman.

Data regarding error to windward and leeward are missing for voyage no. 1. The particulars for this voyage are thus not shown in the tables, and the figures are not included in the statistical values presented here. However, the voyage was made in the Aegean Sea in 1999. The number of legs was 35, comprising a total of 209 nautical miles. The individual errors of estimated course compared with actual course varied from 0 to 25°, giving an absolute average error of 8°. Individual judgements of distance varied between 65 to 133% of real distance, giving an average error of –3% of real distance.

NAVIGATION, VESSELS AND AREAS

When out of sight of land, and when the position of heavenly bodies cannot be measured with enough precision, estimating or measuring the ship's course and distance from its last position, so called dead reckoning, is essential to calculate one's position. Thus the ability to estimate these two factors must have been crucial to navigators of the Viking Age, and this is why the trial voyages focused on them. Some considerations were made on position finding by latitude as well, as this most likely also was done in the Viking Age, but this was not part of the trials discussed here.

A trial voyages with a sun compass and a watch			
voyage no.	2	3	4
year	1999	2000	2005
vessel	Yacht 28′	Viking Age cargo ship	Viking Age cargo ship
area	Skagerrak	Kattegat	North Sea
number of legs	34	24	21
nautical miles, total	386	155	262
error of COURSE			
min-max towards windward	1-15°	2-20°	0-35°
min-max towards leeward	1-42°	0-29°	1-30°
error of DISTANCE			
min-max too short	0-32%	0-54%	0-43%
min-max too long	0-46%	0-83%	0-65%

B trial voyages with no instruments				
voyage no.	5	6	7	8
year	2006	2006	2006	2006
vessel	Yacht 31′	Yacht 31′	Yacht 31′	Yacht 31′
area	Bergen-Shetland	Shetland-the Faeroes	The Faeroes-Shetland	Shetland-the Skagerrak
number of legs	13	15	15	35
nautical miles, total	153	139	152	346
error of COURSE				
min-max towards windward	1-4°	0-27°	1-32°	0-40°
min-max towards leeward	4-22°	1-28°	2-27°	0-13°
error of DISTANCE				
min-max too short	7-23%	0-29%	0-27%	0-32%
min-max too long	4-40%	0-83%	0-67%	0-69%

Table 1   Minimal and maximal values of individual errors regarding course and speed made during one particular trial voyage. – Values rounded to the nearest degree.

According to availability, both modern yachts (trials nos 1, 2, 5 to 8) and reconstructions of Viking Age cargo ships (trials nos 3 and 4) were used (**Table 1**), since the main purpose was navigation, not boat handling. Both kinds of vessels usually sail at a speed varying between 3 to 7 knots. The speed estimations were made in the same way regardless of boat type; by feeling the boat's motion through the sea, or by estimating at which speed the water passed the boat, or a combination of both.

Estimation of the course was also made in the same way on both kinds of vessels. There was probably a somewhat greater possibility that the value of the leeway of the Viking Age cargo ships could be estimated more incorrectly than the yachts', as the former can drift more off course in certain weather conditions than the latter. Regarding other errors, it was assumed that they would apply in the same way to both kinds of vessels.

Except for trial voyage no. 1, all trial voyages were undertaken in the same N. waters as the Viking Age navigators often sailed. During voyages nos 1 and 3, land could be sighted at the horizon, but the information was of limited use to the helmsmen as they were asked to estimate course and distance, not the actual position.

PARTICIPANTS AND CONDITIONS

Trial voyage no. 3 was carried out with the *Vidfamne,* a reconstruction of the find Äskekärrsskeppet, and crewed by members of the Society of Viking Age Ships (Sällskapet Vikingatida Skepp) in Sweden. Voyage no. 4 was made with the *Ottar*, a reconstruction of the find Skuldelev 1, which is owned by the Viking Ship Museum in Denmark, and manned by members of the *Ottar* boat guild. The other trial voyages were mostly carried out by students from or people associated with Fosen folkehögskole in Norway. While the crews' skills ranged from beginner to experienced, the active navigators were experienced or professional sailors. Most of them had been sailing both yachts and square-rigged boats. The author took part in all voyages.

All vessels were using sails for propulsion during the trials. The exception was eight consecutive legs during voyage no. 6 when the engine was used. The reason for this was very light and partly no wind, and a tight schedule due to delays at the outset of the voyage. Whether using the engine influenced the result in a positive or negative way is worth considering. With more or less absent wind and waves it was easier to calculate the boat's leeway, but also more difficult to keep the course.

The wind force varied between 1 to 7 Beaufort, mostly within 2 to 5. As the trials were made during ordinary voyage conditions, all angles of wind direction from beating to running were represented. For safety reasons a weather forecast was obtained every day. Knowledge about the expected wind direction was maybe an advantage, or it may have made the crew less alert to judge the actual wind direction, as this may not have corresponded with the forecast. Recordings were made 24 h a day, and roughly 1/3 of them were made when the sun was barely visible or not visible at all, due to overcast sky or darkness. The only steering aid in those situations was the direction of the wind, the waves and the swell, if noticeable, and sometimes the Pole star.

Two, three or as many as four GPS receivers were on board for recording and safety reasons. The voyages were carried out well away from possible dangers like shallow waters or traffic lanes. The skipper could interrupt the trial at any time and for any reason. On trial voyages nos 1 to 4 the real position was known by only one person on board, who of course kept it secret, while on voyages nos 5 to 8 no one at all knew the real position. In case of poor visibility, it was decided to interrupt those trials with a very good margin to the nearest land.

RECORDING OF TRIALS

Each voyage comprised a number of legs of the same length of time, which coincided in time with the watches and changing of helmsman. The legs varied in length between the voyages from 1 to 3 h. One leg was usually directly followed by another one, but occasionally a row of legs was interrupted by for example vicinity of easily identified land or really bad weather, which made it useless or irresponsible to continue the trial. During voyages nos 5 to 8 there were no such interruptions. The average errors of course and speed for those voyages (**Table 2**) may thereby give a rough clue to a likely total error of dead reckoning during a voyage made under similar conditions during the Viking Age.

The judgement of steered course and sailed distance for each leg was made by each helmsman, who plotted it in the chart at the change of the watch. There were usually three to five helmsmen on each voyage. The navigation was based on dead reckoning only. Since knowledge of actual speed and direction of local current(s) was limited, the current believed to affect the vessel was noted in the form sheet, but not taken into account. Thus it contributed to expand the area of the possible position, without influencing the dead reckoning. The leeway of the vessel was estimated and reckoned with.

Only when a trial voyage was finished were the estimated positions compared with the actual GPS positions for the beginning and end of each leg, The differences in course and distance between the estimated legs and the actual legs were recorded as an error to either windward (–) or leeward (+), expressed in

voyage no.	5	6	7	8
area	Bergen-Shetland	Shetland-The Faeroes	The Faeroes-Shetland	Shetland-the Skagerrak
number of legs	13	15	15	35
nautical miles, total	153	139	152	346
average error of COURSE	+8°	+5°	+3°	–6°
average error of DISTANCE	+5%	–3%	+1%	+3%

Table 2 Average errors for estimated course and distance on trial voyages without any instrument. – Values rounded to the nearest degree. Positive errors are to leeward (course)/too long (distance).

degrees, and as an error of sailed distance, expressed in percentage of actually sailed distance. The distance of each leg varied with the speed, which was not compensated for when calculating the average error. Form sheets with 18 entries were compiled in order to facilitate the discussion of any possible causes of miscalculation of course and distance during a particular voyage. The analysis was based on well-founded guesses, as there could be many reasons for an error, like miscalculations caused by:

1. hardly seen or invisible heavenly bodies due to cloudy/foggy/rainy weather or night/dusk/dawn;
2. misjudgement of the leeway of the vessel;
3. misjudgement of the vessel's speed through water;
4. imperfect knowledge or judgement of tidal streams;
5. imperfect knowledge or judgement of current caused by wind;
6. imperfect knowledge or judgement of permanent currents;
7. inaccurate steering;
8. misreading of the sun compass;
9. the sun compass's gnomon curve made for another date and/or latitude;
10. plotting mistakes in the chart.

During trial voyages nos 5 to 8, when neither watch nor sun compass was used, some possible sources of error were added, such as:

11. inaccurate estimation of the hour;
12. inaccurate estimation of time elapsed;
13. inaccurate observations of the quarters of the sun;
14. inaccurate observations of the direction of the sun compared with the heading of the boat.

Viking Age crews probably knew more about some factors than the modern crews did, and less about others, making it difficult to value if any of the crews would have had any disadvantage regarding the possibilities of correct judging of course and distance.

TRIAL VOYAGES WITH A SUN COMPASS AND A WATCH

The sun compasses on trial were very free interpretations of a find made in 1948 in Uunartoq in Greenland (**Figs 1-2**). Since then, there has been a discussion whether this little piece of wood has been part of a Viking Age navigation device or not. One of several suggestions has favoured the idea of a sun compass (Thirslund 1999). Provided sunshine, of course, and that its gnomon curve is drawn according to the relevant latitude and time of the year, a sun compass usually shows N. more precisely than the magnetic compass, which always has deviation. The gnomon curves used during the trial voyages were constructed mathematically.

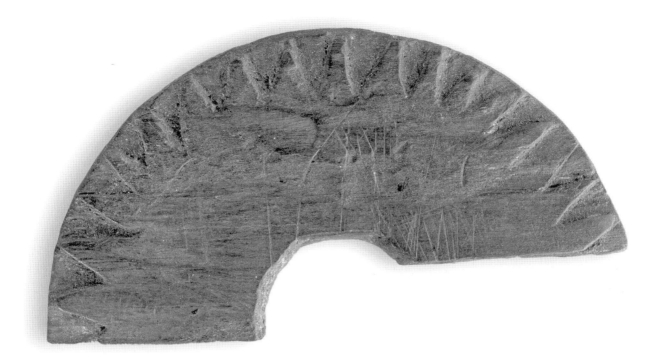

Fig. 1 Among other objects, the Uunartoq find has been suggested to have been a part of a Viking Age sun compass (Photo Werner Karrasch, The Viking Ship Museum, Denmark).

The sun compass was the only instrument to keep the helmsman aware of his bearings during the trial voyages. The possibility of direct observation of the sun was ignored as a help to direction finding. The calculation of sailed distance through the water was based upon the speed estimation, combined with the knowledge of the time elapsed during the watch. This was, when back in harbour, compared with the exact distance over ground measured between the corresponding GPS positions.

TRIAL VOYAGES WITH NO INSTRUMENTS

As nothing is proven about any possible Viking Age navigational aids (Christensen 1992: 151-160), four trial voyages were made from Bergen to the Faeroe Islands and back to the Skagerrak with the same yacht and crew. Apart from a small scale general chart with navigational information covered, neither watch nor any instruments were used, not even a stick to measure the height of the sun with. The position of the sun was the only direction finding help. During the first three voyages the sun was easily seen during 44 % of the legs, sometimes difficult to see during 18 % of the legs, and very difficult or impossible to see during 38 % of the legs due to overcast sky or darkness. For the last voyage, when the sky was clear all the time, the sun was not seen because of darkness during 22 % of the legs. Due to bright nights, the Pole star was not observed until the last voyage, and then just for a few hours.

Waypoints were recorded at watch changes on a GPS with a display covered by tape, so that no one on board would know the actual position during the voyages. The watches, which were supposed to last for 2 h, turned out to be of different length as the exact time was not known. The sun's bearing at sunrise and sunset and the time for those occasions was known, though, which gave the crew a correction of the esti-

Fig. 2 Interpretations of a sun compass, which were used during the trial voyages. The gnomon curves used were constructed mathematically (Photo Vegard Heide, Fosen folkehögskole, Norway).

mated time twice a day. This correction was of course only approximate if the sky was overcast. No attempts were made to find S. by the height of the sun at noon, as the navigation was based upon dead reckoning only. Without an instrument, such a measurement was also considered to be too inexact to rely on. Instead, the crew had to keep track of the time carefully, in order to know in which quarter the sun had moved, and thereby be able to decide where to steer. If the crew believed the time was 1h later then it actually was, this could involve an error in steered course of 15°.

The highest separate error of course was 40°. 78 legs were recorded, and three of them had an error of course greater than 30°, 20 had an error greater than 15°, and 41 of the legs had an error less than 10°. Among them, twelve legs had an error of 1° or 0°.

The average error of dead reckoning was actually smaller than during the voyages made with the help of a sun compass and a watch (**Table 3**). This is interesting, as knowledge of the actual time was essential for direction finding with the help of the quarters of the sun, and knowledge about how long time had elapsed since last noted position was needed for the calculations of sailed distance. Estimation of elapsed time was

	sun compass and watch 79 legs	no instruments 78 legs
COURSE		
average error	+ 4°	0°
average error, absolute	10°	11°
standard deviation	13°	14°
standard deviation, absolute	9°	9°
DISTANCE		
average error	+3%	+1%
average error, absolute	20%	20%
standard deviation	27%	25%
standard deviation, absolute	18%	16%

Table 3 Average errors and standard deviation of estimated course and distance with and without instruments. – Values rounded to the nearest degree. Positive errors are to leeward (course) / too long (distance).

independently made, but estimation of actual time was to some degree dependent on the previous helmsman's estimation. Thus a misjudgement of time in one direction was often followed by another misjudgement in the same direction. Due to this, miscalculations of time sometimes increased from one watch to the next. Errors in time estimation usually varied within 1h, errors of 1 1/2 h were not uncommon, while errors of 2 h were rare.

A likely reason for the relative precision is that the crew, as mentioned, could start the time-keeping from scratch at dusk and dawn. This correction twice a day probably also had a positive influence on how long 2h, or 120 min, were estimated at on the average. The estimated, or at sunrise and sunset corrected, intervals of supposed 2 h varied between 32 and 159 min, but on the average estimations turned out to be 109, 123, 125 and 119 min respectively on voyages nos 5 to 8.

Time-keeping may be seen as a natural way to establish the quarters of the sun, as most modern people are highly aware of the time because of a busy schedule. It required a lot of attention, though. With more experience of light conditions and the sun's height when in different quarters, a glance at the sun now and then would probably have been enough to correct the course steered.

DISCUSSION

In **Table 3** the results from all 157 legs sailed during trial voyages nos 2 to 8 are shown. The average absolute errors show how incorrect the course was on an average to either windward or leeward, and how much too short or too long the distance was estimated. The average absolute errors occurred rather evenly in both directions, thus making the average error much smaller. The standard deviation expresses how much the individual errors were spread compared with the average error. The minimal-maximal values in **Table 1** show how low respectively high the most extreme value for a certain leg was.

The differences of average errors and standard deviation between the methods regarding estimated course and distance turned out to be very small, and in some cases in favour of navigation without any instruments. Conclusions regarding the reasons for this cannot be drawn from this limited material. Yet it should be noted that the sun itself can be used for direction finding for a longer time than the sun compass can be used. The sun compass becomes inexact at sunrise or sunset when the shadow of the gnomon becomes

	yacht 112 legs	Viking Age cargo ship 45 legs
COURSE		
average error	+2°	+1°
average error, absolute	10°	11°
standard deviation	14°	14°
standard deviation, absolute	9°	9°
DISTANCE		
average error	+3%	+1%
average error, absolute	19%	22%
standard deviation	24%	30%
standard deviation, absolute	15%	20%

Table 4   Average errors and standard deviation of estimated course and distance with modern yachts and Viking Age vessels. – Values rounded to the nearest degree. Positive errors are to leeward (course)/too long (distance).

too long for the disc, and it does not work at all when the sky is hazy. In case of an overcast sky, just a glimpse of a pale sun behind the clouds is enough for the experienced navigator to find the approximate quarters, and the course can be held for several hours after this moment with the aid of the direction of wind and waves. The sun compass needs more light to cast a shadow, and more time to be adjusted before it can be read than such a glimpse offers. Estimations of the quarters may be made more exactly with the aid of the sun compass, but it can be done on more occasions in case of bad weather with the help of just the sun. A combination of both methods is of course optimal. But a navigator who concentrates mainly upon the sun compass gets less practice in being observant of the conditions around him, and may thereby become less capable of finding the quarters at times when the sun compass offers no help.

The values in **Table 4** show that errors in estimations of course and distance seem to be made in the same way regardless of the kind of vessel. Thus the results derived from trial voyages made with either Viking Age vessels or modern vessels can be compared.

As the average error for the trial voyages with a sun compass and a watch was towards leeward, it appears as if the helmsmen have been too optimistic regarding the leeway of the vessel.

Due to rough weather during voyage no 4, five legs were steered by the aid of a magnetic compass (not included in the results discussed here). The errors varied from 1 to 11°: one leg to windward with 1° error, and four legs to leeward with errors of 3°, 7°, 10° and 11° respectively. This reminds us that the magnetic compass alone does not guarantee a course without errors.

If the average error would consist only of random errors, the total error of course respectively distance for a particular voyage, measured from start to end, would statistically be the same as the average error, and become smaller the longer one was sailing. However, as the total error is a combination of both structural and random errors, a total error cannot be predicted. Nevertheless, the average absolute error combined with the standard deviation can give a rough clue about what to expect for a particular voyage. About two voyages of three, carried out under the above mentioned conditions, would strictly statistically have a total error in either direction of less than 19° (aver. +1∗std. dev.), and very few of them would have a total error of more than 28° (aver. +2∗std. dev.).

However, if tacking would be needed, giving a zigzagging course, the average error of course might counteract the intended course. This could lead to a higher total error, particularly if the wind does not blow directly against the intended course.

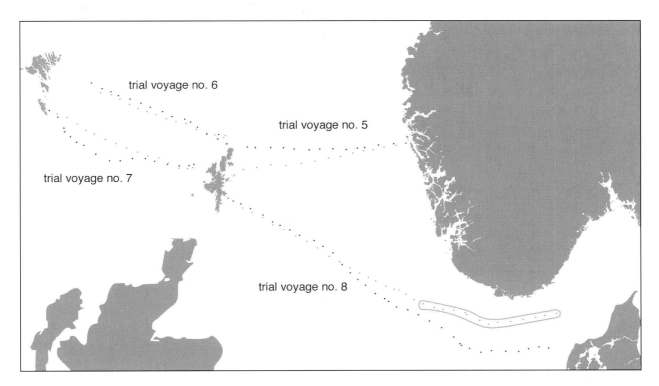

Fig. 3 Trial voyages made without any navigation instruments. Grey dots show estimated positions, black dots show actual positions. Marked positions were believed to be more S. than showed here. Cf. explanation in main text (Computer graphics Rasmus Erlandsson, Fosen folkehögskole, Norway).

Some, or several, of the factors causing errors of course and distance described above will act and counteract each other in different strength and combinations. The influence of some factors may give a structural error, as they make an impact on the course in only one direction. A permanent current, for example, is likely to give an error to either windward or leeward for a certain length of time, as well as a current generated by wind. Both could however be predictable to some extent. The directions of tidal streams at a certain spot in the open sea often complete a full circle during 12 h, thus equalling the impact they have on the ship's course to some extent, depending on the vessel's movements. Estimating the leeway of the boat can be difficult, but not impossible when the navigator is well acquainted with his vessel. Inaccurate steering will probably be done more to one direction than the other by each individual helmsman. Employing different helmsmen could hopefully counteract this probable error somewhat. During no trial voyage was the number of legs in succession where the course error was in the same direction more than seven. Regarding the other factors there are probably no reasons to believe they would dominate in either direction over time, thus giving a random error.

A total error of course of around 10° either way would probably be regarded as acceptable by the Viking Age navigators. When sighting their goal they should have been able, if needed, to correct their course before they would reach any dangerous parts of the coast. Provided that a W. course was set towards the middle of Shetland, it was actually possible to steer 10° off course either way and still make a landfall, even if the islands would be totally hidden by fog. If sailing from Shetland to the Faeroes, the same error of 10° would be acceptable. From the Faeroes to Iceland it was possible to have a total steering error of as much as 18° either way and still find the island in bad visibility. In normal visibility the range expands considerably, since all N. Atlantic islands are large, and in most cases rather high (Haasum 1989: 57).

The individual average estimation of the distance sailed during one leg was around 20% higher or lower than the real distance. The average error of distance based upon all 157 legs was +3% when navigating with a sun compass and a watch and +1% when navigating without any instruments (**Table 3**). Counted on shorter distances, like a particular voyage, the average errors were somewhat higher (**Table 2**). These values may be compared with the speed measuring abilities of the Walker's log, which was still in use 30 years ago. It is stated to show the speed with an error varying between 3 and 4% (Enby 1965: 189).

Fig. 3 shows the effects of the average errors of dead reckoning during the trial voyages without any instrument. The tracks end where land was sighted and the trial was over. The average errors of course and distance for these voyages are shown in **Table 2**. The grey dots on **Fig. 3** represent the estimated positions defining a particular leg, and the black dots represent the actual positions, which correspond with the same leg. Misjudgement of time once resulted in a watch of only 32 min estimated length, as the sun reached the horizon much earlier than expected. The crew realized that the course steered had been too much to the S., and found it likely that an error in time-keeping had occurred already in the morning, as accompanying dolphins then had disturbed the usually concentrated helmsmen for a long period. For this reason the plotting was maintained, but the crew expected the positions marked with shadowed dots to be further S. than showed here.

Even though these voyages were carried out under conditions, which in several ways were comparable to the conditions the Viking Age navigators should have encountered, one important difference ought to be repeated: in order to communicate the estimations of course and speed between the crew, and later to a bigger audience, a protractor, a divider and a general chart in small scale were used. All information for the actual sailing area was photocopied away in advance, leaving the chart blank over the open sea. The chart was probably useful, compared with keeping track of the movements of the vessel only in the navigator's head, as probably was the case in the Viking Age. A new trial voyage will hopefully shed light on how important a chart may be for the precision of navigation, when sailing in waters where the positions of islands are roughly known.

CONCLUSION

As a contribution to the discussion whether the Viking Age navigators made use of any instruments or not, eight trial voyages representing a distance of 1802 nautical miles were carried out in the open sea under realistic conditions. The purpose was to examine the difference in precision between navigation with a sun compass and a watch, respectively with no instruments at all except a chart.

The difference between the two methods regarding average errors of estimated course and distance turned out to be small, and in some cases in favour of navigation without any instruments at all. In spite of the limited material, the results from these trial voyages may stimulate the discussion whether the Viking Age navigators were dependent or not on any instruments for their navigation.

ACKNOWLEDGEMENTS

The author is indebted to Sören Thirslund from the Danish Maritime Museum in Helsingør, and Anton Englert and Max Vinner from the Viking Ship Museum in Roskilde. They all have inspired, and their encouragement and help has been invaluable. I also wish to thank all participating crew members. It is the result of their curiosity, enthusiasm and good seamanship that I have tried to transform into the figures of this paper. – The statistical contents have been revised and approved by Bengt Holm, Man. Dir. at Detector Market Research and Consulting AB.

REFERENCES

Burch, D., 1990, *Emergency navigation*. Camden.

Christensen, A. E., 1992, Vikingenes verdensbilde, skipsbygging og navigasjon. *Norsk sjøfartsmuseums årsbereting*, Oslo, 151-160.

Collinder, P., 1943, *Från Noaks duva till gyrokompassen*. Stockholm.

Crowley, T., 2004, *The Lo-Tech Navigator*. Woodbridge.

Enby, E., 1965, *Navigation under ansvar*. Göteborg.

Englert, A., 2003, *Trial voyages as a method of experimental archaeology: The aspect of speed*. In: *ISBSA 10*, 35-42.

Falk, H., 1995, *Fornnordisk sjöfart*. Skärhamn.

Fisher D., 1995, *Latitude Hooks and Azimuth Rings*. Camden.

Gatty, H., 1943, *The Raft Book*. New York.

1999, *Finding Your Way Without Map or Compass*. New York.

Haasum, S., 1989, *Båtar och navigation under vikingatid och medeltid*. Gamleby.

Karlsen, L. K., 2003, *Secrets of the Viking Navigators*. Washington.

Lagan, J., 2006, *The Barefoot Navigator*. London.

Lewis, D., 1990, *Havets stigfinnare*. Stockholm.

Morcken, R., 1983, *Sjøfartshistoriske artikler gjennom 20 år*. Bergen.

Ramskou, T., 1969, *Solstenen*. København.

1982, *Solkompasset*. København.

Roslund, C., 1985, Hur hittade vikingarna Vinland? *Forskning och Framsteg*, 5, 4-11, 20.

Saugmann, S. A., 1981, *Vikingernes tidsregning og kursmetode*. København.

Schnall, U., 1975, *Navigation der Wikinger*. Hamburg.

Severin, T., 1978, *Brendans resa*. Stockholm.

Sølvær, C. V., 1954, *Vestervejen*. København.

Thirslund, S., 1987, *Trek af navigationens historie*, vol. 1. Helsingør.

1999, *Vikingetidens navigation*. Humlebæk.

Thomas, S., 1987, *The last navigator*. New York.

Vilhjalmsson, T., 1997, *Time and travel in Old Norse Society*. www.raunvis.hi.is/~thv/t_t.html [01.09.2009].

Vinner, M., 1993, *At ramme en række pukkotræer – lidt om »primitiv« navigation i Oceanien*. Roskilde.

1998, *Kompendium i vikingetidens navigation*. Roskilde.

Wallgren. L., 1992, *Lille Orm – en färd i öppen jolle från Birka till Färöarna på vikingavis*. Stockholm.

Winther, N., 1875, *Færøernes Oldtidshistorie*. København.

MIKE BELASUS

TWO RECENT FINDS OF MEDIEVAL SHIPWRECKS IN THE NORTH OF GERMANY

From the 9th to the middle of the 14th c. settlers from the N.W. of Europe moved into the Slavonic territory E. of the rivers Elbe and Saale. This movement culminated in the foundation of towns in the 12th and 13th c. Water transport across the Baltic and along the rivers was of high importance within this development. Vessels of any kind were needed for different purposes, above all to keep the established trading network running and the towns alive. Maritime infrastructure was the vital element of the system and this development caused fundamental changes in the construction of ships. However, for many years this region could hardly be included into research work and archaeological analysis. Due to the absence of material it was difficult to study the development of medieval ships of the area. Until the political change in the early 1990s underwater archaeology along the S. Baltic coast was very restricted and, with a few exceptions, only rarely undertaken.

With the fall of the Berlin Wall the situation has changed. After almost sixteen years of underwater archaeological work in the state of Mecklenburg-Vorpommern, formerly the most N. area of the German Democratic Republic, several medieval ship finds and material from the harbours have opened new options for research projects. In contrast to the material excavated in Poland up to now only one timber of a typical inland craft has been recovered in Mecklenburg-Vorpommern. The fragment of a typical L-shaped floor timber of a flat-bottomed vessel was found in the city of Greifswald (Bleile 1997: 142).

THE ARENDSEE SHIP

Further S. in the state of Sachsen-Anhalt the well preserved wreck of a 13th c. flat bottomed inland craft was found (**Fig. 1**). The wreck was discovered in the Arendsee, a lake in the Altmark region (Altmarkkreis Salzwedel), by the local sport divers Hans-Henning Schindler and Hartmuth Schindler in 1990. The lake is situated in the N.W. of Sachsen-Anhalt about 20 km S. of the River Elbe. The lake only measures 3.5 by 2 km but it is one of the deepest lakes in Germany with an average depth of 29 m. In the history of the lake several landslides were caused by the erosion of layers of salt under the lake by the ground water. Some of them are described in historical documents as early as A.D. 822. In the 9th c. the Altmark region was christianised and later used as starting point for the following conquest of the Slavonic territory E. of the Elbe (Hartmann & Schönberg 2003: 2).

Due to the geological history of the lake, there is an extraordinary wealth of archaeological sites underwater.

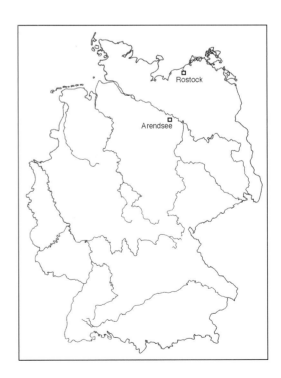

Fig. 1 Germany with the two recently discovered 13th c. shipwrecks mentioned in the text.

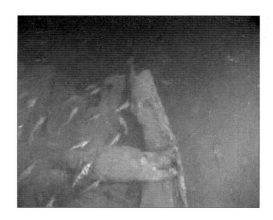

Fig. 2   The Arendsee ship on the ground of the Arendsee lake (Photo H. Lübke, Landesamt für Kultur und Denkmalpflege Mecklenburg-Vorpommern, Schwerin).

Fig. 3   Arendsee ship. – Hollowed-out transition plank on one side of the wreck (Photo reproduced from the video documentation of A. Grundmann, Landesamt für Kultur und Denkmalpflege Mecklenburg-Vorpommern, Schwerin).

Most of them were discovered by the dedicated sport divers of the Lake Arendsee Diving Club. The first contact between the sport divers and the archaeologist from the Landesamt für Denkmalpflege und Archäologie (state heritage authority of Sachsen-Anhalt), Rosemarie Leineweber, took place in 2004. In cooperation with the divers from the Landesamt für Kultur und Denkmalpflege (state heritage authority of Mecklenburg-Vorpommern) the first underwater survey was carried out in April 2004 under the supervision of Harald Lübke. This work continued throughout the following years and was constantly supported by the local diving club. During these diving campaigns several sites discovered by the sport divers were surveyed. In 2005 a 14th c. logboat was raised and will be displayed in the state museum for archaeology in Halle after conservation (Leineweber & Lübke 2006). In 2006 a Neolithic fish trap was documented and partially lifted for conservation and future display (Leineweber & Lübke 2006). In April 2005 the first investigation of the medieval shipwreck was carried out under the supervision of Rosemarie Leineweber and Harald Lübke (Belasus in press).

The wreck

The wreck lies in a depth of about 30 m (**Fig. 2**). To a great extent it is covered with soft lake sediments. Only the upper parts of the vessels sides and the ends of the vessel are visible and give a good impression of its construction. The wreck has a length of 12.3 m and is 2.3 m wide in the midship section. The hull tapers to 1.9 m towards both ends. The flat bottom consists of at least three broad planks laid edge to edge. These planks are bent upwards towards stem and stern. Hollowed-out planks form the transition between the bottom and the vessel sides (**Fig. 3**). L-shaped floor timbers were inserted into the vessel to support the hull (**Fig. 4**). In the visible parts of the construction the upright shorter part of the floor timbers was inserted alternating on both sides. On one end a knee was observed that could have been used on the last floor timber to improve the stability of the hull in this part of the ship (**Fig. 5**). Already during the 1990s a massive beam was lifted from one end of the vessel, which is unfortunately lost today (**Fig. 6**). The only surviving picture of this timber was taken from a video documentation. Presumably this beam was used to stabilise the hull construction in the end of the ship. During the investigation of the ship no further beam was found but it is likely that both ends were constructed in a very similar way. No determination of stem or stern can be made at this stage of research. The upper side planking came loose and fell off on both sides. No connection between the single strakes was observed. The outer planking is fastened to the floor

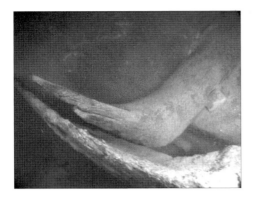

Fig. 4 Arendsee ship. – L-shaped floor timber (Photo reproduced from the video documentation of A. Grundmann).

Fig. 5 Arendsee ship. – Loose knee in one end of the vessel (Photo reproduced from the video documentation of A. Grundmann).

Fig. 6 Arendsee ship. – Massive beam lifted in the 1990s (Photo reproduced from a video of R. Pohlmann, Tauchclub Arendsee, Arendsee).

Fig. 7 Arendsee ship. – Lower side of the bottom planks with traces of iron corrosion (Photo reproduced from the video documentation of A. Grundmann).

timbers with treenails. Traces of iron corrosion were observed on the underside of the bottom planks on one end of the ship but no specific iron feature or object was found (**Fig. 7**).

The wreck from the Arendsee is a bottom-built inland vessel also called »Prahm« in Germany. It is built from local oak that was dendrochronologically dated to after A.D. 1265. A contemporary ship find similar to the vessel from the Arendsee was found for example at Krefeld-Gellep on the Lower Rhine. This could be dated to the 13th and 14th c. Only the foremost part of the ship, consisting of a massive cross beam in the foremost part, L-shaped floor timbers and hollowed out transition planks survived (Ellmers 1976: 47). Wrecks of the same period recovered from the Vistula River, show similar features as e.g. floor timbers and transition plank (Ossowski 2004: 83-95). Most similarities can be found in the late 12th c. ship find from Egernsund in Denmark and the Haithabu 4 wreck in Germany (Crumlin-Pedersen 1997: 300-303; Bill & Hocker 2004: 43; Nakoinz 2005: 123-142). These wrecks were found along the Baltic coast of the Jutland peninsula. Both vessels have L-shaped floor timbers, which are inserted with the upright part alternating on both sides.

Hollowed-out planks form the transition between bottom- and side planking. The bottom planks are bent upward towards the ends where cross-timbers are forming the ends of the hull: beam-like in the Haithabu 4 wreck and rampart-like in the find from Egernsund. In the Haithabu 4 wreck, an additional knee was added to the last L-shaped floor timber at each end of the vessel.

Historical background

Fig. 8   Rostock-Hohe Düne. – Hooked keel plank recovered in the course of dredging (Photo H. Pohl, Landesamt für Kultur und Denkmalpflege Mecklenburg-Vorpommern, Schwerin).

The vessel from the Arendsee was probably used for transport purposes. In 1183 a Benedictine nunnery was founded on the S. banks of the lake on the road between the towns of Salzwedel and Seehausen just 200m off the wreck site (Dehio 2002: 29). The nunnery owned substantial land around the lake and it can be assumed that they transported agricultural products and timber across the lake. In 1208 the settlement of Arendsee was mentioned for the first time and at least in 1289 a warehouse existed here in competition to the Benedictine nuns (Dehio 2002: 29). It might also be possible, that the citizens of the settlement used the vessel for their purposes. Trading contacts to the towns of the Hanseatic League are evident in the historical records of that time. In 1244 for example grain from the Altmark region was sold to Flanders via the city of Hamburg (Hammel-Kiesow 2000: 37). The transport of the grain was probably carried out by inland watercraft on the Elbe.

The lake Arendsee ship is the first medieval bottom-build inland craft found in a lake of N. Germany. The wreck has to be seen in the context of shipbuilding and shipping of that period on the Elbe. Presumably the shipwright was local to the area. To date no archaeological evidence of medieval merchant shipping on the Elbe was recorded.

THE ROSTOCK-HOHE DÜNE SHIP

During the construction of a new marina in Rostock-Hohe Düne, a 14th c. shipwreck was discovered on the mouth of the River Warnow in 2004. The wreck was hit by a dredger. Archaeologists from the Landesamt für Kultur und Denkmalpflege assessed one of the timbers recovered in the course of the dredging and identified it as a part of a hooked keel plank, typical for medieval ships built in the so-called cog-building tradition (**Fig. 8**). While one end of the plank shows the hook that was made from the same piece as the plank the other end shows a vertical scarf. The oak was dendrochronologically dated to after A.D.1304.

In cooperation with the Landesamt für Kultur und Denkmalpflege, the society for underwater archaeology Mecklenburg-Vorpommern under the supervision of Andreas Grundmann and Dirk Hering excavated test pits in spring 2006. The aim of this project was to investigate the vessels construction and assess the extent of destruction caused by the dredger.

The wreck

The vessel lies upside down just a few centimetres beneath the seafloor level in a depth of about 4 m (**Fig. 9**). The wreck has a length of 13.5 m and a beam of 2.7 m. The dredger obviously had caused severe damage. The rear part of the vessel, from midship towards the sternpost, is almost completely destroyed. Just one floor timber, connected to a stringer and two outer planks on the portside, is still in place. The straight sternpost lies on the centreline of the wreck but it was moved inwards (**Fig. 10**). Remains of planks and one rudder gudgeon with an inner diameter of 5 cm are still attached. The sternpost consists of an inner and an outer post. Only a few broken pieces of the outer post survived. While most of the other

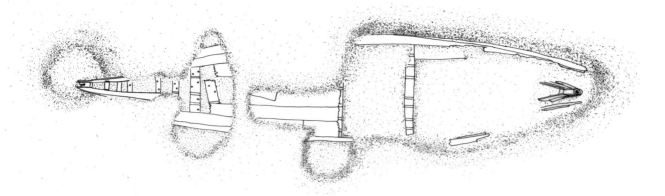

Fig. 9 Rostock-Hohe Düne. – Sketch of the wreck (Drawing M. Belasus).

timbers are lost, remains of the side planking are still in place. These give an idea of the outline of the whole ship.

The foremost part of the vessel was less destroyed. Here extensive parts of the lower hull survived. The outer part of the stem post construction, a few bottom planks and the keel plank are missing, whereas the rest is in a good state of preservation down to the second strake of the side planking. The remaining fragment of the inner stem post shows a horizontal hole for a treenail with a diameter of 3 cm that was used to attach the outer post. The bottom planks were laid edge to edge while the side planking was clinker built. For the connection of the clinker planking 1 cm square iron nails where driven through the planks from the outside to the inside, bent twice and driven into the wood again. The planks are 32 to 37 cm wide and about 4.5 cm thick. Tar soaked moss was used to water tighten the hull of the ship. To keep the moss in the seams it was covered with 2.5 cm wide and 0.5 cm thick laths that were fastened with iron staples (Dutch: *sintelen*). All planks were fastened to the frames with treenails of 3 cm in diameter. The first four frames in the bow section are V-shaped and have limber holes on each side of the

Fig. 10 Rostock-Hohe Düne. – Stern post of the wreck with the rudder gudgeon remains of the side planking (Photo A. Grundmann).

keel plank. The first and the second floor timbers are not attached to the keel whereas the remaining floor timbers are attached with two treenails each. The fifth floor timber is rather U-shaped and the bottom of the vessel gets flatter towards the middle, which is only slightly rounded. All visible frames have square limber holes. These are 6 to 8 cm wide and 3 cm high, cut into the wood in a distance of 15 to 20 cm. The first four frames are 15 to 18 cm wide. From the fifth frame towards the stern the frame size extends to 21 to 25 cm.

The wreck from Rostock Hohe Düne is built in the so-called cog-building tradition. The rather light dimensions of the timbers and the width/length ratio of about 1:5 suggest a medium sized slender vessel that might have been about 15 m in length and 3 m in width. The V-shaped frames in the front cause a sharp bow section. Towards the middle it is fairly beamy with only slightly rounded floor timbers in the midship section. Taking the remains of the rear half of the vessel into account, an outline similar to the bow section can be assumed. It is very likely that the ship used to be a coastal vessel before it ran ashore.

On the other hand, it might have been employed for transport duties. Due to sedimentation processes the warehouses of the medieval town of Rostock were not accessible for larger vessels, consequently smaller ships were used to unload and transport goods along the Warnow.

CONCLUSIONS

Both vessels are examples of the development of shipbuilding in the high medieval period. They are invaluable sources for future research on the development of the medieval ship E. of the Elbe and along the S.W. Baltic coast.

REFERENCES

Belasus, M., in press, Ein hochmittelalterlicher Schiffsfund aus dem Arendsee, Altmarkkreis Salzwedel. *Archäologie in Sachsen-Anhalt*, 4.

Bill, J. & Hocker, F. M., 2004, Haithabu 4 seen in the Context of contemporary Shipbuilding in Southern Scandinavia. In: Brandt & Kühn, *Haithabu*, 43-53.

Bleile, R., 1997, Maritimes Kulturgut aus Stadtkerngrabungen in Rostock und Greifswald. *Jahrb. BMV*, 44, 1996, 133-149.

Crumlin-Pedersen, O., 1997, Viking *Age Ships and Shipbuilding in Hedeby/Haithabu and Schleswig*. Ships and Boats of the North, vol. 2. Schleswig, Roskilde.

Dehio, G., 2002, *Sachsen-Anhalt I, Regierungsbezirk Magdeburg*. Handbuch der Deutschen Kunstdenkmäler. München.

Ellmers, D., 1976, *Kogge, Kahn und Kunststoffboot. 10000 Jahre Boote in Deutschland*. Führer des Deutschen Schiffahrts-museums, no. 7. Bremerhaven.

Hammel-Kiesow, R., 2000, *Die Hanse*. München.

Hartmann, O. & Schönberg, G., 2003, *Der Arendsee in der Alt-mark. Geologie und Entwicklung*. Landesamt für Geologie und Bergwesen Sachsen-Anhalt. Magdeburg.

Leineweber, R. & Lübke, H., 2006, Unterwasserarchäologie in der Altmark. *Archäologie in Sachsen-Anhalt, 4, 127-139*.

Nakoinz, O., 2005, Wrack 4 von Haithabu. Ein Prahm des 12. Jahr-hunderts und seine Parallelen im Ostseeraum. *Arch. Korrbl., 35*, 123-142.

Ossowski, W., 2004, Medieval large river craft from the Vistula River, Poland. In: Brandt & Kühn, *Haithabu*, 83-95.

JENS AUER · REX BANGERTER · FRANCIS MALLON

THE WRECK OF AN ELIZABETHAN MERCHANTMAN FROM THE THAMES

A PRELIMINARY FIELDWORK REPORT

The Princes Channel wreck, also termed Gresham ship after the associated armament, was discovered by the Port of London Authority (PLA) during a pre-dredging survey in the Princes Channel, one of the S. approaches to the Port of London in the Thames Estuary (**Fig. 1**). After initial attempts to disperse the wreck site, which was believed to be the remains of a Thames barge, Wessex Archaeology Ltd., an archaeological contractor based in the S. of England, was asked to undertake a site assessment when cannons and an anchor were found amongst the material grabbed from the site.

A series of geophysical and archaeological surveys followed, in the course of which two large hull sections were recovered by the PLA, because they presented a danger to shipping in the channel. These sections, termed piece 1 and piece 2 were recorded by Wessex Archaeology and dated to the 16th c. by Nigel Nayling, University of Wales (Nayling 2004). When a sidescan survey of the initial wreck site confirmed the presence of a further two hull sections on the seabed, the full excavation of the site was planned.

EXCAVATION AND RECORDING

The excavation and recording commenced in August 2004. The aim was to excavate and consequently remove the two remaining structural elements of the shipwreck as well as all disarticulated artefacts on the site. The excavation was carried out by a combined PLA Marine Services and Wessex Archaeology dive team. A PLA tug was used as diving support vessel. The exposed location of the wreck site in a busy shipping lane and the adverse environmental conditions with strong currents and low to very low underwater visibility necessitated the use of commercial surface-supplied diving equipment. Diving was generally

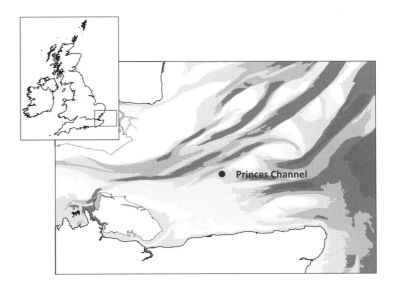

Fig. 1 Princes Channel wreck/Gresham ship. – Location of the wreck site (Drawing J. Auer).

limited to high and low water slack periods and two divers were employed simultaneously to maximise bottom time on site.

Diving tasks prior to full excavation included the tagging of all timbers with unique context numbers and the preparation of a pre-disturbance sketch plan. Due to the lack of visibility, the plan was drawn on the surface, based on observations and measurements conveyed by the diver through the underwater communication system. To keep the recording process as straightforward as possible, traditional offset measuring methods were combined with trilateration for objects located around the wreck site.

Airlifts were used to remove sediment from and around the preserved elements of hull structure. Mesh bags were fastened to the end of the airlifts to allow sieving of the dredged material for small finds. All elements of the cargo that were present on the inside of the timber structures were recorded and consequently lifted. The timber structures were lifted by the PLA salvage vessel *Hookness* using an arrangement of lifting strops and bars. While the recovery of piece 4, the bow section of the wreck, was unproblematic, the side of the vessel, termed piece 3, broke apart while still on the seabed and had to be lifted in two parts, piece 3a and piece 3b. Once lifted, the timber sections were either submerged in barges or covered and kept wet with leaky hose systems while the underwater work continued.

Shoreside recording of timber structures, timbers and finds took place in periods of bad weather during the diving fieldwork and after completion of the diving work. All small-finds were photographed and entered into a MS-Access database. Disarticulated timbers were sketched or drawn at 1:10, photographed and recorded on paper as well as in a database. The three structurally intact hull sections were left assembled and recorded in the same way as the previously lifted sections piece 1 and piece 2. A Leica TCRA 1105 reflectorless total station was used in conjunction with the software packages TheoLT and AutoCAD. While this method allowed rapid and accurate three-dimensional recording of the overall structure, it had to be supplemented by photographs, sketches and 1:10 drawings of selected elements as well as timber record sheets for detailed recording.

DESCRIPTION OF THE HULL REMAINS

Altogether, five coherent hull sections of the Gresham ship are preserved. They include the bow section of the wreck and an approximately 14 m long run of the port side, from a level above the keel to a level above the orlop deck (**Fig. 2**). All sections are made of oak of English origin (Nayling 2004).

The bow section, termed piece 4, has a height of 4.9 m and a length of 2.2 m. It consists of a fragment of the keel, which is joined to the stempost. Stemson and apron are partly preserved. Two V-shaped square rising floor timbers are *in situ* on the inside of the section and a single futtock survives on the port side. Broken treenails and treenail holes indicate the positions of further frames as well as breasthooks. Seven strakes of outer planking, including the garboard strake, are present on the starboard side. As this side was covered by sediment, the planks are well preserved and still show signs of a white protective surface covering. The port side is less well preserved with six heavily eroded strakes from the garboard upward *in situ*.

Piece 3a and piece 3b form the foremost part of the port side. Piece 3a, the lower part of the port side, measures 8.2 by 2.23 m. It consists of six strakes of outer planking. On the inside, the surviving upper ends of the floor timbers are joined to eleven futtocks. All futtocks are broken where piece 3b was joined to piece 3a. Filling frames were inserted between floor timbers and futtocks, presumably to strengthen the turn of the bilge. Two ceiling planks survive *in situ*.

Piece 3b represents the remainder of the ships side from just above the turn of the bilge to the level of the gunports on the orlop deck. It measures 6.3 by 3 m. On the outside, four strakes of planking lead up to a

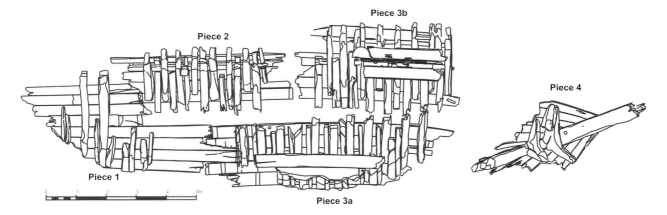

Fig. 2 Princes Channel wreck/Gresham ship. – Overview of the preserved hull sections (Drawing J. Auer, based on data acquired by Wessex Archaeology).

wale, which is composed of five strakes. Above the wale, a complete gunport is visible, with the edge of a second gunport preserved 2.5 m aft of the first. On the inside of piece 3b, the orlop deck construction is apparent below the gunports. Deck beams and planks are missing, but the beam-shelf as well as a half-beam clamp and part of the waterway survive. A sandwiched stringer provides longitudinal strength on the height of the orlop deck.

Piece 1 and piece 2 form the aftermost preserved part of the ship's port side. Both sections were originally joined with piece 2 at the top, but broke apart during the recovery in November 2003. Piece 1 measures 7.48 by 3.34 m. Of the outer planking eight strakes are preserved. On the inside, the upper ends of three floor timbers remain *in situ*. In addition two first futtocks and a number of filling frames are visible. Piece 2 measures 6.11 by 2.29 m. It is composed of five strakes of outer planking, two of which form part of the wale, and was joined to piece1 and piece 3b. As in piece 3b, the orlop deck construction is visible on the inside of this section. The only preserved end of a deck beam is located on piece 2.

THE CONSTRUCTION OF THE GRESHAM SHIP

The most noticeable feature in the construction is a doubling of all framing timbers from the turn of the bilge upwards. The double frames taper from their full moulded dimension to approx. 50 mm and rest on a plank, which is triangular in section. The triangular plank fills the gap between the heel of the outer framing timber and the surface of the first futtock and thus provides a smooth surface for the application of outer planks (**Fig. 3**). The purpose of the double framing was not fully understood until the explanation of the term »furring« was found in the dictionary of Sir Henry Mainwaring: the other, which is more eminent and more properly furring, is to rip off the first planks and to put other timbers upon the first, and so to put on the planks upon these timbers. The reason for it is to make a ship bear a better sail, for when a ship is too narrow and her bearing either not laid out enough or too low, then they must make her broader and lay her bearing higher. They commonly fur some two or three strakes under water and as much above, accordingly, as the ship requires, more or less. »I think in all the world there are not so many ships furred as are in England, and it is pity that there is no order taken either for the punishing of those who build such ships or the preventing of it, for it is an infinite loss to the owners and an utter spoiling and disgrace to all ships that are so handled« (Mainwaring & Perrin 1922). The Gresham ship was furred, presumably either during the construction process or shortly thereafter. The original outer planking was removed and a second layer of framing timbers added. On the level of the orlop deck above the waterline,

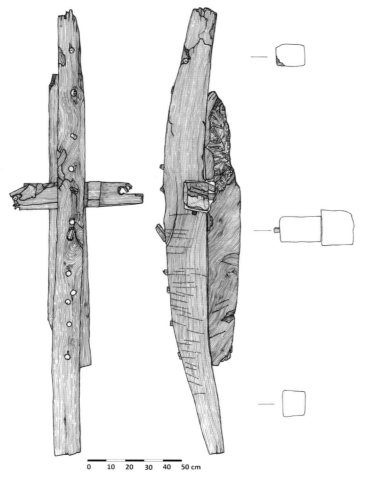

further chocks were inserted between original frames and furring timbers in some places to achieve the desired moulded dimension. The original wale was left *in situ* between original frames and furring timbers and served as a stringer to increase longitudinal strength. The aforementioned plank with triangular section closed the gap between furring timbers and frames and allowed re-planking of the hull. As a result of the furring process the vessel gained approx. 300 mm in width on either side. This increase in fullness is also reflected in the stem rabbet where filling pieces were used to change the angle of the rabbet and accommodate the hood ends of the planks.

Keel

Only a 1.82 m long fragment of the forward end of the keel is preserved (**Fig. 4**). One end is joined to the stempost with a flat vertical scarf joint, while the other end is broken. The keel is made from oak and heavily eroded, moulded and sided dimension appear to be approximately 25 to 30 cm. The upper 90 mm of the moulded dimension is occupied by the between 60 and 65 mm deep rabbets. In addition to treenails and iron bolts securing the scarf joint, four vertical treenails of unclear function were observed in the moulded side of the keel fragment.

Fig. 3 Princes Channel wreck/Gresham ship. – Loose timbers found adjacent to the wreck: furring timber on first futtock (Drawing Rex Bangerter).

Stempost assembly

The preserved part of the stempost has a total length of 4.86 m (**Fig. 4**). The upper part shows signs of a fresh break, while the heel is joined to the keel. The post has an average sided dimension of 200 to 250 mm on the outside and 25 to 35 cm on the inside. The average moulded dimension is 300 mm. Stem rabbets with an average depth of 65 to 70 mm and an angle of approximately 36° are located between 12 cm and 15 cm from the outside of the post. In the lower part of the post, the hood ends of a series of outer planks are fastened in the rabbet with a combination of treenails and iron nails. Tool-marks and cut treenails show that the rabbet angle was modified to reflect the ship's increase in fullness caused by furring. The stemson is fastened to the inside of the stempost with treenails and iron bolts. The visible length is 3.08 m; the sided dimension on the inside is 550 mm. The moulded dimension is about 25 cm. Filling pieces were used to close the gap between post and stemson, and to provide a smooth surface for planking. All elements of the bow section are made from oak. As the bow section was left assembled, the apron and the joint between apron and stemson cannot be described in detail as yet. The bow section will be subject of detailed recording in the post excavation process.

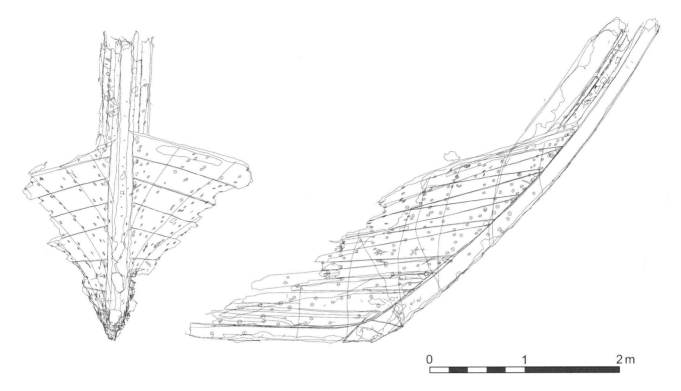

Fig. 4 Princes Channel wreck/Gresham ship. – Side view and front view of the bow section (Drawing J. Auer, based on data acquired by Wessex Archaeology).

Fig. 5 Princes Channel wreck/Gresham ship. – Non-trapezoidal dovetail joint between floor timber and first futtock on piece 3a. – Scale 50 cm (Photo J. Auer).

Framing

All frames were either sawn or converted with an axe from oak and then dubbed with an adze. Floor timbers, first futtocks and second futtocks as well as filling frames are preserved. While the size of the main framing components is fairly consistent with average moulded and sided dimensions between 150 and

Fig. 6   Princes Channel wreck/Gresham ship. – Vertical scarf joint between two outer planks (Photo J. Auer).

250 mm, the filling frames at the turn of the bilge only have sided dimensions between 100 and 150 mm. Floor timbers and first futtocks are joined with double or single non-trapezoidal dovetail joints (**Fig. 5**), secured with a single treenail through the centre of the joint. First and second futtocks and filling frames are not connected to other framing components.

Planking

The planks are sawn from oak. Their lengths vary between 2 m and 6 m. The average plank width is 300 to 460 mm and the thickness varies between 50 mm and 70 mm. All outer planks are joined with flat vertical scarf joints, which are secured with treenails and up to four iron nails with square shanks (**Fig. 6**). The plank seams are waterproofed using a type of setwork rather than caulking. The lower edges of outer planks have been furnished with V-shaped or U-shaped hollow grooves, which are filled with three strands of tarred animal hair. All knots in outer planks have been carefully removed and replaced with small wooden patches fastened with miniature treenails, or in some cases iron nails. On well-preserved planks, a white or cream-coloured surface covering could be observed, possibly the so-called »white stuff« (Lavery 1987: 57).

Fastenings

The outer planks are fastened with cleft and shaved oak treenails, 30 mm in diameter. In most cases the outboard faces of the nails have been split in a V-shaped or cross-shaped pattern to receive caulking. The inboard faces are generally split and wedged. Joints between planks as well as the hood ends are fastened with iron nails or bolts. The iron nails used to secure plank joints are in most cases countersunk, and the holes plugged with tar and caulking material.

Deck construction

The construction of the orlop deck is visible on piece 3b (**Fig. 7**). Recesses show where two deck beams measuring 200 mm by 200 mm rested on the shelf clamp. A 2.34 m long half beam clamp or carling is set between the beams. Mortises of varying size, spaced 360 mm apart indicate the positions of half beams or ledges. The edge of the waterway is preserved above the carling. No evidence for hanging knees could be found and it is currently assumed that the deck construction was reinforced with the help of lodging knees.

Gunports

Two gunports situated above the orlop deck show that the Gresham ship was armed. The ports are spaced 2.5 m apart and are located 700 mm above the orlop deck. The fully preserved forward gunport is 400 mm wide. Due to erosion the gunport height cannot be established.

THE ARMAMENT

Altogether four cannon were recovered from the site. A wrought iron breech loader well preserved in a heavy concretion was found among the grabbed material. Two lifting rings are positioned centrally on the barrel, one of which with remains of cordage.

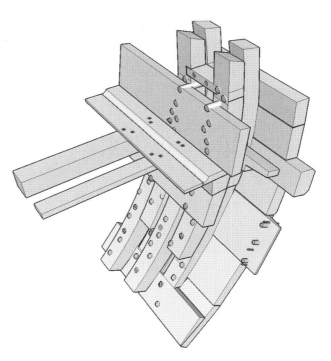

Fig. 7 Princes Channel wreck/Gresham ship. – Schematic representation of vessel construction (Drawing J. Auer).

Another piece of cordage was wrapped around the muzzle end. Near the breech end, and in front of the lifting rings, are pairs of straps for riveting the barrel to the wooden carriage. Fragments of the wooden carriage are preserved in the concretion. The 1.24 m long cannon has a 130 mm bore. The wrought iron breech chamber is 370 mm long and had an apparent calibre of 75 mm. The touch-hole is trapezoidal and fashioned from two iron sheets. A cast iron muzzle loader also formed part of the grabbed material. This gun is 2.32 m long and has an 80 mm bore. It has a pronounced muzzle swell and fairly elaborate mouldings, particularly on the breech. The trunnions, which have a diameter of 100 mm are tapered and show no markings on the trunnion face. The button end of the cascable is missing.

Two further cast iron cannon were recovered during the excavation. One of them remains heavily concreted. It is approx. 2.3 m long and has an 80 mm bore. To allow detailed recording the second cannon was uncovered. It is 2.2 m long and has a bore of 76 mm (**Fig. 8**). The first reinforce is marked with the moulded initials *TG*, the incised numbers *8-0-0* and the moulded emblem of a grasshopper. The initials allowed the identification of the gun founder, Sir Thomas Gresham. Gresham, an Elizabethan financier and merchant, owned a gun foundry in Mayfield in the Weald from 1567 to his death in 1579. He was involved in the arms export and is known to have founded guns for the King of Denmark among others (Teesdale 1991:128). The number *8-0-0* specifies the weight of the cannon as 8cwt or 406.41 kg. It is told to be a rare example of an early English small saker (pers. comm. Nicholas Hall, Royal Armouries 2004). Adjacent to one of the guns, parts of an elm gun carriage were found.

FITTINGS AND ARTEFACTS

Apart from an anchor, which was recovered by grab in 2003, very little of the ship's fittings or equipment survives. The anchor is made from cast iron. It is 3.13 m long and originally had a beam of 1.72 m. The ring

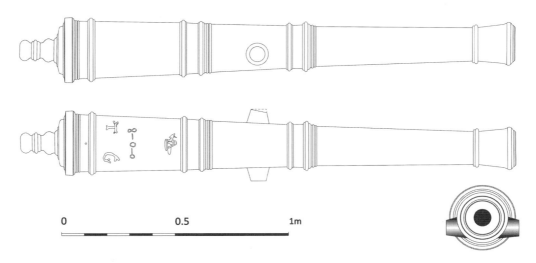

Fig. 8   Princes Channel wreck/Gresham ship. – Small saker founded by Thomas Gresham (Drawing by F. Mallon).

is missing; one arm is broken off 180 mm from the shank which is slightly bent. When raised, the anchor was still fitted with its 3.11 m long, slightly double-tapered wooden stock. This is made from two symmetrical halves tree-nailed together around the anchor shank. The majority of the small finds recovered from the wreck site is still concreted and awaiting treatment. Noticeable small finds include a pewter candleholder, leather shoes and other parts of leather garments, a wooden pike shaft with iron head and fragments of a Spanish olive jar.

CARGO

The ship's cargo consisted of iron bars, lead ingots and tin ingots, the provenance of which has not been identified yet. While other cargo might have been present, no archaeological evidence for this has been found as yet. Two types of iron bars were found on the wreck site. Bars of the first type are narrow with a square section of 30 by 30 mm. They are folded four times to lengths between 1.9 and 2 m. The second type has a rectangular section of 30 by 80 mm and is folded once in the centre of the bar.

The lead ingots are boat-shaped. They measure 600 by 220 by 120 mm and have an average weight of 56 kg. The upper surface of each has been stamped, presumably with a makers mark, up to seven times. The tin ingots measure 520 by 18/16 mm and have a trapezoidal cross section.

PRELIMINARY INTERPRETATIONS

Dendrochronological dating indicates that the Gresham ship was built in, or shortly after 1574 from English oak. The origin of the timbers used for the construction is likely to be East Anglia or Essex (Nayling 2004). The vessel was carvel built. The joints between floor timbers and first futtocks suggest a construction in the so-called »frame-first« method. The vessel was subject to »furring« at some point in its career, possibly during the initial construction process. This resulted in an increase in fullness of approx. 300 mm on either side of the ship. Archaeological evidence suggests that the vessel was a small to medium sized ocean going armed merchantman. The lowest deck in the ship, the orlop deck, also served as a gun deck. While a full

Fig. 9 Drawing of the ship *Emanuell* from the »Fragments of Ancient English Shipwrightry« (Copyright Pepys Library, Magdalene College, Cambridge).

hull analysis and reconstruction of the ship are still outstanding, the preserved hull sections allow a preliminary estimate of her original size. Currently a keel length of 15 to 20 m and a tonnage of approximately 150 to 250 tons are assumed.

The depiction of the small merchantman *Emanuell* of 200 tons with a beam of 26 ft (7.92 m), in Matthew Bakers »Fragments of Ancient English Shipwrightry« (Magdalene College Library, Cambridge: Pepys 2820) can serve as a model for the original appearance of the Gresham ship (**Fig. 9**). While no historical sources regarding the loss of a vessel in the Thames at the end of the 16th c. could be found as yet, salvage reports from 1846 might be associated with the wreck site in the Princes Channel. The Whitstable Shipping and Mercantile Gazette from 2nd May 1846 and Lloyds List mention Whitstable divers salvaging six guns, tin, iron and lead from a wreck on the Girdler Sand, adjacent to the Princes Channel. The Journal of the British Archaeological Association (Anonymous 1846) also reports on Elizabethan artefacts including a knife, a leather shoe and a silk doublet that were found in the same wreck. The iron guns are described as of »very ancient date«, and the amount of tin ingots lifted is quantified as 2700. In addition iron bars, lead pigs and red lead in casks are mentioned. The exact location of the wreck is not specified, but the depth is given as four fathoms (7.3 m) at low water, which is consistent with the depth of the Gresham wreck site. Although there is no proof that the diver salvage of 1846 took place on the latter site, the description of the location and the material lifted makes this highly likely. An earlier salvage would explain the relatively small amount of cargo found on the site and the rope around the lifting rings of the wrought iron cannon. The six guns raised in 1846 would also bring the total armament of the ship up to ten guns, a number consistent with the estimated size of the vessel.

CONCLUSIONS

As the only well preserved example of a small English merchantman of the Elizabethan period, the Princes Channel wreck is of international importance. A full analysis of the vessel will give unique insight into 16th c. ship design and shipbuilding methods and might lead to a re-interpretation of earlier 16th c. ship finds around the British Isles. The wreck is also the only known archaeological example of the practice of »furring«.

ACKNOWLEDGEMENTS

The authors would like to thank the Port of London Authority, in particular the Marine Services Department and the Port of London Authority Dive Team, for their assistance in excavating and lifting the Princes Channel Wreck. Many thanks also go to the other members of the Wessex Archaeology dive and recording team. Furthermore the authors are indebted to Wessex Archaeology for making the primary archive available for further analysis. The authors also thank the Nautical Archaeology Society for giving the Gresham Ship a new home in Horsea Lake, Portsmouth and supporting the post-excavation analysis. The post-excavation programme for the Gresham ship was made possible by the Port of London Authority, the University College of London and the Gresham College.

REFERENCES

Anonymous 1846, Proceedings of the Association, December 9th. *Journal of the British Archaeological Association*, 2, 361-362.

Lavery, B. 1987, *The Arming and Fitting of English Ships of War 1600-1815*. London.

Mainwaring, G. E. & Perrin, P. G. 1922, *The life and works of Sir Henry Mainwaring*, vol. 2. London.

Teesdale, E. B., 1991, *Gunfounding in the Weald in the sixteenth century*. London.

Unpublished Sources:

Magdalene College Library, Cambridge: Pepys 2820 (*Fragments of Ancient English Shipwrightry*).

Nayling, N., 2004, Tree-*ring analysis of framing timbers from the Princes Channel Wreck, Thames Estuary*. University of Wales, HARP Dendrochronology Report 2004/02.

TOMASZ BEDNARZ

GDAŃSK WRECK, W-27 –
AN EXAMPLE OF AN 18ᵀᴴ CENTURY DUTCH MERCHANTMAN

W-27 is, together with W-6 *Solen*, W-5 *Miedziowiec*, W-32 *General Carleton of Whitby* and the site in
Puck, Poland, one of the five most important archaeological sites explored by the Polish Maritime Museum
in Gdańsk (PMM; Centralne Muzeum Morskie). Located six miles N.E. Gdańsk in Gdańsk Bay, in a depth of
26m (**Fig. 1**), the wreck has delivered many valuable artefacts so far, many of which can already be seen in
an exhibition room of the PMM. The relic was discovered on August 10, 1985 during hydrographic
sweeping in the shipping lanes and anchorage area of the N. Port in Gdańsk, carried out by the Maritime
Office in Gdańsk and PMM. From that year on, archaeological work was systematically carried on until
1993. From 2000 to 2005 again PMM archaeologists returned to examine the wreck.

The site covers an area of over 2,000m². Its main part consists of the bottom section of a ship preserved
with keel, keelson, frames and strakes. Many of the artefacts and structural elements of the stern part are
scattered over a considerable distance, about 40m to the S. E. from the main structure, creating group
no.1. Over the years of exploration, the surface of the object has been penetrated, using a metal detector,
and a series of survey excavations have been made with an air lift. The exploration area was extended to
include group no. 2, located in front of the forward part of the wreck.

Fig. 1 Gdańsk W-27 wreck location
(Drawing P. Makowski & T. Bednarz).

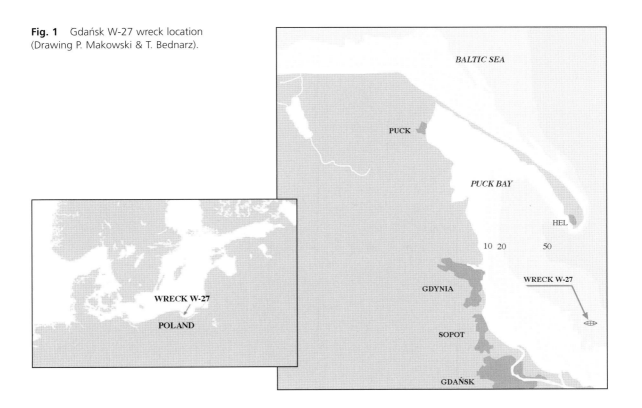

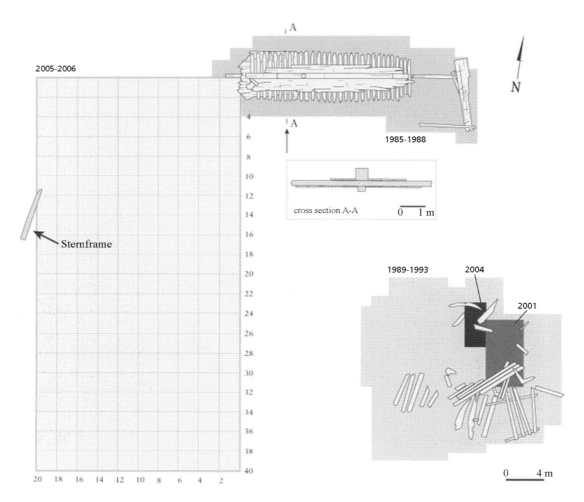

Fig. 2 Gdańsk W-27. – History of research (Drawing T. Bednarz).

The main structure of W-27 (**Fig. 2**) consists of a 26 m long keel, 31 floor timbers, flush-laid bottom planking (five strakes on port side, three strakes on starboard side) and a 17 m long keelson with mast step (50 to 52 cm). A 7 m long rudder (**Fig. 3**) with a 1.4 m wide rudder blade and a 6.1 m long tiller was discovered in 1987. Currently, all these artefacts are in the PMM Conservation Laboratory in Tczew. The wreck's main structure was examined from 1985 to 1988, while from 1989 to 1993, after group no. 1 was detected, investigations moved to the S. E. Repeated surveys of group no. 1 in 2000 and 2001 led to the discovery of further artefacts: More than 10,000 objects have been recovered during 13 exploration seasons including fragments of sails, armament, pottery and glass vessels, the crew's personal belongings, items of kitchen equipment etc. The most interesting finds are an almost complete octant made by URINGS Co., London (**Fig. 4**), a telescope, a paraffin lamp (**Fig. 5**), two rail guns made of bronze (35.0 cm [**Fig. 6**] and 33.7 cm long) and a 80 cm long cannon made of cast iron.

The reasons for the loss of the ship remain a mystery. Since some precious objects of the crew's personal belongings and of ship equipment were found, she might have quickly sunk during bad weather conditions or through collision with another vessel. After sinking, damage was caused to the wreck by sweeping gear, anchors and fishing nets. Identified as a sailing vessel, probably with two masts, the wreck is interpreted as the remnant of a 30 m long flat-bottomed merchantman. As can be traced back from her structure and

Fig. 3 Gdańsk W-27. – Rudder during conservation (Photo T. Bednarz).

dating, the ship represents a Kuff or Galliot-type vessel. Generally built by Dutch shipyards, such types were popular in the Baltic and North Sea in the 18th and 19th c. They had a solid structure and carried a large amount of cargo. Due to their flat bottom, also shallow ports could be entered. The crews consisted of only 8 to 12 persons. Kuffs had two masts; the forward one carrying a gaff sail and two or three square sails, the smaller mizzen a gaff, sometimes with an additional topgallant (**Fig. 8**).

The lengths of Kuff-type vessels varied from about 20 m to more than 30 m. Their cargo capacity could reach up to 120 *lasts*, an amount which can also be estimated for W-27. Galliots usually also had two masts, sometimes three. Characterized by a more slender hull, their stern posts and especially stems were inclined to a larger angle in relation to the keel. Some three-masted Galliots were square-rigged, whereas smaller two-masted galliots carried a mizzen with a gaff sail and a topgallant. Their length varied from more than 30 m to over 40 m. Large differences occurred in both types of ship and it is sometimes difficult to classify some ships as an actual type (Menzel 1997: 118).

The head of the rudder shows the ornament of a sculptured trifoliate clover (**Fig. 9**), which is characteristic for Dutch ships from the 18th and 19th c. A brass snuff-box with an engraved genre piece showing a woman and a man turning in opposite direction is another item indicating a Dutch origin (**Fig. 7**). There is a tree between the figures, on which a lantern is hanging, and a cupid with a lowered bow. The scene is completed with two inscriptions in Flemish. Assisted by the Consulate of the Kingdom of the Netherlands, the inscription has been translated. The phrases read as follows: »*Ik vlugt al voor dat schoon gesigt*« (**Fig. 7**:

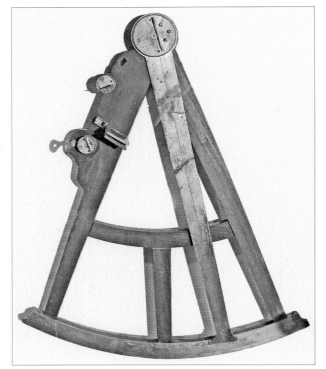

Fig. 4 Gdańsk W-27. – Octant of English origin (Photo T. Bednarz).

Fig. 5 Gdańsk W-27. – Paraffin lamp (Photo T. Bednarz).

Fig. 6 Gdańsk W-27. – Little cannon, 35 cm long (Photo T. Bednarz).

Fig. 7 Gdańsk W-27. – Brass snuffbox with Flemish inscription (Photo T. Bednarz).

right inscription), which means »I escape from a pretty face«; the left inscription reads »*Sip is een lantarn sonder ligt*«, which means »a sad (man) is like a lantern without flame«. Twenty-five Dutch coins were found in the wreck, along with small clay pipes made in Gouda, that are frequently found in many archaeological sites, also prove Dutch connections.

A French copper coin represents the latest of the 77 numismatic finds. Showing the portrait of king Louis XVI, the coin of 1 *Sou* (*Sol*) value was minted between 1778 and 1793. Cargo markings in the form of lead seals provide a supplementary set of dates from within a relatively small chronological scope – from 1784 to 1789. There is an engraved inscription that reads BPAEIN and a date, 1791 on one of the staves found in the wreck. The date is also repeated on another stave. On the basis of analysis of the coins, lead seals and barrels, it is accepted that the ship sank at the end of 18th c., probably in 1791 or a little later.

Fig. 8 Model of a Kuff type vessel (Photo T. Bednarz).

Fig. 9 Gdańsk W-27. – Rudder head (Photo T. Bednarz).

REFERENCES

Binerowski, Z. & Gierszewski, S., 972, Rzemieślnicza produkcja drewnianych żaglowców od XIV do połowy XIX stulecia. In: E. Cieślak (ed.), *Historia budownictwa okrętowego na Wybrzeżu Gdańskim*. Gdańsk, 71-213.

Chapman, F. H.,1768, *Architectura Navalis Mercatoria*. Rostock.

Cieślak, E. & Biernat, Cz.,1969, *Dzieje Gdańska*. Gdańsk.

Diary of an Archeological Research. Wreck W-27, vol.1-5. Centralne Muzeum Morskie, Gdańsk 1986-2005.

Duco, P. H., 1982, *Marken van Goudse pijpenmakers 1660-1940*. Lochem.

Dutkowski, J. & Suchanek, A., 2000, *Corpus Numnorum Gedanensis*. Gdańsk.

Friedrich, F. H. W.,1975, *Pijpelogie, vorm, versiering en datering van de hollandse kleipijp*. Yoorburg.

Gawroński, J.,1991, *Holandia Compendium, a contribution to the history, archaeology, classification and lexicography of a 150 ft. Dutch East Indiaman (1740-1750)*, vols I-III. Amsterdam, Oxford, New York, Tokyo.

Groth, A.,1986, Żegluga bałtycka i jej warunki techniczne w XVII i początkach XVIII wieku na przykładzie portów Prus Królewskich i Książęcych. *Zapiski Historyczne*, 51, 2.2, 21-33.

Ingelman-Sundberg, C., 1978, *Relics from the Dutch East Indiaman, Zeewijk. Foundered in 1727*. Perth.

Litwin, J.,1992, Szkutnictwo i żegluga w Polsce przedrozbiorowej. In: B. Orłowski (ed.), *Z dziejów techniki w dawnej Polsce*. Warszawa, 350-378.

Menzel, H., 1997, *Smakken, Kuffen, Galioten*. Hamburg.

Mikłaszewicz, D., 1992, Fajki z wraków zalegających na dnie Zatoki Gdańskiej. *Pomorania Antiqua*, XV, 265-300.

Mikołajczyk, A., 1994, *Leksykon numizmatyczny*. Warszawa, Łódź.

Ossowski, W., 2003, Archeologiczne badania wraków statków żaglowych z XVIII wieku prowadzone przez Centralne muzeum Morskie w Gdańsku. In: H. Panner & M. Fudziński (eds), *XIII Sesja Pomorzoznawcza*, vol. II. Gdańsk, 313-334.

Rutecki, P.,1995, Wrak W-27. Podwodne badania archeologiczne osiemnastowiecznego statku towarowego w Zatoce Gdańskiej. *Nautologia*, 30.1, 44-54.

Smolarek, P., 1991, The underwater investigations of the Polish Marime Museum in Gdańsk from 1982 to 1985. *Acta Universitatis Nicolai Copernici, Archeologia XV, Archeologia podwodna*, 3, 3-24.

Smolarek, P.,1987, Badania podwodne w Bałtyku w latach 1979-1986. *Kwartalnik Historii Kultury Materialnej*, 35.3, 465-495.

Steffy, J. R., 1995, *Wooden Ship Building and the Interpretation of Shipwrecks*. College Station/Texas.

INLAND NEWS

STEFANIE KLOOSS · HARALD LÜBKE

THE TERMINAL MESOLITHIC
AND EARLY NEOLITHIC LOGBOATS
OF STRALSUND-MISCHWASSERSPEICHER

EVIDENCE OF EARLY WATERBORNE TRANSPORT
ON THE GERMAN SOUTHERN BALTIC COAST

At the German Baltic coast excellent conditions exist for the preservation of archaeological objects, and even for organic material, wood, bark or plant fibre. Due to the worldwide sea level rise and the isostatic land sinking after the Weichselian glaciation, a regular sunken landscape with traces of human dwelling-places and other activities is preserved below the present sea level at the S.W. Baltic coast.

Intensive settlement activities in the terminal Mesolithic and early Neolithic along the sound *Strelasund* is demonstrated by many finds at the sites Prohn, Parow and Drigge. However, a reconstruction of the former landscape and a separation of different settlement phases have not been realized because finds were brought up to light by dredging, without options to document stratigraphies (Lübke *et al.* 2000; Terberger & Lübke 2002; Lübke & Terberger 2005).

Therefore, the discovery of a terminal Mesolithic/early Neolithic coastal site near the medieval city of Stralsund gave opportunity to observe a sequence of shore sediments (**Fig. 1**). As a preliminary survey of a building ground for a water supply reservoir (German: *Mischwasserspeicher*), an area of 60 to 27 m to a depth of 8 m (**Fig. 2**), was excavated by the State Authority for Culture and Protection of Monuments (Landesamt für Kultur und Denkmalpflege [LaKD]), Mecklenburg-Vorpommern. Connected to the settlement site parts of the shore sediments up to 3 m beneath Kronstadt m.s.l could have been investigated (Kaute *et al.* 2005; Mandelkow *et al.* 2005).

Some oak trunks from the Atlantic period have been found in a peat layer together with archaeological artefacts from flint, antler, bone and wood. The material belongs to the terminal Mesolithic phase of Erte-bølle Culture dating from 5000 to 4700 B.C. The most important findings are two dugout canoes lying side by side (logboat 2 and 3). Above the peat, there were marine sand and mud layers again with terminal Mesolithic flint and bone artefacts. A third cultural layer, wherein a third logboat (logboat 1) was found belongs to the early Neolithic Funnel Beaker Culture. Extraordinary well preserved, these three up to 12 m long dugout canoes are the only complete Stone Age logboats of the German Baltic coast to date.

TOPOGRAPHY OF THE COASTAL SITE

The Mesolithic/Neolithic coastal site *Stralsund, no. 225* (*Mischwasserspeicher*), is situated at the N. W. edge of the historical town centre of Stralsund, currently situated at the bank of the sound *Strelasund* opposite to Rügen Island (**Fig. 1**). Seven millennia ago, the dwelling site was situated at a typical island point at the outlet of a secondary sea channel. Since the Middle Ages, a dyke separated the former channel from the sea. The archaeological cultural layers are lying today some meters below the surface, covered by sediments and especially by layers, which have been filled up at the end of the 19th c. to gain new land for the growing city. The excavation only met the fringe of the Stone Age dwelling place in the shallow waters, whereas housing structures might have existed more to the S. E.

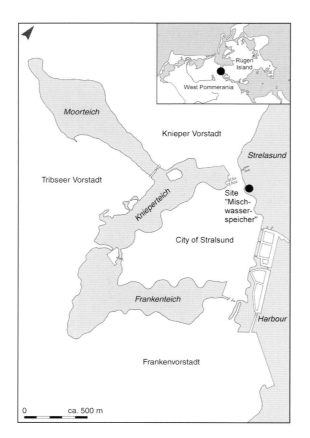

Fig. 1   The site at the edge of the Hanseatic City of Stralsund at the coast of the Baltic sound Strelasund opposite to Rügen Island (Digital drawing B. Froese & H. Lübke, LaKD).

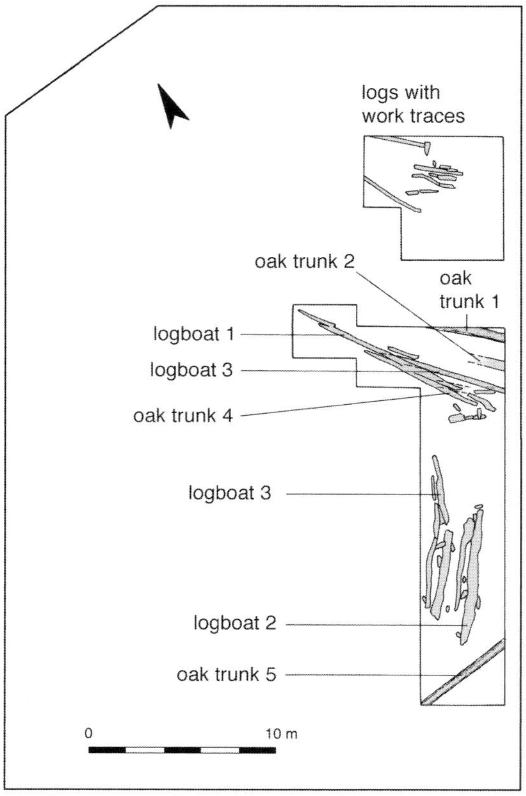

Fig. 2   Stralsund-Mischwasserspeicher. – General plan of the construction area with the excavation trenches. Logboats and oak trunks are labelled (Drawing B. Martin, LaKD).

Fig. 3   Stralsund-Mischwasserspeicher. – The two excavated Mesolithic logboats (Photo P. Kaute & G. Schindler, LaKD).

STRATIGRAPHY

Sediment cores were taken to study the Holocene sedimentation at the site. The core analysis shows, that the Pleistocene channel at its base had late glacial sediments. Above these, sand and mud layers were deposited, which were overgrown by peat. Within the investigated area, peat grew up some decimetres at levels from −3.0 m to −2.2 m. Several oak trunks dated by dendrochronology, sunk into the peat layers. They also contained archaeological artefacts from the Terminal Mesolithic, two logboats inclusive. According to radiocarbon dating, both boats were built in the Atlantic period, between 5000 and 4700 B.C.

During the Littorina Transgression the described area was floated and overlaid by a sequence of marine sand and mud. At the top of this sequence, a small layer with some Mesolithic flint and bone artefacts occurred, and directly above a 0.5 m thick layer of fine marine sand with artefacts of the Early Neolithic Funnel Beaker Culture and the third logboat embeded.

The Early Neolithic layer was overlain by strand border deposits. Also a winged arrow-head with a concave base from the transitional period Late Neolithic/Early Bronze Age was discovered there. The stratigraphical sequence is closed by modern dump deposited to drain the place in the 19th c.

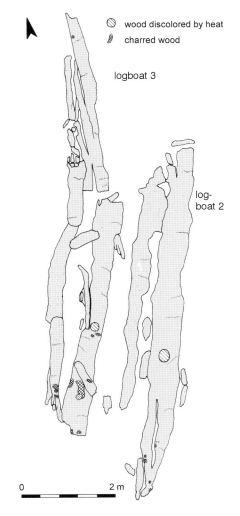

wood discolored by heat
charred wood

logboat 3

logboat 2

0   2 m

Fig. 4   Stralsund-Mischwasserspeicher. – Plan of the Mesolithic logboats 2 and 3. Charred parts of the boats are marked (Drawing B. Martin, LaKD).

THE MESOLITHIC FINDS

The terminal Mesolithic logboats

Logboats 2 and 3 were lying side by side in the slight W. slope of the peat layer, orientated approx. N.S. (**Figs 3-4**). They were pressed totally flat by the overlying deposits. Logboat 2 was made of a large lime trunk (*Tilia sp.*), preserved on 8.0 m length, 0.6 to 0.7 m sided. It was broken into two substantial and several small pieces. The position of bow and stern cannot be identified. A circular spot on the bottom of the boat, not more than 0.2 m in diameter, coloured dark brown from heat, indicates a fire place (**Fig. 5**). As such fire places usually are situated in a boat's centre, it can be concluded, that the boat's E. side was lost. The 9.0 m long and 0.6 to 0.7 m wide logboat 3 was also built from lime tree. Broken into three larger and several small pieces, traces of fire are visible at two positions (**Fig. 6**). Distinct chopping marks of a 2.5 to 3.0 cm adze blade were found specially along the bottom of the dugout (**Fig. 7**). Radiocarbon dates point to the same age, which corresponds to the stratigraphical situation (Lübke 2005). Logboat 2 is dated to 4718±50 cal. B.C.; no. 3 to 4768±44 cal. B.C. (**Table 1**).

Fig. 5 Stralsund-Mischwasserspeicher. – Detail of logboat 2. – The position of a fire place is marked by charred parts on the bottom of the boat (Photo P. Kaute & G. Schindler, LaKD).

Fig. 6 Stralsund-Mischwasserspeicher. – Detail of logboat 3. – The position of a fire place is marked by charred parts on the bottom of the boat (Photo P. Kaute & G. Schindler, LaKD).

Fig. 7 Stralsund-Mischwasserspeicher. – Detail of logboat 3. – Chopping marks of an adze at the bottom of the boat (Photo P. Kaute & G. Schindler, LaKD).

Terminal Mesolithic artefacts

Several flint, bone, antler and wooden artefacts were found in the terminal Mesolithic culture layers. One of the most remarkable finds is a great T-shaped antler axe, 28 cm long, with an edge on one side. The edge was damaged by a crack. Therefore, the axe might had been recycled as raw material. An antler chip was cut out at the neck, and the whole upper side of the antler is missing (**Fig. 8**). Dated by radiocarbon analysis to 4883 ± 53 cal. B.C. (**Table 1**); the tool is the oldest T-shaped antler axe found in the S.W. Baltic region.

NEOLITHIC FINDS

The early Neolithic logboat

Logboat 1 was found in the sand layer with the bow pointing N.W. (**Figs 9-10**). Also made of a lime trunk, the dugout was preserved in two big and several small pieces. The total length of the vessel comes to 12.0 m, the width to 0.6 m. The boat was lying upside down so that internally no fire places or cut marks could be recognized. At the bottom side no traces of bark were visible. The sides were tired off and partly floated away, almost completely on port. At the interior side round holes of 2 to 4 cm in diameter were observed in irregular distances; they might indicate repairs. Logboat 1 is dated to 3858 ± 63 cal. B.C. (Lübke 2005), an age which corresponds well to the dating of a Funnel Beaker potsherd (3776 ± 89 cal. B.C.) found directly on the logboat (**Table 1**).

Early Neolithic Artefacts

Several potsherds of early Neolithic Funnel Beaker ceramics were found in the upper cultural layer (**Fig. 11**). Among other finds, the fragment of a Funnel Beaker type E. Koch II (Koch 1998: 89) seems remarkable. It has a diameter of about 34 cm and a height of at least 27 cm. The rim of the beaker is decorated with a single row of irregular sharp single

find no.	sample no.	age BP	age cal B.C.	d13C	artefact
2001/2168-0209	KIA-20433	4780±31	3574±44	−27.3	wooden board
2001/2168-0383	KIA-20437	4830±30	3598±55	−19.4	human skull
2001/2168-0295	KIA-20435	4964±58	3776±89	−22.4	funnel beaker, charred food crust
2001/2168-0204	KIA-20234	5040±26	3858±63	−25.4	logboat 1
2001/2168-0294	KIA-20434	5194±30	4004±35	−20.0	funnel beaker, food crust
2001/2168-0247	KIA-20235	5853±34	4718±50	−26.1	logboat 2
2001/2168-0246	KIA-20236	5901±34	4768±44	−28.0	logboat 3
2001/2168-0382	KIA-20436	6010±35	4883±53	−24.2	T-shaped antler axe

Table 1 Stralsund-Mischwasserspeicher. – List of radiocarbon datings. – Calibration was conducted with *Calpal* software provided by O. Jöris and B. Weninger (cf. manual *Calpal* or *www.calpal.de*), and based on the calibration curve Intcal98 (Stuiver *et al.* 1998).

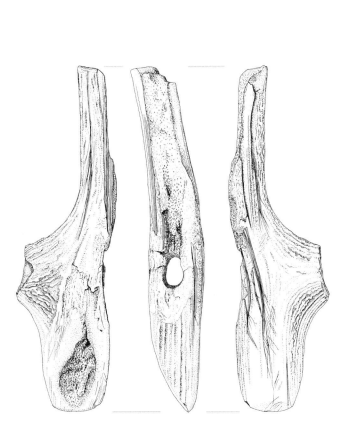

Fig. 8 Stralsund-Mischwasserspeicher. – T-shaped Axe of red deer antler, a characteristic artefact of the terminal Mesolithic Ertebølle culture (Drawing J. Freigang, LaKD).

Fig. 9 Stralsund-Mischwasserspeicher. – The Early Neolithic logboat 1 (Photo P. Kaute & G. Schindler, LaKD).

pricks. A conical bore-hole above the beaker's shoulder indicates a repair. Charred food crusts inside the vessel have been dated by radiocarbon analysis to 4004±35 cal. B.C. (**Table 1**).

Two interesting wooden artefacts belong to the early Neolithic cultural layer (**Fig. 12**): there is a rectangular board from 13 to 38 cm with rounded edges, made of alder (*Alnus* sp.). In the middle an irregular oval handle was worked out all in one piece. Two parallel holes are running through the handle and the upper

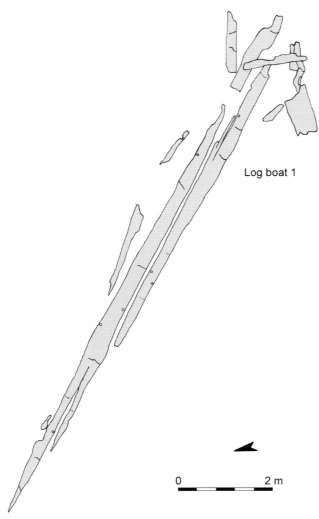

Log boat 1

0   2 m

Fig. 10 Stralsund-Mischwasserspeicher. – Plan of the Early Neolithic logboat with round holes of 2 to 4 cm diameter in the boats hull (Drawing B. Martin, LaKD).

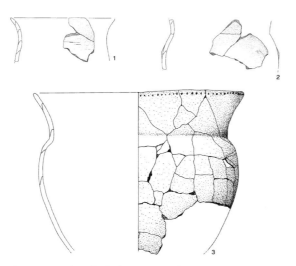

Fig. 11 Stralsund-Mischwasserspeicher. – **1-3** Funnel Beaker pottery (Drawings J. Freigang, LaKD).

side was split off. Inside of one of the openings stuck a thin branch of a fruit-tree (Maloideae). At the other side of the board all the edges were sloped and carefully smoothed like the upper side (**Fig. 12, 2**). A radiocarbon date (AMS) gave an age of 3574±44 cal. B.C. (**Table 1**). To this object no parallel seems to exist. As functional interpretations, the cap for an unknown type of container, a repairing board for a dugout, or a removable transom, which could be fixed at the stern of a logboat, come into mind.

Furthermore, a round stick of hazel (*Corylus avellana*) was found, with some bark preserved. It has a length of 57 cm and a diameter of 3 cm. One ending shows a notch; the other was cut flat from both sides shaped to an oval hole that may have been broken through use (**Fig. 12, 1**). Similar sticks are known from Ertebølle sites at the S.W. Baltic coast, Wangels, Neustadt and Timmendorf-Nordmole I (Klooß in prep.). As well two of such hazel sticks are known from Tybrind Vig, where two well preserved logboats were documented (Andersen 1985: 61, fig. 19). S. H. Andersen (1995: 56, fig. 15) suggested that such wooden objects belong to the construction at the mouth of fish traps according to ethnographic record of Finnish and N. Russian populations (Sirelius 1934: fig. 254).

USE AND FUNCTION OF STONE AGE LOGBOATS

It is reasonable to believe that Mesolithic and Neolithic people who lived at the Baltic coastal waters or at lakes and rivers in N. Germany might have used watercraft for transport and communication as well as for fishing and sealing (Hartz & Lübke 2000). However, assumptions have been hard to prove in the past because of a lack of dated finds. In the meantime, more than 21 Mesolithic boats have been found in Denmark (Christensen 1997: 283) and in N. Germany, where fragments of dugouts occurred in the Wismar Bay and at the site Neustadt-Marienbad in E. Holstein (Labes 2005; Hartz 2005). In general logboats are not exceptional finds in the shore area of terminal Mesolithic coastal settlements of the Ertebølle culture, but frequently they are considerably worse preserved than in Stralsund.

Like most of the other dugouts of the Ertebølle culture (Mertens 2000: 34-55), the Stralsund boats were made of soft wood. Lime wood can grow into large trunks, is easy to work, and compared to other wood species, it is characterized by less weight and less tendency to split. However, after their abandonment, boats broke quickly and the fragile board-shaped fragments were scarred by waves and current in the shore area of the settlements, where they are not easy to identify. Nevertheless, similar find conditions with more than one logboat preserved are known from the Danish sites Lystrup (Andersen 1994), Tybrind Vig (Andersen 1985) and Horskær/-Halskov (Christensen 1997).

According to the radiocarbon analyses, the Stralsund Mesolithic logboats nos 2 and 3 are dating between 4800 and 4700 cal. B.C. Two dugouts, which show similar form, technical details and features from the Danish site Lystrup, Jutland, are a little older. The Lystrup I dugout by way of exception made

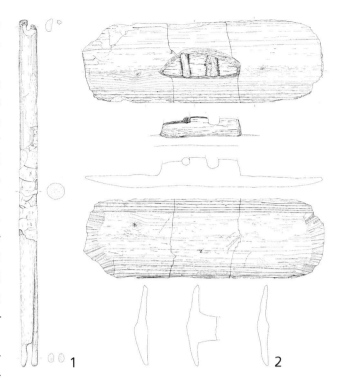

Fig. 12 Stralsund-Mischwasserspeicher. – **1** Hazel stick with worked ends. – **2** Wooden board of alder with a handle (Drawings J. Freigang, LaKD).

of an Aspen trunk (*Populus tremula*) was dated to 5200/5000 B.C., whereas Lystrup II, which was made out of lime, is even about 300 years older (Andersen 1994; 1996). With a length of 6 to 7 m and a width of 0.6 m these two boats are only slightly smaller than the Stralsund finds.

Dated to 4300 cal. B.C. (Tybrind 2) and 4100 cal. B.C. (Tybrind 1), two dugouts from Tybrind Vig already belong to the younger Ertebølle culture (Andersen 1987). Nevertheless, the 9.5 m long and 0.65 m wide Tybrind 1 dugout shares the dimensions of the Stralsund logboats.

Distinct chopping marks from adzes with a worn edge like in Stralsund were seen throughout the interior of the Tybrind and Lystrup boats. These vessels are characterized by open sterns, where a row of holes or a similar construction shows, that their hulls originally had been closed by a transom. Other holes observed at Tybrind 2 and Lystrup I can be interpreted as traces of repairs.

Another remarkable feature of the discussed logboats are evidences of fire places. Especially the boats Tybrind 1, Lystrup 1 and Stralsund 3 are very comparable, in each where two fire places were found. In the case of Lystrup 1 the structure in the stern consisted of a clay package on top of a bed of 1 to 2 mm fine sand (Andersen 1994, 8), and in Tybrind 1 a fire place was made with an isolation layer of sandy clay (1986, 94). In both cases, each a second fire place was indicated by charred areas near the bow at the bottom of the boats.

Comparable clay packages could not be established for the Stralsund logboats, however the dark to black-brown areas coloured by heat, but not charred, point to similar constructed fire places with an isolating bed of sand and/or clay in the forward end of the stern. Different to the findings of Lystrup 1 and Tybrind 1, in Stralsund 3 the second fire place was found near a boat end which appears to be the stern. The existence of fire places in logboats in the terminal Mesolithic is not only proven by Ertebølle findings, but also in context with the S.W. neighbouring Swifterbant culture by a dugout from the site Hardinxfeld-Giessendam De

Bruin (Louwe Kooijmans *et al.* 2001, 455-466). Also in modern times fire places on logboats are well-known from ethnographic records, e.g. of the native inhabitants of N. America. Fire not only was used for heating or cooking on board, but also for fishing to attract fish by night (Andersen 1986: 100; 1994: 9).

Although belonging to the early Neolithic Funnel beaker culture, Stralsund 1 with an age of 3900 to 3800 cal. B.C. is just two or three centuries younger than the Tybrind 1 logboat. So, comparisons with late terminal Mesolithic boats from Denmark seem also reasonable as with the contemporary dugouts from the Åmosen in the interior of Zealand, E. Denmark (Christensen 1990). As with the two elder boats Stralsund 1 was made from lime wood, and working traces on the outer side are very similar to such from the Danish and Dutch dugouts. Although the stern was badly preserved and broken into several pieces, it looks as if it had the same straight end as the Mesolithic logboats. Therefore it seems that Stralsund 1 was build in the same boat building tradition as the finds of the Mesolithic Ertebølle culture.

Nevertheless, with a total length of approx. 12 m and a width of 0.6 m, the logboat Stralsund 1 is the longest established Stone Age log found yet in N. Middle and N. Europe. According to Andersen (1986: 99), logboats with a size of about 10 m like the Tybrind 1 boat carried six to eight persons, including equipment or cargo of comparable weight. Therefore, boats of such considerable dimensions may have been used not only for fishing or sealing, but also for long distance travel, transport and communication along the Stone Age coastline and across the Baltic to S. Scandinavia.

CONCLUSIONS

Through the example of the logboats from Stralsund-Mischwasserspeicher one can see once more the highly developed, long tradition of building large, thin-walled dugout canoes out of lime trunks for thousands of years through the Late Mesolithic and the beginning of the Neolithic at the Baltic coast. Logboats certainly were important watercraft especially at the transition of the terminal Mesolithic Ertebølle culture and early Neolithic Funnel beaker culture. They played a decisive role for extensive fishing, sealing, communication, travel and transport along the coastline, lake shores and rivers, and were an essential part of the material culture of the Stone Age human societies in the S.W. Baltic region.

REFERENCES

Andersen, S. H., 1985, Tybrind Vig. A Preliminary Report on a Submerged Ertebølle Settlement on the West Coast of Fyn. *Journal of Danish Archaeology* 4, 52-69.

1986, Mesolithic Dugouts and Paddles from Tybrind Vig, Denmark. *Acta Arch.* 57, 87-106.

1994, New Finds of Mesolithic Logboats in Denmark. In: *ISBSA* 6, 1-10.

1995, Coastal adaptation and marine exploitation in Late Mesolithic Denmark – with special emphasis on the Limfjord region. In: A. Fischer (ed.), *Man & Sea in the Mesolithic. Coastal settlement above and below present sea level*. International Symposium, Kalundborg 1993. Oxford, 41-66.

1996, Ertebøllebåde fra Lystrup. Ertebølle canoes from Lystrup. *Kuml* 1993-1994, 7-38.

Christensen, C. 1997, Boats and navigation in the Stone Age. In: L. Pedersen, A. Fischer & B. Aaby (eds), *The Danish Storebælt since the Ice Age – man, sea, forest*. København, 282-294.

1990, Stone Age Dugout Boats in Denmark: Occurrence, Age, Form, and Reconstruction. In: D. E. Robinson (ed.), *Experimentation and Reconstruction in Environmental Archaeology*. Oxford, 119-142.

Hartz, S. 2005, Aktuelle Forschungen zur Chronologie und Siedlungsweise der Ertebølle- und frühesten Trichterbecherkultur in Schleswig-Holstein. *Jahrb. BMV*, 52, 2004, 61-81.

Kaute, P., Schindler, G. & Lübke, H., 2005, Der endmesolithisch/frühneolithische Fundplatz Stralsund-Mischwasserspeicher – Zeugnisse früher Bootsbautechnologie an der Ostseeküste Mecklenburg-Vorpommerns. *Jahrb. BMV*, 52, 2004, 221-241.

Klooß, St., in prep., *Endmesolithische Holzfunde von der südwestlichen Ostseeküste*. PhD thesis, Christian-Albrechts-University Kiel.

Koch, E. 1998, *Neolithic Bog Pots from Zealand, Møn, Lolland and Falster*. Nordiske Fortidsminder, Serie B 16. København.

Labes, St. 2005. Endmesolithische Holzfunde von dem submarinen Fundplatz Timmendorf-Nordmole I. *Jahrb. BMV*, 52, 2004, 111-118.

Louwe Kooijmans, L. P., Hänninen, K. & Vermeeren, C. M., 2001, Artefacten van hout. In: L. P. Louwe Kooijmans (ed.), *Archaeologie in de Betouweroute. Hardinxveld-Giessendam De Bruin. Een kampplats uit het Laat-Mesolithicum en het begin van de Swifterbant-cultuur (5500-4450 v. Chr.).* Utrecht, 435-477.

Lübke, H. 2005, Ergänzende Anmerkungen zur Datierung der Einbäume des endmesolithisch/frühneolithischen Fundplatzes Stralsund-Mischwasserspeicher. *Jahrb. BMV*, 52, 2004, 257-261.

Lübke, H. & Terberger, T. 2005, Das Endmesolithikum in Vorpommern und auf Rügen im Lichte neuer Daten. *Jahrb. BMV*, 52, 2004, 243-255.

Lübke, H., Schacht, S. & Terberger, T., 2000, Final Mesolithic and Early Neolithic Coastal Settlements on the Island of Rügen and in Northern Vorpommern. In: F. Lüth, U. Schoknecht, O. Nakoinz, H. Beer, Chr. Börker, H. Schlichterhe, T. Förster, M. Mainberger & J. Riederer (eds), *Schutz des Kulturerbes unter Wasser. Veränderungen europäischer Lebenskultur durch Fluß- und Seehandel. Internationaler Kongreß für Unterwasserarchäologie Sassnitz 1999.* Beiträge zur Ur- und Frühgeschichte Mecklenburg-Vorpommerns 35. Lübstorf, 439-449.

Mandelkow, E., Frenzel, P., Lampe, R., Kaute, P. & Schindler, G., 2005, Paläontologische Untersuchungen von Sedimentprofilen der archäologischen Grabung Stralsund- Mischwasserspeicher. *Jahrb. BMV*, 52, 2004, 263-281.

Mertens, E.-M., 2000, Linde, Ulme, Hasel. Zur Verwendung von Pflanzen für Jagd- und Fischfanggeräte im Mesolithikum Dänemarks und Schleswig-Holsteins. *Prähistorische Zeitschrift*, 75.1, 1-55.

Sirelius, U. T., 1934, *Die Volkskultur Finnlands*, vol. 1, *Jagd und Fischerei in Finnland*. Berlin, Leipzig.

Stuiver, M., Reimer, P. J., Bard, E., Beck, J. W., Burr, G. S., Hughen, K. A., Kromer, B., McCormac, G. & van der Plicht, J. (eds), 1998, INTCAL98 Radiocarbon age calibration, 24,000-0 cal BP. *Radiocarbon 40.3*.

Terberger, T. & Lübke, H., 2002, New evidence on the Ertebølle Culture on Rügen and neighbouring areas. In: R. Lampe (ed.), *Holocene Evolution of the South-Western Baltic Coast – Geological, Archaeological and Palaeo-environmental Aspects. Field meeting of INQUA Subcommission V. Sea-level changes and Coastal Evolution. Western Europe. September 22-27, 2002.* Greifswalder Geographische Arbeiten, no. 27. Greifswald, 47-53.

ROSEMARIE LEINEWEBER · HARALD LÜBKE

THE LOGBOAT OF LAKE ARENDSEE

NEW EVIDENCE OF INLAND WATERCRAFTS IN SACHSEN-ANHALT, GERMANY

Sachsen-Anhalt is a federal state with few inland waters. In the past underwater findings were an absolute exception and mostly originated from the Elbe River water-meadows, whereas the lakes of the state were insignificant. This changed with the discovery of a logboat in Lake Arendsee (Altmarkkreis Salzwedel), in December of 2003.

TOPOGRAPHY AND LAKE HISTORY

Lake Arendsee is situated in the Altmark region near the N. border of Sachsen-Anhalt, close to the Wendland in the state of Lower Saxony (**Fig. 1**). The lake has an area of 5 km² and a maximum E.-W.-expansion of 3.5 km with a N.-S.-expansion of ca. 2 km. With a maximum depth of a little more than 50 m and an average depth of 29 m it is one of Germany's deepest inland waters. The recent lake level is 23.3 m (Arendsee 2000: 75). The shore area in the S. and W. is steep, whereas the shore area in the N. and E. is even. The town of the same name Arendsee was founded at the S.E. shore of the lake. The origins of Lake Arendsee have not been fully researched yet. Already in the late Glacial, at 12,700 B.C., there was a lake to the W. of the present one, which from a geological point of view emerged undoubtedly as a subrosive triggered natural land-subsidence during the pre-Holocene. At that process, freshwater came seeping through and dissolved areas of the anhydride cap rock of the subsoil salt dome, which caused a collapse of the remaining parts of the roof several times during the late-Pleistocene and Holocene so that saline deep water seeped through to the lake bowl (Thormeier 1993: 11). Due to this, size and depth of the lake as well as the location of the collapses changed several times during the Holocene. The lake expanded in the N. due to an area of shallow water in the Atlantic period between 7000 and 4000 B.C. A significant and deep collapse happened in the E. in the following Subboreal until about 750 B.C. (Röhrig & Scharf 2002: 125). Several so-called »lake collapses« are historically registered for the year A.D. 822 as well as 1685. According to observations of the diving club Arendsee (TCA), even nowadays light lake ground descents occur.

Already since the Mesolithic human activity has been established in the area of Lake Arendsee. In the first written source of A.D. 827, the chronicler Einhard (Einhard 827) reports on an event in the year 822, a wall-like bulge of the soil's surface at the *Arnseo*, i.e. »next« to the existent lake (Halbfass 1896: 14; also Felcke 1892: 4-7). O. Hartmann and G. Schönberg (2003: 10) regard this wall formation as a result of the tilt-motion on cracking of the cap rock near the surface or as a pressure zone preceding the collapse. Although the wall disappeared afterwards, it seems the present expansion and depth of the lake resulted from that collapse of 822. A record from 1208 once more refers to the »old« Lake Arendsee (*antiquum Arnesse*) (Müller 1996: 39; Riedel 1859: 2-3). According to A. Brückner (1984: 25) the Slavonic name of this so-called Wendisch lake was *Wlazdejske*, which refers to the word *manor*. These waters were situated in the N. area of the present lake; its shoreline has not been documented.

A second known event is the lake collapse on the 25th November 1685, when on the S.E. shore a mound along with a windmill and several hectares of land sank into the lake (Heinecke 1926: 11ff.; Halbfass 1896: 15; Felcke 1892: 8-9). After G. C. Silberschlag who already focused on depth measurements and the de-

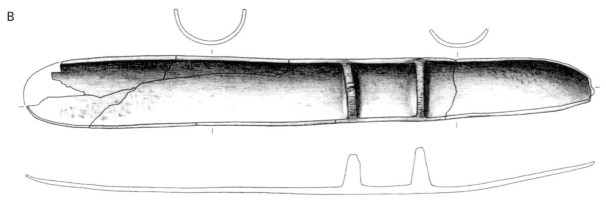

Fig. 5 **A** Photo mosaic of the uncovered logboat (Photos I. Hoffmann, Halle/Saale). – **B** Logboat of Lake Arendsee (Digital drawing based on 3-D-scanning by O. Schröder & M. Wiegmann, LDA).

shore which immediately cleared the water. The soft consistency of the lake's ground accelerated the operation so that after one day's work most of the sediment was removed from the W. starboard side to a depth of ca. 50 cm. Thereby it became apparent that the logboat rested directly on the lake's sediment and consequently was still in its original position upon discovery.

After the uncovering of the starboard side, a raising device consisting of transverse iron bars and sheet steel was laterally shifted into the sediment. Then the excavation of the port side followed. From this side as well, the research divers shifted sheet steel on top of the cross bars underneath the boat. The cross bars were connected to lengthwise bars, which were placed parallel to the logboat (**Fig. 4**). After the completion of that construction, a raising and preservation tub made of stainless steel with an inner dimension of 5 m in length, 1 m in width and 1 m in height was put next to the logboat on the lake's ground with the help of the THW's small ferry, into which the container was lifted. The tub was then taken to the Arendsee harbour and loaded onto a lorry. After the transportation to the conservation lab of the LaKD in Schwerin, the boat was treated with PEG. Salvage and restoration were undertaken with the aim to present the, for the late Middle Ages, unique find at the Landesmuseum für Vorgeschichte in Halle.

CONSTRUCTION AND BOAT TYPE

According to the underwater measuring, the boat hull (**Fig. 5**) is 4.18 m long. Near the forward end width comes to 0.52 m, whereas the stern (top of the tree) is 0.4 m wide. The height increases to 0.33 m towards

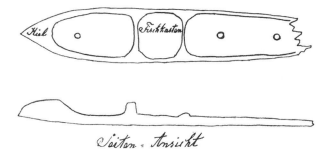

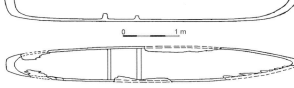

Fig. 6   The logboat of Lake Steinhuder Meer (After Ochwadt 1967).

Fig. 7   The logboat of Lake Klarer See near Grünow (After Raddatz 1957).

the centre (**Fig. 5B**). Both ends are rounded and shaped spoon-like; the square-section is almost semi-circular with a 3 to 5 cm thick profile. In the after part of the boat there are two vertical transverse bulkheads of ca. 5 cm thickness, which form a kind of box (measurements 40 by 43 cm). Marks of a flat hollow adze are scattered over the surfaces. Traces of framing other internals are missing.

The usage of ash tree seems remarkable, since Stone Age logboats were usually made out of lime tree, whereas such of later periods were made from oak. Nonetheless, ash tree has been documented for Bronze Age logboats from Lake Federsee (Billamboz 2000: 42).

LOGBOATS OF THE SAME DESIGN, THEIR INTERPRETATION AND UTILISATION

A characteristic feature of the Lake Arendsee logboat, so far unknown from regional findings (Leineweber & Lübke 2006b), is the interior box-like structure separated by two transverse bulkheads. Only two parallels exist, which can be compared: dugouts from the Steinhuder Meer, Lower Saxony (**Fig. 6**) (Ochwadt 1967: no. 241) and from Lake Klarer See near Grünow (**Fig. 7**), Landkreis Uecker-Randow, Mecklenburg-Vorpommern (Raddatz 1957: 226; Schoknecht 1991: 66).

The origin of the logboat type points already towards its usage as a fishery vessel rather than for transportation. The finding from the Steinhuder Meer also points to such a function; C. Ochwadt identified its internal structure as a fish box (Ochwadt 1967: 334-335). In his essential contribution on N. European dugouts, C. Hirte (1987) does not focus on such a feature, whereas it is mentioned by S. McGrail (1978: 55-58; 69). Although in the description of his examples the boxes never were in the middle of the boat, but towards the rear.

An interpretation of the Lake Arendsee boat as a fishery vessel with a fish-container seems most reasonable. The exceptionally flat and rounded bow of the logboat might has been practical for landing at the shallow shores in the N. of Lake Arendsee. Worked by paddling, the fisherman preferably was seated in the after part of the dugout, where he could store his catch in the fish-container, whilst the forward section of the boat could be used for equipment like nets and weirs. However, historical information on fishery in Lake Arendsee is not known. Records indicate that the lake once belonged to the local abbey. Among others, all the villages adjoining the lake (Arendsee [1208], Genzien [1365], Gestien [1253], Kaulitz [1184 and 1340], Kläden [1271], Leppin [1322], Schrampe [1184], Zehren [before 1235], Ziemendorf [1375?], Zießau [1184] and Zühlen [1331]) were the property of the Benedict convent which was founded in A.D. 1183 (Riggert-Mindermann & Mindermann 2006). The fishery rights are more clearly proved by the abbey's written acknowledgement of the year 1208 (Riedel 1859: 2ff.): »Furthermore everything what they have possessed or could possess between the stagnant water, which is called the old Lake Arendsee, the River Binde and the region Lemgow be it for forest, farming, fishing *or* hunting usage« (English translation after H. Müller 1996: 47). A renewal is dated to the year 1457 (Heinecke 1926: 91). Hence it seems reasonable, that the logboat was used to supply the abbey from the Zießau shore with fish from Lake Arendsee. The vessel may have been sunk intentionally or stored at the lake's ground respectively; alternatively it had accidentally sunk.

PERSPECTIVE

There will be more archaeological research in Lake Arendsee in future. As voluntary appointees of archaeology of the LDA, sports divers are authorized to locate and measure artefacts and structures. By the support of sub-bottom sonar and remotely operated vehicle (ROV), information about relics in and on the lake's ground will be compiled.

ACKNOWLEDGEMENTS

The authors are indebted to the scientific divers Andreas Grundmann (LaKD Schwerin) and Dirk Hering (Walsrode), to the members of the TCA, especially Rüdiger Pohlmann, Hans-Henning and Hartmut Schindler, as well as to the team of the THW Salzwedel and Magdeburg under the direction of the late Hans Hermann Mietz, Clenze. They are grateful also to K.-U. Heußner, DAI Berlin, who directed the dendrochronological analyses. – Timm Weski (München), Christian Hirte (Halle/Saale) and Harm Paulsen (Schleswig) contributed with further clues as to the utilisation of the Lake Arendsee logboat and other comparable dugouts. – I. Riggert-Mindermann and A. Minderman kindly allowed us to read their manuscript on the abbey history of Arendsee.

Translation by Katharina Leineweber

REFERENCES

Arendsee 2000, Arendsee. In: *Die Landschaftsgebiete Sachsen-Anhalts*. Magdeburg, 75-78.

Belasus, M., 2009, Two recent finds of medieval shipwrecks in the North of Germany. *This volume, pp. 73-78.*

Billamboz, A., 2000, Schiffbau und Waldlandschaft am Bodensee. Holzuntersuchungen an Schiffswracks und Uferkonstruktionen. In: *Einbaum, Lastersegler, Dampfschiff. Frühe Schifffahrt in Südwestdeutschland*. Stuttgart, 41-50.

Brückner, A., 1984, *Die slavischen Ansiedlungen in der Altmark und im Magdeburgischen* (reprint Leipzig 1879).

Einhard 827, Einhards Jahrbücher des fränkischen Reiches (Fränkische Annalen). In: *Monumenta Germaniae historica – Scriptores I und V*. Fulda, Xanten (translated by O. Abel, Berlin 1850).

Felcke, A. F. L., 1892, *Chronik der Stadt Arendsee in der Altmark*. Gardelegen 1891-1892.

Halbfass, W., 1896, Der Arendsee in der Altmark. *Mitteilungen des Vereins für Erdkunde zu Halle a. d. Saale 1896*, 1-26.

Hartmann, O. & Schönberg, G., 2003, *Der Arendsee in der Altmark. Geologie und Entwicklung*. Magdeburg.

Heinecke, O., 1926, *Chronik der Stadt Arendsee in der Altmark*. Arendsee.

Hirte, C., 1987, *Zur Archäologie monoxyler Wasserfahrzeuge im nördlichen Mitteleuropa. Eine Studie zur Repräsentativität der* *Quellen in chorologischer, chronologischer und konzeptioneller Hinsicht*. Unpubl. PhD thesis, Christian-Albrecht University Kiel.

Leineweber, R. & Lübke, H., 2006a, Unterwasserarchäologie in der Altmark. *Archäologie in Sachsen-Anhalt, Neue Folge 4. I, 2007*, 127-139.

2006b, Der Einbaum aus dem Arendsee. *NAU*, 13, 33-44.

McGrail, S., 1978, *Logboats of England and Wales with comparative material from European and other countries*. BAR, British Series, no. 51, Oxford.

Müller, H., 1996, Zur Vorgeschichte der Arendseer Klostergründung. *37. Jahresbericht des Altmärkischen Vereins für vaterländische Geschichte zu Salzwedel e. V.* Lüchow, 37-49.

Ochwadt, C., 1967, *Das Steinhuder Meer. Eine Sammlung von Nachrichten und Beschreibungen*. Hannover.

Raddatz, K., 1957, Vernichtete ur- und frühgeschichtliche Funde aus der Uckermark. *Jahrb. BMV, 1957*, 203-271.

Riedel, A., 1859/1862, *Codex diplomaticus brandenburgensis. Sammlung der Urkunden, Chroniken und sonstigen Quellenschriften für die Geschichte der Mark Brandenburg und ihrer Regenten,* vol. A, XVII/XXII. Berlin.

Riggert-Mindermann, I. & Mindermann, A., 2006, Benediktinerinnenkloster Arendsee. In: *Brandenburgisches Klosterbuch 2007*. Berlin, Brandenburg, 106-126.

Röhrig, R. & Scharf, B. W., 2002, Paläolimnologische Untersuchungen zur Entwicklung des Arendsees (Sachsen-Anhalt). In: *Greifswalder Geografische Arbeiten*, no. 26, 123-126.

Schoknecht, U., 1991, Einbäume aus der Region Neubrandenburg. In: *Mitteilungen zur Ur- und Frühgeschichte für Ostmecklenburg und Vorpommern*, 38, 62-67.

Schweichler, J., 1993, Abenteuer Seegrund. In: Arbeitsgemeinschaft der Arendsee (ed.), *Der Arendsee anno 2000? Erstes See-Symposium*. Arendsee, 36-38.

Silberschlag, G. C., 1788, Nachrichten von dem See bey Arendsee in der Altmark. In: *Schriften der Gesellschaft naturforschender Freunde zu Berlin,* no. 8. Berlin, 225-235.

Thormeier, H.-D., 1993, Der Arendsee. Ein spektakuläres Ergebnis normaler geologischer, geochemischer und geomechanischer Prozesse. Neuere Untersuchungsergebnisse über den Salzstock Arendsee von 1984-1986. In: Arbeitsgemeinschaft der Arendsee (ed.), *Der Arendsee anno 2000? Erstes See-Symposium*. Arendsee, 11-14.

JASON ROGERS

DOCUMENTING DUGOUTS FROM BOHEMIA AND MORAVIA, CZECH REPUBLIC

Dugout logboats have in recent years been recognized as a significant source of knowledge regarding early navigation and boat-building technology. Logboat surveys have been undertaken in many countries of Europe, and researchers have assembled detailed records of regional vessels. One gap in this body of work is the Czech Republic, where no comprehensive research was undertaken until relatively recently. Several discoveries within the last decade have prompted new interest in these vessels, and a catalogue of Czech logboats is currently being compiled. This article will provide a summary of dugout vessels from this area, some information on their significant features and characteristics, and a brief analysis of potential use and functionality.

BACKGROUND

The Czech Republic is situated in Central Europe, bordering Poland to the N., Slovakia to the E., Austria to the S., and Germany to the W. (**Fig. 1**). Much of the country consists of uplands and mountains. The Czech lands traditionally have two constituent regions, Bohemia in the W. and Moravia in the E. Bohemia is a fertile basin entirely encircled by mountains and hills, while Moravia consists of highlands, mountains, and

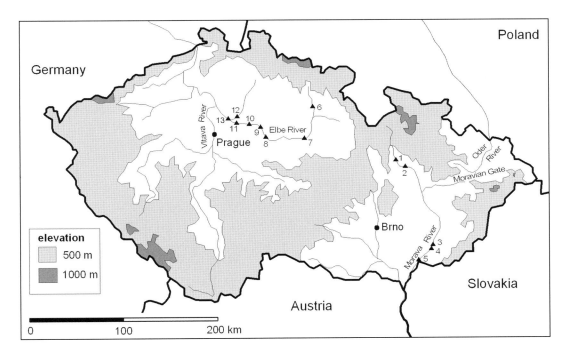

Fig. 1   Location of Logboats mentioned in the text: **1** Mohelnice (okr. Šumperk). – **2** Příkazy (okr. Olomouc). – **3** Spytihněv (okr. Zlín). – **4** Uherské Hradistě (okr. Uherské Hradiště). – **5** Mikulčice (okr. Hodonín). – **6** Černožice (okr. Hradec Králové). – **7** Labětín (okr. Pardubice). – **8** Kolín (okr. Kolín). – **9** Poděbrady (okr. Nymburk). – **10** Přerov nad Labem (okr. Nymburk). – **11** Čelakovice (okr. Praha-východ). – **12** Otradovice (okr. Mladá Boleslav). – **13** Lázně Toušeň (okr. Praha-východ).

the valley of the Morava River. The regions correspond closely to the drainage areas of the country's most important rivers: the Vltava-Labe (Moldau-Elbe) system in Bohemia, and the Morava system in Moravia. This is also one of Europe's main watershed divisions, since the Elbe empties into the North Sea, and the Morava joins the Danube, eventually flowing to the Black Sea.

The presence of sophisticated prehistoric watercraft in this land-locked territory is quite informative, perhaps reflecting some unexpected skills and traditions of the area's early inhabitants. More than 40 logboats are known from the Czech Republic, and at least 19 boats have been preserved in repositories or regional museums (eight in Moravia and eleven in Bohemia). At least two further vessels are known to remain buried *in situ*.

Reliable dating is lacking for most specimens. Only three examples have been dated by absolute methods, and until recently, little analysis had been carried out on these vessels. Among the few early works describing Czech logboats are Bohuslav Novotný's article on ancient Bohemian watercraft (Novotný 1951), and Vilém Hrubý's piece on »old Slavonic« boats in Moravia (Hrubý 1965). Announcements of occasional finds have also appeared in journals, and the four dugouts discovered at Mikulčice in the 1960s and 1970s were described in the official excavation report (Poláček 2000). The newest discoveries have also been recently published: the 10m boat recovered at Mohelnice in 1999 (Kučerová & Peška 2004), and the un-usual fir vessel found at Otradovice in 2002 (Šilhová & Špaček 2004). Also in 2004, the author completed a MA thesis describing and analyzing Moravian logboats (Rogers 2004).

SURVIVING BOHEMIAN AND MORAVIAN LOGBOATS

Eight vessels are preserved in Moravia (**Fig. 1**), including the only Czech logboats with associated absolute dates. Five dugouts are accessible in museums, two are in state repositories, and one remains buried *in situ*. In the spring of 1999, a 10m oak logboat was discovered in Mohelnice Lake in N. Moravia (**Fig. 2, 1**). The discovery location is a former meander of the Morava River, which today is channeled approximately 50m from the site. This vessel measures 10.46m in length, 1.05m in width, with a maximum height of 0.6m. There are four transverse ridges carved from the solid across the floor. The vessel's overhanging platform ends may improve sailing performance as well as providing extra flotation and shielding the crew from spray. Analysis by both dendrochronology and radiocarbon methods revealed a construction date of 281 B.C., making it the oldest dated specimen in the Czech Republic (Kučerová & Peška 2004: 34). Using the minimum freeboard method (Fry 2000), the estimated carrying capacity for this vessel was calculated to be approx. 1077kg (Rogers 2004: 113).

A much smaller logboat was discovered in 1962 at the village of Příkazy, only 30km from Mohelnice along the Morava River (**Fig. 2, 3**). This 4.2m oak vessel contained a wide-bladed iron axe, and investigators concluded that the artifact dated the boat to the Middle Ages. In 2006, dendrochronology samples from the vessel were analyzed at the Agricultural University in Brno, revealing a construction date of A.D. 1532 (Rybníček 2006).

The Příkazy boat features thwarts and a bulkhead carved from the solid. This combination of features is apparent on at least two other Czech logboats and on similar vessels across Europe. According to Ossowski, these are one-man boats used for fishing, where the bulkhead functionally divides the boat into two halves. The »dry« half was reserved for the fisherman, and the »wet« portion was used for storing tackle and fish (Ossowski 2000: 65).

Two boats are held in the Slovacké Muzeum in Staré Město, from the village of Spytihněv and the neighboring city of Uherské Hradiště. These vessels were conserved in the 1960s and have not been dated. The

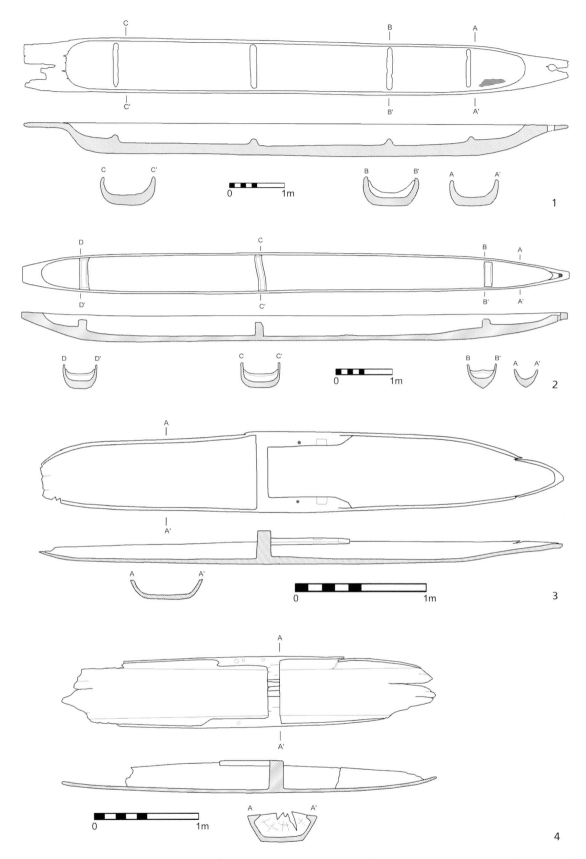

Fig. 2 Logboat from Moravia: **1** Mohelnice (okr. Šumperk), dated after 281 B.C. (After Peška). – **2** Mikulčice 3 Logboat, dated by context to the 10th c. (After L. Poláček 2000). – **3** Logboat from Příkazy (okr. Olomouc) dated after A.D.1537 (After M. Rybníček 2006). – **4** Poděbrady 2 Logboat.

3.8 m Spytihněv boat is quite similar to the Příkazy vessel above, featuring a bulkhead and thwart carved from the solid, with apparent grooves for a seat-board. There are tapering blocks or protrusions on the 5.2 m Uherské Hradiště vessel, one in the bow and two in the stern, whose function is unknown.

The final Moravian logboats are held in the museum at the Mikulčice national cultural monument in S. Moravia. The early Slavonic citadel of Mikulčice dates from the 7th to the 11th c. and was excavated between 1959 and 1984. Three complete vessels, and half of another, were found during the course of excavations. These boats, dated by context to the late 10th c., feature beveled transverse ridges across the floors (**Fig. 2, 2**). The carrying capacity of the largest vessel, Mikulčice 3, was calculated at approximately 635 kg (Rogers 2004: 113). The last boat to be unearthed, during the 1984 excavations, was so fragile that it was reburied and left *in situ*. Wood samples taken from this vessel were dated by ^{14}C to A.D. 1180±40 (Poláček 2000: 206).

Of more than 20 reported dugouts from Bohemia (**Fig. 1**), at least eleven still exist. The majority of Bohemian vessels come from the region's dominant waterway, the Elbe River. A large number of historically documented examples were also found in the same area, although they have now been lost or destroyed. No vessels from Bohemia have been dated by any absolute method.

The vessel found farthest upstream on the Elbe is a 6.22 m oak dugout recovered during bridge construction at Černožice, now held in the Jaroměř-Josefov museum (**Fig. 3, 1**). This logboat is unique among Czech examples in that it has a nearly square profile in cross-section. The square overhanging platform ends are perforated by rectangular holes, one at the presumed bow and two at the stern. Width at the bow is 0.46 m, stern width is 0.56 m, and maximum height is 0.31 m. Vessel walls are 3 to 5 cm thick, and there are no bulkheads or transverse ridges. The low height is a result of the parent log being split lengthwise in half, in order to obtain two identical boats from a single trunk. The holes in the platform ends may have used to attach strengthening elements, making the two hulls into a single raft. The form suggests that this was one hull of a paired or multi-hull raft, while the sloping transition from the open bow and stern may have facilitated rolling barrels into and out of the vessel.

Nearly identical vessels have been found in adjacent areas of Poland, especially the upper reaches of the Oder River. These logboats, known as Lewin-type vessels, are characterized by square or trapezoidal cross-section, rectangular hull-ends, and low height of the sides in relation to vessel length. In addition, nearly all the Lewin-type boats have a single hole in the bow and two at the stern. Lewin-type logboats were used as paired hulls, joined by transverse poles. The Polish vessels date from the early centuries A.D. and are associated with the Przeworsk culture (Ossowski, pers. comm.).

Several vessels from Bohemia's central Elbe region share a different construction and morphology. Logboats from Labětín, Kolín, and Přerov nad Labem were all hollowed from single oak logs, retain a circular or semi-circular shape in cross-section, and lack bulkheads and transverse ridges. The Labětín vessel was discovered on the Elbe River in 1957, and is now at the Eastern Bohemian Museum in Pardubice (**Fig. 3, 2**). The vessel's stern is missing and was likely broken off when the boat was pulled from the riverbed. The remaining torso is 8 m in length, approx. 0.7 m wide, with a maximum height of 0.62 m. The bow was cut to a rough wedge shape, with no overhang or platform, leaving a massive portion of solid wood at the vessel's forward end. Several holes 4 to 5 cm in diameter perforate the sides, and wall thickness varies from 5 to 9 cm. Attempts to date the Labětín boat by dendrochronology were so far unsuccessful.

Fig. 3   Logboat from Bohemia: **1** Černožice, similar to Lewin-type vessels from Poland. – **2** Labětín (okr. Pardubice). – **3** Otradovice (okr. Mladá Boleslav). – **4** Lázně Toušeň (okr. Praha-východ).

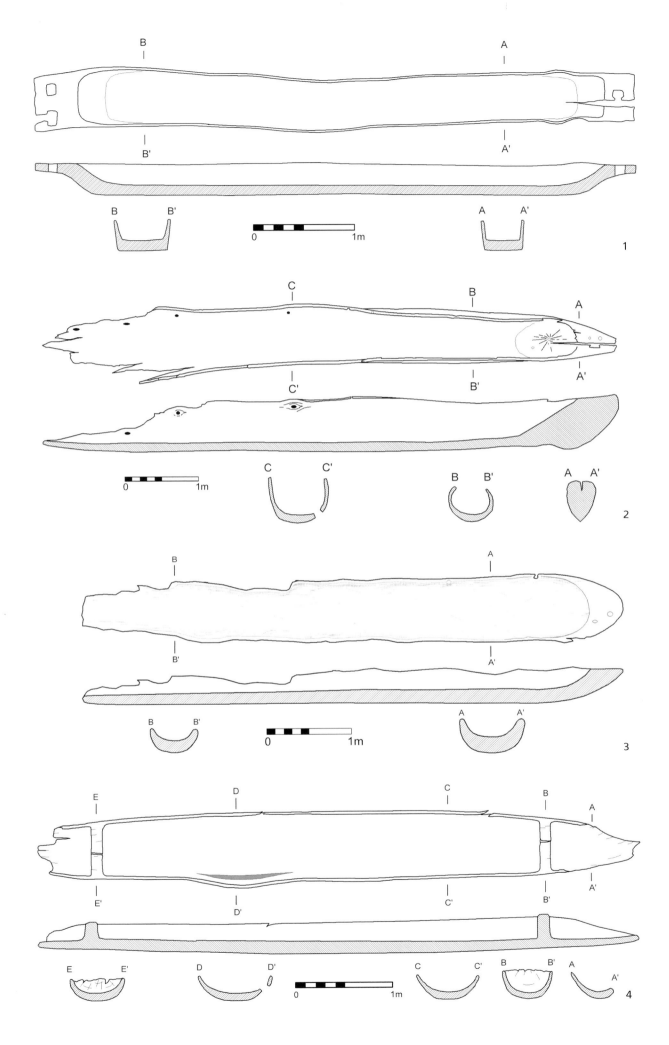

1

2

3

4

0   1m

Of several logboats discovered in the town of Kolín at least one survives, recovered in 1921, and is now displayed in the National Museum in Prague. The complete vessel is 9.45 cm long, 0.66 m wide, and 0.55 m high. Similar to the Labětín boat, there are no bulkheads or transverse ridges, and several round holes (2 to 3 cm in diameter) perforate the vessel's upper sides. The holes were initially interpreted as outrigger attachment locations (Niederle 1923: 34). The bow and stern taper to narrow overhanging ends, both of which are incised by narrow slots. The stern slot is cut in the shape of a »T«, possibly a niche for a steering oar. Hrubý (1965: 127) described a nearly identical feature on a Moravian vessel, which was later destroyed. The Kolín logboat was conserved in the 1920s, and has not been dated.

A logboat of the same type was found in Přerov nad Labem in 1954, but was recovered only in 1957. The vessel form is quite similar to the Labětín logboat. In construction, the bark was scraped from the parent tree, and the inside hollowed. The floor is smooth without ridges or bulkheads, and there are holes through the upper walls. As a result of being stored outdoors, the vessel today consists of several indistinct fragments.

At least five logboats have been found along the Elbe near the town of Poděbrady, also in central Bohemia. Portions of three vessels have survived, and are held in the cellar of Poděbrady castle. All three Poděbrady logboats differ markedly from the previously described Bohemian examples in that they feature bulkheads or transverse ribs. One vessel (Poděbrady 2) is nearly complete, and is quite similar to the boats from Spytihněv and Příkazy with a bulkhead to separate the »wet« and »dry» functional spaces (**Fig. 2, 3-4**). Poděbrady 2 measures 3.62 m in length, 0.68 m in maximum width, and is 0.4 m high. The hull is trapezoidal in cross-section, with a sharp chine. The two other logboats (Poděbrady 1 and 3) survive only as floor segments, one measuring 4.96 m and the other 3.64 m in length. The fragmentary boats are similar in construction, each with two transverse ridges and a distinct chine where the walls meet the floor. Widths of these vessels may be estimated at 0.7 m and 0.6 m respectively, although original lengths cannot be determined from the surviving fragments.

Two logboats are held in the Čelákovice municipal museum, one discovered in the spring of 2002. The recovery location near the village of Otradovice is on the Jizera River only 4.5 km from its confluence with the Elbe (**Fig. 3, 3**). This vessel is the single example of a Czech logboat not made from oak (*Quercus sp.*); the wood species employed to build this boat is silver fir (*Abies alba*). There are very few European logboats made of fir; this timber is not cited on McGrail's list of ethnographic and archaeological logboats (McGrail 1987: 60) and the sole published examples are several early modern vessels from Switzerland's Aegerisee (Arnold 1983: 276). In the Czech Republic this species grows only at elevations above 300 m, meaning the vessel was likely constructed along the Jizera's upper reaches, and then sailed downstream to the Elbe basin (Šilhová & Špaček 2004: 30). The surviving portion, probably the bow, measures 6.65 m in length, 0.8 m in maximum width, with a height of 0.4 m. This vessel also lacks bulkheads or transverse ridges across the floor.

The second logboat at the Čelákovice museum was recovered locally on the Elbe in the 1940s, and was constructed quite differently from the Otradovice vessel. This boat has a central transverse ridge and two bulkhead walls at either end. The stern does not survive; the bow is completely hollowed and comes to a point. The hull is trapezoidal in cross-section, narrowing to a V-shape at the bow. The surviving length is 6.72 m, maximum width is 0.62 m, and height is 0.34 m. The walls have a very uniform 2 to 3 cm thickness. Several 2 cm holes perforate the vessel's sides, and there is a 5 cm oval opening near the point of the bow.

A floor fragment and a nearly complete vessel held in the town of Brandýs nad Labem complete the inventory of Bohemian logboats. The floor fragment is almost 5 m in length, and a maximum width of 0.56 m survives. Remains of two transverse ridges and a distinct chine are apparent, giving a trapezoidal profile in cross-section. The second vessel, from the neighboring village of Lázně Toušeň, is nearly complete

vessel	river system	length (cm)	beam (cm)	height (cm)
Pod brady 2	Elbe	362	68	40
Spitihněv	Morava	383	60	30
Příkazy	Morava	418	65	30
U. Hradišt	Morava	522	76	34
Jaroměř	Elbe	622	50	31
Lázně Touše	Elbe	635	70	26
Mikulčice 4	Morava	672	75	26
Mikulčice 2	Morava	883	66	36
Kolín	Elbe	945	66	55
Mikulčice 3	Morava	988	71	45
Mohelnice	Morava	1046	105	60

Table 1   Basic dimensions for complete vessels.

(**Fig. 3, 4**). The surviving length is 6.35 m, although missing portions at the bow and stern mean the vessel was originally nearly 7 m long. Constructed from a trunk split lengthwise in half, the hull shape closely follows that of the parent tree. There are two large bulkheads, one near the bow and one at the stern. Maximum width is approximately 0.7 m, and the vessel's height is 0.3 m.

There are many other logboats in both Bohemia and Moravia known from historical sources, which have disappeared or were destroyed. At least one, at the village of Skorkov, was reburied and is presumed to remain *in situ*. It is likely that many vessels were lost during deepening and straightening of river channels in the 1920s and 1930s. Even today, vessels stored outside or without adequate shelter are disintegrating.

DISCUSSION

Currently, the main difficulty in proceeding with a description of chronological development lies in the lack of dating for Czech logboats. Only three vessels have been analyzed by ^{14}C or dendrochronology: Mohelnice (after 281 B.C.), Mikulčice 4 (A.D. 1180±40), and Příkazy (A.D. 1537). Radiocarbon samples for a fourth logboat (Otradovice) are currently being analyzed. In Poland, Waldemar Ossowski has determined that the evolution from logboats to plank boats took place along the coast by the 9th c., and on inland waterways between the 13th and 15th c. (Ossowski 1999: 221). It is likely that even later development took place in the Czech Lands, situated still further from the sea. Despite the lack of chronology for Czech logboats, some remarks can be made concerning vessel morphology, distribution, and use.

Dimensionally, the complete and reconstructed vessels range in length from 3.62 to 10.46 m, in breadth from 0.5 to 1.05 m, and in height from 0.26 to 0.6 m. Several incomplete vessels (Labětín, Čelákovice, and Otradovice) originally attained lengths of at least 7 to 9 m. Basic dimensions for complete vessels are shown in **Table 1**.

Morphologically, the boats in this study exhibit a range of features and constructional styles. Several observations regarding vessel form and elements can be made. All logboats from the Morava River watershed feature transverse ridges, interior bulkheads, or other floor elements carved from the solid. In contrast, at least five vessels from the Elbe River system have smooth floors with no ridges or other protrusions. (Jaroměř, Labětín, Kolín, Přerov, and Otradovice). On both river systems, those hulls with ridges and bulkheads generally have trapezoidal or U-shaped cross-sections, whereas vessels with smooth floors are more circular in cross-section, with hull shapes that closely follow that of the parent trunk.

Most Czech logboat sites and remains are clustered along the country's two dominant rivers, the Elbe and the Morava (**Fig. 1**). In Moravia, the discovery sites range from the foothills of the Jeseníky Mountains in the N. nearly to the Morava's confluence with the Danube. The major concentration of Moravian logboats (ten existing or historically known vessels) occurs between Uherské Hradistě and Mikulčice. Nearly all Logboats in Bohemia have been found along the Elbe River, concentrated between Pardubice and Mělník.

The Czechs' geographic position is important in this context, as these lands provide one of very few lowland passages between N. and S. Europe. High mountain ranges oriented E.-W. across Europe (the Alps, Carpathians etc.) tend to channel transportation in those directions. It is more difficult to move directly N. or S. One key N.-S. route across Europe runs through Moravia, where the headwaters of the Morava River come to within a few kilometers of the headwaters of the Oder. This passage connecting the Polish Plain with Pannonia and the Danube is called the Moravian Gate. The Elbe River has likewise been an important transportation link for many centuries, providing a useful route from the Bohemian heartland to Saxony and N. Germany. Logboats found in the major Czech river systems should thus be seen not only in the context of local riverine resource exploitation, but also medium and long-distance trade, travel, and communications.

REFERENCES

Arnold, B., 1983, Les dernières pirogues monoxyles de Suisse centrale. *Helvetia archaeologica* 14, 271-286.

Fry, M., 2000, *Coití: Logboats from Northern Ireland*. Northern Ireland Archaeological Monographs, no. 4. Antrim.

Hrubý, V., 1965, Staroslovanské čluny na našem území. *Z dávných v ků* 2(1), 119-136.

Kučerová, I. & Peška, J., 2004, Monoxyl z Mohelnice. *Sborník přednášek z odborného semináře pro technologii a ochrany pamatek (STOP)*, 2004, 32-38.

McGrail, S., 1987, *Ancient Boats in N.W. Europe. The Archaeology of Water Transport to AD 1500*. London.

Niederle, L., 1923, Nález člunu v Kolin . *Obzor praehistorický*, II.1, 32-34.

Novotný, B., 1951, Nejstarši plavidla na Českých vodách. *Národopisný v stník Československý*, 32, 253-292.

Ossowski, W., 1999, *Studia nad Łodziami Jednopiennymi z Obszaru Polski*. Gdańsk.

2000, Some Results of the Study of Logboats in Poland. In: *ISBSA 8*, 59-66.

Poláček, L., 2000, Holzfunde aus Mikulčice. In: *Studien zum Burgwall von Mikulčice*, vol. 4. Brno, 177-302.

Rogers, J., 2004, *Logboats of the Moravian Gate: Monoxyl Dugout Vessels from Central Europe*. Unpublished MA thesis, East Carolina University, Greenville/N. Carolina.

Rybníček, M., 2006, Závěrečná zpráva: Příkazy – Hynkov (okr. Olomouc) – monoxyl člunu. Report prepared by Mendelova Agricultural and Forestry University, Dendrochronology Laboratory, Brno.

Šilhová, A. & Jaroslav, Š., 2004, Monoxyl z Čelákovic a jeho konzervace. *Sborník přednášek z odborného semináře pro technologii a ochrany pamatek (STOP), 2004*, 29-31.

TIMM WESKI

LOGBOATS AND LOCAL BOATS IN BAVARIA, GERMANY

A SUMMARY OF CURRENT RESEARCH

Bavaria is situated in the S.E. part of Germany. Contrary to common belief, it consists not only of the Alpine region, but it is much larger. The S. border is formed by the Alps with several lakes at their N. edge. The most significant ones are the Ammersee, the Starnberger See and the Chiemsee. In the S. part of Bavaria all rivers flow to the Danube, which runs to the Black Sea (**Fig. 1**). The main river in the N. part is the Main; it empties into the River Rhine, which gives access to the North Sea. There is only a very low watershed between these two European water systems. Therefore it is not surprising that at different periods three canals were dug through it. The first one, the Fossa Carolina or Karlsgraben, was started to be built in A.D. 793. Though it is uncertain whether this canal was ever completed its remains are still visible today (Koch 2002). The second one, the Ludwigs Kanal, was opened in 1845 and remained in service until 1945. The last one, the Rhein-Main-Donau-Kanal, was completed in 1992.

The river system of the Danube was used intensively in Roman times, though it must be stressed that before canalisation this river was flowing in meanders. Apart from the river patrol boats from Manching-Ober-stimm, Pfaffenhofen a.d. Ilm district, dating to the beginning of the 2nd c. (Bockius 2002), harbour structures were discovered in Straubing (Prammer 1988). Near Seebruck, Traunstein dist., a Roman landing place at the shore of the Chiemsee was investigated (Burmeister 1998: 27, figs 5-14).

S. of the Danube several of the rivers are flowing so fast that only downstream traffic with rafts is possible. On lakes rafts were towed with ropes (Gödde 1997: 43) or sails were used (Raff 1985: 40). Rafts transported not only wood, but goods and passengers as well. There was even a weekly raft service from Munich to Vienna before the railway line was established in1860 (Schattenhofer 1983: 78). On the Danube, and on some other rivers, plank boats of different sizes were known. Larger ones, so-called Ulmer Schachteln, were used for the passage to Vienna or even further downstream. Such vessels were flat bottomed with raised ends instead of stem and stern, thus avoiding bending the planks in more than one direction during the building process (**Fig. 2**). Vessels with a stem and stern typical for the River Main area were introduced not until the opening of the Ludwig-Kanal. A passage from Ulm to Vienna lasted eight to ten days. Going upstream, apart from very small boats that could be rowed or poled, the vessels were towed initially by men and later by horses. It took ten to twelve weeks to travel from Bratislava, Slovakia, to Rosenheim, Germany, or twelve to fourteen weeks from Budapest, Hungary, to Regensburg, Germany (Neweklowsky 1958: 30). The current of the river was so strong that at certain places rings were placed in the rock of the river bank, as at Weltenburger Enge, or at bridges to pull the vessels through. At the bridge Steinerne Brücke in Regensburg built in A.D. 1147 a motor winch with a wire cable was used still in the 20th c. (Heilmeier 2008). Traditional plank boats can still be seen on the River Danube, though they are rapidly replaced by modern ones. In 1976 during dredging at the mouth of the River Altmühl into the Danube at Kelheim-Kelheim-winzer, Kelheim dist., remnants of a plank boat were discovered. The wreck is preserved to a length of 5.85 m, a width of 1.4 m and a height of about 0.5 m. To a length of 1.55 m the flat bottom is raised. The seams were caulked with moss (*Drepanocladus aduncus* and *Calliergonella cuspidate*). Different to vessels from the Danube, where all traditional boats are characterized by a hard chine section (**Fig. 2**; Sarrazin *et al*. 1996), the section shows a double chine (OA BLfD 7037/1017). The latter is typical for boats of the River Rhine and its tributaries (e.g. Keweloh 1993). According a map drawn around 1820, the Kelheimwinzer

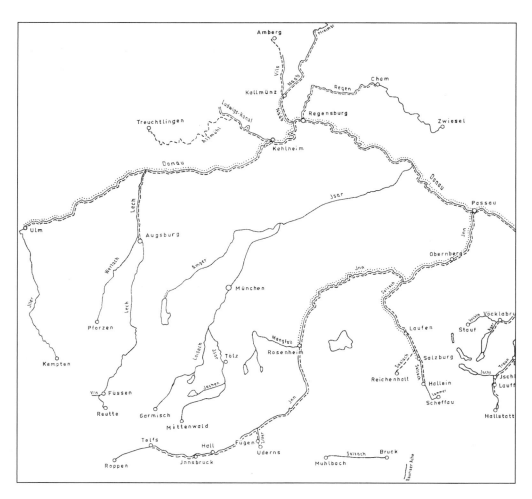

Fig. 1 Navigable rivers in S.E. Germany and W. Austria around 1900. – Straight line: rafts. Dashed line: rowing boats. Dotted line: steamers (After Neweklowsky 1958: app. 1).

site was already dry land. An uncalibrated ^{14}C date of 120±60 (KI-1147) points to an age of the vessel between A.D. 1640 and 1800 at the latest (Herzig & Weski 2009: 93).

Plank boats were also used on lakes, for instance for transporting wood (Gödde 1997: 46). Apart from the Chiemsee all traditional plank boats on lakes have been replaced. However, some of the fishermen still keep alive tradition by using boats, which are constructed out of stainless steel or aluminium, but retain traditional design. As late as in the 1920s, a sail boat was introduced, which became a popular local dinghy class. Though people of Bavaria are very proud of their heritage, very little systematic research has been done on plank boats on lakes.

Logboats were used on the several lakes by fishermen until around 1900. Such vessels on lake Starnberger See had raised ends and could carry up to six persons (von Westenrieder 1784: 37). A document notes 50 logboats and 79 plankboats used on this lake in 1842 (Erhebung 1842). On other lakes such as the Chiemsee boats commonly had a raised bow only (Höfling 1984: 45; 1987: 88). On the nearby Mondsee in Austria such vessels survived up to the 1950s; the final dugout was built in 1965, though never used for fishing (Kunze 1968).

In the 1980s records listed at least 20 logboats found in Bavaria (Hirte 1987, cat. no. 210). Most of them were recovered without any documentation. Along the River Main several logboats were not recorded in

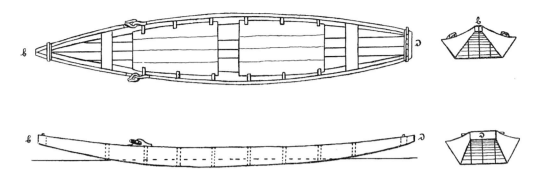

Fig. 2 *Waidboot* of 7.6 m length around 1900 (After Brunner 103: figs 25-28).

place	dating	type of dating	material	references
Starnberger See, Roseninsel	900 B.C.	Dendro	Oak *quercus*	Bauer 1992
Chiemsee, Feldwies	300 B.C.	14C		Pflederer 2005
Starnberger See, Kempfenhausen	250 B.C.	14C		Pflederer 2002
Laufen-Pfaffing	42 B.C.	Dendro	Oak *quercus*	Weski 2005
Schonungen	A.D. 53	Dendro	Oak *quercus*	Bauer 1992
Barmsee 1	A.D. 580	14C		Hirte 1987
Langbürgener See	A.D. 760	14C	Oak *quercus*	Pflederer 2001
Starnberger See, Ambach	A.D. 800	14C	Oak *quercus*	Hirte 1987
Starnberger See, Leoni 2	A.D. 900	14C		Hirte 1987
Starnberger See, Leoni 1	A.D. 950	14C		Hirte 1987
Starnberger See, Seeheim	A.D. 1080	14C		Pflederer 1999/2002
Schweinfurt	A.D. 1207	Dendro	Oak *quercus*	Herzig 2003
Brunnensee	A.D. 1250	14C		Hirte 1987
Wessobrunn-Blaik	A.D. 1343	Dendro	Fir *abies*	Weski 2005
Chiemsee, Kailbacher Winkel	A.D. 1350	14C	Oak *quercus*	Pflederer 2005
Volkach-Ostheim	A.D. 1369	Dendro	Fir *abies*	Bauer 1992
Chiemsee, Prien 2	A.D. 1370	14C		Pflederer 2005
Bergrheinfeld-Garstadt	A.D. 1375	14C		Hirte 1987
Staffelsee	A.D. 1460	14C		Hirte 1987
Barmsee 2	A.D. 1470	14C		Hirte 1987
Pflegersee	A.D. 1570	14C		Hirte 1987
Falkenseebach	A.D. 1630	14C		Hirte 1987
Starnberger See, Feldafing	A.D. 1790	14C	Confir	Hirte 1987
Chiemsee, Prien 1	A.D. 1800	14C	Oak *quercus*?	Pflederer 2005

Table 1 Dating and wood species of logboats from Bavaria.

the past, because they were misinterpreted as pontoons of modern boat mills (Prof. Dr. B. Abels., pers. comm.). Thanks to the activities of the society »Bayerische Gesellschaft für Unterwasserarchäologie« during the last two decades, some dugouts have been excavated and documented properly (Beer 1988; 1990; Pflederer 2001: 24; 2002; 2005). In spite of the fact that there are radiocarbon dates for several of the vessels plus a few dendro-dated finds (Bauer 1992), the majority remained unpublished (Dannheimer 1980: 7; Brandl 2004: 219). Most of the logboats belong to medieval and later periods, though there are some older ones. Oak was the favourite material, though fir is also recorded (**Table 1**).

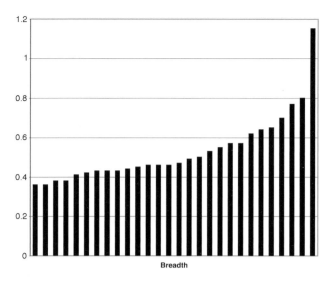

Fig. 3 Width of logboats from Bavaria.

Discoveries of logboats are usually associated with big rivers or lakes, but some cannot be connected with either. Instead they were found in bogs connected to brooklets, which nowadays seem unsuitable for any kind of water transport. Other dugouts also came to light in unusual geographical setting, e.g. in lake Pflegersee, Garmisch-Partenkirchen district, which lies high up in the mountains at 850 m above sea level (Weski 2005: 275). In spite of the fact that logboats were in use still at the beginning of the 20th c., very little ethnographic research had been done. Therefore, it is very difficult to give a general picture of this type of watercraft in S.E. Germany.

Several of the Bavarian logboats seem to be too narrow to float on their own without capsizing. Boats of such proportions were meant to be used as paired ones (McGrail 1978: 44). Some of them also show holes that could be used for tying the hulls together. Detlev Ellmers divided paired logboats into a Weser, Gaul and Oder type by using archaeological finds (Ellmers 1973: 50). A couple of years later Seán McGrail introduced a scheme of three types based on ethnographic evidence. Though he discussed Ellmers' study at great length he never linked it to his own scheme. Due to the different data, it is difficult to quote the two systems for research. Christian Hirte perhaps made the right step, when he distinguished on the one hand paired logboats, which could float on their own either, on the other hand buoyancy timbers, which could only be used as pairs, though only one part of the craft has survived in general. On the other hand, he failed to give a proper definition for the two types. A diagram showing the breadth of logboats from Bavaria does not indicate such a difference (**Fig. 3**). The breadth is sometimes difficult to determine, because only parts of the vessels have survived. As there are so few drawings, it is not possible to include the shape of hull section into the argumentation. On the other side there is ethnographic evidence from New Guinea of especially narrow logboats (e.g. Scofield 1962: 599), in some of which people had to stand inside (e.g. Scofield 1962: 585; Helfrich 1984: fig. 3; Bildarchiv). The exact width of these vessels is hard to prove as the only published drawing is without scale (Neyreth 1974: 150, fig. L.G4e1). There are reports of a width as little as 0.3 m, but it remains uncertain whether such a measure refers to logboats with outriggers (Erdweg 1902: 363; Haddon 1937: 303). Also on logboats without outriggers from New Guinea it is reported that they were so unstable that even in a little seaway, paddlers squatted on the floor, while accompanying women and children had to lie down in the hull (Parkinson 1900: 32). Extraordinary narrow plank boats are also recorded from the River Thames, Great Britain[1]. Hence perhaps some of the narrow logboats in Bavaria were also used as single vessels.

There are several cases when individual vessels, which were usually used on their own, were paired for carrying heavy or bulky loads, e.g. from Hasselø, Denmark (Rasmussen 1953: 43). The same method is recorded also from the lakes Chiemsee, Mondsee, and Steinhuder Meer (Kunze 1968: 196; Weski 2000: 157), but also from Russia or from Native Americans (Raipon; von Württemberg n.d.: 262).

One of the drawbacks when discussing paired logboats is that usually only one part of craft is found. Therefore, it remains uncertain by what method or construction the hulls were connected. A recently discovered vessel sheds new light on this problem. In 2001 Joachim Tröster, member of the water guard Schweinfurt, discovered a logboat in the Main near Schweinfurt. After it had been recorded in 2002 by Franz Herzig from the Bayerische Landesamt für Denkmalpflege, it again was sunk in an old river arm. Unfortunately there was a big flood a year later, which most likely destroyed the vessel. It was cut out of a 270 year old oak tree. The outermost year-ring could be dendro-dated to A.D. 1207/1208. The dimensions of the dugout were 3.5 by 0.5 by 0.4 m (Herzig 2003: figs 1-3; Brandl 2004: 218). At the bow there was an oak pole of 7 cm diameter fixed to the hull with two 16 cm long and 2.5 cm thick oak pegs. It still had a length of 1.1 m, from which a section of 0.57 cm was jutting out on starboard. At the stern two similar holes were found, through which another pole may have been attached to. About midships and near the stern there were two rectangular notches cut into the gunwale, in which large cross beams could be inserted (**Fig. 4**). The hull certainly formed one part of a paired logboat, probably of the catamaran type. With a maximum cargo capacity of 1 ton it may have been a local ferry, which could only carry a couple of people with their belongings or small animals.

Next to the catamaran type another solution for paired logboats can be discussed. On the River Dunajec in Poland four or five narrow, slightly wedge shaped logboats were lashed together to form a kind of raft. Such a vessel was very stable and suited well the fast flowing rough river. The craft was used to transport cargo or persons downstream. When the destination was reached, the logboat units were separated and pulled back, one behind the other by the boatmen who often had to wade in the water. Nowadays similar constructed plank boats are used for touristic purposes (Boczar 1966: 219; Litwin 1995: 61-66 figs 13-18).

Most likely similar water crafts were used in the Middle Ages on the Main. During the last winter a logboat was dredged from gravel pit near Oberhaid-Staffelbach, Bamberg dist. Its dimensions are 4.55 by 0.445 by 0.26 m. The sides and the bottom are flat. Both ends are equally shaped, each with four holes, which are now slightly oval shaped due to the shrinkage of the untreated wood. Surprisingly two of these holes appear in the bottom of the hull. As they were drilled perpendicular into the bottom, they must be part of the original concept of the vessel (**Fig. 5**). Perhaps ropes that held a cross beam were led through the holes, which were then closed with pegs. The shape of the logboat is typical for paired ones, like those on the Dunajec.

A slightly smaller logboat with the same kind of holes was discovered a couple of decades ago in a neighbouring gravel pit, though this one has a proper flat stern. The end section of another dugout was uncovered at Schweinfurt 2, the outermost year-ring of the vessel dated to A.D. 1483. Unfortunately both have to be published yet. The remains of a similar vessel, though without holes in the bottom, found near Volkach-Astheim, Kitzingen dist., were dendro-dated to A.D. 1369 (Bauer 1992: 81). Another two were discovered 1956 in Zapfendorf-Unterleiterbach, Bamberg dist. (Losert 1986: 57, fig. 20).

Close to the latter place two logboats were reported in 1936 (OA BLfD 5931/0075). Their dimensions were 4.0 by 0.35 m each, and holes were observed in both ends and in the sides. The finders claimed that the hulls were tied together side by side. Unfortunately one of these boats was destroyed *in situ* and from the other one proper records are missing.

All mentioned finds indicate that paired logboats similar to those known from the Dunajec were common on the Main in the Middle Ages. The purpose of such watercraft remains open, but as some have raised ends on both sides they may have been used as ferries.

This kind of water craft may offer also an explanation for the gold model of a vessel discovered in a grave dated to the Latène B1 period (around 400 B.C.) on the Dürrnberg near Hallein. As the site is just 300 m from the German-Austrian border, the author feels entitled to include this object to this paper. In the upper burial context of barrow no. 44, next to a sword the 6.6 cm long gold miniature of a boat was discovered. The archaeological publication sketches two oars or paddles, each placed in holes in the starboard side (Penninger 1972: 78, figs 42.9; 116.4). Detlev Ellmers argued this to be the wrong position, because it would be impossible to operate the oars or paddles respectively. Accordingly, they had to be fastened with

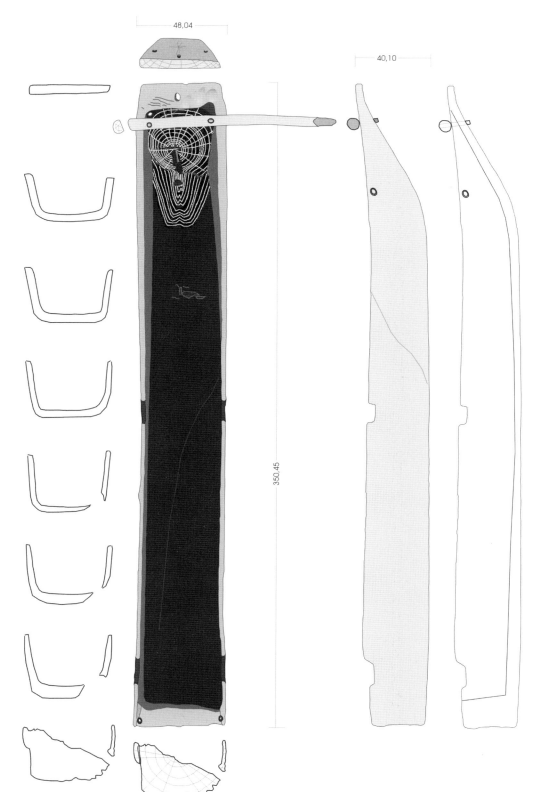

Fig. 4 Paired logboat from Schweinfurt, Wasserwacht (Drawing Fr. Herzig, Bayerisches Landesamt für Denkmalpflege).

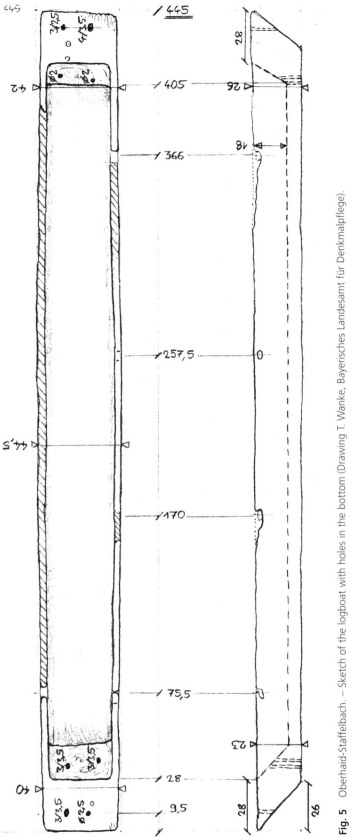

Fig. 5 Oberhaid-Staffelbach. – Sketch of the logboat with holes in the bottom (Drawing T. Wanke, Bayerisches Landesamt für Denkmalpflege).

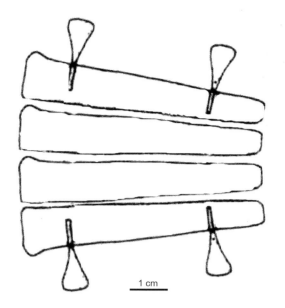

Fig. 6 The gold model of Dürrnberg barrow 44 as part of paired logboats (After Penninger 1972: pl. 42.9).

loops on top of the gunwale. Unfortunately there are no photos from the excavation to prove this argument. Elmers further stated that the model represents a cargo vessel for transporting salt in barrels, which were rolled on board through the open bow (Ellmers 1996: 60).

The function of the gold model is hard to specify. Ships certainly did not belong to the group of popular Celtic symbols (Pauli 1978: 267). Thus, it has been assumed that the Dürrnberg miniature may represent the boat passage to the underworld (Torbrügge 1970: 89; Polenz 1982: 208), a theory which seems less convincing because it reflects Classical religion rather than Celtic. Moreover, the question arises as to what extent the miniature depicts an Iron Age boat. As not a single plank boat from this period has been found in continental N. Europe, the gold miniature may well represent a logboat. The reason for the oars or paddles being assembled to one side may have been that the object originally was exposed for lateral view. Nevertheless, when crossing a river with a strong current, oars or paddles are commonly used on one side as long as conditions do not oblige shifting (Sarrazin *et al.* 1996: 193). However, the Dürrnberg miniature may also be interpreted as part of a watercraft, which originally was based on paired logboats. With its straight sides and wide ends it fits well into this scheme. However, such a craft consisting of three or four buoyancy timbers seem suitable for transporting cargo from the prehistoric salt mines of the Dürrnberg downstream rapid alpine rivers (**Fig. 6**).

Apart from the find from Schweinfurt there are good reasons to assume that some of the logboats found in Bavaria were used by pairs as rafts. Quite surprisingly there is no ethnographic evidence for this kind of craft from recent periods. In the years 1899 and 1900, Albert Voß (Voß 1899; 1900) started a comprehensive questionnaire about old fashioned boats in Germany (Acta 1900), which was published sporadically only (Messikomer 1902; Brunner 1903; Traeger 1904). Amongst the published answers to be found in the archives of the Berlin Völkerkunde Museum are notes on logboats on the Starnberger See (Brunner 1903: 1). Here again only fishermen's logboats were mentioned, but there are no clues for buoyancy timbers or paired logboats. Meanwhile a complete list of all boats in Bavaria has been compiled (Pflederer & Weski 2009), further a MA thesis on logboats in Bavaria is recently appeared (Kröger 2009).

NOTE

1) The author is grateful to Damian Goodburn for drawing attention to this fact.

REFERENCES

Acta, 1905, *Acta betreffend alter Schiffstypen.* Materialsammlung der Deutschen Gesellschaft für Anthropologie, Ethnologie und Urgeschichte. Unpublished manuscript Völkerkunde Museum Berlin.

Bauer, S., 1992, Wasserfahrzeuge aus Bayerns Vorzeit. *Das archäologische Jahr in Bayern, 1991,* 80-82.

Beer, H., 1988, Unterwasserarchäologische Untersuchungen bronzezeitlicher Siedlungsreste und eines Einbaums in der Flachwasserzone der Roseninsel. *Das archäologische Jahr in Bayern, 1987*, 58-60.

Beer, H., 1990, Unterwasserarchäologische Ausgrabung und Bergung eines prähistorischen Einbaums aus der Flachwasserzone der Roseninsel. *Das archäologische Jahr in Bayern, 1989*, 84-87.

Bildarchiv: http://ub.bildarchiv-dkg.unifrankfurt.de/ Bildnr. 024-0275-21, CD/6264/3051/3194/6264_3051_3194_0022.

Bockius, R., 2002, *Die römerzeitlichen Schiffsfunde von Oberstimm in Bayern*. Römisch-Germanisches Zentralmuseum, Monographien, no. 50. Mainz.

Boczar, M. L., 1966, The Craft in Use at the Rivergate of Dunajec. *MM*, 52, 211-222.

Brandl, A., 2004, Einbäume – Urtümliche Wasserfahrzeuge aus Unterfranken. *Beiträge zur Archäologie in Unterfranken, 2004 = Mainfränkische Studien*, 71, 215-225.

Brunner, K., 1903, Zur Forschung über alte Schiffstypen auf den Binnengewässern und Küsten Deutschlands und der angrenzenden Länder. B. Donaugebiet. *Correspondenz-Blatt der deutschen Gesellschaft für Anthropologie, Ethnologie und Urgeschichte*, 34, 1-13.

Burmeister, S., 1998, *Vicus und spätrömische Befestigung von Seebruck-Bedaium*. Materialhefte zur Bayerischen Vorgeschichte, no. A 76. Kallmünz.

Dannheimer, H., 1980, Einbäume aus oberbayerischen Seen. *Freundeskreisblätter*, 12, 7-15.

Ellmers, D., 1973, Kultbarken, Fähren, Fischerboote. Vorgeschichtliche Einbäume in Niedersachsen. *Die Kunde*, NF 24, 23-62.

1996, Celtic Plank Boats and Ships 500 BC-AD 1000. In: R. Gardiner & A. E. Christensen (eds), *The Earliest Ships. The Evolution of Boats into Ships*. London, 52-71.

Erdweg, P. M. J., 1902, Die Bewohner der Insel Tumleo, Berlinhafen, Deutsch-Neu-Guinea (Schluss). *Mittheilungen der Anthropologischen Gesellschaft in Wien*, 32, 317-399.

Erhebung, 1842, *Erhebung die kleinen Fahrzeuge auf bayerischen Seen betreffend*. Unpublished manuscript Staatsarchiv München, AR 3704.

Gödde, G., 1997, *Die Holzbringung aus dem Einzugsgebiet des Königssees*. Nationalpark Berchtesgaden, Forschungsbericht, no. 38. Berchtesgaden.

Haddon, A. C., 1937, *The Canoes of Melanesia, Queensland and New Guinea*. = A. C. Haddon & J. Hornell, Canoes of Oceania, vol. II. *Bernice P. Bishop Museum, Special Publication*, no. 28. Honolulu.

Heilmeyer, H., 2008, Der elektrische Schiffszug bei der Steinernen Brücke zu Regensburg – ein technisches Unikat. *Donau-Schiffahrt*, 9, 81-107.

Helfrich, K., 1984, Boote aus Melanesien und Australien. In: G. Koch, *Boote aus aller Welt*. Berlin, 33-54.

Herzig, F., 2003, Ein Einbaum aus dem Main bei Schweinfurt. Zur Holzbearbeitung und Dendrochronolgie. *NAU*, 10, 61-64.

Herzig, F. & Weski, T., 2009, Neues zu Altfunden von Booten in Bayern. *NAV*, 15, 93-104.

Hirte, C., 1987, *Zur Archäologie monoxyler Wasserfahrzeuge im nördlichen Mitteleuropa. Eine Studie zur Repräsentativität der Quellen in chorologischer, chronologischer und konzeptioneller Hinsicht*. Unpublished PhD thesis, Christian-Albrecht-University Kiel.

Höfling, P., 1984, Der Einbaum des Chiemsees. *Vom Einbaum zum Dampfschiff*, 4, 45-48.

1987, *Die Chiemsee-Fischerei. Beiträge zu ihrer Geschichte*. Beiträge zur Volkstumsforschung, 24. München.

Keweloh, H.-W., 1993, Traditionelle Boote in Deutschland – 1: Die Ruhrfähre von Oefte. *Deutsches Schiffahrtsarchiv*, 16, 211-228.

Koch, R., 2002, Fossa Carolina. Neue Erkenntnisse zum Schiffahrtkanal Karls des Großen. In: K. Elmshäuser (ed.), *Häfen – Schiffe – Wasserwege. Zur Schiffahrt des Mittelalters*. Schriften des Deutschen Schiffahrtsmuseums, no. 58. Bremerhaven, Hamburg, 54-70.

Kröger, L., 2009, *Einbäume aus dem Main*. MA-thesis, Otto-Friedrich-Universität Bamberg.

Kunze, W., 1968, Der Mondseer Einbaum. *Jahrbuch des Oberösterreichischen Musealvereins*, 113, 173-202.

Litwin, J., 1995, *Polskie Szkutnictwo Ludowe XX Wieku*. Prace Centralnego Muzeum Morskiego w Gdansku, no. 10. Gdansk.

Losert, H., 1986, Die Vor- und Frühgeschichte des Zapfendorfes Raumes. In: T. Gunzelmann (ed.), *Zapfendorf. Landschaft – Geschichte – Kultur*. Zapfendorf, 39-85.

McGrail, S., 1978, *Logboats of England and Wales with comparative material from European and other countries*. BAR, British Series, no. 51. Oxford.

1998, *Ancient Boats in North-West Europe. The Archaeology of Water Transport to AD 1500*. London.

Messikommer, H., 1902, Zur Forschung über alte Schiffstypen auf den Binnengewässern und Küsten Deutschlands und der angrenzenden Länder. A. Die Schweiz. *Correspondenz-Blatt der deutschen Gesellschaft für Anthropologie, Ethnologie und Urgeschichte*, 33, 36-42.

Neweklowsky, E., 1958, Die Schiffahrt auf der oberen Donau und ihren Nebenflüssen. *Deutsches Museum Abhandlungen und Berichte*, 26/3, 5- 53.

Neyret, J., 1974. *Pirogues Océaniennes 2: Polynésie, Mirconésie, Indonésie, Inde, Autres Continents*. Paris.

OA BLfD 5931/0075: unpublished. Archive Bayerisches Landesamt für Denkmalpflege Fundstellennummer 5931/0075.

OA BLfD 7037/1017: unpublished. Archive Bayerisches Landesamt für Denkmalpflege, Fundstellennummer: 7037/1017, Archäologische Staatssammlung München, Einlaufnummer: E 1976, 12.

Parkinson, R., 1900, Die Berlinhafen-Section. *Internationales Archiv für Ethnographie*, 13, 18-54.

Pauli, L., 1978, *Der Dürrnberg bei Hallein III*. Auswertung der Grabfunde. Münchner Beiträge zur Vor- und Frühgeschichte, no. 18.1. München.

Penninger, E., 1972, *Der Dürrnberg bei Hallein I*. Münchner Beiträge zur Vor- und Frühgeschichte, no. 16. München.

Pflederer, T., 2001, Aktuelle Forschungen in bayerischen Seen. *NAU*, 8, 21-26.

2002, Ein Einbaum der Latènezeit aus dem Starnberger See. *NAU*, 9, 17-19.

2005, Einbäume des Chiemsees. *NAU*, 11-12, 37-43.

Pflederer, T. & Weski, T., 2009, Einbäume und Boote in Bayern. *Bericht der Bayerischen Bodendenkmalpflege*, 50, 62-69.

Polenz, H., 1982, Münzen in latènezeitlichen Gräbern Mitteleuropas aus der Zeit zwischen 300 und 50 vor Christi Geburt. *Bayerische Vorgeschichtsblätter*, 47, 27-222.

Prammer, J., 1988, Der römische Donauhafen von Straubing-Sorviodurum. In: K. Schmotz (ed.), *Vorträge des 6. Niederbayerischen Archäologentages, Deggendorf*. Deggendorf, 149-155.

Raff, T., 1985, Flößerei auf dem Ammersee. *Vom Einbaum zum Dampfschiff*, 5, 36-51.

Raipon: www.raipon.org/Web_Database/photo/itelmen5_pic1.jpg

Rasmussen, H., 1953, Hasselø-Ege. *Kuml*, 1953, 15-46.

Reitinger, J., 1975, Das goldene Miniaturschiffchen vom Dürrnberg bei Hallein. *Mitteilungen der Gesellschaft für Salzburger Landeskunde*, 115, 383-405.

Schattenhofer, M., 1983, Aus der Geschichte der Isarflößerei. In: M.-L. Plessen, *Die Isar. Ein Lebenslauf. Ausstellungskatalog Münchener Stadtmuseum*. München, 64-78.

Scofield, J., 1962, Netherlands New Guinea. *National Geographic*, 121.5 (May), 584-602.

Torbrügge, W., 1970/71, Vor- und frühgeschichtliche Flußfunde. Zur Ordnung und Bestimmung einer Denkmalgruppe. *Berichte der Römisch-Germanischen Kommission*, 51-52, 1-146.

Traeger, P., 1904, Zur Forschung über alte Schiffstypen. C: Schiffsfahrzeuge in Albanien und Macedonien. *Correspondenz-Blatt der deutschen Gesellschaft für Anthropologie, Ethnologie und Urgeschichte*, 35, 25-38.

Voss, A., 1899, Ueber Schiffsfunde. *Correspondenz-Blatt der deutschen Gesellschaft für Anthropologie, Ethnologie und Urgeschichte*, 30, 116-117.

1900, Fragebogen zur Ermittlung und Beschreibung der noch in Gebrauch befindlichen oder ehemals gebräuchlichen Schiffsfahrzeuge einfacher Bauart und Einrichtung. *Correspondenz-Blatt der deutschen Gesellschaft für Anthropologie, Ethnologie und Urgeschichte*, 31, 125-128.

Weski, T., 2000, Local Boats of the Steinhuder Meer near Hannover. In: *ISBSA 8*, 155-160.

2005, Unfinished and Paired Logboats from Bavaria, Germany. *IJNA*, 34, 269-281.

von Westenrieder, L., 1784, *Beschreibung des Würm- oder Starnbergersees und der umliegenden Schlößer etc. samt einer Landkarte*. München.

von Württemberg, P. W., n.d., *Reise nach dem nördlichen Amerika in den Jahren 1822 bis 1824*. München.

Zeller, K. W., 1994, Die Fürstenzimmer. In: *Salz. Katalog der Landesausstellung Hallein, 30. April bis 30. Oktober 1994*. Hallein, 175-238.

IRENA RADIĆ ROSSI

DUGOUTS OF CROATIA

Logboats have been rarely mentioned in the Croatian archeological and ethnological literature. The main reason is the fact that no organized research has been undertaken until today. Besides that, most finds belong to Modern History, especially to the period between the 16th and 20th c., which rarely pose any interest to archeologists, while ethnologists pass them up as archeological finds. Even though the above mentioned reasons do not justify the lack of interest for this particular group of artifacts, they do explain why the Croatian dugouts have remained rather unknown to the international and the Croatian scientific community.

The initial interest upon any discovery, displayed by the local community, dissipates with time. The time consuming process of preservation of waterlogged wood, which requires a great deal of effort and financial backing leads to an eventual abandonment of the conservation project, which inevitably causes the artifact's deterioration (Malinar 2007). This situation is no exception; it is reminiscent of similar situations elsewhere in Europe (Greenhill & Morrison 1995: 101).

The dugouts found in the continental waters are mainly occasional discoveries made by the local population during digging or low tides. Some logboats were taken to the local museums while the others were destroyed or left to rot in the open rural areas. Dugouts found in the Adriatic met a better fate mostly through their secondary usage, which prolonged their life well into the second half of the 20th c. and caused them to end up within the local museums, monasteries, or private collections[1].

GROUPS OF DUGOUTS

The dugouts of Croatia can be divided into two major groups. The first group refers to finds from Central and E. Croatia, from the mountainous W. regions towards the Panonian Basin. This region is dominated by three large rivers, the Danube, Drava, and Sava, which along with their tributaries played a significant communication role throughout history. During research on the early Iron Age settlement at Donja Dolina, at the Bosnian side of the River Sava, at the beginning of the 20th c. two large dugouts were uncovered, while in the late Bronze Age settlement at Ripač a small scale miniature of a dugout was found (Truhelka 1902; 1906; Ćurčić 1908; 1910). These findings did not only prove that dugouts were used in prehistoric times onward, but have also commenced an interesting ethnographic study in the nearby village of Gornja Dolina led by the Bosnian scholar Vejsil Ćurčić.

At the beginning of the 20th c., life along the banks of River Sava was still quite traditional and could not be imagined without boats made from a single piece of wood. Used for transport and fishing, the dugouts presented an appropriate vessel during the adverse weather conditions, described by Ćurčić: »during floods these people cannot live without their boats, their whole life seems to take place on the water, they do not marry or die without them; they need them in any season and for any occasion« (Ćurčić 1910: 387).

The people populating the Sava basin used logboats for various purposes resulting in at least three types, which are known as *korab, ladja*, and *čun*. All three terms are of old Slavic heritage, proving once again the extreme antiquity of their usage. The *korab's* length ranged from 8 to 14 m. It was usually made of oak. It was used for transport of people and cargo, and could accommodate up to 20 people. Simple clay hearths and a tent were the usual gear of this type of dugouts. It is interesting to note that the prehistoric

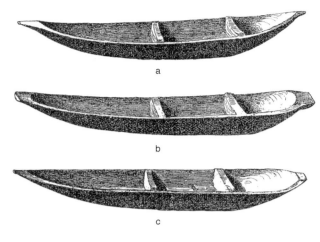

Fig.1 »Male« (a), »female« (b), and »male-female« type (c) of dugout (After Ćurćić 1910: 395, fig. 11).

dugout from Donja Dolina bears traces of ashes, which suggest that the boat's fire place was used (Ćurćić 1910: 390).

Ladja was built from a lighter poplar wood. This type was shallower than *korab* and reached up to 7 m in length. It could take up to ten people at the time. Due to its greater maneuverability this type was mainly used for fishing. Both of the described boats had bulkheads; *ladja* only one, often in the rear whereas *korab* had two at both ends. The smallest boat was named *čun*. This boat, whose total length never exceeded 5 m, was used by one person only. It was also equipped with bulkheads at both ends, and by the shape of its extremities it was usually determined as »female«, »male« or »male-female« (**Fig. 1**). *Čun* was used for traffic near the house because its small size allowed for greater maneuverability in the swampy areas. Even a worn out one had its further purposes; researchers notice that some of them were used to feed the cattle, the others as doorsteps while one was even used as a bed by its owner (Ćurćić 1910: 393).

Dugouts known under the name of *kerep* were used as rafts or other floating vessels, in which case the trunk was hollowed out while in many cases the bark was left intact. Their shape and construction are reminiscent of medieval finds from Mandelsloh and Evensen (Gräf 2006, 144-147[2]). These vessels were mainly used as rafts and as boat mills, which according to written records appeared some 1500 years ago[3] and could have still be found around the Drava and Sava at the beginning of the 20th c. (**Fig. 2**; Gojković 1954; Ribarić 1959; Janjić 1978). The importance of *kerep* is best illustrated by the fact that during the excavation of a prehistoric dugout at Donja Dolina about a century ago, scholars were wary of transporting this find over surface roads fearing that their bad condition would damage the artifact. Instead, a special raft was built, which transported the dugout to the nearest railway station, from which it could safely be transported to Sarajevo (Ćurćić 1910: 390).

That the dugouts were used on the Adriatic tributaries as well is evident from numerous written records and old photographs (Fortis 1774 [1987]: 209; Milošević 2003: 14). The concrete finds are rare; a fragment which was held in the Museum of Sinj has disappeared without trace.

In the Neretva region, a specific type of vessel that survived until today is called *trupa*, and it seems certain that it originates from a dugout. Unfortunately, there is not a specimen made of a single piece of wood which survived till today (Volpi Lisjak 2004: 105). These vessels are built of four planks, two at the bottom and two on the sides.

The special group of dugouts is the one used for fishing in the Adriatic Sea. They are usually called *ladva*, *ladja*, or *copul*[4]. They were often described by various Slovenian, Italian, and Croatian writers, but the most accurate work was done by Bruno Volpi Lisjak, who compiled a large documentation on Slovenian examples (Lorini 1903; Šoljan 1938; Lenček 1950; Barbalić 1957; Bonino 1980; 1981; Marzari *et al.* 1994; Volpi Lisjak 2004). Describing them as very primitive vessels, Petar Lorini, the Fishing Superintendent of the Marine Government in Trieste, noted in 1903: »*Copul* is the type of vessel invented by our ancestor Adam, if he used to fish or sail« (Lorini 1903: 61).

These boats were used for fishing up and down the Croatian coast throughout medieval times, as recorded in the statutories of many coastal cities. During the centuries the term was attributed to such types of

Fig. 2 Boat mills on River Sava at Slavonski Brod at the beginning of the 20th c. (Courtesy of the Museum of Brodsko Posavlje, Slavonski Brod).

vessels, whose construction originated from a dugout but conserved just a bottom made of a single piece of wood (Volpi Lisjak 2004: 104-105; Šoljan 1938). Therefore, all the records which mention only the name and not a full description of a vessel are not a reliable proof of existence of dugouts. However, they suggest a long tradition and a dugout's widespread construction form. Extended dugouts of the Adriatic can be recognized in old photographs (Ružić Barbić 2004: 181) which clearly show a dugout bottom to which planks are attached with the help of frames, thus giving the vessel the more suitable width. Studies of photographs are quite limited; so in the case of future research it will be

Fig. 3 Rowing with the help of an outrigger joist (After Lorini 1903: 62, fig. 13).

necessary to trace some records from the 1930s which remained unpublished (mentioned by Barbalić 1957: 178).

The seafaring dugouts are quite different in form from other vessels that can be found in the continental part of Croatia. Their shape is defined by a flat bottom and almost vertical sides, giving its cross-section quite a rectangular form. Although the similar cross-section is not an exception compared to European finds (e.g. Ossowski 1999: 144-151), it seems that in Croatia it does only appear in coastal areas and lakes near the coast.

The most common way of rowing as shown in old drawings and photographs (Lorini 1903: fig. 13; Šoljan 1938: 187) was done by the help of an outrigger joist[5] (**Fig. 3**), which served to improve the boat's stability, ease the strain of rowing and exclude the eventual noise. These characteristics made *ladva* suitable for night fishing. Thus, on the preserved finds there can still be observed a grill attached to the bow which served to lighten a fire to attract fish.

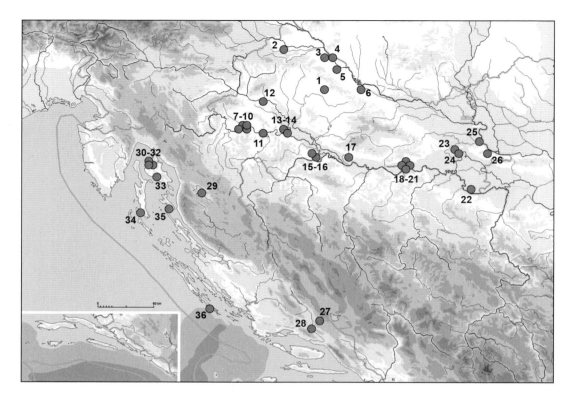

Fig. 4 Distribution of dugout finds in Croatia.

Unfortunately, due to the outrigger joist, *ladva* used to occupy a lot of space on the water; it was difficult to dock sideways and the crew had difficulty moving about (Šoljan 1938). After World War I its popularity fell and only some isolated specimens can be traced. The extended dugouts could still be found after World War II and were mainly used for tuna fishing.

LIST OF DUGOUTS

This paper represents the first attempt to collect information about all the Croatian dugouts known through records, photographs, and professional research results (**Fig. 4**). After surveying the field, the number of dugouts has doubled. At the moment 36 vessels have been put in official evidence, six of which do not exist any longer. These do not include the data about the dugouts known to exist in the river beds but which, due to limited funds and conservation space, have not yet been excavated. None of the citations listed below include a thorough data analysis; only basic data and a preliminary photograph or a sketch is included.

Dugouts from River Drava and its tributaries

1. Narta near Bjelovar, River Česma (l. 4.05 cm; w. 0.99 m; h. about 0.28 m; Municipal museum of Bjelovar, inv. no. 2265; Malinar 2007: 94-95, fig. 12). – Found in 1962. Vessel with rounded stern, pointed prow and two bulkheads to the boat's edge. Part of the stern on the port side missing.

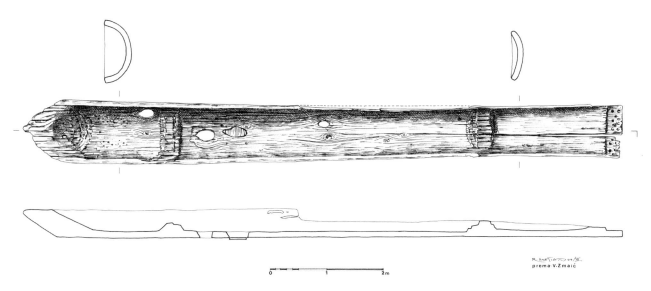

Fig. 5 Dugout from Podravske Sesvete (Drawing K. Rončević, after V. Zmaić).

2. Pleta – Novi Marof, River Bednja (l. 2.36m; w. 0.53m; h. 0.25m; Municipal museum of Varaždin; Registar 1997: 123). – Bottom of a dugout. Accidental find in 1960, during the regulation of Bednja. On the opposite river bank, there is evidence of a Roman settelment.

3. Hlebine near Koprivnica, River Drava/former river bed (l. 12.10m; w. 1.46m; h. 0.9m; Municipal museum of Koprivnica; Malinar 2007, 102-104, fig. 30). – Found in 1999. Dugout defined as *kerep*; part of a boat mill or raft. Evenly shaped on one side while on the other pointed; traces of two bulkheads. On the even side, there is a socket with many openings and wooden pegs, which served to fasten the vertical planks. On several spots, there are metallic threads and other parts meant to tighten the vessel's parts. The boat is damaged at the pointed side while the hull shows many cracks. [14]C analysis dates the vessel to the 19th c. (Ruđer Bošković Institute – Radiocarbon measurements, vol. 44, No. 2, Z 2903 and Z 2904, p. 6, 2002).

4. Legrad near Koprivnica, Drava (l. 1.03m; w. 0.6m; h. 0.47m, Municipal museum of Koprivnica, unpublished). – Found in the 1950s. Pointed prow with a vertical hole for ropes.

5. Podravske Sesvete, Drava (**Fig. 5**; l. 10.57m; w. 1.15m; h. 0.32m; Cultural centre of Đurđevac, Malinar 2007: 104-105, fig. 32; Radić Rossi 2006: 92). – Found in 2001. Extensively damaged *kerep* dugout intended for transport, or part of boat mill or raft. Pointed on one side and evenly cut on the other. On the evenly cut side, there is an array of rounded portholes, which served to tighten vertical planks. In its current state, two bulkheads are visible even though the records mention four (Malinar 2007: 104). Along the entire hull traces of metal and wooden pins for various purposes were found.

6. Gaćište, River Brežnica (l. 1.96m; w. 0.6m, h. 0.22m; Municipal museum of Virovitica, inv. no. 111, unpublished). – Arrived in the museum in 1953. Pointed forward part of the dugout; two bulkheads are noticed. The stern bulkhead is partly damaged.

Dugouts from Rivers Kupa, Sava and their tributaries

7. Zorkovac lijevi near Ozalj, Kupa (l. 5.5m; w. 0.8m; h. 0.4cm; The Old Castle of Ozalj; Malinar 2007: 99-101, figs 21-22). – Found in 1977. Dugout with evenly cut prow and stern. The stern is elongated with a depressed oarsman's seat. Three bulkheads. At the starboard part of the prow, a chain for tying the boat is fastened. [14]C analysis dates the dugout to the 20th c. (Ruđer Bošković

Institute – Radiocarbon measurements, vol. 21, No.1, Z 563, p. 135, 1979).

8. Karlovac, Kupa (l. 11m; w. unknown; h. unknown; destroyed, once in the Municipal museum of Karlovac; Malinar 2007: 95-96, figs 13-14). – Found in 1970. According to photos, this was an extensively damaged dug-

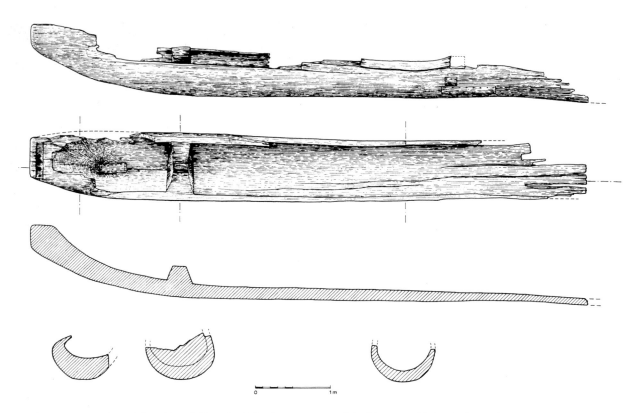

Fig. 6   Dugout from Svibovski otok (Drawing I. Petrinec; courtesy of the Museum of Prigorje, Sesvete).

out whose both ends were missing. Remnants of two bulkheads. The dugout was conserved, but had been left in the open air, which caused its disintegration. [14]C analysis dates the dugout back to the 17th c. (Ruđer Bošković Institute – Radiocarbon measurements, vol. 15, no. 2, p. 436, Z 164, 1973).

9. Karlovac(?), Kupa (l. 3.1 m; w. 0.64 m; h. about 0.2 m, Municipal museum of Karlovac; unpublished). – The date of arrival to the museum is unknown. Dugout with missing ends. Three bulkheads. Sides are not preserved in their entire height.

10. Koritinja, Kupa (l. 3.0 m; w. 0.65 m; h. about 0.2 m; private ethnographic collection, J. Žunac, Rečica near Karlovac; unpublished). – Found in 1977. Forward section of a dugout with two bulkheads. The prow is elongated and pointed.

11. Brkiševina, Kupa (l. 4.0 m; w. 0.8 m; h. unknown; Ethnographic Museum, Zagreb; Eckhel 1993: 42). – Purchased for the museum in 1923. It is kept in the museum depot, not accessible.

12. Svibovski otok, Sava/old river bed (**Fig. 6**; l. 7.5 m; w. 1.1 m; h. 0.6 m; Museum of Prigorje, Zagreb-Sesvete;

Sokol 2006: 6). – Found in 1999. Partly preserved dugout of *kerep* type; part of a boat mill or raft. Several repairs present on the hull. The section is slightly elevated. Remnants of two bulkheads. Original length estimated to 10 m. [14]C analysis dates the dugout back to the 17th c. (Ruđer Bošković Institute – Radiocarbon measurements, vol. 44, No. 2, Z 2962 and Z 2963, p. 452, 2002).

13. Sisak, Kupa/1 (l. 5.5 m; w. 0.8 m; h. 0.4 m; destroyed; unpublished). – Found in 1983. According to photograph this was a relatively well preserved dugout with pointed ends. [14]C analysis dates the dugout back to the 2nd to the 1st c. B.C. (Ruđer Bošković Institute – Radiocarbon measurements, vol. 26, No. 2, Z 1147 and Z 1147 and Z 1148, p. 452, 1984).

14. Sisak, Kupa/2 (l. 6.0 m; w. 0.5 m; h. 0.2 m; Municipal Museum of Sisak; Jurišić 1993). – Excavated in 1993. Partly damaged dugout; long and straight; rounded ends. According to a sketch, there was a bulkhead at one end. The boat broke down into several pieces after being raised, and due to the uncompleted conservation process the situation became worse. [14]C analysis dates the dugout back to the 1st c. B.C. (Ruđer Bošković Institute – Radiocarbon measurements, vol. 36, No. 2, Z 2426 and Z 2427, p. 452, 2002).

Fig. 7 Dugout from Hrvatska Dubica (Photo I. Radić Rossi).

15. Hrvatska Dubica, River Una/1 (l. 10 m; w. 0.6 m; h. unknown, destroyed; Vjesnik newspaper, 11/12 February 1973, 13; Radić Rossi 2006: 92). – Found in the year 1973. According to the photograph preserved in the Ministry of Culture of the Republic of Croatia, this was an almost entirely preserved dugout with pointed prow and slightly rounded stern, with two bulkheads. As the local inhabitants can remember, it was stored in the courtyard of the local school for a long time. During the reconstruction of the building, the boat was probably thrown away. [14]C analysis dates it back to the 16th c. (Ruđer Bošković Institute – Radiocarbon measurements, vol. 17, No. 1, Z 251 and Z 255, p. 150).

16. Hrvatska Dubica, Una/2 (**Fig. 7**; l. 9.7 m; w. 0.85 m; h. 0.31 m; in the village, on the river bank; Radić Rossi 2006: 92). – Found in 1996. Extremely narrow and elongated dugout, with pointed prow, straightly cut and elongated stern. The stern has been damaged, and there are two vertical holes on it, probably intended for tying up the vessel with ropes. Towards the extremities there are two bulkheads. The whole boat bears traces of damage caused by drying.

17. Donja Varoš, Sava (l. 5.57 m; w. 0.78 m; h. 0.29 m; Municipal Museum of Nova Gradiška; unpublished). – Found in 1983. Dugout with evenly shaped stern, three rounded holes and elevated prow. In the forward section there is one bulkhead. The prow is cracked, whereas the stern has been disintegrated into several parts. There are some wooden repairs on the hull. According to photographs, a rectangular metal plate was attached to the

prow. The shape of the boat and the arrangement of the openings suggest that it belonged to a paired dugout (compare to Osowski 1999: 156, fig. 140).

18. Novigrad, Sava (l. 13.8 m; w. 1.5 m; h. unknown; destroyed, once in the Museum of Brodsko Posavlje, Slavonski Brod; Malinar 2007: 98-99, fig. 19). – Found in 1975. *Kerep* type dugout, used as part of a boat mill or raft. Both ends open, showing grooves for fastening vertical planks. After the conservation it was kept in the open air, so it has disintegrated and got lost. [14]C analysis dates the dugout back to the 17th c. (Ruđer Bošković Institute – Radiocarbon measurements, vol. 21, No. 1, Z 553, p. 135, 1979).

19. Oprisavci near Slavonski Brod, River Bidž – former river bed/1 (l. 4.79 m; w. 0.61 m; h. 0.17 m; Museum of Brodsko Posavlje, Slavonski Brod, inv. no. 642; unpublished). – Purchased for the museum in 1935. Dugout with pointed ends, incomplete height and length. On the hull there are two well preserved bulkheads, and near one end there are still traces of another bulkhead, which might have been removed.

20. Oprisavci near Slavonski Brod, Bidž – former river bed/2 (l. 4.2 m; w. 0.58 m; h. 0.24 m; Museum of Brodsko Posavlje, Slavonski Brod, inv. no. 643; unpublished). – Purchased for the museum in 1935. Dugout with pointed prow and rounded stern, and with three bulkheads.

21. Oprisavci near Slavonski Brod, Bidž/former river bed/3 (l. 3.4 m; w. 0.53 m; h. 0.17 m; Museum of Brodsko

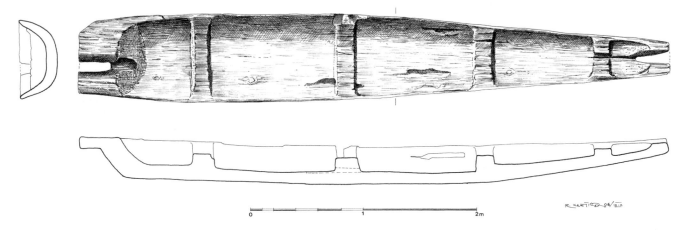

Fig. 8   Dugout from Bosutski virovi (Drawing K. Rončević).

Posavlje, Slavonski Brod, inv. no. 644; unpublished). – Purchased for the museum in 1935. Hardly damaged dugout with pointed prow and probably rounded stern, the end of which is missing. Three bulkheads.

22. Račinovci near Županja, Sava (l. 14.1 m; w. 0.8 to 1.5 m; h. about 1.0 m; in the village, on the open air; Malinar 2007: 104, fig. 31). – Found in 2000. Dugout of *kerep* type; used as part of a boat mill or a raft. Narrow, straightly cut prow and wide, protruding stern. On the starboard side there was a line of vertical openings, probably intended to fasten other constructional elements. The boat was left in the open air, so it has disintegrated in several pieces. [14]C analysis dates the dugout back to

the 17th c. (Ruđer Bošković Institute – Report no. BO 18/01, Z 3026 and 3027).

23. Bosutski virovi near Vinkovci, River Bosut/1 (**Fig. 8**; l. 5.24 m; w. 0.78 m; h. 0.3 m, Municipal Museum of Vinkovci; Radić Rossi 2006: 92). – Dugout with pointed prow and evenly cut stern, on which there is a rectangular groove. Four bulkheads.

24. Bosutski virovi near Vinkovci, Bosut/2 (l. 3.91 m; w. 0.68 m; h. 0.26 m; Municipal Museum of Vinkovci; Radić Rossi 2006: 92). – Dugout with narrowed but damaged ends. One bulkhead well preserved, the other one only by small remnants.

Dugouts from the Danube

25. Vučedol, Danube, (l. 5.93 m; w. 1.28 m; h. unknown; disappeared; Malinar 2007: 96). – Found in 1972. According to a photograph and a description, the forward section of a dugout, from which only the prow and parts of the sides survived. [14]C analysis dates the dugout back to the 18th c. (Ruđer Bošković Institute – Radiocarbon measurements, vol. 15, No. 2, Z 224, 1973, p. 436).

26. Sotin, Danube (**Fig. 9**; l. 4.0 m; w. 0.79 m; h. 0.23 m; Municipal Museum of Vukovar; Radić Rossi 2006: 92). – Found in the 1980s, it arrived to the museum several years later. Dugout with pointed prow and rounded, damaged stern. Two bulkheads.

Dugouts from the Adriatic river basin

27. Otok, River Cetina (l. about 1.5 to 2.0 m; disappeared; once in the Museum of the Sinj Region, Sinj; unpublished). – Arrived in the museum in 1958. According to the reports of former museum employees and the preserved inventory card, dugout with missing prow.

28. Trilj, River Ruda (dimensions unknown; temporary storage in the Archaeological Museum of Zadar; Milošević 1992: 88). – A piece of prow raised about 1992. It belongs to a dugout which remained *in situ*. [14]C analysis dates it back to the 14th c. (Milošević 1999: 209).

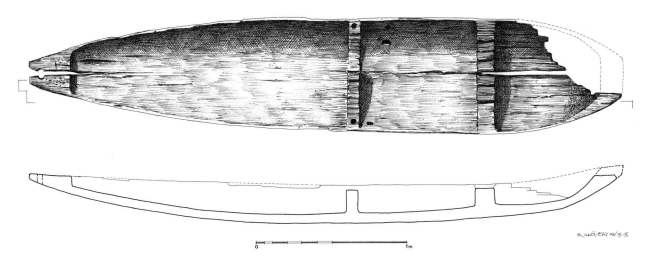

Fig. 9 Dugout from Sotin (Drawing K. Rončević).

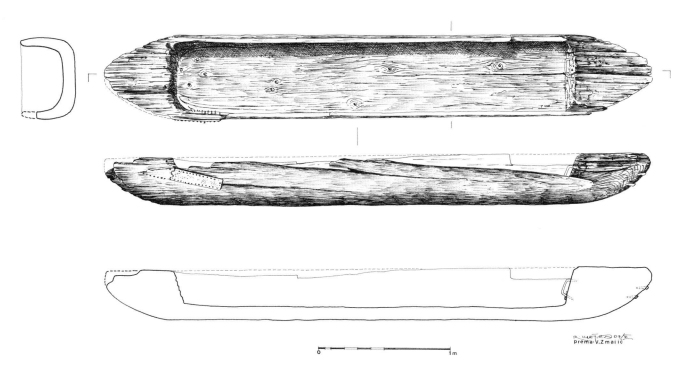

Fig. 10 Dugout from the national park of Plitvice (Drawing K. Rončević, after V. Zmaić).

Dugouts from lakes

29. Plitvice Lakes, lake Kozjak (**Fig. 10**; l. 4.1 m; w. 0.7 m; h. 0.44 m, National Park of Plitvice; unpublished). – Found in 1984 or 1985. Dugout of rectangular cross-section, and with pointed ends. At the prow there is a wooden repair. Metal joints occur on several positions. The hull cracked and damaged in the upper part.

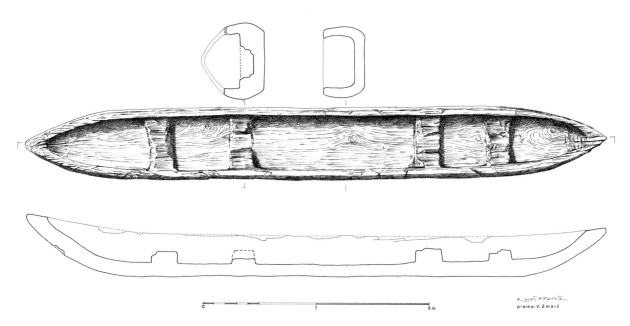

Fig. 11   Dugout from the island of Krk at the Naval and historical museum of Hrvatsko primorje (Drawing K. Rončević, after V. Zmaić).

Dugouts from the Adriatic Sea

30. Bogovići, Island of Krk (**Fig. 11**; l. 4.96 m; w. 0.57 m; h. 0.3 m; Naval and Historical Museum of Hrvatsko primorje, Rijeka, inv. no. 1558; Barbalić 1957: fig. 1; Malinar 2007: 94). – Purchased for the museum in 1957. Well preserved dugout of rectangular cross-section with pointed ends and four bulkheads.

31. Kremenići, Island of Krk/1 (l. 4.72 m; w. 0.66 m; h. 0.38 m; private ethnographic collection, J. Šamanić, Sv. Vid – Malinska; unpublished). – Dugout of a rectangular cross-section with pointed ends. Over-dried and damaged at one end. The boat served as a cattle feeder.

32. Kremenići, island of Krk/2 (l. 3.5 m; w. 0.58 m; h. 0.3 m; ethnographic collection of the Franciscan Convent at Porat – Malinska; unpublished). – Dugout with rectangular cross-section, and with pointed forward end, where a grid for lighting a fire during night fishing is attached. Evenly cut stern, closed with a wooden joist. The boat served as a cattle feeder.

33. Miletići, island of Krk (l. 4.64 m; w. 0.63 m; h. 0.38 m; collection of the Franciscan Convent at the island of Košljun – Bay of Punat; Malinar 2007: 94). – Purchased for the museum around 1953. Dugout with rectangular cross-section; extremities are cut and replaced with metal endings. At the prow there is a grid attached for lighting

a fire during night fishing; along the sides are fittings to rig oars, and an outrigger joist are attached. Inside the hull there are four bulkheads, and two repairs made out of boards occur. The whole boat is thickly covered with tar.

34. Radiboj bay, Island of Cres (l. 4.3 m; w. 0.47 m; h. 0.31 m; Archaeological Collection, Osor; Imamović 1980: 126-127, fig. 1). – Raised from the sand of a shallow bay in the 1970s. Dugout with rectangular cross-section, and with pointed ends. The bottom elevates at prow and stern.

35. S. Eufemija bay, Island of Rab (l. 1.61 m; w. 0.5 m; h. 0.3 m; Naval Collection of the shipyard *Brodosplit* at Split; Barbalić 1957: 179). – Arrived at the museum in 1949. The ends of the dugout were cut off and only the central part of the boat was preserved. In the open air for years which caused its deterioration.

36. Island of Lavsa, Archipelago of Kornati (**Fig. 12**; l. 4.05 m; w. 0.55 m; h. 0.32 m; Naval Collection of the Croatian Academy of Science and Arts, Zadar; Kozličić 1993: 46, fig. 27; Županović 1995, 113). – In the 1940s blown by wind to the Kornati area. Arrived at the museum around 1955. Dugout with rectangular cross-section, and with pointed ends. The bottom elevates at prow and stern.

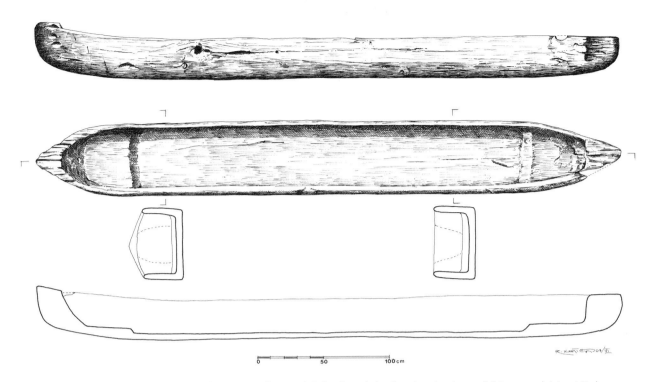

Fig. 12 Dugout from the Archipelago of Kornati at the Naval Collection of the Croatian Academy of Science and Arts at Zadar (Drawing K. Rončević, after I. Čondić).

CONCLUSIONS

According to the list of dugouts it is obvious that there is not a single find that would belong to prehistoric times. Prehistoric dugouts from the neighboring countries, found in the same rivers, which flow through Croatia, refer to the fact that they surely existed. A 12 m deposit which the excavators of Donja Dolina had to remove in order to uncover a boat dating to the late Iron Age (Ćurčić 1910: 390) clearly signifies one of the reasons why prehistoric finds are hard to reach.

Dugouts stored in Croatian museums were mostly found during low tides and only occasionally by sand or gravel digging. The age of dated vessels does not exceed several hundred years, except in the case of two finds belonging to the Roman period. However, out of 36 known dugouts only ten were provided by ^{14}C dating, and not a single one was submitted to a dendro-chronological analysis. Apart from the Adriatic and lake samples, for which usage at the beginning of the 20th c. can be presumed, 17 undated finds theoretically could belong to an earlier age.

Two dugouts found in Sisak (*Siscia*) were dated to the 2nd and 1st c. B.C. (cat. nos 13 to 14). In the Municipal Museum of Sisak three more dugout sites are recorded. Considering the circumstances, in which they are preserved, they obviously belong to the Roman period as well. Due to the lack of adequate conditions for their conservation and presentation they have not been yet explored. Unfortunately, a dugout found in 1983 has fallen apart and does not exist anymore, while the other has been excavated, but hardly documented. Even during the excavations and first conveyance the dugout had fallen apart into several pieces, and because of an unfinished conservation procedure the process of disintegration has not yet been stopped.

The majority of inland dugouts could be included in a group of boats intended for fishing and performing everyday activities. Their average length amounts to approximately 5 m, and the better preserved specimens have two or three bulkheads. In two cases the length of the boats exceeds 5m, indicating that they might have been used for cargo transport as well (cat. nos 15 to 16). In a single case, a dugout with only one bulkhead might have belonged to a pair of logboats (cat. no. 17).

Five dugouts (cat. nos 3; 5; 12; 18; 22) belong to a group intended for rafts and water mills. Their length of 10 to 14m considerably complicates their conservation and storage. One of them had disappeared forever (cat. no. 18), one lies abandoned in the middle of a village (cat. no. 22), while two have been adequately conserved and stored under pretty good conditions. Series of pegs used to fasten vertical planks, which were closing the stern (Gräf 2006: 145, fig. 222) appear frequently. Also exist different metal elements, used for securing the dugout itself or constructional components.

Unfortunately, at the moment nothing specific can be said about dugouts of the Adriatic river system. The only significant find was lost (cat. no. 27).

In the group of the Adriatic Sea dugouts (cat. nos 30 to 36), where the Plitvice Lakes find can be included (cat. no. 29), three varieties can be clearly distinguished. There are boats 4 to 5m long, out of which some are simply made without bulkheads or other internals (cat. nos 31 to 32). Others are characterized by a bottom elevated towards the prow and the stern (cat. nos 34; 36), while the third group represents logboats with several bulkheads (cat. nos 30; 33). It is hard to estimate whether these are characteristics of a local manufacture or is it a case of different purposes, for which they were intended. Bulkheads concentrate to the longer vessels.

Huge oak forests, which have existed, and still do in the area, most probably contributed to the popularity of dugouts. The vast majority of them are made out of oak (*Quercus robur*), which abound in the Slavonian plains, while for the Adriatic area it was fetched from the Velebit mountain range that spreads along the coast. In only one case (cat. no. 30) the wood species could be determined as elm (*Ulmus laevis)*, found on the island itself. Very few of the analyses have been expertly confirmed. Most of them have been undertaken on the spot and based only on the primary characteristics of the wooden material.

Dugouts in the Croatian area, similar to other parts of Europe, have long stayed in usage and have therefore been transferred from the domain of archeological to ethnological heritage. They are reflections of a tradition, dating from prehistoric periods to modern times. Although the continual usage of dugouts cannot definitely be confirmed, it is sure that with the arrival of the Slavs this tradition gained a new boost and has continued almost to the present day. The interesting fact is that it encompassed all water surfaces, including the Adriatic coast, where dugouts less than a hundred years ago used to thread the distance between the land and numerous E. Adriatic islands.

As already stated, this paper represents the first attempt at unifying the basic data on Croatian dugouts[6]. The next step would be their comparison to other European finds, with the aim of noting similarities and differences, which could contribute to their more detailed interpretation.

ACKNOWLEDGEMENTS

The author is grateful to the colleagues from the Croatian museums for their kind assistance in collecting information and data.

NOTES

1) Despite B. Volpi Lisjak's detailed description of Croatian finds he missed a few finds from the island of Krk, which remained unpublished, and a few pieces of information about dugouts from Zadar and Split.

2) The term has a Hungarian origin (*kereb*), probably from Greek κάραβς, S. Slavic *korabja*, which means a boat, a dugout (Skok 1972: 152). Sometimes the term *komp* or *kompa* is used, also of Hungarian origin, but it mostly refers to a raft.

3) With Gräf 2006 a detailed literature on both findings is provided.

4) As the first comprehensive study of floating mills, D. Gräf quotes Procopius who saw such on the Tiber in 537 (Gräf 2006: 15).

5) The Croatian terms are *igo* or *jaram*, both meaning an outrigger. It describes a diagonal plank, which was fastened on the abaft

third of the boat. Its length is equivalent to the half length of the entire boat or little longer; tholes are attached to both ends (Šoljan 1938: fig. 1; Volpi Lisjak 2004: fig. on p. 148).

6) The collection of entire documentation about preserved finds has been started. In the case of the Sisak dugout a successful conservation process using PEG is being undertaken, while for the rest of the unpreserved and damaged dugouts an initiative for their preservation has also been taken.

REFERENCES

Barbalić, R. F., 1957, Ladva – novi ekspozit Pomorske zbirke Narodnog muzeja u Rijeci, *Riječka revija*, 6, 178-179.

Bonino, M., 1980, Barche e navi antiche tra Aquileia e Trieste. *Antichitá Altoadriatiche*, 7, Aquileia, 57-87.

Bonino, M., 1981, Rafts and dugouts in central Italy. The primitive phase of local inland boat building. *MM*, 67.2, 125-148.

Ćurčić, V., 1908, Prehistorička sojenica iz brončanog doba u Ripču, kraj Bihaća u Bosni. *Glasnik zemaljskog muzeja u Bosni i Hercegovini*, 20, 149-179.

1910, Ribarski alati. Korabovi, čunovi, ladje, in Narodno ribarstvo u Bosni i Hercegovini. *Glasnik zemaljskog muzeja u Bosni i Hrcegovini*, 12, 387-396.

Eckhel, N., 1993, Pokupske vedute. In: *Pokupska sjećanja*. Etnografski muzej Zagreb. Catalogue of the exhibition. Zagreb, 33-45.

Fortis, A., 1987, *Viaggio in Dalmazia* (1st edition, Venezia 1774), ed. Eva Viani. Venezia.

Gojković, J., 1954, Posljednje vodenice. *Osječki zbornik*, 1954, 164-166.

Gräf, D., 2006, Boat Mills in Europe from Early Medieval to Modern Times. *Bibliotheca Molinologica*, no. 19. Dresden.

Greenhill, B. & Morrison, J., 1995 (1976), *The Archaeology of Boats and Ships*. London.

Imamović, E., 1980, Pomorstvo Cresa i Lošinja u prethistorijsko i antičko doba. *Otočki ljetopis* (Mali Lošinj), 3, 121-149.

Janjić, S., 1978, Suvlasničke vodenice na Savi u bosanskoj Posavini. *Etnološki prikazi* (Zagreb), 1, 217-225.

Jurišić, M. 1993 Nalaz monoksila u Kupi kod Siska. Obavijesti Hrvatskog arheološkog društva, XXV. 3, 68-69.

Kozličić, M.1993 *Hrvatsko brodovlje – Croatian Shipping*. Književni krug Split. Zagreb.

Lenček, R., 1950, Poročilo o čupi. *Izvjestije Srednjih šol v britsko-ameriškem Pasu Svobodnega Trzaškega Ozemlja, za skolsko leto 1949-1950*. Trieste, 3-7.

Lorini, P., 1903, *Ribanje i ribarske sprave pri istočnim obalama Jadranskoga mora*. Beč (reprint Zagreb 1995).

Malinar, H., 2007, Konzervacija arheološkog drva. *Godišnjak zaštite spomenika kulture*, 29-30, 2005-2006, 85-110.

Marzari, M., Dedenaro, R., D'Ercole, R. & Furlan, A., 1994, Il mare degli zoppoli. *Archeologia Viva*, N.S. 45, Maggio – Giugno, 58-64.

Medas, S., 1997, Le imbarcazioni monossili: Letteratura antica e archeologia. In: *Atti del convegno nazionale di archeologia subacquea, Anzio, 30-31 Maggio e 1 Giugno 1996*. Bari, 271-286.

Milošević, A., 1992, Arheološki nalazi u koritu rijeke Cetine u Sinjskom polju. *Arheo*, 15, 86-88.

1999, Archäologische Probeuntersuchungen im Flussbett der Cetina (Kroatien) zwischen 1990 und 1994. *Arch. Korrbl.*, 29, 203-210.

2003, *Numini Hippi fluvii*. Muzej hrvatskih arheoloških spomenika. Exhibition catalogue. Split.

Novak, G., 1932, *Naše more*. Mjesni odbor II. Jadranske straže. Zagreb.

Ossowki, W., 1999, *Studia nad Lodziami Jednopiennymi z Obszaru Polski/Study on Logboats from Poland*. Polish Maritime Museum's Proceedings, no. XI. Gdańsk.

Radić Rossi, I., 2006, Monoksili. In: *Trgovina i razmjena u pretpovijesti*. Arheološki muzej Zagreb. Catalogue of the exhibition. Zagreb, 92-93.

Registar 1997, *Registar arheoloških nalaza i nalazišta sjeverozapadne Hrvatske, drugo dopunjeno izdanje*. Mzejsko društvo sjeverozapadne Hrvatske, Sekcija arheologa i preparatora. Bjelovar.

Ribarić, J., 1959, Mlinovi na Muri i Dravi u okolici Varaždina i u Međimurju. In: *Rad kongresa folklorista Jugoslavije u Varaždinu 1957*. Zagreb, 41-43.

Ružić Barbić, A. 2004, *Bakaračke tunere*. Katedra Čakavskog sabora »Ljubo Pavešić«. Rijeka.

Šilić, Č., 1993, *Atlas drveća i grmlja*. Svjetlost – Sarajevo, Zavod za udžbenike i nastavna Sredstva – Beograd. Sarajevo.

Skok, P., 1972, *Etimologijski rječnik hrvatskoga ili srpskoga jezika*, vol. II. Jugoslavenska akademija znanosti i umjetnosti. Zagreb.

Sokol, V., 2006, *Kelti, Rimljani … i hrvatski monoksil*. Muzej Prigorja. Sesvete, Zagreb.

Šoljan, T., 1938, Ladva, jedan naš ribarski čamac na umoru. *Jadranska straža*, no. 5, 187.

Truhelka, Ć., 1902, Sojenica u Donjoj Dolini. Drugo iskopavanje 1901. *Glasnik Zemaljskog muzeja u Bosni i Hercegovini*, 14, 129-144.

1906, Sojenica u Donjoj Dolini. Peto iskopavanje god. 1904. *Glasnik Zemaljskog muzeja u Bosni i Hercegovini*, 18, 99-228.

Volpi Lisjak, B., 1997, *Čupa – Čoln slovenskih ribičev v Tržaškom zalivu, Etnolog*. Ljubljana, 43-62.

2004, *Čupa – prvo slovensko plovilo in drevaki. Prispevek k etnologiji in vprašanju etnogeneze Slovencev*. Trieste.

Županović, Š. 1995, *Hrvati i more*. Prva knjiga. Zagreb.

INLAND NAVIGATION AND ITS VESSELS

KATRIN THIER

PADDLING, ROWING AND STEERING IN WORD AND DEED

PREHISTORY OF A WORD

In many ways, historical linguistics, the study of the history of languages, is similar to archaeology; it often involves similar methods, such as typologies, and relative and absolute dating, along with all the problems associated with these. The main difference is that historical linguistics deals not with artefacts, but with words and the concepts behind them.

Rowing and paddling are very closely linked conceptually as well as technologically. Both involve a shaft with a broad flat end, pushing against the resistance of the water. In effect, rowing is a development of paddling, making the technique more efficient by turning the implement against a pivot and taking advantage of the resulting leverage. Consequently, no distinction was made between oar and paddle in Europe[1] until as late as the 17th c. (OED3 2005 at PADDLE n.[1]; Thier 2005: 289-290).

Most European languages as well as some languages of the Near East and India are thought to derive from a single ancestor language, which cannot be securely dated but must predate its first recorded descendants, Hittite (mid-2nd millennium B.C.) and Greek (late-2nd millennium B.C.). This language is usually known as Proto-Indo-European or Indo-European. From the various reflexes in recorded languages an Indo-European form for the verb »to row« has been reconstructed as *h_1reh_1-, more traditionally written as *(e)rē-[2]. This short form is known as the root, the essential part of a word; derivatives can be composed by adding letters and syllables (suffixes) to this root.

The root of the verb »to row« has reflexes in Vedic Sanskrit, the earliest decipherable Indic language, which reached India from the Near East in the second half of the 2nd millennium B.C. (Mallory & Adams 2006: 33). The Vedic words are *aritār* »rower« and *aritra* »oar« (Rigveda; Monier-Williams 1899: 88), and their presence suggests that the word goes back to the earliest stages of Indo-European, before the Indic languages came to India. Reflexes are also attested in the very earliest layers of Greek, as Mycenean Greek *e-re-e* »to row« (which does not survive) and *e-re-ta* »rower« (which corresponds to classical Greek *eretēs*, modern Greek *eretis*). These inscriptions come from the second half of the 2nd millennium B.C. from Pylos and Knossos (13th c. or earlier; cf. e.g. Ventris and Chadwick 1973: no. 15, 53, 55), not long after the earliest images of the use of oars from the Thera frescoes (probably 17th c. B.C.; Wachsmann 1998: 106-107). Since the word at the time was old enough to be present in India as well as the Aegean, it can be assumed to pre-date the development of rowing at least in the Mediterranean and to have previously referred to propulsion by paddle. In classical Latin, the root only survives as *rēmus*, which can denote an oar as well as a paddle and is the ancestor of a word for »oar« in modern Romance languages, e.g. Italian *remo*. In the language groups of N.W. Europe (Celtic and Germanic), the vowel *ē* of the root was replaced by *ō*, so that all the equivalent words in these languages effectively descend from a root *rō- »to row« (which in the Celtic languages regularly changed to *rā- (in the course of the Iron Age). So in Common Celtic a word *rāmo- for »oar« can be reconstructed, formed similarly to the Latin (with the same -mo- suffix), but clearly not borrowed from Latin, because the vowel has a different history. Hence the Old Irish word for oar is *rámae* (modern Irish *rámha*), while Welsh has a word *rhawf* »spade«, which has descended from the corresponding word for »oar«. (Welsh *rhwyf* »oar« was borrowed from Latin in early first millennium A.D.). In Germanic, finally, the verb survives as Old English *rōwan* (English *to row*), Old Norse *róa*. In

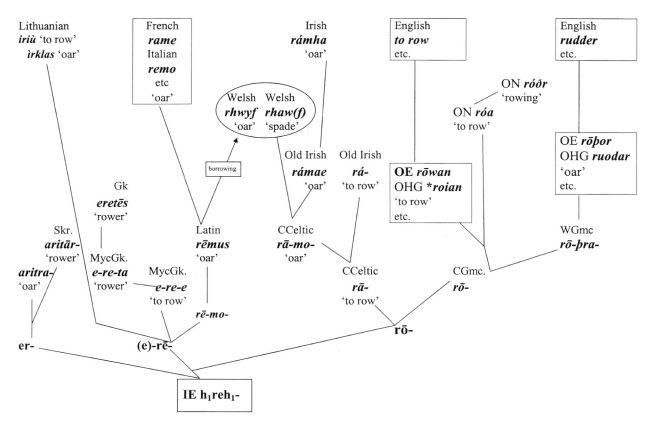

Fig. 1 Family tree of the Indo-European word for paddling or rowing.

the W. Germanic languages (i.e. the Germanic languages discussed here except Old Norse[3], the tool is denoted by a derivation with the suffix -*þra*- (used for a tool or agent, like -*mo*- in Celtic and Latin): e.g. Old English *rōþor*, Old High German *ruodar*. The parallel derivative in N. Germanic (i.e. Scandinavian, represented by Old Norse), *róðr*, however, denotes the act of rowing and was formed separately from the W. Germanic word. Old English *rōþor* eventually developed into English *rudder*, which no longer means »oar« and which I will therefore return to later (**Fig. 1**).

At this point some reference should be made to the development of paddling and rowing in N.W. Europe. There is not very much evidence, and an almost complete lack of linguistic material. The Celtic languages of Britain and Ireland are well attested only from the middle of the first millennium onwards, although there is enough earlier evidence to make reconstructions possible (Mallory & Adams 2006: 15-18). Aside from names and some short Runic inscriptions, W. Germanic languages are first known from the 7th to the 8th c. onwards (Old English, Old Saxon, later also Old Frisian: van der Wal & Quak 1994), N. Germanic languages from the Viking Age (Faarlund 1994; Jesch 2001)[4].

PADDLING AND ROWING

A small gold model of the 4th c. B.C. from Hallein is often regarded as the earliest evidence of rowing N. of the Alps (McGrail 1998: 213). However, its interpretation is uncertain, and even if it does depict a rowing boat (cf. T. Weski, this volume, pp. 123-132), it is so isolated that it may merely represent minor and temporary technological influence from the Mediterranean.

By contrast, there is clear evidence from Hjortspring in Denmark that paddles were still being used to power large craft in the 4th c. B.C. As late as the 1st c. A.D., the Roman writer Tacitus describes how ships of the Suiones (in the S. Baltic Sea) were propelled in a markedly different way from Roman ships: »the shape of their ships is different in such a way that a bow at each end always serves as a fore-part, ready for landing; they do not use sails, and they do not join their »oars« in a row to the sides: the »rowing« is loose, as in some river-craft, and flexible, if necessary, [going] this way or that« (Germania 44)[5]. This cannot describe rowing in the modern sense, since the presence of oar pivots and perhaps even a steering mechanism would fix the craft in its direction, whereas Tacitus stresses that these ships could change ends apparently spontaneously. It is significant that the word Tacitus uses for the tool is *rēmus*, here clearly denoting a paddle, but at the same time the normal word for »oar« (cf. above). Within the Roman Empire, the technique of rowing was known in N. Europe and it appears to be a fair assumption that the technique spread from the Empire to the neighbouring peoples. There is a large amount of pictorial evidence as early as the 1st c. A.D., showing oars even on ships, which appear to be built in non-Roman traditions, e.g. on the memorial for Blussus, now in Mainz (Boppert 1992: 53; Mott 1997: 107). In the Atlantic W., there is some interesting evidence challenging the perception that the expansion of the Roman Empire alone was responsible for the spread of the technology of rowing. A gold model found off the coast of Broighter in the N. of Ireland represents a boat with as mast as well as a set of eight rowing benches, 15 surviving long narrow oars, as well as loops to serve as pivots (Farrell & Penny 1975: 19, 23). Even though the model was found in a severely damaged state, the sum of these features allows interpretation of the craft as a large ship that could be sailed and rowed, dated to the 1st c. A.D. In this location, it is unlikely that the presence of such a sophisticated ship reflects a recent and direct impetus from Rome, it rather seems the result of a longer period of internal development. It is worth bearing in mind here that the Old Irish *rámae* is not a loan from Latin *rēmus*, but related to it and of the same ultimate origin. It is therefore likely that the Irish and Latin words developed further from »paddling« to »rowing« senses mostly independently and in parallel.

So by the 2nd c. the following picture has emerged: the Latin word *rēmus* normally designates the oar on rowed craft, but it is also applied to Barbarian paddles. The Celtic word *rāmo-* is not yet attested, but must have existed[6], and there is evidence of rowing technology outside the Empire, which it will have referred to. There is still no evidence of a Germanic term, but since the reconstructed verb *rō-* cannot be a loan from Celtic or Latin (different vowels), it must have been there already, probably in the sense »to paddle«, since the evidence from Scandinavia seem to point at paddling as the principal mode of propulsion. The tempting conclusion would be that there was a contrast in sense between the Germanic N. and E. and the Celtic and Latin S. and W., and that the technology along with the sense development spread from the latter to the former aided by the increasing influence of the Roman Empire.

This picture is altered by the find of a number of rowlocks from a ship-breaking site at Mangersnes in W. Norway, the earliest of which is dated to at least the 2nd c. (Christensen 1995: 75). It is a fully developed complex device, with a thorn-like spike curved backwards to take the oar, and a triangular grommet hole. It is clearly an ancestor of the later Scandinavian rowlocks; it is not, however, in any way similar to the Roman ones, which had upright pegs around which the grommet was laid.

MORE ON ROWING

The next stage in the development of word and technique is overshadowed by the decline and withdrawal of the Empire in the N. Not much changed in the Celtic and Roman worlds, although the 4th c. sees images of apparently native craft propelled by paddles from Trier, the N. centre and contemporary capital of the

Empire. These are unique, but their interpretation is debated, and the paddles may be used for purely tactical reasons (e.g. silent approach) or for topographical ones (e.g. narrow waterways). Apart from these there is still no tangible evidence from the continental Germanic area. The W. Germanic word *rōþra-* may have existed at this stage, but even this cannot be inferred with any certainty.

The most significant changes can be seen in Scandinavia. The site at Mangersnes continues (Christensen 1995), and rowlocks are also found with the broken oak boat at Nydam, now dated to approx. A.D. 250 (Rieck *et al.* 1999: 34). The 4th c. boats from Björke in Sweden and Halsnøy in Norway show evidence of rowing (Westerdahl 1985: 129; Crumlin-Pedersen: pers. comm.), and in the 5th and 6th c., major rowing boats are depicted on stones in Gotland (e.g. Bro; Lindquist 1942: 62-64; Nylén 1978: 22-23). Amid all this, the ancestor of modern English *oar* is found in Scandinavia, probably in the form *airo-*, later attested as Old Norse *ár*. It is unrelated to the rowing/paddling word discussed above, but its origin is otherwise unknown, as is its age. It does not appear to be of Indo-European origin. Outside N. Germanic, it only appears in languages apparently borrowing it from N. Germanic, most notably Finnish. Finnish *airo* exactly mirrors the form the N. Germanic ancestor of Old Norse *ár* must have had, confirming that the borrowing into Finnish must go back some time. Also, Finnish *airo* only ever denotes the oar, unlike the older term *mela*, which can be either a paddle or an oar (Koivulehto, pers. comm.) and thus functions similarly to the Indo-European group discussed at the beginning. Unfortunately, the sound changes involved are not datable, so that the origin of *ár* cannot be narrowed down further chronologically (OED3 2004 at OAR n.; Thier 2002: 102). Old Norse *ár* is first attested in 11th c. poetry (cf. Jesch 2001: 154).

Interestingly, it coexists with another term, *ræði*, which descends from the Indo-European paddling/rowing word, and is already disappearing, when it is first attested in Viking Age poetry (Jesch 2001: 155); it does not survive into the Middle Ages. It is quite possible that this was originally the word for »paddle«, which could not successfully complete the change to the sense »oar«, because *ár* was already present and sufficient to cover this sense. Further evidence of unusual and probably indigenous developments in Scandinavia can be found in other elements of rowing terminology: the word for the rowlock is *keipr*, a word of debated, though probably Germanic origin, but unparalleled in either form or sense in any language outside the N. Germanic group. It first appears on a Runic inscription of the beginning of the 8th c. in W. Norway (de Vries 1961 at KEIPR 1). Then there is *hár* »oar«, first attested in a 7th c. Runic inscription and of Germanic origin, but again, unparalleled in exact form and sense in other languages. It was borrowed into Finnish as *hanka* (de Vries 1961 at HÁR). Old Norse *hamla* »oarlock, grommet«, finally is similarly unique, though also of Germanic derivation (de Vries 1961 at HAMLA 1). The latter two were borrowed into Old English in the Viking Age, where they co-existed briefly with the native *þol* »rowlock« and *wiððe* »grommet« (both of the W. Germanic tradition)[7], but did not survive.

ROWING AND STEERING

The interaction of the words for »oar« and »rudder« in the Germanic languages mostly happened later and is therefore better documented. Since much of the best evidence comes from glosses, i.e. word lists or interlinear translations of Latin texts, here is a short list of some relevant Latin terms. These are often more precise than the Germanic translations:

remus, the main word for »oar« (or »paddle«, as discussed above); *palmula* »oarblade«, apparently never »rudder-blade« (sometimes understood by glossators as an alternative term for »oar«); *tonsa*, a medieval word for »oar«; *gubernaculum*, the main word for »rudder«; *aplustrum* »stern decoration« (understood to mean »stern« or »rudder« by some Germanic glossators); and *clavus* »helm, tiller«.

By the time of the Roman Empire in the Mediterranean, a ship's steering mechanism was clearly distinguished from its means of propulsion, and perceived as separate. It consisted of a pair of blades over both sides of the ship, with long tillers operated by a single helmsman (Casson 1971). There was no overlap between words for »oar« and »rudder«. There is evidence of the presence of ships with Mediterranean-style steering arrangements in Imperial N. Europe, e.g. from the 2nd c. seagoing ship found at County Hall in London (Marsden 1994: 109-130), and the Late Roman river patrol ships of Mainz (Bockius 2006). There is also a rudder blade of the 1st c., from the Roman camp at Newstead in S. Scotland, which appears to have belonged to a similar arrangement in a small boat (Curle 1911: 313). Yet there is also evidence in N. Europe for steering arrangements using a single rudder. From within the Empire (and not paralleled outside it) there is the gravestone of Blussus mentioned above, which shows a single sweep mounted over the back of the boat. From Ireland comes the Broighter boat model, also mentioned above, which has a single quarter rudder mounted over the port side of the vessel (Farrell & Penny 1975: 23-24). The Irish evidence is similar to that of the Germanic world, where single rudders used over the side of a boat are known from at least as early as the 4th c. B.C.: some of the paddles found with the Hjortspring boat were different from the others, with broader blades and positioned at the extreme ends of the vessel. These are the earliest evidence of specialised paddles (or later oars) used to steer a ship, and thus arguably the earliest instances of a kind of rudder in N. Europe. Large oar-like implements used for steering are also depicted on some of the stones from Gotland in the 5th and 6th c. (Nylén 1978: 22-23), and a find of such a »steering oar« from Alsodde has also been dated to this period (7th c.; Crumlin-Pedersen 1990: 108). It is notable that both the Hjortspring and Gotland ships seem to have such steering oars both at the bow as well as the stern. More efficient is the next step in the development, which is a firmly mounted quarter rudder. A fully developed example of this was found with the Nydam pine boat of A.D. 300/320. When the W. Germanic languages are first attested, the word for the oar, *roþra- must already have existed[8], but these developments are still recent (or perhaps even ongoing, in their final stages). This led to an association of the word for oar with steering. There is also a Germanic word for steering (the ancestor of English *steer*), but this was used originally as a verb, not as a noun describing the apparatus. So the steering apparatus was also called *rōþra-*, like the oar.

As a result, *rōþra* became ambiguous, and to make the distinction the W. Germanic languages developed different strategies of disambiguation. The *rōþra* was increasingly used to denote the rudder, while the oar came to be known by different names. Only in English has this development been completed and is traceable in detail. There is only very incomplete and late evidence from Frisian and Low German (or Old Saxon, in its earlier form). The Frisian evidence from the 15th c. shows the Germanic term (now in the form *roer*) primarily used for the rudder, while the oar is denoted by the unambiguous word *rēme*, which was borrowed from Latin *rēmus*, prob. during the late Empire. Old Saxon in the 12th c. only shows the compound *stiurrōðer* »steering-oar, steering-rudder« in contexts clearly referring to steering, suggesting that the function still needed to be specified. Similarly, in German, the Latin loan *rieme* »oar« is attested from the mid-13th c., and the form of the word shows that it must have been in the German language at least as early as the 8th or 9th c. This is the antecedent of the modern technical term *Riemen*. In the 10th and 11th c., the compound *stiurruoder* suggests a continuing need for disambiguation, and a new noun *stiura* (from the verb *stiuran* »to steer«) appears also, the antecedent of the modern popular (i.e. non-technical) term *Steuer*. On its own, Old High German *ruodar*, is first attested around the same time in the sense »oar«, but even in the 11th c., it also glosses Latin words for the steering apparatus (or parts of it), and from then on is consistently ambiguous. Even in modern popular use it still denotes the oar, while in technical register it is used exclusively for the rudder. The record for English is equally detailed, and begins earlier, so *rōþer* can be seen as the word for an oar as early as the 8th c., in a glossary, which is likely to have been copied

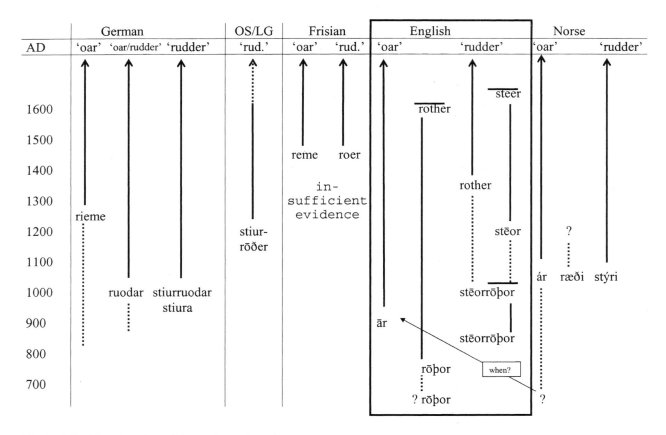

Fig. 2 Disambiguation of words for rowing and steering.

from a 7th c. original (*Épinal Glossary* 986). By the 9th c., the compound *stēorrōþer* is evidence for a certain amount of ambiguity in the term: as in other languages, the prefixing of the »steering« word makes the sense clear. From the 12th c., a simplex noun *steor* is attested in the same sense. The sense »oar« has meanwhile been taken over by the unambiguous Scandinavian loan *ár*, which is first attested in the 9th c. (*Anglo-Saxon Chronicle* 897) and could be a Viking-Age borrowing, but it may also have come into English at an earlier date[9]. As the language now had a separate word for »oar«, *rōþer* was free to be used for the steering apparatus, which in the course of the early second millennium increasingly developed away from any obvious association with oars. Stern rudders appear in the mid-12th c. while side-rudders are in evidence as late as the 14th c. (Mott 1997: 149). It is in this context that in the 14th c. the word *rother* on its own (and now spelt like this) is first attested to mean »rudder«. It is last attested meaning »oar« around 1600 (OED2 at RUDDER n.). No longer needed to distinguish oars from rudders, the noun *steer* »rudder« disappears in the 17th c. (cf. OED2 at STEER). Current English is left with two unambiguous terms, *oar* and *rudder*. It is also in the 17th c. that the word *paddle* is first used for the hand-held implement previously also denoted by *oar* (cf. above), thus making the disambiguation of terminology complete (**Fig. 2**).

No such developments seem to have been necessary in the Scandinavian languages which by the 11th c. already had the unrelated and unambiguous terms *ár* »oar« and *stýri* »rudder«. The sole derivative of the Indo-European oar-word, *ræði*, is attested in 11th c. poetry, but has disappeared by the time of the sagas (from the 13th c.), apparently surplus to requirements.

So by the time the stern rudder has taken over as the main technology, the following linguistic picture presents itself (based on glosses of the Latin terms detailed above): where in the earlier period, there was much

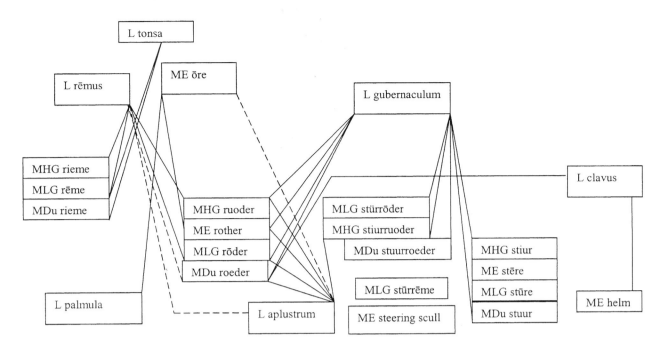

Fig. 3 Distribution of senses in the Middle Ages.

apparently chaotic ambiguity, the terminology has now fallen neatly into two groups of words clearly denoting the oar and words clearly denoting the rudder. An overlap however remains for the un-compounded Old W. Germanic word, but the trend for this to become less ambiguous continues in the following centuries, even though this process has not been completed in all languages yet (**Fig. 3**).

Interestingly, there seems to have been occasional need to describe the older type of rudder, and the origin of this construction as a specialised oar is still recognised, as evidenced by Middle Low German *stūrreme* (Schiller & Lübben 1878 at STÜRREME), Middle English *steering scull* (OED2 at STEERING, vbl. n.). When in the 19th c. the word *steering oar* is coined by English-speaking antiquarians, the development has come full circle.

ACKNOWLEDGEMENTS

The author is grateful to J. Koivulehto, C. Westerdahl, and O. Crumlin-Pedersen whose comments at some time or another have contributed to this paper.

NOTES

1) Much of this is also true in other parts of the world, but this paper will limit itself to the Mediterranean and W. Europe.

2) The asterisk means that this form is not actually recorded, and the letter h_1 refers to a sound, which is not known exactly, but has left traces in later development, in this case making the vowel consistently long and prefixing a further vowel in some languages (cf. Mallory & Adams 2006: 48-50). Long vowels in ancient languages are marked with a horizontal bar, or macron, over the top. For more information about Proto-Indo-European and its descendents cf. Mallory & Adams 2006.

3) The E. Germanic branch, solely represented by Gothic, is not relevant here, because no words for paddling, rowing or steering appear in surviving texts.

4) Some Old Norse poetry is datable to the 11th c., but the manuscripts, and therefore the bulk of the evidence, only date from the 13th c. and later: Jesch 2001.

5) *Forma navium eo differt, quod utrimque prora paratam semper appulsui frontem agit; nec velis ministrant, nec remos in ordinem lateribus adiugunt: solutum, ut in quibusdam fluminum, et mutabile ut res poscit, hinc, vel illinc, remigium.*

6) It can be reconstructed from Welsh and Irish evidence, the earliest of which dates to the 8th or early 9th c. (Old Irish, St. Gall Glosses: 90)

7) Old English *þoll* (8th c.: Corpus Glossary S 182), English *tholepin*, German *Dolle*; Old English *wiððe* (11th c.: Antwerp Glossary 231, 2; 234, 7), English *withe*; Old English *hā, hamele* (both 11th c.: Anglo-Saxon Chronicle 1039, 1052): Thier 2002: 104-106.

8) As would the ancestor of Old Norse *ræði*, though the chronology is more difficult to establish in the case, and the actual evidence is later (for the earliest attestations cf. Jesch 2001: 155).

9) The age of this word in English is impossible to tell on the grounds of its form, and it may have come from Scandinavia as early as the beginning of Anglo-Saxon settlement.

REFERENCES

Anglo-Saxon Chronicle: Plummer, C., 1892 (ed.), *Two of the Saxon Chronicles Parallel*. Oxford.

Anglo-Saxon Chronicle: Swanton, M., 1996 (tr.), *The Anglo-Saxon Chronicles*. London.

Antwerp Glossary: Kindschi, L., 1955, *The Latin-Old English Glossaries in Plantin-Moretus MS 32 and BM MS Add. 32, 246*. Unpublished PhD dissertation, Stanford University.

Bockius, R., 2006, *Die römerzeitlichen Schiffswracks aus Mainz*. Monographien des Römisch-Germanischen Zentralmuseums, no. 67. Mainz.

Boppert, W., 1992, *Zivile Grabsteine aus Mainz und Umgebung*. Corpus Signorum Imperii Romani. Corpus der Skulpturen der Römischen Welt, Deutschland. Germania Superior, vol. II. 6. Mainz.

Casson, L., 1971, *Ships and Seamanship in the Ancient World*. Princetown/New Jersey.

Christensen, A. E., 1995, Boat Fragments from Mangersnes. In: O. Olsen *et al.* (eds), *Shipshape – Essays for Ole Crumlin-Pedersen*. Roskilde, 73-80.

Corpus Glossary: Hessels, J., 1890, *An Eighth-Century Latin-Anglo-Saxon Glossary Preserved in the Library of Corpus Christi, Cambridge*. Cambridge.

Crumlin-Pedersen, O., 1990, Boats and Ships of the Angles and Jutes. In: S. McGrail (ed.), *Maritime Celts, Frisians and Saxons*. CBA Research Report 71. London, 98-116.

Curle, J., 1911, *A Roman Frontier Post and its People. The Fort of Newstead in the Parish of Melrose*. Glasgow.

de Vries, J., 1961, *Altnordisches Etymologisches Wörterbuch*. Leiden.

Ellmers, D., 1977-1978, Die ersten bildlichen Darstellungen zu Schiff fahrender Sachsen aus dem römischen Trier. *Die Kunde*, N.F. 28-29, 99-104.

Épinal Glossary: Pheifer, J. D. (ed.), 1974, *Old English Glosses in the Épinal-Erfurt Glossary*. Oxford.

Faarlund, J. T., 1994, Old and Middle Scandinavian. In: E. König & J. van der Auwera (eds), *The Germanic Languages*. London, 38-71.

Farrell, A. W. & Penny, S., 1975, The Broighter Boat – a Reassessment. *Irish Archaeological Research Forum*, 2.2, 15-28.

Germania: M. Kretschmer (ed.), 1986, *Tacitus: Germania*. Münster.

Jesch, J., 2001, *Ships and Men in the Late Viking Age*. Woodbridge.

Lindquist, S., 1942, *Gotlands Bildsteine*, vol. 1. Uppsala.

Mallory, J. & Adams, D., 2006, *The Oxford Introduction to Proto-Indo-European and The Proto-Indo-European World*. Oxford.

Marsden, P., 1994, Ships of the Port of London: First to Eleventh Centuries AD. *English Heritage, Archaeological Report* 3. London.

McGrail, S., 1998, *Ancient Boats of North-West Europe: The Archaeology of Water Transport to AD 1500*. London (2nd edition).

MED: Kurath, H., *et al.* (eds), 1952-2001, *Middle English Dictionary*. Ann Arbor / Michigan.

Monier-Williams, M., 1899, *A Sanskrit-English Dictionary*. Oxford.

Mott, L., 1997, *The Development of the Rudder: A Technological Tale*. London.

Nylén, E.,1978, *Bildstenar*. Visby.

OED2: Simpson, J. A. & Weiner, E. S. C. (eds), 1989, The *Oxford English Dictionary*. Oxford (2nd edition).

OED3: dated by individual entry, *Oxford English Dictionary Online*. Oxford. URL: http://dictionary.oed.com/ [all information correct on 28th Feb. 2006]

Rieck, F., *et al.*, 1999, … som samlede Ofre fra en talrig Krigerflok. Status over Nationalmuseets Nydamprojekt 1989-97. *Nationalmuseets Arbejdsmark*, 1999, 11-34.

1994, The Iron Age Boats from Hjortspring and Nydam – New Investigations. In: *ISBSA 6*, 45-54.

Rosenberg, G., 1937, Hjortspringfundet. *Nordiske Forntidsminder*, vol. III, 1. København.

Schiller, K. & Lübben, A., 1878, *Mittelniederdeutsches Wörterbuch*, vol. IV. S-T. Bremen.

St Gall Glosses: Stokes, W. & Strachan, J., 1903, *Thesaurus Palaeohibernicus*, vol. II. Cambridge.

Thier, K., 2002, *Altenglische Terminologie für Schiffe und Schiffsteile*. BAR, Internat. Series, no. 1036. Oxford.

Thier, K., 2005, Das Paddel – eine Minikulturgeschichte. In: H. Eilbracht *et al.* (eds), *Itinera Archaeologica vom Neolithikum bis in die frühe Neuzeit*. Rahden (Westf.), 281-294.

van der Wal, M. J. & Quak, A., 1994, Old and Middle Continental West Germanic. In: E. König & J. van der Auwera (eds), *The Germanic Languages*. London, 72-109.

Ventris, M. & Chadwick, J., 1973, *Documents in Mycenean Greek*. Revised edition. Cambridge.

Wachsmann, S., 1998, *Seagoing Ships and Seamanship in the Bronze Age Levant*. London.

Westerdahl, C., 1985, Sewn Boats of the North. *IJNA*, 14, 33-62; 119-142.

MARC GUYON · ÉRIC RIETH

THE GALLO-ROMAN WRECKS FROM LYON, PARC SAINT GEORGES (FRANCE)

NEW ARCHAEOLOGICAL DATA
ON ANCIENT INLAND »BOTTOM-BASED SHIPBUILDING«

During the building of an underground car park in Lyon, on the level of a fossil bank of the River Saône, archaeological rescue operations were carried out by the French Institute of Preventive Archaeological Research (Institut National de Recherches Archéologiques Préventives; INRAP) on commission of the Ministry of Culture. Field works, directed by Grégoire Ayala (INRAP), took place from October 2002 to June 2004. Inside a cofferdam an area of approx. 4000 m² was investigated to a depth of 10 m according to the traditional methods of terrestrial archaeology. Within a few months, 16 wrecks were uncovered and documented (**Fig. 1**) under the direction of Marc Guyon (INRAP).

Due to the large number of wrecks, their dimensions, and because of the restricted time of excavation imposed by the building contractors, it was necessary to define archaeological strategies applied to each wreck as rigorously as possible:

– dredging of the sediments boxing;
– manual excavation of the architectural remains;
– photographic recording and drawing (dimensions, architectural details etc.);
– systematic selection of samples (wood, cloth, coating, organic material etc.) for analyses;
– permanent protection of the wrecks by watering.

Taking into account the scientific and heritage interest in such a bulk of wrecks for the knowledge of regional river craft over a long period ranging from Antiquity to Modern Times, with great consequences on the technical and financial plans, the decision was made to save the best preserved and representative wrecks for museum display. Thus, from three of the six Gallo-Roman wrecks, (wrecks Ep. [épave] 4, Ep. 7

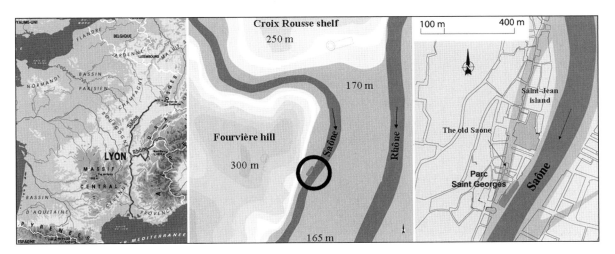

Fig. 1 Lyon, Parc Saint Georges. – Topography of the archaeological site.

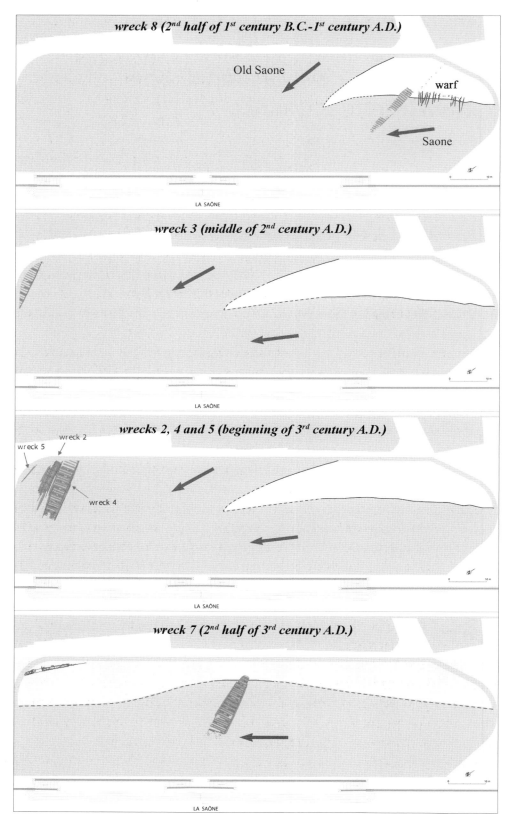

wreck 8 (2nd half of 1st century B.C.-1st century A.D.)

Old Saone

warf

Saone

LA SAÔNE

wreck 3 (middle of 2nd century A.D.)

LA SAÔNE

wrecks 2, 4 and 5 (beginning of 3rd century A.D.)

wreck 5

wreck 2

wreck 4

LA SAÔNE

wreck 7 (2nd half of 3rd century A.D.)

LA SAÔNE

Fig. 2 Lyon, Parc Saint Georges. – The site between the 2nd half of the 1st c. B.C. and the 2nd half of the 3rd c. A.D.

and Ep. 8) 22 sections of 2 m length on average were cut out. These sections were extracted from the archaeological area of excavation and transported towards a provisional storage site before being treated in the near future by the laboratory ARC-Nucléart at Grenoble where the conservation will be realized. On the other hand, the Gallo-Roman wrecks Ep. 2, Ep. 3 and Ep. 5 were dismantled on the site and later deposited in a store in Vienne (Isère). This operation made it possible to prolong detailed studies of each of the wrecks in laboratory, and to supplement the documentation already recorded *in situ*.

In addition to already published papers (Ayala & Horry 2003; Ayala 2004; Ayala, Horry & Laurent 2005; Ayala, Guyon & Laurent 2005), in the meantime twelve volumes of the scientific excavation report have been completed. A series of monographs, of which one will be devoted to the ship finds, is in preparation. The museum display of the conserved and restored wrecks, namely three Gallo-Roman wrecked barges, two medieval logboats, five younger (16th c.) wrecks of fishing boats, and the remains of an 18th c. barge will have to await a certain number of years, probably the next ten years, to be treated.

THE ARCHAEOLOGICAL SITE OF PARC SAINT GEORGES: HARBOUR INSTALLATIONS AND WRECKS

The site is located on the level of an ancient right bank of the Saône, near its mouth into the River Rhône (**Fig. 2**). Lying in the middle of the town of Lyon, from the point of view of water transport, the place appears to be a strategic junction zone. Harbour activities results are reflected archaeologically by installations at the bank, but also on the bed of the river by artefacts and, obviously, by wrecks. From the Gallo-Roman period, the discovered harbour structures are primarily indicating a wooden wharf. Many bits of amphoras, are obvious as being the traces of cargo handling, point to harbour activities particularly of the 1st and 3rd c. A.D. After a period of interruption, or displacement, during the early Middle Ages, the site was occupied again during the High Middle Ages, when, in particular, stone built harbour installations existed. The medieval pier has been replaced, during the 16th c., by stone constructions, at about the same time with an urbanization of the district around *Port Sablé*, which was illustrated for the first time on a scenographic plan of Lyon dating to 1550. Importantly the seven wrecks of fishing boats reveal economic activities of an urban district directed towards its river environment. It is only during the 19th c. that the construction of a high quay has isolated the ancient harbour site from the Saône.

The six Gallo-Roman wrecks have been found in a N.-S. orientation, each lying obliquely to the shore line of the ancient bank of the Saône. Four of these wrecks were uncovered at the W. end of the excavation area: Ep. 5 was situated at a level above Ep. 3, which is parallel to the wrecks Ep. 2 and Ep. 4. Ep. 7 came to light in the middle of the site, and the wreck Ep. 8 at its E. edge. The reasons why all of the Gallo-Roman wrecks shared the same orientation remain obscure. Despite the many geomorphologic results on the river environment and the hydro archaeology of the Saône throughout various periods, nothing sheds light on the specific distribution of the ancient wrecks: had those vessels been abandoned, were they temporally beached in the course of repair, or did the ships accidentally drift downstream?

Chronogically, the Gallo-Roman wrecks span a period ranging from the 1st to the 3rd c. A.D. (**Table 1**). As a striking feature, wrecks Ep. 3, Ep. 4 and Ep. 5, located at the W. edge of the site, share very close dating. However, this chronological proximity of tree felling data does not necessarily fix the chronological relation on the level of building and, of course, of deposit.

The Gallo-Roman ship finds are characterized by different states of preservation: Apart from wreck Ep. 5, preserved with less than 10 m length and less 1 m width, the other vessels are more preserved either in length, with a little more than 14.50 m to almost 20 m, and in width, with almost 3 to 5 m (**Table 1**).

wrecks	length (m)	width (m)	height (m)	dendrochronological dating: Catherine Lavier, Laboratoire de Chrono-écologie, Besançon
Ep. 8	17.41	2.80	0.50	A.D. 55
Ep. 5	7.30	0.83	0.55	A.D. 150
Ep. 4	18.53	4.67	1.15	A.D. 158-185
Ep. 3	14.64	3.05	0.25	A.D. 160-185
Ep. 2	15.11	2.83	1.10	A.D. 210-215
Ep. 7	19.82	5.05	1.13	A.D. 254-260

Table 1   Dimensions and dating of the Gallo-Roman ships from Lyon.

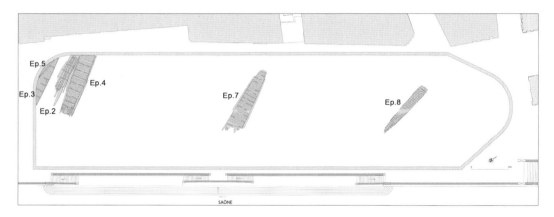

Fig. 3   Lyon, Parc Saint Georges. – Gallo-Roman wrecks *in situ*.

It should be emphasized that the archaeological documentation is based on precisely dated wrecks, which for the majority are well preserved. Delivering important data, not at least from the point of view of their historical interpretation, they all belong to the same hydrographical system formed by the rivers Rhône and Saône.

MAIN ARCHITECTURAL CHARACTERISTICS OF THE GALLO-ROMAN WRECKS

The Gallo-Roman wrecks were built according to the »bottom-based« principle of ancient ship construction (**Fig. 3**). Their architecture is defined in correlation to their flat, keelless bottom, by the conceptual level of design (shape, dimensions, structure) by the practical aspects of shipbuilding. From this architectural point of view, the flat bottom and the sides do not form the same continuous structure, as in the case of a »shell first« or »frame first« constructions based on keel, but two distinct structures.

According to the character of their structure, these »bottom-based« wrecks can be divided into two individual groups (**Fig. 4**): the first group (Ep. 2, Ep. 3, Ep. 4, Ep. 5 and Ep. 7) consists of barges with a monoxylous structural element, an oak L-shaped chine strake, reduced but however still able to be identified, combined with a lower side planking in shape of one (or two) half-log of fir. Group II, which includes only wreck Ep. 8, is characterized by plank-built structure with a composite plank chine and flush-laid side planking (**Fig. 5**).

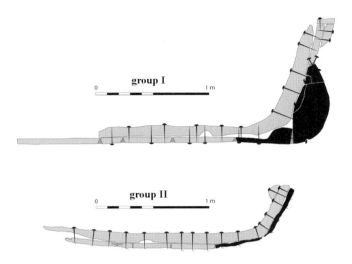

Fig. 4   Lyon, Parc Saint Georges. – Sections of group I and II wrecks.

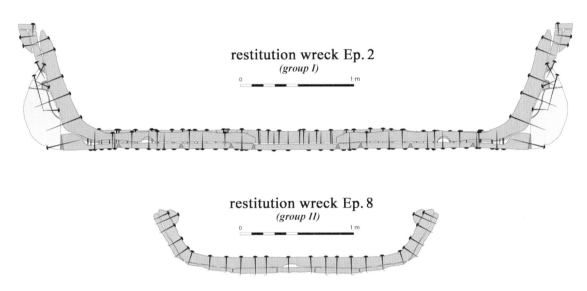

Fig. 5   Lyon, Parc Saint Georges. – Sections of wrecks Ep.2 and Ep.8.

Group I

The flat bottom of group I barges was built from oak planks with bevelled edges. At the sides, the bottom is girded by chine strakes, i.e. monoxylous elements, whose upright sections are reduced each to a short but solid lip. Oak ribs are composed of flat floor timbers and paired L-shaped half-frames spaced in two different sequences. Strong frames are fastened to the bottom planks with large blind iron nails driven from inboard and outboard. The side planking includes a lower fir strake made from one or two half-logs, and an upper flush-laid oak strake. The lower part of the half-log strake comes to cover the vertical arm of the chine strake matching the system of an »integrated« flat bottom (Beaudouin 2001: 22). Half-log and chine strake were fastened with large iron nails driven from outboard. The half-log strake and the upper flush-laid strake as well were attached to the frames by large iron nails driven from inboard. Luting made from

tightness of the plank seams

Fig. 6 Lyon, Parc Saint Georges. – Luting.

pitched fabric, which filled all of the plank seams provided for water tightness. Finally, the interior face of the planks was protected by a pitched coating (**Fig. 6**).

Group II

As the only representative of group II, wreck Ep. 8 shows a composite plank chine and flush-laid side planking. The flat bottom is laid by oak planks with bevelled edges. Oak frames are connected to the bottom planks by large iron nails driven from inboard. Outboard, the nails are single-clenched to the external face of the bottom planks. The flush-laid side planking consists of one oak strake fastened to the frames by large iron nails driven from inboard. As in the case of the wrecks of group I, the base of the side planking strake comes to overlap the edge of the bottom planking according to the system of the so-called »integrated« flat bottom. Likewise, in the plank seams pitched fabric occurs as luting material.

Further to such characteristics typical for group I and II vessels, other constructional details remain concentrated on individual wrecks, which are belonging to the one or other architectural group: bottom planking of wrecks Ep. 7 and Ep. 8 were pre-assembled by means of iron nails driven through tetrahedrical shaped notches tangentially into the edges of adjacent planks. Additionally, the bottom planking of wreck Ep. 8 was pre-assembled by un-pegged mortise-and-tenon joints scattered along the seams. As a unique feature, the seams of bottom and side planking of vessels Ep. 2 and Ep. 4 had been covered internally with lead ribbons, attached by nails. This method resembles caulking systems, e.g. the French palâtrage, using small timber battens, which are typical for inland shipbuilding.

How to interpret the characteristics of the shipwrecks found in Lyon, Parc Saint Georges, in terms of their meaning to the history of Romano-Celtic (or Gallo-Roman) tradition of »bottom-based« shipbuilding?

Fig. 7 Architectural fingerprints of the »Rhône-Saône« group: **1** Iron nail tangentially driven in the edges of the planks from tetrahedral sink. – **2** Mortise and un-pegged tenon. – **3** Lead strips internally nailed to bottom planking.

A REGIONAL GROUP OF »BOTTOM-BASED SHIPBUILDING«:
»THE RHÔNE-SAÔNE« GROUP?

In the most recent synthesis related to the »Romano-Celtic bottom-based shipbuilding« tradition, Frederick M. Hocker emphasizes the existence of regional groups. He writes: »these vessels fall into clear groups usually named for type vessels, based on configuration, shape and construction« (Hocker 2004: 67). Within the »Rhenish« group, Hocker distinguishes two sub groups, the one of Zwammerdam type, the other of Bevaix type, according to the polygonal shape of the hull and the orientation (axial or oblique) of the bottom planks (Hocker 2004: 68).

From an architectural point of view, characteristics of the Lyon Parc Saint Georges wrecks indicate the existence of regional shipbuilding procedures, limited to the Rhône-Saône river system. There are two features, most frequently attested as regional »ship-architectural fingerprints«: Firstly, the specific lower side strake of the Lyon, group I vessels consisting of one or two half-logs; secondly, the method to make ships watertight. For the latter it was carried out in all wrecks by means of pitched fabric, in particular found in the seams of bottom planking. This luting procedure, which appears very different from that considered as traditional of the »Romano-Celtic« barges[1], is attested by two further wrecks of the same hydrographical Rhône-Saône-area: the Place Tolozan wreck, in Lyon, excavated in 1990 (Becker & Rieth 1995; Rieth 1999), and the wreck found next to pile no. 3 of the Roman bridge of Chalon-sur-Saône (Saône-et-Loire) a few years later (Lonchambon 2000). Both are dated to the 1st c. A.D.

Two wrecks from Lyon Parc Saint Georges (**Fig. 7**) indicate the pre-assembly of the bottom planks, reflected by tangential nailing and edge-joining with mortises and un-pegged tenons. The same features are also met with the Place Tolozan wreck and the barge found in Chalon-sur-Saône. The use of lead strips nailed to the bottom seams of two of the wrecks from Lyon, Parc Saint Georges can be taken as another regional peculiarity of the hydrographical Rhône-Saône-area.

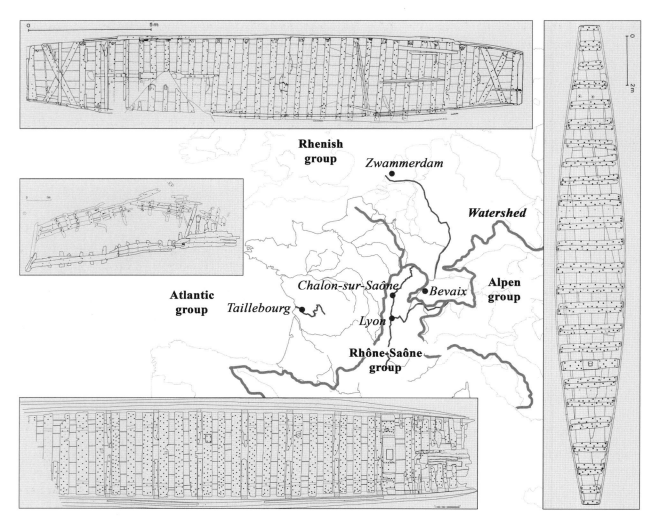

Fig. 8 Different regional groups of bottom-based shipbuilding: a proposal.

Some of these regional »fingerprints« seem to reflect an influence of ship-architectural practices specific to Mediterranean maritime shipyards. That might be true in the case of vessels, where mortises and un-pegged tenons occur, but also for the luting system of pitched cloth and nailed lead strips[2]. In which ways such an influence of Mediterranean maritime techniques would have reached the boatyards of the Rhône and Saône will be discussed in another place.

CONCLUSIONS

At the ISBSA 10 meeting in Roskilde, the hypothesis of an »Atlantic« group of bottom-based shipbuilding has been advanced in relation to the EP1-Taillebourg wreck, a late Roman barge found in the River Charente (Rieth 2006). By the six Gallo-Roman wrecks from Lyon, Parc Saint Georges, and two wrecks previously discovered in Lyon, Place Tolozan, and Chalon-sur-Saône[3], an additional regional group of the Gallo-Roman bottom-based shipbuilding tradition can be defined (**Fig. 8**). Further to the »Rhenish« and »Alpine« groups, the recent archaeological discoveries in France result in a more detailed geographical picture of ship architecture. Apparently, the grouping corresponds to the nautical conditions of ancient Gaul, as formed by its watershed system, but also to historical and cultural borders[4].

Vessels from the hydrographical Rhône-Saône-area reflect different regional practices of bottom-based shipbuilding, of which some might be influenced by techniques used from Mediterranean maritime shipyards. Thus, the Gallo-Roman wrecks from Lyon, Parc Saint Georges, suggest a more diversified and detailed perception of the bottom-based shipbuilding tradition than understood before. The fresh architectural scope resulting from the study of these river barges, indicates that the historical concept of bottom-based shipbuilding ought to be discussed again.

NOTES

1) Based on organic material (moss in general), fastened by series of small nails and additionally held in place by wooden laths: Arnold 1977.

2) On the subjects of assembly and caulking in particular as cultural based indications of technological transfer cf. Bockius 2002.

3) According to a paper given during ISBSA 11 (Long, Rival & Marlier, this volume pp. 277-287), a new Gallo-Roman wreck –

Arles-Rhône 3 – discovered in 2004 in the Rhône, in the city of Arles (Bouches-du-Rhône), could be added to the corpus.

4) It is interesting to note the correspondence between »bottom-based shipbuilding« of regional tradition attested by archaeological data of the »Rhône-Saône« area and Westerdahl's cartographical concept of »zone of transport«, no.17a including the Saône-Rhône river system (Westerdahl 1995: 227).

REFERENCES

Arnold, B., 1977, Some remarks on caulking in Celtic boat construction and its evolution in areas lying northwest of the Alpine arc. *IJNA*, 6.4, 293-297.

Ayala, G., 2004, Le port fluvial gallo-romain. *Archeologia*, 415, 38-39.

Ayala, G., Guyon M. & Laurent, L., 2005, Lyon Saint-Georges (France): la fouille d'une berge de Saône. In: H. Stoepker (ed.), *Archaeological Heritage Managment in riverine landscapes*. Rapportage Archeologische Monumentenzorg, no.126. Amersfoort, 89-94.

Ayala, G. & Horry, A., 2003, A l'époque de Louis XIV sur les rives de Saône. *Archeologia*, 403, 8-14.

Ayala, G., Horry, A. & Laurent, L. 2005, Au cœur de Lyon, mille ans de navigation fluviale. *Archeologia*, 419, 40-48.

Beaudouin, F., 2001, *Les bateaux garonnais. Essai de nautique fluviale (II)*. Les Cahiers du Musée de la Batellerie, 45. Conflans-Sainte-Honorine.

Becker, C. & Rieth, É., 1995, L'épave gallo-romaine de la place Tolozan à Lyon: un chaland à coque monoxyle-assemblée. *L'arbre et la forêt, le bois dans l'Antiquité*. Publication de la bibiothèque Salomon Reinach, Université Lumière-Lyon, no. 2. Lyon, 77-91.

Bockius, R., 2002, Abdichten, Beschichten, Kalfatern. Schiffsversiegelung und ihre Bedeutung als Indikator für Technologietransfers zwischen den antiken Schiffbautraditionen. *Jahrb. RGZM*, 49, 189-234.

Hocker, F. M., 2004, Bottom-based shipbuilding in Northwestern Europe. In: F. M. Hocker & C. Ward (eds), *The Philosophy of Shipbuilding. Conceptual Approaches to the Study of Wooden Ships*. College Station/Texas, 65-93.

Lonchambon, C., 2000, Un bateau monoxyle-assemblée à Chalon-sur-Saône (Ier siècle après J.-C.). In: L. Bonnamour (ed.), *Archéologie des fleuves et des rivières*. Paris, 174-178.

Rieth, É., 1999, L'épave gallo-romaine de la place Tolozan à Lyon (France). In: *TROPIS V*, 339-348.

2006, A preliminary report on the hull characteristics of the Gallo-Roman EP1-Taillebourg wreck (Charente-Maritime, France): archaeological evidence of regional practices of ancient flat-bottomed construction? In: *ISBSA 10*, 78-83.

Westerdahl, Ch., 1995, Traditional zones of transport geography in relation to ship types. In: O. Olsen, J. Skamby Madsen & F. Rieck (eds), *Shipshape. Essays for Ole Crumlin-Pedersen*. Roskilde, 213-230.

BÉAT ARNOLD

A GALLO-ROMAN NAVAL BUILDING YARD
AT AVENCHES/EN CHAPLIX

Planks intended for the construction of barges were found at the mouth of the port-canal, which linked Avenches (Aventicum, capital town of Roman Helvetia) to Lake Morat, as well as other elements, amongst which an inscription enables the probable identification of a boatyard located at a place called En Chaplix. The analysis of tool marks and traces of construction on these planks, similar to those found on planking of the Bevaix Gallo-Roman barge, tends to prove the existence of a shipyard, which used stocks for bottom-based ship building. What happened to these vessels after they were abandoned is also dealt with: the dismantling of boats and the different options to re-use the planking (building of new barges, embankment construction, storage of recycled timbers and perhaps firewood).

INTRODUCTION

The Roman town of Aventicum was founded shortly before Christ. It developed rapidly and by A.D. 70, the settlement received the status of colonia. Five kilometres of walls surrounded the town located in a short distance to Lake Morat and to neighbouring zones, which often were inundated.

The initial planning of the A1 motorway was slightly altered in order to preserve the area enclosed by the town wall[1]. Nonetheless, a large number of Roman remains were discovered, particularly at a place called En Chaplix, where a remarkable funerary and religious ensemble was uncovered, consisting of two large dismantled mausoleums (**Fig. 1**). Halfway towards the town, a watermill was found; it has been tree-ring dated to A.D. 57 to 58, and was abandoned around A.D. 80 (Castella 1994). Furthermore, one extremity of a canal made around A.D. 125 was uncovered closer to the lake.

The banks of the canal, measuring close to 800 m long by 7 m wide, were reinforced by planks upheld by posts, particularly numerous at both ends of the canal. It was restored several times up to A.D. 170 (Bonnet 1982). Prior to the construction of the canal, the lake had been filled up over a surface of 100 m by 30 to 35 m, forming some sort of quay with buildings dating to A.D. 5 to 6. These harbour installations were linked to the town by a straight road, which was bordered by a graveyard named Le Port, where chiefly cremation burials are found.

A remarkable feature of the graveyard was the large number of adult males buried there, probably men having worked in that particular area (Castella 1987). In one of the better preserved tombs, cremation tomb no. 3, bones were placed in an iron-clad wooden box that also contained a bent saw-blade, originally measuring 60 cm long, an adze and shears (Castella 1987: 51-55, pl. 38), rather than in a glass or ceramic urn. Excavation records of cremations practically always mention the presence of small nails. These were studied in detail to determine whether discarded boat planking and caulking were used as firewood for pyres. Quite a number of nails were found similar to those used on the Bevaix barge to keep the caulking in the cracks of planks, but they were of a kind also used in other fields. Nonetheless, only three specific large-headed nails were identified, of a type used to fasten caulking to the seams. The overall impression is that planking was not usually used for pyres except at one or two occasions at most. The »*bustum*« type cremation no. 36 containing 90 nails may be a prominent example. Finally, in some rare cases, a single large nail

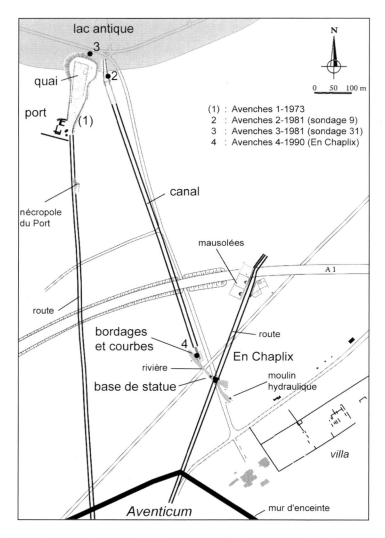

Fig. 1 Location map of the area between the town wall of *Aventicum* and Lake Morat with the find spots (1-4) of planks (After Bonnet 1982; Castella 1994; 1998).

similar to those used to assemble barges was found in the tombs. The hypothesis of D. Castella (1987: 32, note 202) is that of magical nails, also referred to by other authors.

Close to the road leading to the mausoleums, a remarkable monument was built in the 2nd c., lining the axis of the canal[2]. A large statue, of which nothing remains, had been raised on a 3.7 m high limestone column, on which an inscription was found dedicating the monument to both Neptune, god of the sea and terrestrial waters and protector of mariners, and to Silvanus, god of the forests and protector of woodcraft artisans. The monument had been built by Aprilis, an upper class slave belonging to C. Camillius Paterus, patron of one of the most influential families from the Helvetian aristocracy. A large villa located at a place called Russalet[3] no doubt belonged to him.

The reason why the canal ran halfway between the villa and the town could partly be answered by the location of the river and watermill. According to the published general plans of the area, it seems likely that the watercourse was diverted into the canal to keep it clean and prevent it from silting up.

REMAINS OF A BOATYARD

The question relating to the existence of a naval building yard at the top S. end of the canal was raised when isolated pieces of wood were discovered and studied on the site, supported by the remarkable inscription on the monumental column. The topography of the site appears ideal to establish a boatyard: large open space, a road nearby allowing planks and other wood material to be transported for boat construction, although they could have been shipped across the lake also. Finally, with the proximity of Aventicum and its specialised workshops (e.g. forges) and traders, a boatyard[4] would have found the necessary infrastructure to develop.

There was no need first to level down ground in order to establish the building yard as barges were assembled on horizontal stocks. In time, the ground would have been covered with tons of wood-chips from boat construction keeping the yard dry and free of mud. The neighbourhood to the town, where the demand for fuel (for cooking and heating) and wood for building as well was doubtless substantial, might have promoted a new market for recycled chips and other waste of wood. The building of a full-scale replica of the Gallo-Roman boat of Bevaix, named *Altaripa,* exellently illustrates the amount of waste produced during construction. From 64.8 tons of raw oak material at the beginning, the boat when launched weighed a mere 7 tons (Arnold 1999). Thus the offcut quantity was still sufficient to build a small house and a forge.

Amongst the wood found in the central part of the S. end of the canal, two large planks are worth mentioning (**Figs 2-3**). One had the right measurements to have been used as a boat plank (nos 1990-2). This plank seems to have been assembled initially to form the bottom of a barge, but was almost immediately removed as no marks of fastening nails are visible. The other plank also had been part of the planking of an abandoned boat. On it, some 50 holes are discernible, caused by nails. When the vessel was dismantled, nails were extracted, and the holes subsequently concealed by small square treenails (nos 1990-1), allowing the plank to be re-used on a new barge. These two timbers obviously have been stored in the canal, doubtless to protect them from drying out and from harmful insects, much longer than initially intended.

Other relics of planking and frames, found at the W. bank of the harbour-canal (**Fig. 4**) may be interpreted as stock material stored on a foundation made up of four planks. These artefacts clearly demonstrate the existence of a boatyard, as per the inscription on the limestone column, but reveal only just a small part of the building activities that took place. With regard to the needs of the capital city it seems probable that a number of barges were built simultaneously, possibly up to a few dozens at a time.

BEGINNING AND END OF A BARGE

The recycled planking from Avenches-En Chaplix and the remains of the Gallo-Roman Bevaix barge were built mostly of oak trees, with those from the Bevaix wreck felled in A.D. 182. They show distinctive regional features common to later barges, which were built around the lakes of Neuchâtel, Bienne and Morat, and the River Aar. In fact, the existence of a separate region more S. with its own ship architecture was identified with the remarkable discovery of the of the Gallo-Roman vessels in Lyon, Parc Saint-Georges from 2002 to 2004. The use of composite chine-girders with the bottom of the sides made up of slightly fashioned resinous half logs is characteristic. Unused round treenails found on both the Bevaix barge and the Yverdon-2 boat (Arnold 1992a: 81-94; 1992b: 26-27) show that they had been assembled on stocks, the treenails temporarily fixing the planking whilst frames have been nailed. This type of assembly was missing on the Yverdon-1 barge.

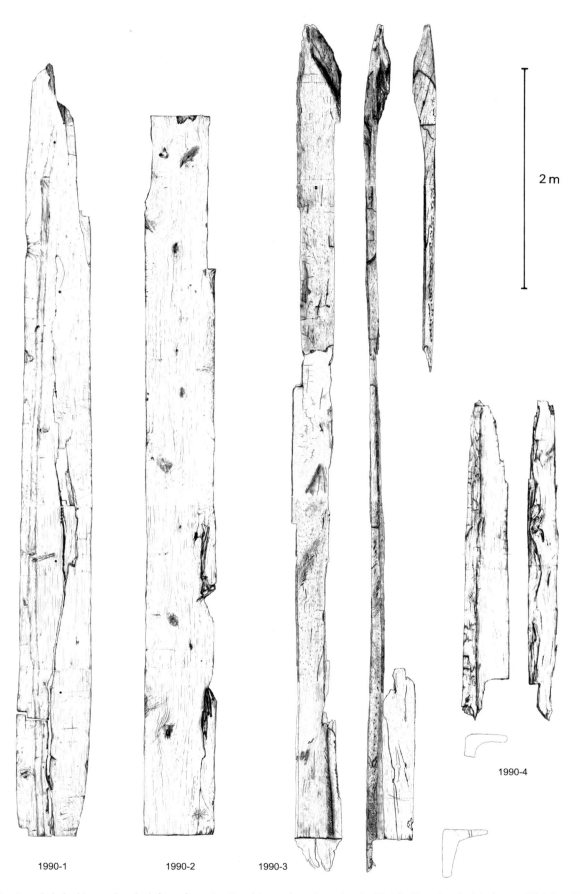

Fig. 2 Recycled planking and a plank free of constructional traces from Avenches-En Chaplix (Drawing Archéodunum; Béat Arnold).

1990-1

1990-2

1990-3

1990-4

2 m

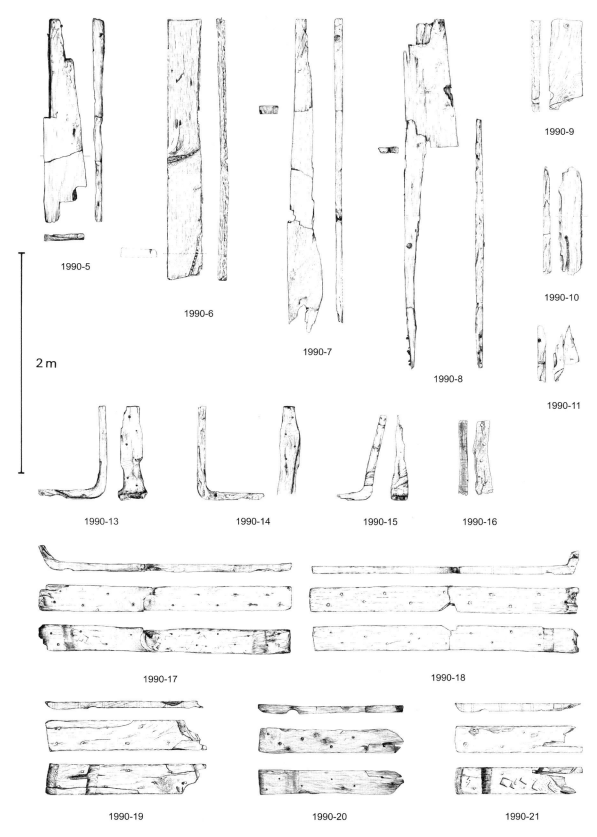

2 m

1990-5

1990-6

1990-7

1990-8

1990-9

1990-10

1990-11

1990-13

1990-14

1990-15

1990-16

1990-17

1990-18

1990-19

1990-20

1990-21

Fig. 3 Knee fragments discovered at the S. end of the harbour-canal (Drawing Archéodunum).

Fig. 4   Platform built with recycled parts of a barge. On the left, a spoon-shaped chine-girder fragment is visible (Objects 1990-3; photo Daniel Castella).

On the other hand, similar features were found on both the recycled planking from Avenches-En Chaplix and the after portside chine-girder of the Bevaix barge (Arnold 1992a: 92-93). In the latter case, there were two series of round treenails: one in line with the treenails, which have been used to assemble the barge; the other corresponding to those used to assemble the previous boat, which was discarded later. On the same plank, a number of small squared treenails were detected that concealed holes caused by the extracted nails. Similar treenails were found on the recycled planking from Avenches-En Chaplix and plank C of the Bevaix barge (**Fig. 5**). As there was no further series of round treenails on the latter plank, an alternative technique fixing only the chine-girders but not the bottom planking, might have been chosen initially.

All these elements suggest the presence of a common practice employed when vessels had been dismantled. This technique was still widely used during the 19th c. on many lakes and rivers to save wood for small needs or as extra building material. In France, one would talk of boats being »torn apart«. Whether by chance or not, one of the few nail extractors, with a large notch on its base conceived to remove large nails, was discovered at the end of the harbour-canal (Duvauchelle 2005: pl. 18-19).

CONCLUSIONS

The Avenches-En Chaplix boatyard was identified thanks to a number of minor and more significant elements, mainly an area to store undressed wood underwater, specifically recycled ready-to-use planks, and

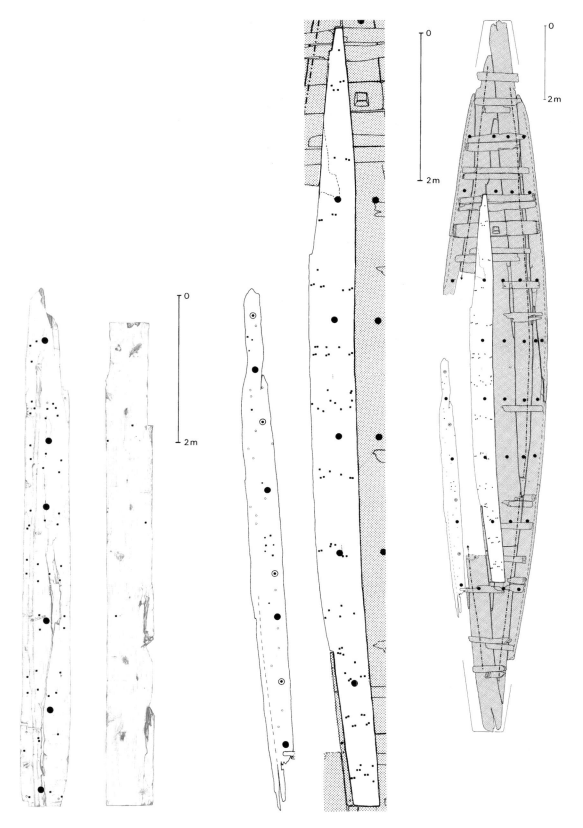

Fig. 5 Recycled planking from Avenches-En Chaplix and of the Bevaix Gallo-Roman barge (Arnold 1992a: 92-93). The round treenails provided to fix the bottom planking on the stocks. The squared treenails filling in the holes left when the fastening nails were removed during dismantling of the boat.

the inscription mentioning Neptunus and Silvanus; an important monument would not have been erected just for the construction of a few isolated boats. In other circumstances, it is difficult or impossible to identify such sites as usually little evidence is available to prove activities that took place.

The temporary assembly of planks on stocks was a common technique confirmed by the presence of round or square treenails found on barges where they no longer served a purpose. These were used to steady the planking until frames were being fixed. They are also an important element to prove that watercraft had been dismantled, and that the less worn planks were put aside for new constructions.

Another inscription discovered at Avenches indicates the existence of a corporation of watermen on the River Aar. Apart from the boat construction itself, much more is involved in a boatyard, namely the activity of a whole population; shipping consumes goods and, in the case of Avenches, many thousand tons of stone, transported from the N. shores of Lake Neuchâtel, were needed to build houses, monuments and the town wall of the Roman Helvetian capital.

INVENTORY

All wooden artefacts (**Figs 2-3**) are made of oak.

Avenches 1990-1 (B-271): recycled plank (7.02 m long; 60 to 65 cm wide), showing a draining-groove, which suddenly curves 1 m from the end of the plank, probably on the spot of the uprising ship bottom. Six round treenails are located lengthwise, the first one found 23 cm from the preserved end of the plank, the others are distant one from the other at 1.07, 1.21, 1.37, 1.09 and 1.36 m. A group of almost 50 small square treenails fill up the holes made when the fastening nails were extracted from the previous barge. It had probably been assembled on stocks, the plank temporarily treenailed prior to the final nailing of the frames. Thus prepared, the plank was ready for use on a new construction. Apparently raw material. – Avenches 1990-2 (B-270): complete plank, 6.54 cm long and 60 to 61 cm wide, part of a strake. On one extremity, four square treenails and a scarf on one of the edges show that the plank was fitted when the bottom of a barge was assembled, but then shortly removed as there is no trace of fastening nails. Apparently raw material. – Avenches 1990-3 (B-111a+b): spoon-shaped section of a chine-girder from the fore port side or aft starboard. Preserved length 7.69 m; width 32 cm. – Avenches 1990-4 (B-111c): fragment of a chine-girder, 2.93 m long, lengthwise split, with a scarf to fit another chine-girder segment. – Avenches 1990-5 (B-106): bottom plank with one preserved end. Preserved length 1.85 m; max. width 37 cm. – Avenches 1990-6 (B-110): plank fragment with a knot and caulking in a crack. Length 2.33 m; width 32 cm. – Avenches 1990-7 (B-95): long triangular shaped plank fragment. Preserved length 2.83 m; max. width 0.30 m. The narrow part is fixed with a large nail driven at right angles into the plank edge prior to the fitting of the next plank. – Avenches 1990-8 (B-101): plank with a narrow end. The end measures 2.01 m long and max.0.19 m wide; total length preserved 3.18 m; width 0.46 m. The narrow shape is underlined by a strong large headed nail driven from outside. – Avenches 1990-9 (B-904): extremity of a plank. Preserved length 82 cm; width 30 cm. – Avenches 1990-10 (B-108): plank fragment with a caulked crack. Preserved length 98 cm; width 21 cm. – Avenches 1990-11: shapeless planking fragment with a large nail driven into the plank's edge. Size: 52 cm to 24 cm. – Avenches 1990-12: extremity of a plank. Size: 30 cm and 13 cm. – Avenches 1990-13 (B-109a): knee with the vertical section, at right angles, complete (max. height 85 cm). – Avenches 1990-14 (B-109b): knee with the vertical section, at right angles, complete (max. height 86 cm). – Avenches 1990-15 (B-115): knee with the vertical section, at an angle of 102°, and a horizontal section (preserved height, at right angles of the bottom 77 cm). – Avenches 1990-16 (B-116): vertical section of a knee (height 68 cm). – Avenches 1990-17 (B-90+103): knee with a horizontal part/floor timber, complete (bottom length 2.15 m), with two limber holes. The lower end of the vertical section forms an angle of 114°. – Avenches 1990-18 (B-102): horizontal section of a knee/floor timber, incomplete (a single limber hole). Preserved length 2.37 m. – Avenches 1990-19 (B-98): extremity of the horizontal section of a knee/floor-timber. Preserved length 1.42 m. – Avenches 1990-20 (B-97): extremity of the horizontal section of a knee/floor-timber. Preserved length 1.28 m. – Avenches 1990-21 (B-107): extremity of the horizontal section of a knee/floor-timber. Preserved length 1.42 m.

ACKNOWLEDGEMENTS

The Avenches-En Chaplix excavation was part of the project »RN1 excavation – Archéologie cantonale vaudoise; commission Archéodunum SA, director Daniel Castella«. – The author sincerely thanks Anne Hochuli-Gysel, curator of the Roman Museum of Avenches. He is particularly grateful to Daniel Castella, archaeologist, for his useful comments, to render archaeological data from the excavations accessible and, not at least for requesting the author to observe and study all material relevant to naval constructions as they were being discovered, and for allowing the recording of all the constructional details even before objects were going into conservation.

Translation by Dominique Robert Bliss

NOTES

1) Much has been published on the town wall but the main source for the data presented here is taken from Castella 1998.

2) It is not possible to give a precise tree-ring dating of the supporting base of the construction as the trees were felled in young age.

3) Outside the area concerned by the roadworks.

4) Whose activities do not leave much evidence behind.

REFERENCES

Arnold, B., 1992a, *Batellerie gallo-romaine sur le lac de Neuchâtel*, vol 1. Archéologie Neuchâteloise, no. 12. Saint-Blaise.

1992b, *Batellerie gallo-romaine sur le lac de Neuchâtel*, vol. 2. Archéologie Neuchâteloise, no. 13. Saint-Blaise.

1999, *Altaripa: archéologie expérimentale et architecture navale gallo-romaine*. Archéologie Neuchâteloise, no. 25. Neuchâtel.

Bonnet, F., 1982, *Le canal romain d'Avenches. Rapport sur les fouilles exécutées en 1980 et 1981*. Bulletin de l'Association Pro Aventico, no. 27. Avenches.

Castella, D., 1987, *La nécropole du Port d'Avenches*. Cahiers d'archéologie romande, 41. Lausanne.

1994, *Le moulin hydraulique gallo-romain d'Avenches »En Chaplix ». Fouilles 1990-1991*. Cahiers d'Archéologie Romande, 62. Lausanne.

1998, *Aux portes d'Aventicum. Dix ans d'archéologie autoroutière à Avenches*. Documents du Musée Romain d'Avenches, no. 4. Avenches.

Castella, D. & Flutsch, L., 1990, Avenches VD. Une inscription inédite en Chaplix. *Archéologie Suisse* 13.4, 185-186.

Duvauchelle, A., 2005, *Les outils en fer du Musée Romain d'Avenches*. Documents du Musée Romain d'Avenches, no. 11. Avenches.

WALDEMAR OSSOWSKI

THE ORIGINS OF FLAT-BOTTOMED RIVER CRAFT ON THE ODRA AND VISTULA CATCHMENTS

In the existing Polish publications devoted to inland watercraft it is the logboat and the raft that were considered as the earliest watercraft sailing in the Odra and Vistula river basin (Smolarek 1985; Litwin 1995). Through centuries they underwent an evolution marked both by development of the boat and the raft and by their mutual interaction (**Fig. 1**). Therefore, inland watercraft were formed in the following development line: logboat – plank-built boat – river craft, or raft – raft-shaped craft – pointed-bow craft, with possible crossings between those lines (Smolarek 1985). The craft formed as a result of those transformations underwent in turn further evolution. It is emphasized that in the course of those transformations the silhouettes and structures of the gradually developing cargo ships were influenced by such factors as the nature of water conditions, abundance of excellent boatbuilding material, technological level, organizational forms of inland navigation and the type of transport needs at specific stages of its development. As no wrecks have been found, which could illustrate the transformations in river boatbuilding, this purely theoretical evolutional pattern has been based mainly on the numerous iconographic images of Vistula river craft from the 16th to the 18th c. (Smolarek 1985). The views concerning the origin of river craft were also significantly affected by etymological and lexicological studies of linguists basing on numerous noted names of watercraft occurring in the Polish language area and in the dialects of the Vistula river basin. Such terms are for instance *komięga* and *dubas*, often noted in Old Polish as of the 16th c., but also very popular in Russian and Ukrainian meaning both a logboat and paired logboats, and a vessel used for grain floating at a later time.

In this evolutional approach the route of development from a logboat to a flat-bottomed plank-built craft led through bottom extension. The process consisted in pairing two logboats whose two adjacent sidewalls

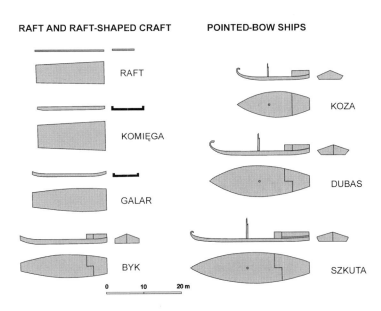

RAFT AND RAFT-SHAPED CRAFT POINTED-BOW SHIPS

RAFT

KOMIĘGA

GALAR

BYK

KOZA

DUBAS

SZKUTA

0 10 20 m

Fig. 1 Silhouettes of different river craft types in Poland (According P. Smolarek 1985).

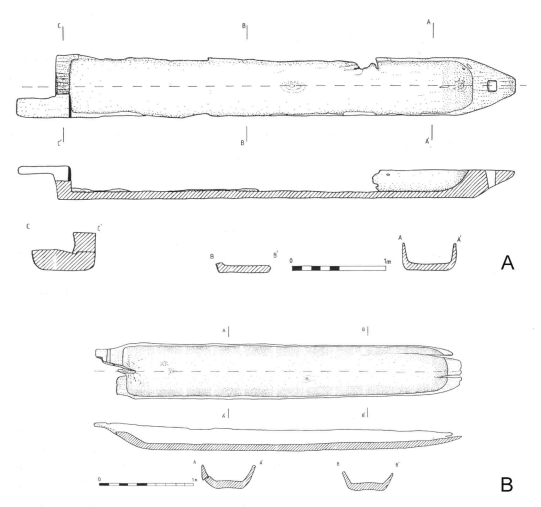

Fig. 2 Bronze Age logboats: **A** Pinczów, dated after 1220 B.C. – **B** Trzcianka, radiocarbon dating 14th to 6th c. B.C.

were removed and the bottom was joined by an additional plank placed in the middle. With time, strake planks were attached to the sides or a plank structure was used instead of extreme logboat sections. Only one example of such an artefact is known among the old boatbuilding artefacts originating in Poland. It is a logboat extended by a plank which was used on the San River in the 20th c. in the locality of Majdan Zbidniowski (Litwin 1985: 328).

LOGBOATS

The most numerous categories of sources for studies on old river craft in the Odra and Vistula river basin are logboats (Ossowski 1999). In the course of inventory works covering logboats from the area of Poland that have been conducted over ten years, information about 218 logboats were gathered. From these, the age of 124 artefacts was determined by absolute dating methods, 13 artefacts were dated by archaeological methods, whilst the chronology of just 39 objects remained undefined. As could be shown, most of the examined logboats from Poland originate in the medieval period and in the modern times. Hence, there is not too much to say about the use of logboats from earlier periods. As much as 37 vessels are ethnographic artefacts – as it should be remembered that the tradition of building boats of such type has survived on the Bug River to date. The number of logboats from Polish territory is supplemented by numerous archival data about artefacts that were lost during World War II, the number of which is also considerable. Significant objects for consideration on the origin of watercraft appear to be extended logboats, which can be interpreted as transitory before plank-built craft started to be made. The records include many paired logboats, however there are fewer examples of logboats with side planking.

The earliest examples of paired logboats are two middle and late Bronze Age finds (**Fig. 2**). Oak hulls with a rectangular or trapezoid cross section, without bulkheads show sterns with blunt-ending overhangs. Those vessels were made in such a way so as to ensure the largest loading capacity and accommodate several 100 kg of cargo. The one discovered in Pińczów, was used for water transport on the Nida River, whereas there is no information about the other logboat from the collection of the Trzcianka Museum, although the place of discovery might be related to the Noteć River.

The Trzcianka logboat has a hollowed-out groove with a trapezoid cross-section on the upper stern over-hang surface – a detail that is noted in paired logboats from the 1st c. A.D. from the Upper Odra River (**Fig. 3**). Three oak dugouts used for pairing are preserved. There are no close similarities of these Odra river vessels to logboats known from the adjacent areas. Archives are telling about numerous discoveries of similar artefacts from that area suggesting that such logboats were very common (Hellmich 1912; 1919). However, all these discovered at the turn of the 19th and 20th c. were lost during World War II. Research conducted on similar boats in Lewin Brzeski and in the Archaeological Museum in Kraków in the 1990s provided the opportunity to look anew at this specific group of logboats (Ossowski 1999).

All the discussed artefacts share large dimensions (more than 10 m long) and a similarity of boatbuilding methods. The Lewin type logboats are characterized by a small height of sides limited by the use of a log, torn in half to build them. Theoretically, by employing such boatbuilding techniques it was possible to obtain two twin hulls from one log. In case of paired logboats this technique had the advantage that it facilitated later the ability to pair similar hulls, which were identical in length and had been obtained from one log. A huge log was split in half in such a way that it retained the conic parent log shape when viewed from above. Afterwards the lower log section was cut down to make the bottom flat and the sides were formed to obtain a trapezoid cross-section.

Typical for the dugouts from Lewin and Kraków is a smooth transition of the bottom into flat stern and bow overhangs, a feature that distinguishes such logboats from those described by Hellmich, all the more because the drawings of which are characterized by simplifications and a schematic approach to details. The presence of transverse hollows, which accommodated triangular planks, must be a trace of hollowed-out hulls, which were joined to form pairs. Such a way of pairing was noted in case of the logboat excavated in the Odra near Roszowicki Las (Ellmers 1973: 31; Paret 1931: 99-103).

Round or close to rectangular holes found in the boat ends may have served both for mooring or towing as well as to fasten fittings for steering and navigating. Most probably they were used to tie additional strengthening elements that join single hulls into a raft and reinforce the whole structure. The discussed boats were discovered in the Celtic area of Poland, which was inhabited by Przeworsk culture peoples in the first centuries A.D.

Important transport routes ran through that area and intense economic progress was traced manifesting itself, inter alia, in the form of highly developed metallurgy. The Przeworsk culture is known for their trading with Celtic and Italic centres, and at a later time, with Roman provinces and the neighbouring peoples, where amber trading was of great importance. Logboats of such type could serve for carrying even large cargos. The calculated load capability of the Lewin I logboat was 640 kg with a draught of 10 cm, and up to 1600 kg with a draught of 20 cm.

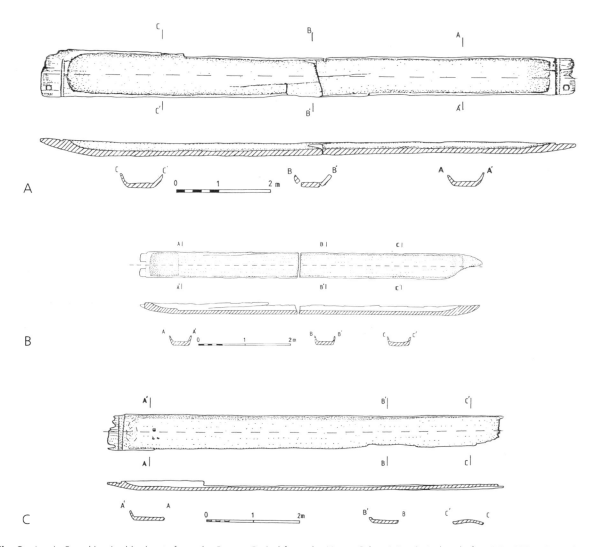

Fig. 3 Lewin Brzeski paired logboats from the Roman Period from the Upper Odra: **A** Lewin I, dated after A.D. 372. – **B** Lewin II, dated after A.D. 418. – **C** Kraków, radiocarbon dating 4th c. B.C. to A.D. 2nd c.

Subsequent finds of paired logboats were noted on Polish territory from the medieval period. The earliest paired logboats of such type are dated to the 10th c., the period of the beginnings of the formation of the first Polish state of the Piast dynasty; the latest originate from the 14th c. They were made from large oak tree trunks mainly by hollowing out the inside, which gave them a semicircular trunk-shaped cross-section, preventing them from floating on their own (Ossowski 1999: 104-112). These logboats were 7 to 15.6 m long (**Fig. 4**). It has been calculated that a 10 m long logboat from the Szczecin Museum's collection could carry approx. 3 tons of cargo at a draught of 45 cm and a freeboard of 15 cm (Szymczak 1997). Such vessels were without bulkheads, and the roughly shaped hull at the outside showed bough remains, which were difficult to remove. The stern ends were often closed by transoms. At the side edges there were openings used for forming a raft. Some of them had also bore holes for calibration indicating that boat builders endeavoured to obtain the smallest possible side thickness, the purpose of which must have been to decrease the boat's weight. The sides were so thin with respect to the height that it became necessary to reinforce the hulls with frames. Such logboats were discovered in the Vistula River and its tributaries, i.e. the

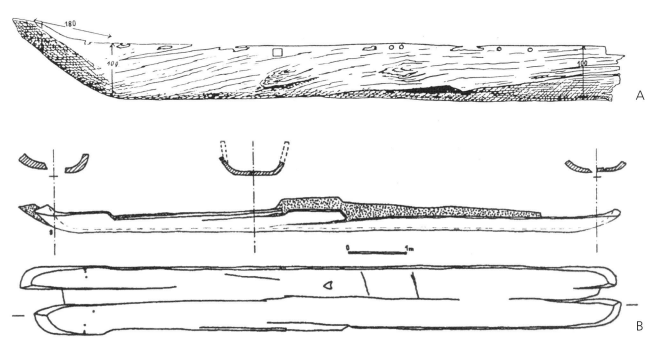

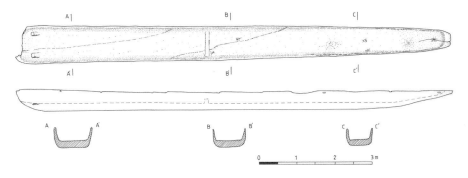

Fig. 4 Paired logboats from the early medieval period: **A** Nowa Cerkiew, dated to A.D. 959 (After Krieg 1933). – **B** Szczecin, radiocarbon dating 9th to 11th c. (After Szymczak 1997).

Fig. 5 Logboat from Machów dendro-chronologically dated after A.D. 1568.

rivers Bug, the Narew and the Pisa. Two similar finds, which have not been preserved, from the early 20th c. originate from the Upper Odra at Wróblin and Wrocław-Osobowice (Hellmich 1912: 19-21). The existence of such a type of watercraft is also confirmed by a customs tariff for Szczecin published around A.D. 1255, wherein *navis que dicitur gewerdebordeth* and *navis simplex sine borth* is mentioned, interpreted as modified logboats, and a *navis linguata* which is understood as »paired« logboats (Mielcarek 1981).

Dugouts continued to be joined to larger watercraft until modern times. The artefacts preserved in Polish museums show that they were carefully shaped, with trapezoid cross-sections. A 16th c. logboat, 11.67 m long, discovered in 1955 during the cleaning of the River Vistula near Machów may serve as example (**Fig. 5**). The openings at the upper side edges suggest that the Machów vessel has been part of a larger craft intended to perform floating or barge functions (Ossowski 1999: 156-157). The tradition of making

Fig. 6 13th c. wreck from Kobyla Kępa during investigation in 2000.

such crafts continued to the recent times. The most recent vessels made of dugouts were used in the Pieniny Mountains up to the late 1960s (Litwin 1995: 60-63).

Less numerous are findings of extended logboats with frames and additional planking. Further to the destroyed artefact from Gdańsk, Królik bastion (Conwentz 1898), the best known proof of that type is a 14th c. logboat discovered at the waterfront of a medieval town in Kołobrzeg (Polak 1998).

The abundance of excellent raw-material is surely one of the main reasons why paired logboats belong to the most numerously representatives of watercraft serving to float goods downstream or to transport them across the river since the Bronze Age to recent times, discovered in Poland. No special skills were required to make relatively simple inland craft of such a type. It is known that in modern times it was a domain of the rural and small town population, where such vessels were built by carpenters to gain additional income. The craft usually made a journey only downstream, where timbers were sold as fire wood after the freight had been unloaded. Their deadweight capacity was limited by the trunk size, though some logboats longer than 15 m could carry substantial quantities of goods.

BARGES

The earliest remains of flat-bottomed river craft from the Lower Vistula River originate in the 13th c. Archaeological discoveries from Poland and the preserved iconographic sources show that specific types of vessels adapted for navigation on the Upper Vistula, the Vistula Bay and coastal waters were built in the late Middle Ages.

There is evidence of five wrecks and numerous other sources of boatbuilding activities from the 13th to the 16th c. (Ossowski 2004a-b). The best preserved ship was discovered near Elbląg in 1920 (Ehrlich & Steegmann 1923). Similar ship finds are a 13th c. wreck from Kobyla Kępa (**Fig. 6**), a 14th c. wreck from Gdańsk-Green Gate (Ossowski & Kościński 2003), two wrecks from the vicinity of Elbląg (Salemke 1973), and numerous finds of isolated boatbuilding elements from the city of Elbląg and the River Elbląg. The archaeological sources are supplemented by two images of river craft from other cities located on the Lower Vistula: Kwidzyn and Toruń (**Fig. 7**).

The characteristic features of those ships are mostly a flat, keelless bottom, which clearly points to river craft. Their narrow silhouettes running into a more or less sharp bow, and a lengthwise bent bottom were to decrease the hull's resistance in water, i.e. to increase speed on rivers with slower currents. Owing to their curves, properties and type of propulsion those ships could navigate both down and up the river.

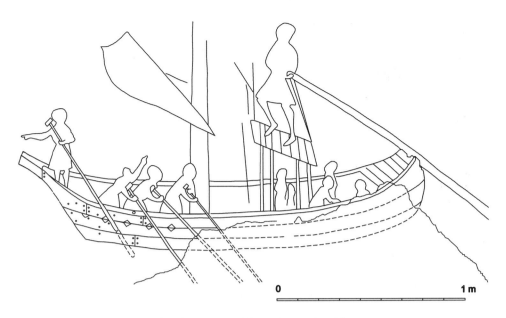

Fig. 7 River craft from the 15th c. fresco in Toruń (Drawing A. Piasecki).

The intersection between the bottom and the side was formed by grooved timbers with an »L« cross-section, which formed the chine. Such a solution strengthened the whole structure lengthwise and ensured better hull tightness at the transition of bottom to sides. The longer side section of the profiles parted at an angle of 120° in relation to the bottom. Chine planks were flush-laid to the bottom strakes and fastened by pinewood pegs, which have been inserted diagonally to the floor timber edge.

The bow of such ships usually shows an inclined stem post, e.g. a wreck found at Elbląg from about A.D. 1500. However, a similar stem from the early 14th c. was discovered during dredging works in the River Elbląg. Inclined stems are also seen on the images of ships depicted on church frescos in Kwidzyn and Toruń: one has been propelled by a square sail hoisted on a mast, which was set in a rectangular mast step relatively distant from the forward end.

The planking of those ships was caulked by means of iron staples (*sintels*), which fastened wooden laths fixing moss, i.e. a procedure unknown in that area earlier. The *sintels* from the wrecks in question correspond to the types described by Karel Vlierman (1996). The earliest finds of *sintels* from Poland were discovered during archaeological investigations conducted in Elbląg, where fragments of planking and floor timber reused for padding a yard's ground were discovered (**Fig. 8**). Those remains, which are dated to the years between 1239 and 1280, are similar to the staples of the Kobyla Kępa and Gdańsk-Green Gate wrecks. The latter correspond to D1 and D2 type *sintels* originating from wrecks dated for the years 1275 to 1325. Type C and D *sintels* are commonly and in large quantities found in the layers of medieval Baltic Hanseatic towns in Poland, e.g. in Elbląg, Gdańsk, Szczecin, and Kołobrzeg. Earlier single ones were discovered in the early medieval city layers in Gdańsk from the turn of the 12th and 13th c., probably relicts of Lübeck merchantmen, which were repaired in Gdańsk.

Similar finds are known from Szczecin (Filipowiak 1996). At the Vistula estuary *sintel* caulking disappeared during the 16th c., whereas at the Upper Vistula and the River San the tradition survived in small boats and barges up to now (Litwin 1995: 83-95). 18th c. authors mention that staples were used on the Upper Odra and Vistula (Hoyer 1793), however artefacts are still to be found as yet.

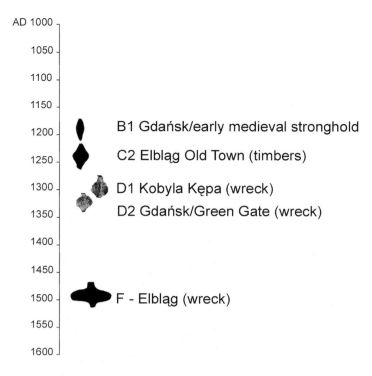

AD 1000
1050
1100
1150
1200   **B1 Gdańsk/early medieval stronghold**
1250   **C2 Elbląg Old Town (timbers)**
1300   **D1 Kobyla Kępa (wreck)**
1350   **D2 Gdańsk/Green Gate (wreck)**
1400
1450
1500   **F - Elbląg (wreck)**
1550
1600

Fig. 8   Types of *sintels* from the Lower Vistula.

As shown by dendrochronological analysis, most of the ships were made from various trees growing in the same period, and that the timber was transported to the ship yards from various, possibly very distant regions (Ossowski & Krąpiec 2001). Differences chiefly concern the side planking: in the case of all of the Gdańsk-Green Gate ship strakes, and certainly in the case of the chine strake of the Kobyla Kępa, wreck planks were flush-laid, whereas the Elbląg ship strakes were overlapping conventionally, reversely the top strake.

The use of those watercraft might have been related to the economic and social conditions of the Lower Vistula area in the 13th c., when the state of the Teutonic Knights was established and new urban centres appeared. Long-distance trade played an important role in the economic development of cities such as Elbląg and Toruń. Its heyday was related to the extensive resource background of the Prussian cities spread over Poland, Slovakia and Russia. Agency in barter exchange between those areas and W. Europe became the basis of the economic position of those cities in the Middle Ages. From the end of the 13th c. and in the 14th c. the major Hanseatic trading centre on the Lower Vistula was Elbląg. The dynamically developing trade required the port and its facilities to be developed and appropriate boats and ships to be built in order to ensure transport from the hinterland to allow deliveries of goods and products. In the social and economic history of the Polish Kingdom of the 16th to the 18th c. cargo transport on the Vistula was of great importance (Smolarek 1985).

Similar ships could be used on the Lower Odra section, however the only evidences of that are large river craft in the customs tariff of Szczecin from 1255 (*navis que vocantur bordinc*: Mielcarek 1981) and 14th c. images of a ship on the Goleniów seal, a Hanseatic town located at the navigable River Ina, one of the right tributaries to the Odra.

Unfortunately, there is not any substantial find of ships from that period, apart from two decorated stems found in the Vistula region at Kazimierz Dolny and Sandomierz. On the basis of numerous iconographic images and historical documents, it is known that the largest and most popular craft was the Vistula *scuta* (**Fig. 9**). Her sides were made from six to eight overlapping strakes sticking outside to a considerable extent. Equipped with a solid stem post, which at the top often was decorated with religious emblems, the narrowing hull at the stern was closed with a transom adjoined by a superstructure, which was placed in the stern section containing the skipper's room. The ship was driven by oars from up to 20 oarsmen, and by a square rig. Her rudder with a large pole was operated by a helmsman standing on top the superstructure roof or, more often, a special scaffold.

Similar but smaller craft built in E. provinces were called *dubas*. Raft-derivative craft continued to be used in river freight floating including *komięga* (by the end of the 18th c.) or *galar*, which locally existed, even still in the 20th c.

The Odra as a transport route encountered considerable difficulties to the same degree as the Vistula. It was a river winding in many sections, often changing its course, and navigation was hindered by various

Fig. 9 Engravings showing the *scuta* manoeuvring in Gdańsk harbour (After A. Dickmann 1617).

water damming structures, which often had too narrow passages for ships or did not have any passages at all. A factor considerably limiting the river transport were customs duties and also the storage rights granted in the 13th c. to the towns of Szczecin, Frankfurt and Wrocław. They started to be abolished as late as in the 18th c., when hydraulic works facilitating navigation were commenced on a larger scale.

An important element affecting the development of inland navigation was the building of canals connecting the Odra with Elbe and Vistula. The Finowski Canal between Odra and River Hawela was built from 1744 to 1746. In 1774 Bydgoszcz Canal was inaugurated which connected Vistula and Odra through the rivers Brda, Noteć and Warta. Canals constructed at a later time connected Vistula and Dnepr (Royal Canal), and Vistula and Niemen respectively.

Records on Odra river craft by the second half of the 18th c. are scarce. Sources related to navigation include some ship names: *Scutha, Schiff, Pram, Schale, Kahn, Oderkahn*. Either barges with a stem post and a stern transom and slender boats and ships known in Polish literature as *odraks,* or *odrzaks* (German: *Oderkahn*) navigated on the Odra in the 17th and 18th c. These were particularly useful in navigation on rivers and canals because of certain characteristics: their strong hull, relatively small width and parallel sides facilitated canal navigation and against the current. Ships ends were made of bottom planks bent upwards, so-called *kaf*. Bow and stern *kafs* of late 18th c. *odraks* each shared a length-ratio of about 30 % of the total ship length (Mielcarek 1974).

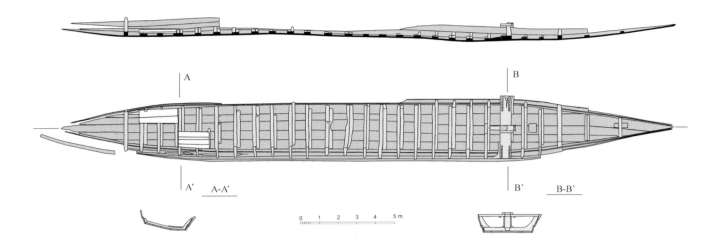

Fig. 10   18th c. wreck from Krosno Odrzańskie.

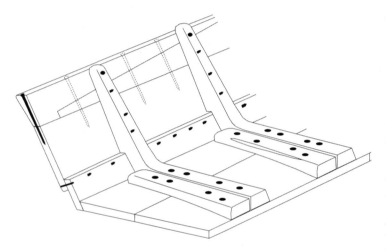

Fig. 11   Construction features of the flat-bottomed ship from Krosno Odrzańskie przekrój.

The only wreck of this type was discovered in 2003 in Krosno Odrzańskie, on the left bank of the Odra, not far from the old Bóbr river mouth to the Odra (Ossowski 2004a-b). The hull was 34.3 m long and 3.6 m wide (**Fig. 10**). In a horizontal projection the ship was characterized by narrow proportions, a spindle-shaped ground-plan, with a pointed, elongated bow and stern. In a lengthwise projection the craft was characterized by a positive sheer, even in the stern and bow sections. No traces of stem joinery were observed from the remains, indicating the existence of kaf-construction.

The slightly inclined sides were formed by three to four flush-laid strakes, overlapping except for the first and second strake. Two bottom strakes, made of oak-wood were joined to each other by inwards hooked iron nails. Nails of the same type were also used to fasten the 2nd to 4th side strakes to the frames. The top strake was made of pinewood and its thickness increased from 7 cm at the lower edge to 14 cm at the top edge. Such a profile fulfilled the role of an additional stringer to reinforce the side edge. The sides were additionally reinforced by metal bolts hammered vertically across the strakes (**Fig. 11**).

In the Krosno Odrzańskie wreck a caulking method was used different from other Vistula river craft of the 13th to the 16th c. The seams of side planking were covered by laths fastened by small nails to a hallowed groove, which was caulked with soaked fabric. A similar way of caulking was observed in the wreck of a 19th c. lighter discovered in the Gdańsk Bay. Scarce remains of river craft show that the method was also known on Odra and Vistula in the 18th and 19th c. The earliest example of such technique revealed in Gdańsk from underwater structures of the 16th c. (Owsianowska 2003: 341). Further investigations are required to clarify the issue whether this procedure replaced the above mentioned *sintel* technique disappearing in the 16th c. and when exactly it started to become widespread.

The position of the mast step was near to the bow. A characteristic feature of *odraks*, either found with the Krosno Odrzańskie wreck was one mast set in the crafts fore section – usually at 1/3 of the length from the bow. Contrary to the square sail typical for Elbe and Vistula barges in the 18th c., according to iconographic sources *odraks* were rigged with spritsails.

Numerous traces of repairs could be seen on the walls: boards fastened by nails bear witness to a long-term usage of that ship. Dendrochronological analysis shows that the craft, which had been built around 1774, was repaired after 1785. The ship still s ailed after 1799, which is evidenced by the dating of the samples taken from the pinewood boards of the deck located on the stern. According the same analysis the ship was used for over 25 years, which is a very long period compared to an age of just 12 years which are indicated by written sources dealing with such watercraft.

At the same time new ship types with narrow, elongated hulls called *łyżwa* and *berlinka* occured on the Vistula. Scholars believe that the new ship type figured under the name *odrzak*, which sailed to the Vistula through the Bydgoszcz Canal constructed from 1773 to 1774, and which started to become widespread under the name of *berlinka* after having undergone certain adaptations in Polish boat yards (Litwin 1995: 44).

The *berlinka* recorded by an Austrian engineer on the River San in 1796 was defined by him as »Berlinka, ein Oder Kahn« which may be regarded as a Polonization of a German term. Drawings show a so far unknown Vistula river craft type which apparently was adopted to the new navigation conditions after the canals had been opened. In the 19th c. several ship types were still operated, however the largest and best documented ship type remains the *berlinka*, which was used either on Odra and Vistula.

Relics of river craft discovered in recent years prove diversified transformations in river boatbuilding rather than a simple evolutionary development. They are most strongly manifested through a series of alterations in the social and economic development of individual regions reflected by the type of demands in respect of river transport and organizational forms of river navigation. The archaeological finds show the existence of centuries old traditional river boatbuilding seen in the form of the craft, simple in technical terms, such as extended logboats. In the early medieval period there is a similarity in the appearance of paired logboats used for water transport and the time when the first Polish state was established based on the prince's law. Many boat finds from that period confirm that inland waters were convenient and intensively used transport routes. Taking into account the royal sovereignty over all water traffic systems and, apart from several exceptions, the lack of trade exchange on a mass scale, cargo transport in that period must have been connected with obligations if not servitude towards the ruler or his representatives.

First larger river craft have been in the Vistula estuary areas so far noted in the 13th c. The 12th c. is a period of social and economic transformation manifesting itself, *inter alia*, by the process of initiating municipality, by urbanization, the development of mining and trade relations, and certainly by crafts of larger dimensions. In the context of boatbuilding conditions alter through a separation of specialized shipmen and craftsmen who built ships and were joined in guilds, and through the origin of permanent shipyards. In case of S. Baltic harbours, related to the influx of new settler population, the great role of the Hanseatic long-distance trade as a catalyst for the cultural unification of that region and its amalgamation of various technologies have to be taken into account.

The first written evidence of permanent boatbuilding centres in the upper Vistula course and its basin goes back to the early 17th c. The introduction of commercial boatyards might have led to the development of local boatbuilding traditions and skills. However, the present lack of wrecks hinders tracing the process of change of more complicated forms of ships built by specialists such as *dubas* or *szkuta* used on a mass scale to water transport in the 16th to the 18th c.

Research conducted so far on boatbuilding sources from Poland has shown the co-existence of various river craft types in particular historic periods, and not a subsequent occurrence of phenomena in the course of time. Hence, it is difficult to make considerations about innovations, turning points and changes occurring in boatbuilding in a diachronic order. Instead the author was obliged rather to look for links related to structural interrelations and transfer of technology, and to focus options of evolution of certain types as a result of the development of local centres.

REFERENCES

Conwentz, H., 1898, Der überhöhte Einkahn aus Danzig. *Amtlicher Bericht Westpreussen Provinzial Museum*, 18, 37-44.

Ehrlich, B. & Steegmann, E., 1923, Der Fund eines alten Flussschiffes bei Elbing. *Elbinger Jahrbuch*, 3, 152-163.

Ellmers, D., 1973, Kultbarken, Fähren, Fischerboote. Vorgeschichtliche Einbäume in Niedersachsen. *Niedersachsens Frühzeit*, no. 3, Hildesheim.

Filipowiak, W., 1996, Archeologia a uprawa morza. In: E. Wilgocki (ed.), *50 lat archeologii polskiej na Pomorzu Zachodnim*. Szczecin, 103-130.

Hellmich, M., 1912, Einbäume in Schlesien. *Schlesiens Vorzeit in Bild und Schrift*, 6, 17-32.

1919, Einbäume in Schlesien (Nachtrag). *Schlesiens Vorzeit in Bild und Schrift*, 7, 127-128.

Hoyer, J. G., 1793, *Versuch eines Handbuches der Pontonnier-Wissenschaften in Absicht ihrer Anwendung zum Feldgebrauch*. Leipzig.

Krieg, H., 1933, Der Einbaum von Neukirch, Kr. Grosses Werder. *Mitteilungen des Westpreussischen Geschichtsvereins Danzig*, 32, 26-28.

Litwin, J., 1985, The development of folk boats in Poland from the example of structures used on the San and the Bug rivers. In: *ISBSA 3*, 327-350.

1995, Polskie szkutnictwo ludowe XX wieku. *Prace Centralnego Muzeum Morskiego*, X. Gdańsk.

Mielcarek, A., 1974, Statek odrzański (Odrak). *Materiały Zachodniopomorskie* 20, 377-394.

1981, O statkach występujących w szczecińskiej taryfie celnej z XIII wieku. *Materiały Zachodniopomorskie*, 27, 201-208.

Ossowski, W., 1999, Studia nad łodziami jednopiennymi z obszaru Polski. *Prace Centralnego Muzeum Morskiego* XI, Gdańsk.

2004a, Medieval large river crafts from the Vistula River, Poland. In: Brandt & Kühn, *Haithabu*, 83-96.

2004b, Wraki z Krosna Odrzańskiego – nowe źródło do badań żeglugi odrzańskiej. *Biblioteka Środkowego Nadodrza*, no. 2, 363-372.

Ossowski, W. & Kościński, B., 2003, Pozostałości średniowiecznego statku spod Zielonej Bramy w Gdańsku. *Pomorania Antiqua*, 19, 155-176.

Ossowski, W. & Krąpiec, M., 2001, Das Wrack eines Flußschiffes aus dem 13. Jahrhundert von Kobyla Kępa bei Sztutowo. *Deutsches Schiffahrtsarchiv*, 23, 395-414.

Owsianowska, A., 2003, Wyniki badań sondażowych na stanowisku »Katownia« w Gdańsku. In: H. Paner & M. Fudziński (eds), *XIII Sesja Pomorzoznawcza*, no. 2. Gdańsk, 335-348.

Paret, O., 1931, Die Einbäume im Federsee und im übrigen Europa. *Prähistorische Zeitsschrift*, 21.1-2, 76-116.

Polak, Z., 1998, Kołobrzeska łódź-dłubanka. In: M. Rębkowski (ed.), *Archeologia średniowiecznego Kołobrzegu*, no. 3, 183-196.

Salemke, G., 1973, Mittelalterliche Flusschiffsfunde bei Elbing in der Zeit zwischen 1920-1944. *Das Logbuch*, 9.4, 129-131.

Smolarek, P., 1985, Vistula cargo ships from the 16th-18th centuries. In: *ISBSA 3*, 165-191.

Szymczak, A., 1997, *Łodzie dłubanki ze zbiorów szczecińskich*. Materiały Zachodniopomorskie, 42, 31-59.

Vlierman, K., 1996, »... Van *Zintelen, van Zintelroeden ende Mossen* ...« *Een breeuwmethode als hulpmiddel bij het dateren van scheepswrakken uit de Hanzetijd*. Scheepsarcheologie I, Flevobericht 386. Lelystad.

PETR SOROKIN

FLAT-BOTTOMED BOATS FROM NORTH-WESTERN RUSSIA

Based on archaeological material from the territory of N.W. Russia, distinct constructional types of vessels existed in the Viking Age and the Middle Ages (**Fig. 1**). They probably comprise the main vessel type which is known from written sources (Sorokin 2000; 2002).

Remains of flat-bottomed boats are well-known from archaeological layers of the 9th c. and later in N.W. Russian towns: Ladoga, Novgorod, and Pskov. Most ship components were adapted to second use. The material can be distinguished to single elements and constructional parts of vessels. In the former case often fittings and equipment occured, e.g. oars, rowlock and rigging parts which do not prove the specific type of boat they belonged to, whereas other objects as knee-shaped frames at least signify the hull type. Apparently re-used in settlement architecture, all relicts were taken from abandoned vessels.

Substantial parts of barges were found in building constructions for the new purposes more or less altered in size and shape to fit the parameter of building structures. Side and bottom planking, and frames as well could be identified by nail holes. Such material was found as flooring constructions inside and outside

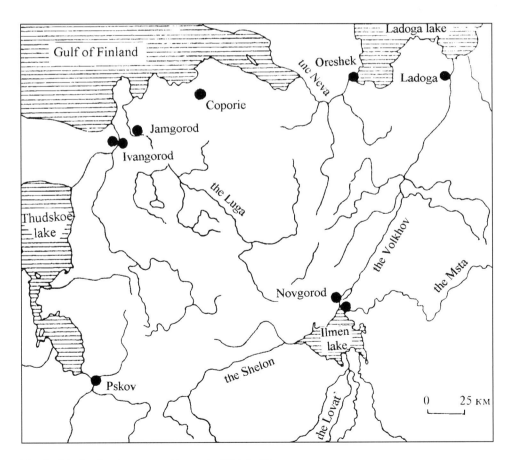

Fig. 1 Medieval waterways and towns in N.W. Russia.

Fig. 2 Barge elements reused as floor construction of wooden houses in (Photo P. Sorokin).

Fig. 3 Barge elements in the floorings outside houses in Staraya Ladoga (Photo P. Sorokin).

houses (**Figs 2-3**). Beyond that, ship timbers were widely used as road surface. They represent larger hull sections, which could belong to one and the same boat. Due to their shape and sectional flatness it seems in particular barges have been reused.

Records about the concentrations of ship finds in the N.W. Russian towns list 25 sites of the 9th and 10th c. in the Staraja Ladoga settlement (not region), which were excavated from 1930 to 1990 by V. I. Ravdonikas,

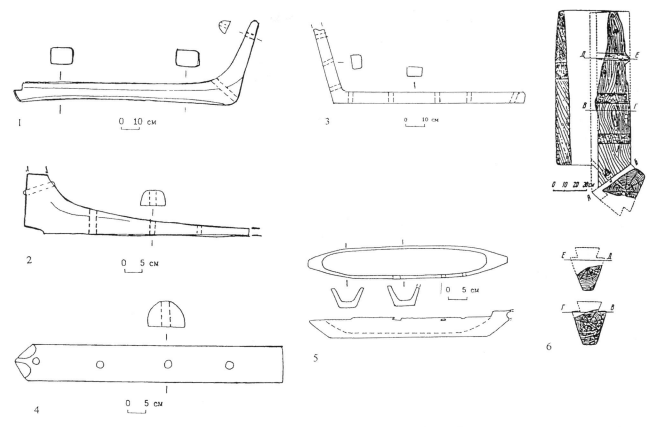

Fig. 4   Barge elements and boat model from Staraya Ladoga, Novgorod and Pskov, 10th to 12th c.: **1-3** knee-shaped floors made from knee-timber; **4** straight floor; **5** wooden model of a flat-bottomed boat; **6** stem (Drawings S. N. Orlov).

E. A. Rjabinin and V. P. Petrenko. In Novgorod about ten find spots from the middle of the 10th to the 15th c. were investigated over the same time by V. L. Janin and B. A. Kolchin. One complex of mid-14th c. and single objects were uncovered in Pskov, the latter without closer dating and careful documentation. However, some detailed descriptions, drawings and photographs of those excavations are available, though most of the finds have not been preserved.

To be interpreted as barges or ferry boats, the ship remains pointed out flat bottomed vessels with steep sides. The material comprised of side and bottom planking, connected in carvel construction, planks of L-shaped profile to form the transition of the ship's bottom to the walls, floor-timbers and grown knee-shaped frames, and also straight posts (**Fig. 4**).

Comparable material, i.e. L-shaped transition planks, side and bottom planking, straight floors and knee-shaped ribs, were excavated near a house in the central part of the medieval settlement Staraja Ladoga between 1948 and 1981 (Grozdilov 1948; Ryabinin & Sorokin 1998; Sorokin 2006). Re-used as architectural elements of wooden street construction of the A.D. 930s, two fragments of L-shaped planking have been dendrochronologically dated to A.D. 807 and 808. It can be deduced from this that the re-use of the dismantled barge took place about 120 years after the building of the vessel. There are different interpretations of such an evidence that ship remains found in an archaeological layer are for many years older than the date of the layer: repeated re-use of constructional elements in shipbuilding and settlement architecture or long-lived vessels. The relicts indicate barges of about 0.8 m high sides and 35 to 50 cm wide planks of 3.5 to 4 cm thickness. The elements were fastened by tree nails about 2.5 cm in diameter.

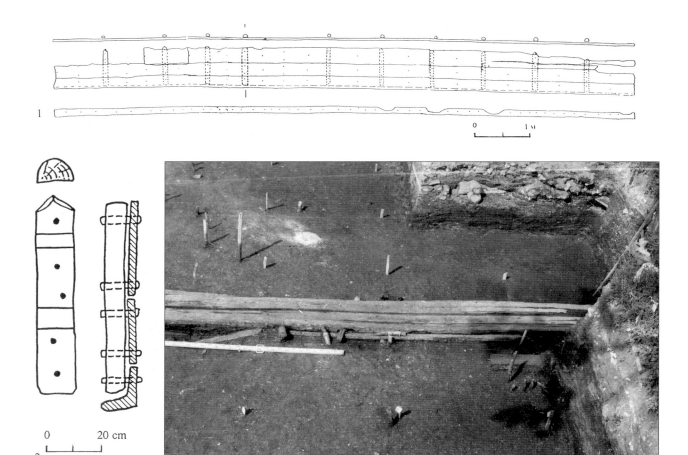

Fig. 5 Barge elements found at Ladojka River (Drawings and Photo [*in situ*] V. P. Petrenko).

Remains of a barge, floor-timbers and two planks which were found in the same area belonged to a vessel up to 3.2 m wide. Based on the analysis of the stratigraphical context it was dated to A.D. 865 to 930. The barge was built with two layers of bottom planks.

The biggest barge fragments were excavated on the left bank of Ladojka River in 1976/1977 (**Fig. 5**), where they had been used for street bridges dated to the years A.D. 900 to 924 (Petrenko 1977). The preserved part was 14.3 m. long and about 75 cm consisting of two planks, an L-shaped transition plank and floor-timbers (**Fig. 6**). Measurements are as follows: plank width 22 to 30 cm, thickness 2.5 to 3.5 cm; width of the L-shaped plank at the vertical section 16 to 25 cm, at the horizontal section 10.5 to 12 cm. The frames had been made from half-trunks of pine tree, each 67 to 74 cm long, with half-rounded cross-section, 8 to 13 cm sided and 7 to 8 cm moulded. They were fastened to the planks with treenails of 2.2 to 3 cm diameter. The Intervals between fastening holes were 35 to 50 cm. On the other hand, holes in the bottom section of the L-shaped plank showed intervals of just about 11 to 38 cm. That probably indicates the fastening of an additional bottom plank.

Small oak wedges inserted on every 14 to 19 cm into the plank edges point to a system of caulking which included narrow wooden laths originally fastened to the seams (Sorokin 1997:119). Analogies are known from Falsterbo, barge no. VI, dated to the late 1340s, and from the Netherlands where the oldest evidence of this method could be dated to A.D. 913±13 (Nilson, Krapiec & Ossowski 2002: 73-74; 76-78).

Knee-shaped frames found in Ladoga especially reveal the shape of hulls with ship´s sides inclining to about 90 to 110°. The later development of the Ladoga barges' building tradition remains unknown because of the bad preservation of organic material in archaeological layers later than the 11th c.

Attempts to reconstruct vessel types mentioned in written sources were made on the Novgorodian material. They comprise the *Korabl* type of the 12th and 13th c., associated with terms as *Ushkui*, *Uchan* or *Strug* (Kolchin 1968; 1989). Certainly the identification of barges by names from historical documents seem less reliable.

Planks with triangular-shaped ends belong to the bottom section of ship ends. Some of them at their lateral surface show nail holes which derive from joints of neighbouring planks (Dubrovin 2000: 153). There is a stem in a Novgorod collection dating to the 12th c., 1.55 m long and 36 cm wide. It was attached to a bottom plank at an angle of about 130°. Knee-shaped frames from Novgorod and Pskov reveal inclined ship's sides of about 100 to 110°. In general constructional details and shape of barges from Ladoga, Novgorod and Pskov are comparable.

Fig. 6 Barge elements (cf. fig. 5) dismantled (Photo V. P. Petrenko).

Wooden and bark models of boats were uncovered in Novgorod and Pskov in the 11th to 15th c. layers. Some of them show realistic features of form and construction. Therefore, they can be interpreted as miniatures of contemporary types of vessels, usually flat-bottomed boats (**Figs 4-5**).

Based on archaeological material in N.W. Russia the traditional usage of barges has been proved for the period from the beginning of the 9th to the 15th c. Vessels were made mostly from pine and fir. This kind of boat had a flat bottom and upright boards with the angle of connection about 90° and about 100 to 110°.

The shape of N.W. Russian barges resembles that of boats from Falsterbo and Treiden, which show pointed bows and transom sterns (Blomquist 1950; Ellmers 1972: 104), notwithstanding that other shapes could have existed. As geometrical data of this kind of watercraft because of the poor preservation are limited, not even a tentative reconstruction would be reasonable: the length of barges could exceed 14.3 m, their width may have reached up to 3.2 m; the height can be estimated at approx. 0.6 to 0.9 m, perhaps as much as 1.2 m.

The vessels were built in carvel construction, 2.5 to 4 cm thick side and 4 to 7 cm thick bottom planking combined with L-shaped transition profiles. Some of the boats had double bottom planking [cf. comment above] – two layers of bottom planks. Two variants of frames occur, knee-shaped and straight ribs which were arranged at intervals of 0.35 to 0.90 m. Fastenings were made mainly with treenails of 2 to 3 cm diameter.

Caulking systems included the use of moss and tow, and there is evidence of wooden laths fastened either with wooden wedges or by sewing technique (**Fig. 7**). The method to attach laths to the planking seams with iron clamps has been wide-spread in N.W. Russia since the end of the 12th c. It can be considered as

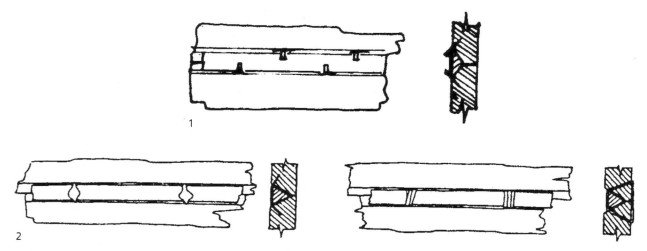

Fig. 7 Types of caulking: **1** Barges from Staraya Ladoga, beginning of the 10th c. – **2** Ferry boats from Novgorod of the 11th to 14th c. (After B. Kolchin).

Fig. 8 Steering-oar rowlock found in archaeological layers from Staraya Ladoga of the 10th c.

Fig. 9 Ferry-raft on an East European river (Drawing by Gustav Meerberg, mid-17th c.).

W. influence to Russian boatbuilding at the time of the beginning of intense communications with towns of the Hanseatic League. This type of caulking was most often used for medieval Russian barges and in traditional boat building of N.W. Russia the method survived till the end of the 20th c.[1]

The identification of rigging and equipment belonging to such barges is more difficult. Two large bifurcated rowlocks origin from archaeological layers at Staraya Ladoga of the 10th c. Due to their dimensions (height 1.02 and 1.20 m; width at the top 22.5 and 25 cm; cross-section at the base approx. 8 to 3 cm), the fittings would have been suited to carry oars with a shaft diameter of approx. 10 cm (**Fig. 8**). An analogy is shown by an illustration of Gustav Meerberg from the mid-17th c. which portrays a ferry-raft on an East European river (**Fig. 9**).

type of boats	historical dating	Russian/foreign	general terms	see/lake/river	war/cargo/passenger
Uchan (Ouchan)	A.D. 1271-1480...	3/2	*Lodia Sudno Shneka Porom Cheln*	– / 3 / 4	2(?) / 4 / 1
Porom	A.D. 1238-1418...	2 / –	*Pavosok Lodia Nasad*	– / – / 1	
Pavosok	A.D. 1374-1446 ...	1 / –	*Lodia Porom*	– / – / 2	– / 1 / –

Table 1 Types of flat-bottomed boats according to medieval documents from N.W. Russia.

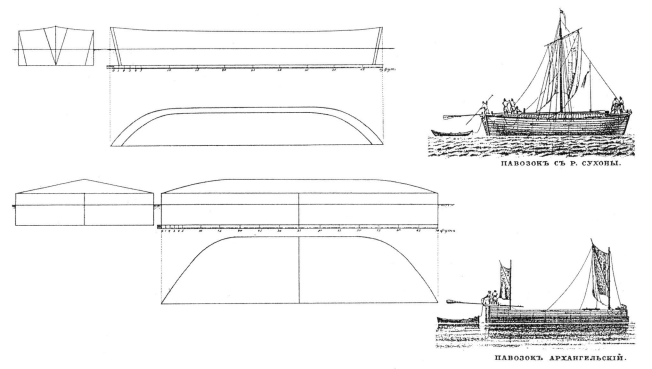

ПАВОЗОКЪ СЪ Р. СУХОНЫ.

ПАВОЗОКЪ АРХАНГЕЛЬСКІЙ.

Fig. 10 Pavosok barges with parallel sides from Severnaja Dvina basin, end of 19th c.

In medieval documents such as chronicles, acts and the birch letters of N.W. Russia, there appear terms which meant vessels in general or certain classes, e.g. *Korabl*, *Lodia*, *Sudno*, whilst *Uchan*, *Porom* and *Pavosok* meant a ship type, obviously barges (**Table 1**; Sorokin 1997: 53-55).

The name *Uchan* was known only in N. W. Russia. Such craft were used to transport people across Ilmen Lake in A.D. 1471, whereas the Novgorodian birch letter no. 232 of the end 14th c. mentions cargo, i.e. firewood and hay. *Uchans* were employed by the German Order at war against Pskov in A.D. 1271 for evacuation of lost soldiers and in A.D. 1480 as branders. In a contract between Novgorod and the Hanseatic League of A.D. 1436 the Russian term *Uchan* was translated to German to »ene praem«.

The first mentioning of *Porom* is in the Novgorodian birch letter no. 232 (dated A.D. 1238 to 1268). In the medieval town of Pskov the left bank of the Velikaja River was called »Paromjane«, which marks a landing place of ferries.

The *Pavosok* was known in the Volga basin as a big flat-bottomed boat for cargo transport since A.D. 1374. Forty *Pavosoks* with cargo from Novgorod, Moscow and Novotorjec visited Torjok, a town south from Novgorod, in A.D. 1446.

Another flat-bottomed vessel named *Strug* is documented since the 11th c. The type was used on the rivers Dnepr and Zapadnaja Dvina, and in theVolga basin. Since the 15th c., *Strugs* also operated as war boats.

The main types of Russian medieval barges correspond to traditional Russian boats types of the 18th to the beginning of the 20th c. The *Pavosok* (**Fig. 10**), *Poludnische* and *Barja* which belong to the type of flat-bottomed cargo vessels with straight ship's sides were known in N. Russia in the Severnaja Dvina basin till the end of the 19th c. Driven by sails and oars, the former two types were 12 to 18 m long, 2.4 to 4 m wide and 1.5 to 1.8 m high, with a draught of 0.9 to 1.2 m. The inclinations of boards were approx. 90 to 110° as with the medieval boats. Spread on the Volga basin, the biggest barge, *Beljana* was up to 61 m long and 19 m wide with a height of 3.05 m (Bogoslovski 1859: 57; 162).

The nature of Russia with its many shallow and rapid rivers contributed to the development and spreading of flat-bottomed types of watercraft. Easy to be made and designed for different navigation conditions to sail on rivers, lakes and sometimes coastal waters, they usually have much space and displacement for cargo. Due to their small draught they overcome obstacles on waterways. Such boats and ships were used also for transport purposes across rivers and fisheries as it is also known from ethnographical records of the Nordic countries.

The rich forest resources of Russia, its long distances and difficulties to go upstream favoured one-way traffic by vessels which were exploited for some three years. Navigating downstream, they were dismantled and sold as timber or firewood. Ship timbers were used for the building of houses, bridges and other constructions. This transport system flourished from the medieval time to the beginning of the 20th c. As a result this circumstance may have caused the determination of conservation of old traditional boat building technology.

Building traditions in Europe often included Roman and local elements. The word *Parom,* meaning flat-bottomed vessels, is found in different transcriptions in the majority of Slavonic languages. This suggests that the popularity of this type continues among the Slavs even up to the time of their colonization of the Danube area where Slavonic water craft including boats for ferrying across rivers were often mentioned in the Byzantine written sources of the 6th and 7th c. Could such a neighbourhood have caused influences, on the other hand the international sea contacts in the Baltic region doubtless also promoted the share of new technological ideas in boatbuilding. The traditions of local Finnish inhabitants and the boatbuilding technology, brought by Novgorodian Slovene from their native land must be taken into consideration.

NOTE

1) Traditional boats with a similar system of hermetic sealing of seams are preserved on Tchudskoe and Ilmen lakes up to the end of the 20th c.

REFERENCES

Blomquist, R., 1950, *Falsterbohus. Kulturen.* Lund, 142-181.

Bogoslovski, P. A., 1859, *O kupecheskom sudostroenii Rossii, rechnom i pribrejnom.* vol. 1, Album. St. Petersburg.

Dubrovin, G. E., 2000, *Wodnii I suhoputni transport srednevekovogo Novgoroda X-XV v. v.,* vol. 1. 2. Moscow.

Ellmers, D., 1972, *Frühmittelalterliche Handelsschiffahrt in Mittel- und Nordeuropa.* Offa-Bücher, no. 28. Neumünster.

Grozdilov, G. P.,1950, Raskopki w Staroj Ladoge w 1948g. *Sovjetskaya Arheologiya,* XIV, 139-170.

GVNP, 1949, *Gramoti Velikogo Novgoroda i Pskova.* Moscow, Leningrad.

Kolchin, B. A.,1968, *Novgorodskie drevnosti. Derevjannie izdelia.* SAI. EI -55. Moscow.

1989, *Wooden Artefacts from Medieval Novgorod.* BAR, Internat. Series, 495, part 1. Oxford.

Nilson, M., Krapiec, M., and Ossowski, W., 2002, Medieval Barges from Falsterbo, Sweden. In: Brandt & Kühn, *Haithabu,* 71-81.

Petrenko, V. P., 1977, Otchet o raskopkah v Staroj Ladoge bliz Varjagskoi ulici v 1977g. *Arhiv IIMK RAN*f. 35, 1977.

Ryabinin, E. A. & Sorokin, P. E., 1998, Nekotorye sudovye nakhodki iz raskopok v Staroy Ladoge. In: *Izuchenye pamiatnykov morskoi arkheologyy,* vol. 3. St. Petersburg., 187-194.

Sorokin, P. E., 1997, *Vodnye puti i sudostroenie na Severo-zapade Rusi v srednevekov ye.* St. Petersburg.

2000, The Medieval Boatbuilding Tradition of Russia. In: *ISBSA 8,* 37-44.

2002, The medieval boats in north west Russia. In: *Bottnisk kontakt XI. Maritimhistorisk konferens.* Harnosand, 140-145.

2006, Staraya Ladoga: a seaport in medieval Russia. In: *ISBSA 10,* 157-162.

DARINA L. TULLY

THE TRADITIONAL BOATS AND FISHERIES
OF THE WATERFORD ESTUARY, IRELAND

In the S.E. of Ireland three major rivers, the Barrow, the Nore and the Suir, come together to form the Waterford Estuary (**Fig. 1**). The Port of Waterford is presently one of Ireland's strategic ports, and the nearest deep-water port to Europe. A variety of vernacular craft co-exist here, alongside modern bulk carriers and container traffic. The traditional fisheries carried out are drift, draft and snap netting, eel trapping, shell fish collection of mussels, cockles and oysters, crab and lobster potting, along with the operation of large sprat and white fish weirs. Vernacular craft are also used for hunting, wildfowling, the collection of reeds, and, up to recently, for short distance trading.

In A.D. 155 Waterford was known as *Cuan-na-Grian*, the harbour of the sun (Marmion 1855: 589). The River *Birgos* (Barrow) can be identified on Ptolemy's 2nd c. map. There are a number of promontory forts and early Christian sites in the area. The Scandinavians established the Port of Waterford and named it *Vader Fiord*.

The Port of New Ross, up the River Barrow, was essentially a Norman establishment, and the area attracted a number of Medieval Orders including Franciscans, Crutched Friars, Dominicans, Augustinians and Knights Templar. The Anglo-Norman Cistercian Abbeys of Dunbrody, Graiguenamanagh and nearby Tintern (minor), provide some of the earliest documented evidence for the fisheries in the Estuary. The origins of Buttermilk Castle weir, near Dunbrody, can be traced back to monastic times (Colfer 2004: 63) and is still

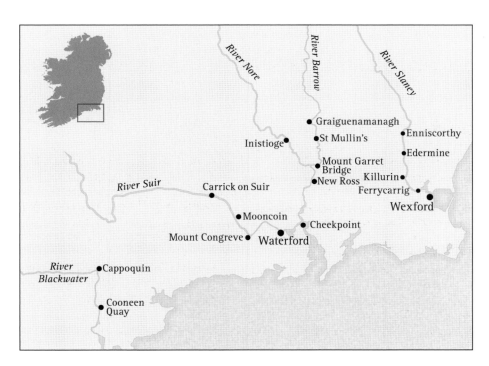

Fig. 1   Map of the Waterford Estuary, Ireland.

Fig. 2   A round hulled keelless prong.

licensed to catch salmon. The area had close connections with the Grand Banks fishery, and in the 18th c. a Waterford Colony was set up in Newfoundland. Over the last decade, an ongoing independent research project has recorded the vernacular craft of the area, and the way they have traditionally been used.

PROJECT METHODOLOGY

Fieldwork was undertaken using long open-ended interviews, audio recording and note taking, along with stills photography and digital video where appropriate. Lines plans and constructional details were drawn for each boat type. One of the best ways to understand and comprehend the forms and functions of maritime traditions is to take part in the day-to-day activities of the community. The premise underlying participant-observation, as this approach is called, is that the researcher becomes a more effective observer by taking an active role in the performance of regular activities (Taylor 1992: 29-30). The capabilities and performance of the boats, and the skills and dexterity of the fishermen is really only appreciated by close observation.

ETHNOGRAPHIC APPROACH

Ethnography gives written descriptions of customs, beliefs and behaviour of particular cultures, from data and information collected through fieldwork, while ethno-archaeology uses data collected from living groups of people as a basis for understanding the peoples of the past. This ethnographic approach to the study of the current use of traditional boats and their communities can be used to better understand the use of boats in the past.

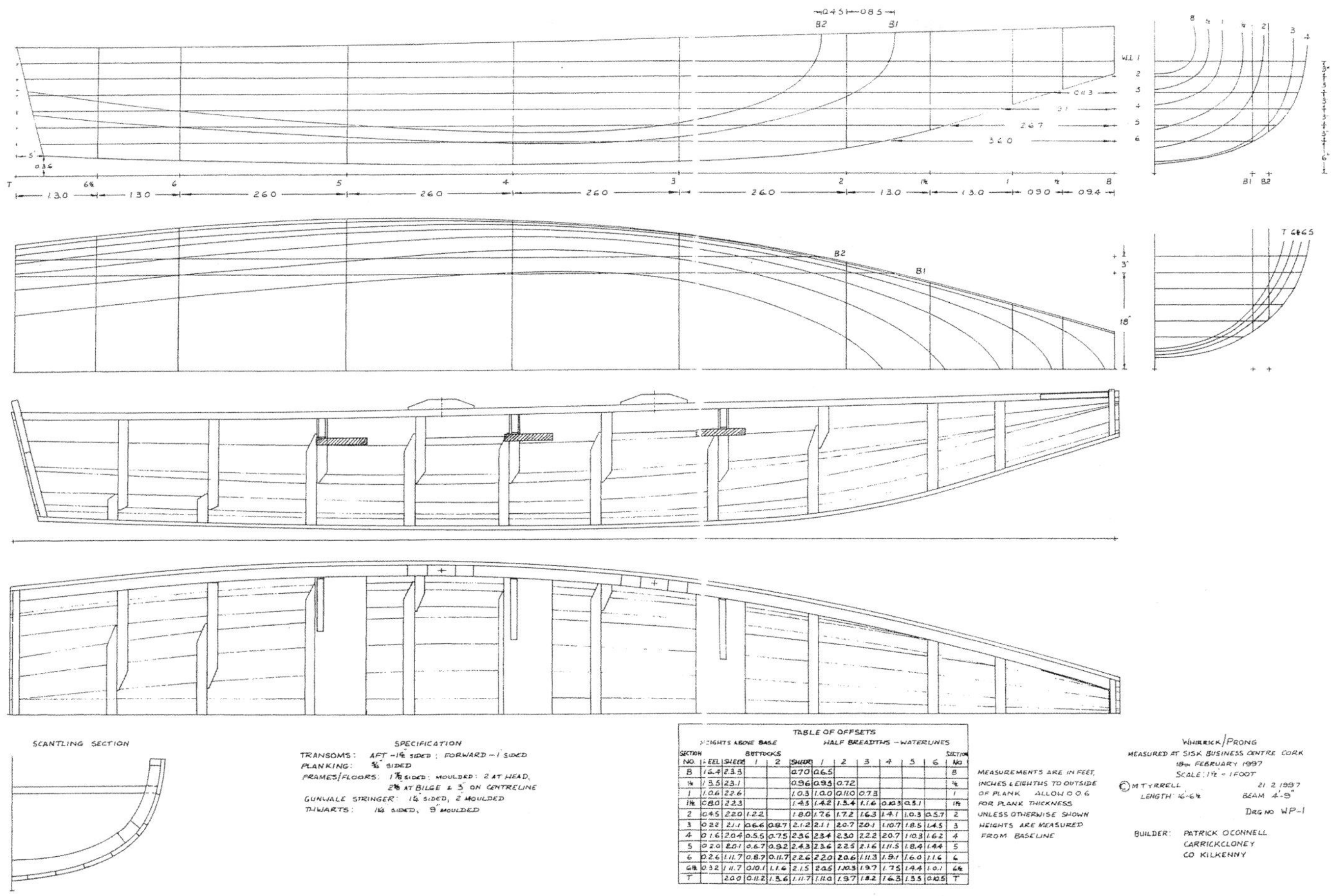

TABLE OF OFFSETS

SECTION NO.	HEIGHTS ABOVE BASE: KEEL	SHEER	BUTTOCKS 1	BUTTOCKS 2	HALF BREADTHS – WATERLINES: SHEER	1	2	3	4	5	6	SECTION NO.
B	1.6.4	2.3.3			0.7.0	0.6.5						8
½	1.3.5	2.3.1			0.9.6	0.9.3	0.7.2					½
1	1.0.6	2.2.6			1.0.3	1.0.0	0.11.0	0.7.3				1
1½	0.8.0	2.2.3			1.4.3	1.4.2	1.3.4	1.1.6	0.10.3	0.3.1		1½
2	0.4.5	2.2.0	1.2.2		1.8.0	1.7.6	1.7.2	1.6.3	1.4.1	1.0.3	0.5.7	2
3	0.2.2	2.1.1	0.6.6	0.8.7	2.1.2	2.1.1	2.0.7	2.0.1	1.10.7	1.8.5	1.4.5	3
4	0.1.6	2.0.4	0.5.5	0.7.5	2.3.6	2.3.4	2.3.0	2.2.2	2.0.7	1.10.3	1.6.2	4
5	0.2.0	2.0.1	0.6.7	0.9.2	2.4.3	2.3.6	2.2.5	2.1.6	1.11.5	1.8.4	1.4.4	5
6	0.2.6	1.11.7	0.8.7	0.11.7	2.2.6	2.2.0	2.0.6	1.11.3	1.9.1	1.6.0	1.1.6	6
6½	0.3.2	1.11.7	0.10.1	1.1.6	2.1.5	2.0.5	1.10.3	1.9.7	1.7.5	1.4.4	1.0.1	6½
T		2.0.0	0.11.2	1.3.6	1.11.7	1.11.0	1.9.7	1.8.2	1.6.3	1.3.5	0.10.5	T

Fig. 3 Prong lines drawing (Drawing M. Tyrrell).

»There is a great deal to be learned about the development of boats from detailed study of modern examples, providing that we do not assume that things were necessarily the same in the past as they are now, but use the study as a source of ideas and an inclination of what is possible« (Greenhill 1976: 22).

By studying traditional boats in the developed world, where there have been known contacts or influences with various cultures of the past, one may be able to identify particular distinguishing features or characteristics which originated long ago, but are still retained in the craft and communities of today.

»The outstanding interest of Ireland for the student of European origins, lies in the fact that it's historic literature, language and social organisation, as well as it's folklore and folk customs, illustrate the marginal survival of archaic elements of the Indo-European world« (Evans 1957: xiv). While the W. of Ireland has been long recognised as a study area by European folklorists, the E. and S.E. coasts also present many opportunities in the study of traditional boats and fisheries.

THE PRONGS AND THE DRAFT NET FISHERY

One of the most distinctive boats of the area is the round-hulled keelless prong (**Figs 2-3**). They have all the characteristics of a Scandinavian pram, but are carvel built. There is absolutely no sheer at the gunwale and the prong is often compared to a bottle or barrel cut in half. The prongs are 5 to 5.2 m long, by around 1.48 m in the beam. The building process starts with laying down a central plank, which is raised fore and aft with blocks to give some rocker. A U-shaped bow board and the semi circular transom, along with the frames, which are round in profile, are attached. The frame is then inserted, as is common practice in Ireland, and planked bottom up, with the fixing of pairs of bevel edged planks of pre-defined ratios fore and aft, to fit the bow and sternpost, as in building a pram dinghy.

The boats were mainly involved in a draft net fishery. Draft netting uses a large purse seine net around 600 m long. The net is carefully folded into the stern from where it pays out freely as the boat sweeps out in a long arc. A man on shore holds a warp attached to the end of the net while the boat comes back to the shore encircling the fish.

Due to the ease with which the round hull can be launched and retrieved at all states of the tide, the prongs were perfectly suited to clandestine fishing activities, locally called *Pouching* (poaching). Due to the phasing out of the draft net fishery, development of the port, and changes in fishery practice, the numbers of prongs have reduced dramatically in the last decade.

THE WATERFORD PUNTS AND DRIFT NET FISHERY

There are approx. one hundred carvel punts engaged mainly in a drift net fishery. They are also used for eel fishing, collecting shellfish, longline fishing and tending stake weirs. All the punts are of similar design and build, and are around 5 m in length. The drift net is a rectangular net approx. 400 m long. The top rope is buoyed, and there is a lead line on the lower rope. Marked at the ends by buoys, the gill type net is paid out completely, and set adrift on the tide. The boat follows and retrieves the net after around 20 to 30 min. The entire length of the estuary is fished. The various drifts (preferred drift netting locations) all have names and optimum times to set a net, and are fished in an orderly sequence by the different crews to share the available sites.

THE STAKE WEIRS

Another feature of the maritime cultural landscape of the estuary is the large number of fish weirs. There is literary evidence for the use of weirs, from Monastic times through to the 19th c. (Maddock 1990: 542-543), while a large body of literary evidence also exists for their operation since the dissolution of the Monasteries in the 16th c. (Went 1955, 60: 47-56). A large number of weir sites are recorded on the 1837 first edition Ordnance Survey Maps. Around fifteen sprat and white fish weirs are still in use in the vicinity of Cheekpoint. These stake weirs (**Fig. 4**) are an adaptation of the older Salmon weirs, which (with the exception of Buttermilk Castle Weir) were outlawed in the1860s (Went 1959).

In the archaeological medium, weirs are usually studied when they have been abandoned, so the Waterford estuary is rare in that it affords one the opportunity to study stake weirs in current operation. These sprat stake weirs, like salmon head weirs, work on the principle that fish move up and down an estuary with the tide. Most of the weirs on the river are set up as ebb weirs, as the fish have a habit of dropping back on the ebb. A few weirs are also set up as flood weirs.

The V-shaped stake weirs have an entrance about 3 m wide flanked by two large poles called *Coolalagh's* The sides are made up of large poles made into a loose, fence-like structure. The crossbeams are called *Robberies*. Set in the entrance is a conical or *Coghill* style net, up to 14 m long, with an opening around

Fig. 4   A stake weir still in operation above Great Island.

3 m in diameter, which narrows progressively down to about 45 cm. Metal hoops called *Gads*, that encircle and slide up and down the entrance poles, are attached to the open end of the net. These hoops are used to open and close the mouth of the net and are controlled by a rope known as the *Gob* rope.

The weir is tended at slack tide by boat, and the net is emptied from the narrow end, where a peg is removed. The net then has to be re-anchored in position. The weirs are emptied everyday, or lifted and tied up when not in use. To erect the weirs, an arrangement of chains are wrapped around the pole, which is slung between two large yawls, then using the chains for grip they are pile driven into the muddy ground. Oak poles from abandoned weirs are re-used in repairing working weirs. Poles of larch and steel are also used.

THE COTS OF THE RIVERS NORE, BARROW, AND SUIR

The term *cot* refers to small, open canoe-like boats used on many Irish rivers and lakes. It derives from the Irish word *coite* with the Irish for logboats being *coti* (Fry 2000: vii). Literary evidence shows us that *cots* were a persistent feature of inland water transport. A statute was passed in 1537 for the River Suir, regulating traffic by »necessarie boates, scowts, wherries, claruns, cottes and other vessels, loden and bestowed with goods« (McCraith 1912: 73). Gerald Boate wrote in 1652 »Both Oure (Nore) and Barrow are portable many miles into the country, the Oure only with little boats and with cots, they call in Ireland things like

Fig. 5   A cot snap netting: the fisherman has to manoeuvre the boat and control the net at the same time.

boats, but very unhappily being nothing but square pieces of timber made hollow, very common throughout Ireland both for to pass rivers in and to carry goods from one place to another« (Lucas 1963: 64)

The cots operate in the upper reaches of the rivers, which are tidal up to 60 km inland. Each river has its own variation of cot, but with similar characteristics giving a narrow low profile craft. There is a total of around 250 cots, mainly engaged in an ancient form of fishing called snap netting (**Fig. 5**).

The snap net is rectangular in shape, just 10 to 15m long, and the bottom or *sole* rope is weighed down with two ovoid stones of 0.5 kg each. To use the snap net, the cots work in pairs, some with two men to each boat, and paddle in tandem with the net stretched between the two boats. One cot man controls the paying out of the net, while both paddle to keep the cots on a straight course while drifting with the tide. A sense of rhythm and timing is essential for the pairs of boatmen to work effectively. The cot men display great skill and dexterity to »snap« the bottom and top rope closed, trapping the salmon by quickly drawing the two boats together with their single paddles.

The cot men have an intimate knowledge of the movements of the river and fish. Each *ledge*, or *scrape*, as the fishing pools are called, along with the riverbanks, have a host of local names passed down in the oral tradition. When not in use the cots are kept in »stocks«, which are perpendicular cuts into the riverbank, or are drawn up into mud berths called *leaba na mbad* (bed of the boat).

There are a few local variations on the boats, depending on the builders, but the double-ended cot typically measures 5.2 to 5.5 m in length overall, and has a maximum beam of just over 1 m (**Fig. 6**). They have a flat bottom with slight rocker, and the sides are planked clinker style, onto fine frames called *brongs*. They are built double ended or with transom sterns. The National Museum of Ireland holds an interesting example of a planked but frameless cot collected in 1976.

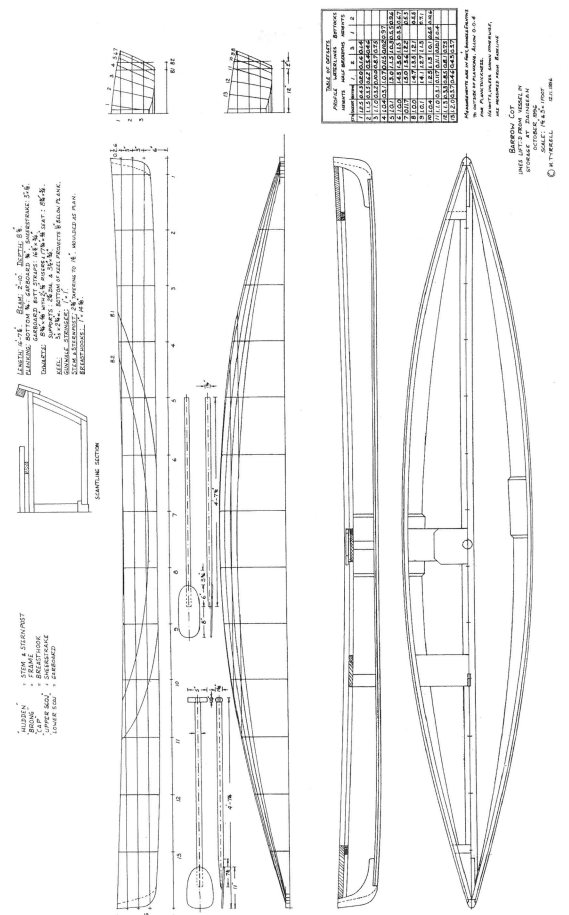

Fig. 6 Barrow cot lines drawing. Most of the river cots have light frames. This particular example of a cot has no internal framing (Drawing M. Tyrrell).

CONCLUSION

While preserving traditional forms of fishing, the traditional boats of the S.E. are also a focus for the continuity of a great range of traditions within their communities. They are a catalyst for the transmission of knowledge and awareness of the rivers, fishing, boat building and associated crafts, and the oral traditions associated with the fishery. Nevertheless, the continuation of these traditional inland fisheries, like that of their coastal counterparts, is under severe pressure from many sources.

ACKNOWLEDGEMENTS

The author is grateful to *The Traditional Boats of Ireland Project* for use of figures 3, 5, and 6.

REFERENCES

Colfer, B., 2004, *The Hook Peninsula*. Cork.

Evans, E., 1957, *Irish Folkways*. London.

Fry, M. F., 2000, *Coiti, Logboats from Northern Ireland*. Belfast.

Greenhill, B., 1976, *The Archaeology of the Boat*. Connecticut.

Lucas, A., 1963, *The Dugout Canoe in Ireland, The Literary Evidence*. Varsberg Museum Arsbok, Sweden.

Maddock, F., 1990, *The Cot Fishermen of the Nore*. In: W. Nolan & K. Whelan (eds), *Kilkenny History and Society*. Dublin, 541-565.

Marmion, A.,1855, *The Ancient and Modern History of the Maritime Ports of Ireland*. London.

McCraith, L. M., 1912, *The Suir from its Source to the Sea*. Clonmel.

Taylor, D. A, 1992, *Documenting Maritime Folklife*. Washington.

Went, A. E. J., 1955, Irish Monastic Fisheries. *Journal of the Cork Historical & Archaeological Society*, 60, 47-56.

1959, Sprat or White-Fish Weirs in the Waterford Estuary. *Journal of the Royal Society of Antiquaries of Ireland*, 89, 91-93.

LAWRENCE E. BABITS

THE PERIAUGER –
AN EXAMPLE OF ADAPTING AN EUROPEAN BOAT TYPE
TO THE NORTH CAROLINA SOUNDS
A RECONSTRUCTION

The S.E. United States coastline is made up of barrier islands and inland waterways providing access to the mainland. Roads were few, poorly built, and rarely maintained, even as late as 1900. Woodlands and marshes made overland travel difficult, dangerous, and costly. Although too shallow for ocean-going vessels to get far inland, the inshore network of rivers, streams, and islands provided an inland waterway protected from the ocean. Smaller, shallow-draft vessels were developed to lighter cargo on the inland streams. One of these, the periauger, combined a European hull form with N. American timbers to produce a very useful watercraft called the »periauger«.

HISTORY

The Indians developed dugout canoes as swift and convenient transportation; by 1740, Europeans were operating on S.E. waterways in a variety of vessels including native canoes, sloops, schooners, and – according to the travel diaries of John Lawson – periaugers: »As we row'd up the [Santee] River, we found the Land toward the Mouth, and for sixteen Miles up it, scarce any Thing but Swamp and Percoarson, Affording vast Ciprus-Trees, of which the French make Canoes, that will carry fifty or sixty Barrels. After the tree is moulded and dug, they saw them into two Pieces, and so put a Plank between, and a small keel, to preserve them from the Oyster Banks [...] They carry two Masts, and Bermuda Sails, which makes them very handy and fit for their Purpose« (Lefler 1967: 16-17).

The periauger, as a split log, dugout hull form, appears to have been developed in S.W. France (Alford 1992; 1993a; 1993b; Alford et al. 1996). By circa 1700, it was common in the Carolinas, and its use later extended to Georgia and Florida. The periauger was probably the most common inland water work boat until the mid-19th c. when it was supplanted by a variety of other specialized watercraft. It might well be likened to the modern pickup truck for its utility. No obvious periaugers have been found archaeologically and only one specifically identified illustration exists.

The South Carolinians defended themselves against Spanish and Indian attacks from Florida with »Six Cyprus Periaugers, fourty foot Long and five foot wide, att Least with Seaventy Eight pair of oars« (Fleetwood 1995: 30). In this description, it seems unlikely that six 40 ft. long vessels would be rowed with seventy-eight pairs of oars, so perhaps the writer meant »seven to eight« per boat. These examples demonstrate a need for researchers to critically analyze the accounts.

The lack of visual evidence describing periaugers has made them the subject of debate among maritime historians. English grammar and spelling were not only different from today, but were inconsistent within their own time. Some thirty or more terms were used for this vessel (Parry 2000: 448), in an area approx. 1,000 km N. S. and 300 km E.W., over a time span of only 300 years. Regardless of any one hypothesis, this type of question shows another reason for critical interpretation.

Did different terms refer to different vessel types? Was periauger a »generic« term? Were scout boats named for their function or their design? Were periaugers, petiaugers and scout boats the same basic vessel or did the terms correspond to specific, and different, and very specialized, characteristics (Pecorelli 1993)? Particular details of these craft cannot be resolved until more evidence is found. While exact details have significant relevance for reconstructing a specific boat, it is still possible and worthwhile to build a typical representative type so that other approaches for understanding these craft are possible.

Since periaugers could be built in crude conditions, shipyards and chandleries would not be necessary. Large cypress trees were abundant and in »diameters of eight feet and more [...] Cypress wood is both easy to work and very resistant to rot« (Alford 1993a: 2). The logs were shaped wherever the log was found, and »the partially shaped boat is then floated and rowed, or perhaps towed, to the builder's home or settlement where it is completed« (Alford 1992: 201).

It appears that both periauger and petiauger were generic names for a particular class of vessel: a split-dugout Cypress log with a plank keel inserted in the center, sometimes with an upper strake added to increase freeboard, propelled by oars or sails, and two masts which could be stepped when not rowing (Alford *et al.* 1996). Some could carry large cargoes and travel up streams and rivers where deeper draft vessels could not. Some went to sea as far as Bermuda.

Once built, vessels could take the name for which it was used. William Stephens described them according to use: trade boat, guard boat, or express boat (Merton Coulter 1958: 86; 92; 96). Intended use would determine adaptations made to a vessel. Some were reported as being decked over and rowed by two or four oars; others, such as the scout boats, were more streamlined and had more oars for maneuverability and speed.

RECONSTRUCTION

To reconstruct a traditional boat deals with more than just the logistical problems of funding, purpose, and maintenance. Existing boat reproductions show that making new versions is possible and can shed light on how the original vessel handled. Examples range from Iron Age vessels (Crumlin-Pedersen & Trakadas 2003), to Viking ships (Anderson *et al.* 1997), Revolutionary War gondolas (Bratten 2002) and 1813 Brigs (Rybka & Heerssen 2006); for which there were plans and/or originals to work from. Unlike most replica watercraft, there is no archaeological or extant periauger to work from. All information regarding the periauger is documentary material that recorded its existence and what it was used for. No examples have been found.

Based on research by Alford, Pecorelli, Babits and O'Reagan, the possibility of building a 10 m long reproduction periauger was put to several coastal North Carolina historic sites. No one was interested until it was pointed out that Abraham Saunders, owner of the Newbold White House mentioned a periauger in his will. The Perquimans County Restoration Association applied for grants to build a reproduction in conjunction with the Newbold White House, East Carolina University and the North Carolina Maritime Museum. Eventually, over $120,000 in cash, grants and matching funds was raised, and the project went forward.

One immediate question about authenticity came about because it would be criminal to cut down a cypress tree over 2 m in diameter. There is no longer the ability to tell if the tree is intact; that is, it may not have »shakes«, where the wind, in bending the tree, caused fibers to separate. A tree with shakes would be useless for a periauger as can be seen in the term »shakes« also being used for shingles. Shingles were a byproduct of boat/ship construction to use up otherwise useless pieces and keep workers busy. Conse-

Fig. 1   Reconstructing a periauger (Photo M. B. Alford).

quently, since there were no trees available, and because there was no extant example, it was decided to build up the log with glued cypress blocks (**Fig. 1**), following a design produced by Mike Alford. The artificial log would then be shaped in traditional fashion to form the half hulls, center log and the bow and stern chunks. This work was accomplished during the winter and spring 2004. Mike Alford and the author had little control over the issues of authenticity in the boat yard or with deadlines. Consequently more modern elements were utilized than the two mentioned would have preferred.

SAIL TRIALS

The periauger was launched in early May 2004 and subjected to stability and flotation tests (**Fig. 2**). Then it was »taken home« over summer 2004. This »Odyssey« served as the sail trials and a great deal about the vessel and its handling was learned. The crew was composed of volunteers.

Fig. 2 Sailing a periauger (Photo J. Ernst).

The first volunteers were not ideal. They all came from a power boat squadron, and were not sailors. In light winds, they had to row and they were not up to it. They also did not understand the urgency of line handling while under sail. Later volunteers were sailors and improvement was noted. This was part of the learning experience, dealing with volunteers while acquiring a feeling for how the periauger handled under varying conditions.

It seemed that rowing was a fairly simple process but most volunteers were not used to it. After two years experimentation, now the sweeps are used immediately and people got thinking about rowing, before setting the sails. This is also an instruction period. It was found that the boat could be moved with six oars at a speed in excess of 2 knots. With experience, the crew also learned that the periauger handled fairly well if people planned ahead while rowing.

Sailing was a lot easier but brought a new set of problems. The periauger is heavy and does not have a keel. Leeward drift was a constant factor and, since there is no record of lee boards, such were not used. Now volunteers were shifted around to get the leeward gunwale lower so as to limit drift. Setting sails led to many changes and alterations. The masts were initially 1.5 m shorter than designed due to bridge heights. Two sets of masts were made. One was solid pine and correct, but quite heavy. The other was a much lighter composite that could be stepped readily with three people. In the past, two men could probably have stepped the pine logs by themselves but during the trials, the masts were a problem:

Tacking is always an exercise in judgment. The periauger sailed well with a quartering breeze. Speeds in excess of 6 knots were noted on many occasions. When the boat ran out of space and had to come about, a sudden, and dramatic, drop in speed was faced. To counter this, the crew tried backing the sails, pulling the bow through with an oarsman, or roll tacking. Rolling tacking is definitely a modern technique where weight is shifted to one side and it was not altogether satisfactory. Using a sweep to propel the bow through the eye of the wind worked quite well but seemed like extra work for a small crew. Backing the sail could be done by one person while the helmsman handled the sails and it represented the best combination of traits if momentum was lost.

Turning rapidly was impossible. What appeared to be a smooth handling vessel with a quartering breeze changed to a slow moving tub with lighter wind. The periauger did not respond readily to the helm. The tiller bar was also set wrong because the helmsman's knees were in the way if he sat down. A longer tiller and a change in the angle of the tiller were necessary, and implemented when the rudder broke, another indication that the design was wrong.

There were numerous adjustments to lines, blocks and cleats the crew was tried to make the rig more efficient. All cleats broke off the masts because they were not anchored sufficiently to withstand sweating the lines or even moderate sailing conditions. Numerous block and tackle arrangements were rigged to allow one person to handle all sails if necessary. The lines by which sails were bent onto the masts were adjusted to make them looser so the sail could come down in a hurry – the classic response in a blow.

The crew spent a lot of time trying to make the combined throat and peak halyard arrangement work. Eventually it was decided that separate blocks and lines had to be made to the throat and peak. This adjustment was not necessary and was not implemented until the masts were broken.

DAMAGE AND REPAIR

Both composite masts broke because they were not plugged high enough. In fact, the thwart mast partners served as the fulcrum to snap the mast in rough water. The stubs of the masts now serve as the masts when the vessel is trailered in local parades. When the masts were repaired, they were lengthened to the original design specification. This 1.52 m addition solved numerous problems, especially those associated with a single halyard for the throat and peak. The additional height meant that the gaff could be brought high enough to spread the sail at the cuff and the peak could then be drawn up further to spread the sail along the leech.

The rudder broke, probably because it was not big enough and did not sit deep enough in the water. These corrections were made midway along the voyage home and then improved the following winter, by increasing the rudder's depth and moving it slightly forward.

After two years of being in and out of the water, there is another type of damage. Sunlight has damaged the epoxy glues. What is interesting about this damage relates to the age old problem of logboats. The wood grain is exposed at the ends of the vessel. As it turns out, the damage at the modern bow and stern matches similar damage seen on skiffs built in the same tradition that have survived.

CONCLUSIONS

Over the last two years, experimental trials shed light on periaugers, knowledge that has been lost for the last 130 years. While we tried to improve speed, handling, and many other things, this is typical of virtually all sailors. Local volunteers and East Carolina University students regularly sail the periauger and learn something about North Carolina's sailing heritage. However, this specific reproduction met four or five of Ole Crumlin-Pederson's reasons for building a replica (Crumlin-Pedersen 2006: 3).

The whole exercise is best summed up by Bill Anderson, a teacher who works with special children: »Although Periauger is sailed by a bunch of older people [...] the legacy she leaves is for the younger generation ... it is our hope that we can inspire at least a few of those kids to become interested in sailing or preserving our maritime history through programs like ECU's Maritime Studies and the NC Maritime Museum or that someday they'll buy an old wooden boat and preserve it with their children, otherwise this history will be lost to the future [...] perhaps they'll remember a group of wacky old people playing with sails on the lawn and throwing the balls up in the air and think [...] »I want to go sailing [...] That's the gift we leave with Bath [...] and North Carolina« (Bill Anderson, 16 October 2005).

The question Seán McGrail posed in Roskilde (McGrail 2006: 8) »does experimental boat building have a future, especially in our visual and tactile world?« should be answered with a resounding yes.

ACKNOWLEDGEMENTS

This paper would not have been possible without the assistance of Michael B. Alford, retired curator, North Carolina Maritime Museum, Paul Fontenoy, North Carolina Maritime Museum staff and volunteers at the North Carolina Maritime Museum, and the Friends of the Periauger, Hertford County, North Carolina.

REFERENCES

Alford, M. B., 1993a, *French Sources of Vernacular Boatbuilding Practices in the Carolinas*. Paper presented to The Conference on Underwater Archaeology, Society for Historical Archaeology, Kansas City/Kansas.

1993b, Periauger, Pettiagua, Petty Puzzler: Kunner, Cooner, Colloquial Conundrum. *Tributaries*, 5, 31-33.

Alford, M. B., Babits L. E. & Pecorelli III, H., 1996, *A Working Definition of Periauger*. Paper presented to the Society for Historical Archaeology. Cincinnati/Ohio.

Andersen, E., Crumlin-Pedersen, O., Vadstrup, S. & Vinner, M., 1997, *Roar Ege Skuldelev 3 Skibet som Arkaeologisk Eksperiment*. Roskilde.

Bratten, J. R., 2002, The Gondola Philadelphia and the Battle of Lake Champlain. *Studies in Nautical Archaeology*, no. 6. College Station/Texas.

Crumlin-Pedersen, O., 2006, Experimental Archaeology and Ships – Principles, Problems and Examples. In: *ISBSA 10*, 1-7.

Crumlin-Pedersen, O. & Trakadas, A. (eds), 2003, *Hjortspring, a pre-Roman iron-age warship in context*. Ships and Boats of the North, vol. 5. Roskilde.

Fleetwood, W. C., Jr.,1995, *Tidecraft*. Tybee Island/Georgia.

Lefler, H. T. (ed.), 1967, *New Voyage To Carolina by John Lawson 1709*. Chapel Hill/N. Carolina.

McGrail, S., 2006, Experimental Boat Archaeology: Has it a future? In: *ISBSA 10*, 8-15.

Merton Coulter, E. (ed.), 1958, *The Journal of William Stephens: 1741-1743*. University of Georgia Press. Athens, Georgia.

Parry, M. H. (ed.), 2000, *Aak to Zumbra. A Dictionary of the World's Watercraft*. Newport News/Virginia.

Pecorelli III, H., 1993, *The Scout Boat*. Unpublished Student Paper, Program in Maritime History, East Carolina University. Greenville/N. Carolina.

Rybka, W. & Heerssen, W. (eds), 2006, *U.S. Brig Niagara Crew Handbook*. Flagship Niagara League. Erie/Pennsylvania.

RESEARCH METHODS

WILFRIED STECHER

DIMENSIONS OF ANCIENT BIGSHIPS:
CAN MODERN SHIP THEORY HELP TO SOLVE THIS ENIGMA?

In order to estimate the size of ancient fighting ships bigger than the Athenian trireme, it will help always to keep in mind that there are no archaeological finds to support such efforts. Based on written evidence and on the dimensions of the ship sheds in which triremes were stored when being out of commission, repaired or maintained, Morrison and Coates (Morrison & Coates 1990) have managed to reconstruct an Athenian *trieres*, to build and to test it at sea. Compared with images on ancient works of art this replica comes as close to its historical model as possible.

HOW TO DEDUCT DETAILS OF LARGER WARSHIPS FROM THOSE OF THE BASIC TRIEREME?

The principal dimensions of a trireme were determined by the number of oarsmen, of other crew members and officers she was intended to carry while under commission. When marine tactics gradually shifted to the concept of ramming opposing ships, the number of marines – *epibata*i – could be reduced as fighting of men against men was no longer intended as the outstanding tactic. However, soon after the end of the Peloponnesian war this development reverted and larger ships were built to board larger numbers of marines, and different kind of artillery. This was inevitable as the trireme could accommodate neither larger fighting crews nor heavier equipment.

Length – beam – draft

Length, beam and draft are the principal dimensions of a ship. The length and the beam of an ancient fighting ship are determined by the number of oarsmen she is designed to carry. The longitudinal distance between oarsmen in their working position is called the *interscalmium* by Vitruvius (*De architectura* 2, 21). It ranges from 0.88m to slightly more than 1m (Bockius 2000).

The beam of a »Four«

If, e.g. eight oarsmen are seated in every vertical section (**Fig. 1**), four on both sides of the ship, whereof two as *thranites* on the top level, one as *zygites* on the center level and one as *thalamitis* on the lowest level, the beam could be not less than four times 0.6m, the latter figure being the average shoulder width of an oarsman. Other requirements may lead to an increased beam. For this example the beam is fixed on the basis of Bockius' drawing as 6.33m.

Computation of length from estimated beam

The length of an ancient fighting ship is closely related with the total number of oarsmen and the beam assessed by the fore-going step. The total number of oarsmen divided by the number of oarsmen in a

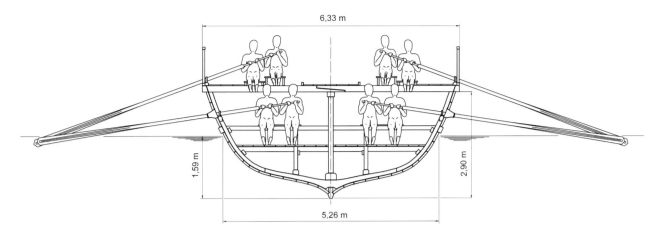

Fig. 1 Hypothetical hull-section of the *quadiremis* as proposed by Bockius (1997: appendix).

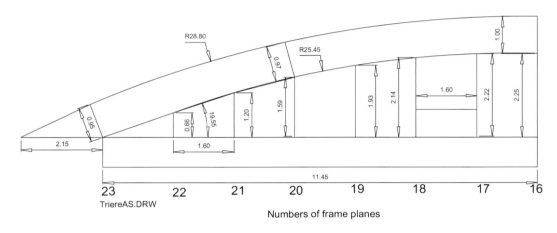

Fig. 2 After deck area of the Athenian trireme with additional contours of the *quadriremis* (Drawing W. Stecher).

vertical section yields the number of *interscalmia* amidships where the sides are parallel. For the *quadriremis* the number of oarsmen is estimated as 200 (Bockius 2008: 94). Divided by eight oarsmen per vertical section, the result is 25. Multiplied with the length of the *interscalmium*, in this example fixed as 0.9 m, it yields the length of the midship section: 25 m. The fore and the aft part of the ship where the sides are curved towards the fore and aft stems respectively measure 9.6 m forward and 11.45 m aft (**Figs 2-3**). The circular radius of the curvature on the triereme is about 21 m forward and 26-29 m aft. But the contour can also be approximated by an elliptic or a Bezier Curve. The differences are negligible.

As shipbuilding timber cannot be bent freely, these values apparently represent a limit which the ancient shipbuilders did not step below. 2 m increase of beam produce an increase of length of 1.96 m forward and 2.15 m aft.

Consequently the length (over all) is:

LOA = 22.5 m + 9.6 m + 11.45 m + (1.96 + 2.15) * (6.33 – 4.56)/2
LOA = 47.19 m

It is assumed that the shell planks of the *quadriremis* were thicker than those of the trireme in accordance with the three-dimensional scale factor, which will be computed below.

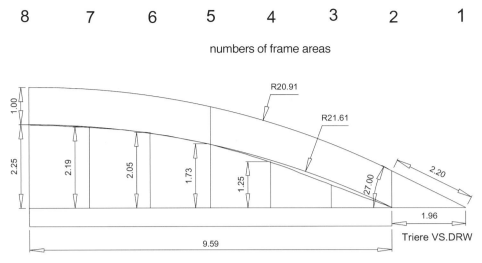

Fig. 3 Fore deck area of Athenian trireme with additional deck contour of the *quadriremis* (Drawing W. Stecher).

The draft

The draft of an ancient fighting ship is determined by the vertical distance between the lowest oar ports and the waterline. Differently than on a cargo ship it can be changed only within very narrow limits. This is the reason why fighting ships must be ballasted if the draft is substantially less than moulded.

Offset table

The offset **Table 1** is a compilation of the beam(s) of a ship at a number of vertical planes and of waterlines, both with equal distances between them. The offset table of the quadrireme is obtained by multiplying all elements of the offset table of the triere with the applicable scale factors for length, beam and draft.
The frame planes or waterline planes are computed within Windows Excel using Simpson's Rules as applicable. Any other algorithm for numerical integration can be used as well. Software for personal computers is available in the market at relatively high prices.

Froude's number: What does it mean?

Froude's number (FN) describes the relation between the speed through the water and the length of the waterline of a ship. It is computed by using the term:

$$FN = V/\sqrt{9.81 * LWL}$$

with V = speed through the water in m/s and LWL the length in the waterline in m. Obviously FN has no dimension. Ships of identical Froude's numbers generate identical wave patterns. When the speed is increased the FN will increase also. When the FN reaches a value of 0.4 the resistance will start to rise, because the wave resistance share will no longer be negligible. This is the point where a further substantial increase of propulsive power will yield no appreciable increase of speed.
Ancient warships generally were not able to operate against increasing wave resistance. This means that for any obtainable speed the FN should remain below 0.4. **Table 3** below shows that this was the case with the exception of the trireme which came close to the border when running at action speed.

Waterline m	#	22	21	20	19	18	17	16	9	8	7	6	5	4	3	2	1	SH m	Waterline area M²			
2.0	10	1.06	1.56	1.94	2.14	2.20	2.26	2.28	2.28	2.28	2.20	2.06	1.74	1.26	0.64	0.06	0.02	2.0				
1.8	9	0.94	1.50	1.92	2.12	2.18	2.22	2.26	2.26	2.26	2.18	2.04	1.72	1.24	0.64	0.06	0.02	1.8				
1.6	8	0.80	1.36	1.80	2.06	2.08	2.16	2.18	2.18	2.18	2.14	1.98	1.68	1.20	0.64	0.06	0.02	1.6				
1.4	7	0.60	1.16	1.66	1.94	1.96	2.08	2.12	2.12	2.12	2.08	1.82	1.80	1.18	0.64	0.06	0.02	1.4				
1.2	6	0.24	0.92	1.48	1.60	1.80	1.94	2.02	2.02	2.02	1.98	1.80	1.50	1.08	0.58	0.06	0.02	1.2	106.1			
1.0	5		0.54	1.20	1.30	1.64	1.78	1.86	1.86	1.86	1.84	1.68	1.38	0.96	0.50	0.06	0.02	1.0	94.9	94.9		
0.8	4			0.78	0.88	1.10	1.56	1.66	1.66	1.66	1.66	1.48	1.18	0.78	0.40	0.06	0.02	0.8	79.6	79.6	79.6	
0.6	3			0.28	0.60	0.84	1.18	1.38	1.38	1.38	1.38	1.22	0.92	0.56	0.24	0.06		0.6	63.1	63.1	63.1	63.1
0.4	2				0.40	0.36	0.62	0.80	0.80	0.80	0.68	0.70	0.44	0.22	0.08			0.4	34.3	34.3	34.3	34.3
0.2	1				0.06	0.1	0.18	0.22	0.22	0.22	0.20	0.18	0.12	0.02				0.2	9.0	9.0	9.0	9.0
0.0	0					0.1	0.18	0.20	0.20	0.20	0.20	0.18						0.0	8.0	8.0	8.0	8.0
		Frame areas m²							Frame areas m²													
		6.04	13.81	20.20	23.64	26.57	29.84	31.44	31.44	31.44	21.99	19.81	16.00	10.83	5.52	0.78	0.23		Displacement m³			
																			66.8	46.9	29.7	24.3

Table 1 Offset table for *Olympias* (Data taken from Morrison & Coates 1990: 222).

However, the test runs performed by Morrison and Coates (1990) were executed at somewhat lower speeds. This implies that Olympias had a slightly lower hull speed than computed on the basis of her dimensions. Equally, the hypothetical larger fighting ships – *quadriremes* or *quinqueremes* – were with high probabilty only able to be operated at speeds below FN 0.4.

The displacement

The offset table also can be used to compute the displacement of the ship at any arbitrarily chosen draft. The waterline areas are added up using Simpson's formula as a first step. The results are the displacements at the drafts chosen as reference points. A curve of best fit is then produced by the relative function of the Excel programme used. The curve for the *quadriremis* is represented by the square equation:

$$y = 135.33 * x^3 – 694.88 * x^2 + 1356.1 * x – 789.52$$

wherein y is the displacement and x is draught. The equation is applicable for those ranges of draught, which can occur with the ship in commission.

Speed through the water

In order to assess whether the development from *triremis* to *quadriremis* resulted in superiority of the latter in military use, as all the time in naval action, the attainable speed through the water is an important criterium. Speed can be computed if resistance and/or propulsion are known.

Resistance $R_T = \rho/2 * c_T * V^2 * A$

In this formula ρ is the density of water around the ship, c_T is the coefficient of resistance for the hull. The values published by (Baumgärtel 2000: 144) for the trireme have been used for the other types too. Any differences are believed to be negligible as the hulls were similar. *V* is the speed through the water, and A is the immersed surface of the hull, computed by using a modern formula. Again any discrepancies are

Datum	Triere	Inshore-Bireme	Trireme Puteoli	Quadrireme Alba Fucens	Quinquereme Praeneste
LOA	36.17 m	30.4 m	47.4 m	44.8 m	50.2 m
LWL	29.8 m	25.07 m	39.09 m	36.9 m	41.4 m
WOA	4.56 m	3.68 m	5.27 m	5.4 m	6.64 m
WWL	3.42 m	3.32 m	4.83 m	4.9 m	4.98 m
Depth	2.1 m	1.72 m	2.90 m	2.3 m	2.38 m
Draught	1 m	0.64 m	1.2 m	1.59 m	1.54 m
Number of Oarsmen	170	48	148	200	283
Cruising speed	9.88 knots	5.75 knots	10.0 knots	8.7 knots	7 knots
Action speed	13.98 knots	8.15 knots	14.16 knots	12.3 knots	9.2 knots
Weight of hull	21 t	11.7 t	24.2 t	33.7 t	48.1 t
Crew & equipment	17 t	4.8 t	11.0 t	20.5 t	29.0 t
Marines & weapons	8.9 t	18.0 t	2.0 t	100.0 t	96.0 t
Froude's number Cruising/Action	0.32 / 0.45	0.17 / 0.24	0.26 / 0.37	0.26 / 0.37	0.28 / 0.39

Table 2 Data of four types of super ships originate from trireme data.

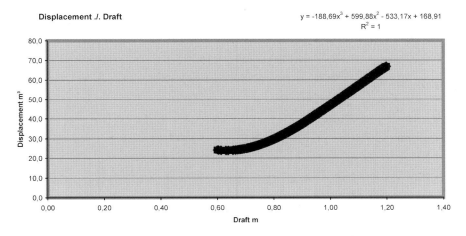

Displacement ./. Draft

$y = -188,69x^3 + 599,88x^2 - 533,17x + 168,91$
$R^2 = 1$

Table 3 Displacement as a function of draught of *Olympias*.

believed to be negligible. With more than one oarsman seated on the same side of the thwart the outboard oarsmen probably could not apply force in the same way as the center oarsmen. This would reduce the product of force and way and thus the speed of the ship. It has to be assessed whether an increase in force was feasible to compensate for the decrease of way.

Speed and power

The development from the trireme to bigger warships obviously created the technical basis for the transition from ramming tactic to gunning and boarding which slowly started to govern naval battles climaxing at *Actium*. However, did it actually put the obsolescent ramming completely out of use? One reason could have been that super ships were substantially slower than triremes.

Again this can be assessed by computation. Speed through the water of the »five« discussed here was 7.0 knots under cruising conditions and 9.2 knots in action. With 9.9 knots cruising and 14 knots in action the trireme was faster. However, with the bigger ships and their stronger construction the surplus in speed may not have been enough to inflict letal damage to bigger ships. All considerations referring to a »four« are equally applicable to other larger ships or to ships for special service such as inshore or fluvial. The table below shows results for four types discussed by Bockius (1997).

The data in **Table 3** are approximations. A large number of marginal conditions had to be estimated. Test of scale models in a towing tank could lead to deviating results. However, it can be accepted that larger ships were not substantially faster, possibly noticeably slower than the reference, the Athenian triere. Larger ships, however could embark large numbers of marines and/or naval versions of artillery such as onagers. The potential use of these assets in action is beyond the scope of this paper.

Before taking a decision to model one or the other types simulation with the Excel Wizard for displacement and/or the Excel Wizard for length programmes used for the above computations could help to find the most economic solution. Even if ancient emperors were willing to spend any amount of money to win a war, their funds were never unlimited so that they had to be spent in the cheapest way to accomplish their military and/or political objectives.

CONCLUSIONS

The author has tried with this contribution to demonstrate to nautical archaeologists that ship theory offers means and methods suitable to provide answers to questions which were put forward repeatedly in the past, and still asked in the present. He will be pleased to share the results of his research on ancient bigships with every scientist who is interested. This includes the provision of copies of the programmes developed by him for these purposes.

Caution though must be recommended. Ship theory is no pastime activity. Popular textbooks frequently are volumes of many hundred pages. New, modern textbooks of wooden shipbuilding are very rare. Most titles go back to at least the end of WWII. They are sometimes difficult to read and to understand because older textbooks may still use the old units foot, inch, pound, and pint, while computations nowadays are done using the SI units. Thus a close cooperation between scientists from both disciplines is recommended.

REFERENCES

Baumgärtel, F., 2000, Rechnergestützte Analyse des hydrodynamischen Leistungsverhaltens historischer Schiffe. *Jahrbuch der Schiffbautechnischen Gesellschaft*, 94, 136-146.

Bockius, R., 1997, Vegetius und die Klassifizierung römischer Kriegsschiffe in der kaiserzeitlichen Flotte. In: D. Baatz & R. Bockius, *Vegetius und die römische Flotte*. Monographien des Römisch-Germanischen Zentralmuseums, no. 39. Mainz.

2000, *Gleichmaß oder Vielfalt? Zum interscalmium bei Vitruv (De architectura I2,2If.)*. In: *Studia Antiquaria. Festschrift für Niels Bantelmann zum sechzigsten Geburtstag*. Universitäts-forschungen zur Prähistorischen Archäologie, no. 63. Bonn 2000, 111-125.

2008, Model reconstructions and full-scale replicas. Ships and boats in the Museum of Ancient Navigation, Mainz, and their museological purpose. In: M.-J. Springmann & H. Wernicke (eds), *Historical boat and ship replicas*. Conference-proceedings on the scientific perspectives and the limits of boat and ship replicas, Torgelow 2007, 91-95. Friedland/Mecklenburg.

Morrison, J. S. & Coates, J. F., 1990, *Die athenische Triere*. Mainz.

FRÉDÉRIC GUIBAL · PATRICE POMEY

ANCIENT SHIPWRECKS, NAVAL ARCHITECTURE AND DENDROCHRONOLOGY IN THE WESTERN MEDITERRANEAN

Several methods exist to date shipwrecks. By cargo analysis the last voyage of a ship can be dated by means of typology: e.g. as far as ancient shipwrecks are concerned, wrecks can be dated by amphora assemblages. Besides that, applying radiocarbon dating or dendrochronology to wooden hull elements can date the shipbuilding. In all dating attempts, ^{14}C successfully supplies a time range connected with the formation of the tree rings (Bowman 1990; Evin & Oberlin 2001). Meanwhile, dendrochronology is able to date more exactly to the felling year of trees from which architectural elements were made provided that the ship ring-width series are reliably crossdated with a well replicated tree-ring calendar or master chronology (Baillie 1982). Hence the most important tool for a dendrochronological dating is the master chronology. In Central and W. Europe, specific types chronologies are available each several centuries long (Baillie 2002). In the European part of the Mediterranean establishing master chronologies meets difficulties which are caused by a lesser frequency of wooden artefacts due to a lesser use of timber material in that region in the past. In addition to that, except in coastal areas, the soil conditions are often disadvantageous to the preservation of organic material such as wood (Guibal 1992; 1996).

However, there is a wealth of archaeological remains provided by ancient shipwrecks from the French Mediterranean seashore. This heritage is of high interest, not only for dendrochronology, but also for ancient maritime, economical and naval history studies. Ship timbers are most valuable from an archaeological perspective in order to document shipbuilding techniques; additionally, their dendrochronological analysis can shed light on morphological and anatomical details of wooden elements which is also helpful to the interpretation of ship construction: dendrochronology can determine (1) which tree species were used in ancient shipbuilding, (2) how timber was converted into architectural elements, and (3) where the ship could have been built (Rival 1991). Finally, dendrochronology provides any kind of ship archaeological research with very accurate dating (Guibal & Pomey 2003).

Large amounts of samples taken from numerous different architectural elements of the above mentioned ancient shipwrecks were analysed by dendrochronology. Capable to resolve chronological questions raised by shipwrecks, dendrochronology also benefits from data supplied by wrecks of which many make up homogeneous collections (1st c. B.C. to Late Roman Empire) in order to adapt W. Mediterranean master chronologies. Nevertheless, in spite of the advantage provided by the many shipwrecks available for analyses, ignoring of the place where the ship was built and ignoring of the geographical area where the trees grew, is a serious drawback that slows down cross-correlation between wrecks. Indeed, although research on ship cargo or shipboard items allows to determine the ultimate route of a ship, and to estimate the area where the cargo was loaded, it can neither provide the dating of shipbuilding nor information about the location of shipyards.

Meanwhile dendrochronological analysis of ring-width series can assess the felling dates of trees used for ship construction and geographical areas where those trees grew by developing a network of master chronologies spatially dense enough in order (1) to warrant dating, (2) to localize a potential area where the trees could have grown, and (3) to where the ship could have been built.

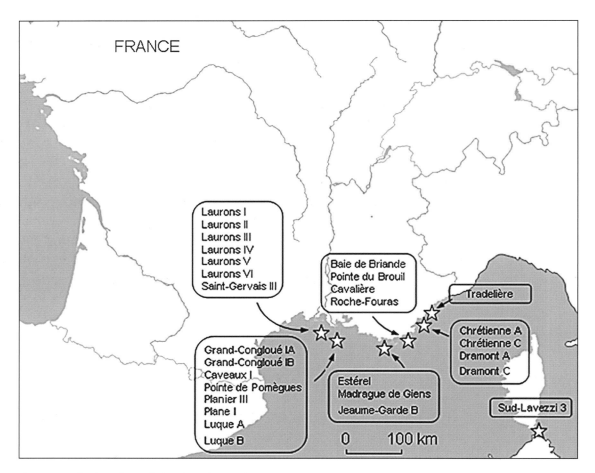

Fig. 1　Localisation of sampled ancient shipwrecks.

In order to answer these questions and to build up a master chronologies network for dating ring-width series in the W. Mediterranean area, a research project called »Dendrochronology and Dendromorphology of Ancient Mediterranean Shipwrecks« has been launched since 1991 by the Centre Camille Jullian (CNRS – Université de Provence), Laboratoire de Chrono-Ecologie (CNRS – Université de Franche-Comté), and since 1994 in collaboration with the Institut Méditerranéen d'Ecologie et de Paléoécologie (CNRS – Université d'Aix-Marseille Paul Cézanne), assisted by the Département des Recherches Archéologiques Subaquatiques et Sous-Marines, and with support by the French Ministry of Culture.

MATERIALS AND METHODS

Sampling is based on well-known shipwrecks which are selected according to geographical, archaeological and chronological criteria. That involves: (1) geographical areas where several wrecks are reported; (2) shipwrecks which are known to provide representative valuable wooden remains; (3) and, for which the probability is high to obtain, high cross-correlation between mean ring-width chronologies.

So far, nine fieldwork campaigns have been carried out during which 28 shipwrecks have been sampled in seven geographical areas (**Fig. 1**): Gulf of Fos, Bay of Marseilles, Hyères islands, W. Maures coast, Esterel coast, Bay of Cannes, Straight of Bonifaccio (S. Corsica). Based on the analyses of cargo, shipboard items and – sometimes – coins, those wrecks are dated between the 2nd c. B.C. and the 4th c. A.D. Some of the remains had disappeared after their initial excavation. All together, 21 shipwrecks were considered. Chrétienne A and Chrétienne C wrecks were analysed by S. Wicha (1997: 45-46), Dramont A and Dramont C wrecks by Ch. Dagneau (unpublished).

Each of the architectural elements were sampled for wood anatomy identification. For dendrochronological analysis, for each tree species, at least 12 pieces were sampled among those which offered the longest ring series. The selection was carried out also with the aim to proof repairs or timber re-use as sources which illuminate the history of a ship. To that purpose, transverse sections of each timber had to be examined carefully. Samples were kept waterlogged in order to cut off one to three fresh radii using a razor blade. Then ring-widths were measured with a 1/100 mm precision. Afterwards, all the elementary series (Kaennel & Schweingruber 1995) of a same tree species are compared by using correlation statistical tests, and by comparing the visual correspondance of ring-width curves (Baillie 1995). Once two elementary series from the same ship timber are cross-dated, a mean chronology is built up; then cross-correlations between pieces are traced by the same method so as to build up a mean chronology for the ship.

RESULTS

Wood anatomy

Out of 1400 samples, 25 tree species representative of three biogeographical units have been identified. In terms of present geographical distribution, out of 25 species, eight species are located at low elevation in the Mediterranean vegetation stage and therefore are often present near the seashore: *Pinus halepensis*, *Pinus pinea*, *Pinus maritima*, *Olea europaea*, *Quercus sp.*, *Quercus ilex*, *Castanea sativa*, *Celtis australis*. Eleven species are characterized by a wide geographical distribution, from medio-temperate Europe to low elevation Mediterranean areas restricted to river edges and lagoons: *Acer sp.*, *Alnus glutinosa*, *Carpinus betulus*, *Cornus sp.*, *Fagus silvatica*, *Fraxinus oxyphylla*, *Juglans regia*, *Populus sp.*, *Salix sp.*, *Tilia sp.*, *Ulmus campestris*. Six species are conifer trees from mountain and subalpine vegetation stages: *Abies alba*, *Larix decidua*, *Picea abies*, *Pinus leucodermis*, *Pinus nigra*, *Pinus silvestris*.

Tree species identified on each wreck are so numerous and come from so diverse biogeographical regions that usually no reliable limitation of geographical areas where ships were built could be given. The only exceptions were two wrecks (Pointe de la Luque B; Cavalière) for which taxonomy of the hull proofed was very homogeneous, and the identified species (*Larix decidua*, *Pinus leucodermis*) were characterized by a restricted geographical distribution (Guibal & Pomey 2003). Therefore, dendrochronology also appears essential not only in dating shipbuilding but also in assessing the geographical area of shipbuilding by means of correlations gradients throughout the different chronology networks.

Dendrochronology

The current state of chronologies which have been based on eight tree species among the most frequently encountered on ancient ship finds off the French Mediterranean coast is summarised in a bar diagram (**Fig. 2**). On the X-axis are reported rectangles whose length is proportional to the ring-width chronology, and width is proportional to the number of elementary series which are included in the ship chronology. These chronologies are not established firmly in time because they have not been dated by means of ring-width patterns; nevertheless, in order to sketch their timely distribution, dating based on cargo, shipboard

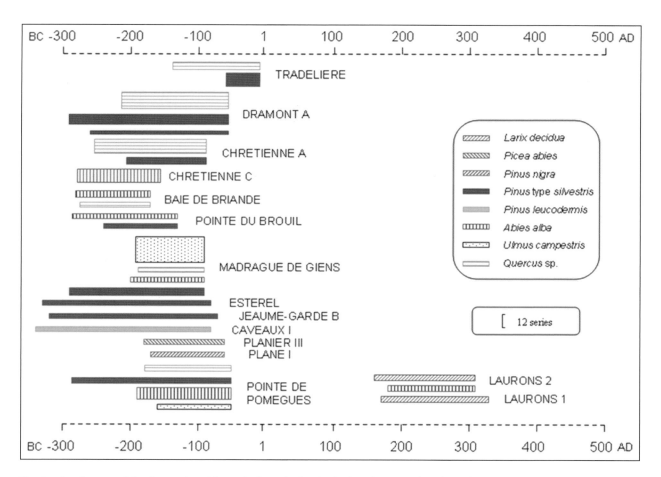

Fig. 2 Bar-diagram of floating ancient shipwreck chronologies. Dashed x-axis means that chronologies are not anchored in time.

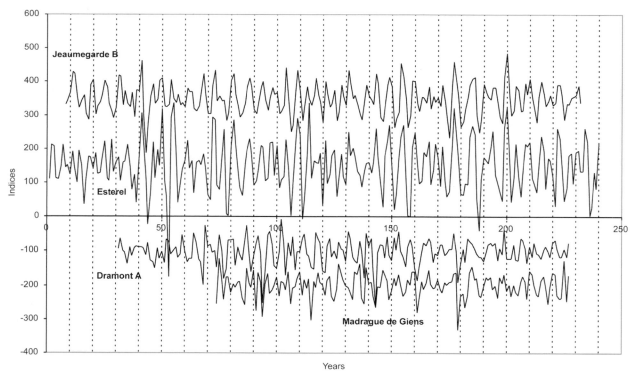

Fig. 3 *Pinus silvestris* cross-correlated shipwreck indexed chronologies.

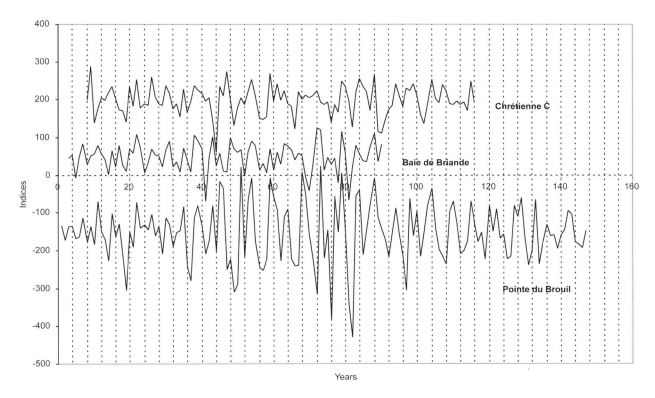

Fig. 4 *Abies alba* cross-correlated shipwreck indexed chronologies.

items and/or coins appears along the X-axis. There are shown only chronologies representative of tree species whose ring-width series can be accurately cross-dated; for that reason chronologies of willow or poplar are missing. All together, eight tree species are considered here: six conifer species (*Abies alba, Larix decidua, Picea abies, Pinus leucodermis, Pinus nigra, Pinus silvestris*) and two broad-leaved species (*Quercus sp., Ulmus campestris*).

Chronologies span between the end of the 5th c. B.C. and the first half of the 4th c. A.D. Year sequences of the 3rd, 2nd and 1st c. B.C. are outstandingly well represented. Three tree species (Scots pine, white fir, oak) and seven sites are involved in significant cross-correlations between shipwrecks:

– Scots pine (*Pinus silvestris*) at Jeaume-Garde B, Cap de l'Estérel, Dramont A, and Madrague de Giens (**Fig. 3**),

– White fir (*Abies alba*) at Chrétienne C, Baie de Briande, and Pointe du Brouil (**Fig. 4**),

– Oak (*Quercus sp.*) at Baie de Briande and Dramont A (**Fig. 5**).

Such a coincidence involving high-frequency interannual variations between two curves means that timber used for these hulls comes from trees that grew under similar climate conditions. That does not mean they grew in the same forest: in mountain areas, locations could be close, whilst at low elevations, they could be a couple of hundred kilometres distant, sometimes even more.

Besides that, the example of the synchronism between the Scots pine growth curves of Dramont A and Madrague de Giens (**Fig. 6**) has different meaning. Again, there is a fair correspondence involving the high-frequency variations evidencing trees developed under similar climate conditions. However in addition to that, there is a remarkable synchronization involving the low and middle-frequency variations which attest that the trees were similarly affected by small disturbances which are due to very local factors, and evidencing how a same pine forest was used for producing strakes used for two different merchant ships.

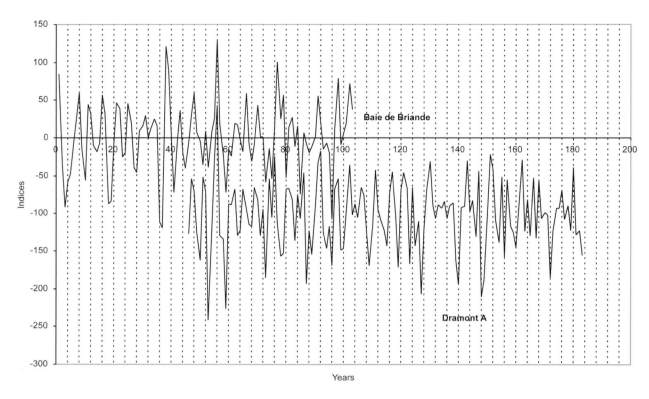

Fig. 5 *Quercus* sp. cross-correlated shipwreck indexed chronologies.

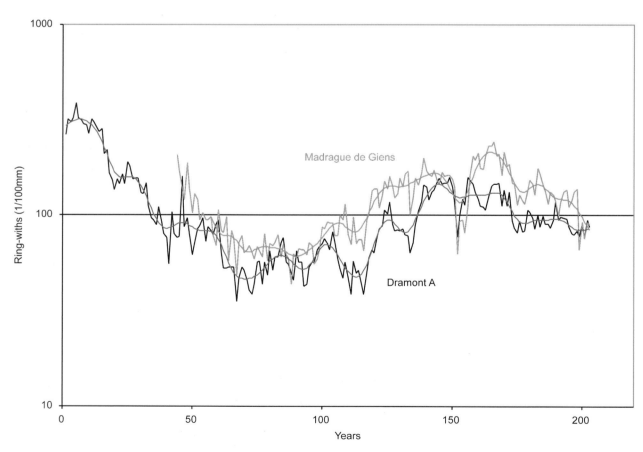

Fig. 6 Synchronised *Pinus silvestris* raw-data mean chronologies from the ship finds Dramont A and Madrague de Giens.

This result shows that in that forest whose geographical location remains unknown, Scots pine trees were devoted for naval architecture during at least 20 or 30 years, that is to say the time interval between the supposed construction of the ships Madrague de Giens and Dramont A.

Moreover, it must be stressed that on the same ships, another common tree species (oak) was identified allowing to establish a mean oak chronology for each shipwreck. These oak chronologies were compared to each other but without an acceptable cross-correlation. This failure can be interpreted as follows: the availability of oak whose biogeographical characteristics suggest stands close to the sea and, so, close to the shipyards, was much higher than Scots pine trees. Many oak stands close to the seashore might have been available for supplying shipyards, therefore increasing the diversity of origins.

DISCUSSION

Difficulties in crossdating mean chronologies obtained from different shipwrecks probably result to a large extent from the fact that trees used for shipbuilding may have grown in different site conditions or in different geographical regions, characterized by too different bioclimatic conditions. However, although the ships are contemporaneous, the overlap between two mean ship chronologies may be too short to provide reliable crossdating if we consider that trunks were sawn to produce strakes which do not extend to the outermost ring (Kaennel & Schweingruber 1995). Therefore external rings may have been lost during woodworking, shortening the potential extension of a mean ship chronology. Also the number of individual series included in some site chronologies may be too small; even if the number of elementary chronologies included in mean site chronology is high, the representativeness of the latter is sometimes low due to the fact that most of the elementary chronologies may come from a single tree as it is often the case for most of the strakes that make up the hull. That was done deliberately by ancient shipbuilders in order to optimize the use of timber (Guibal & Pomey 2004).

It seems probable that ignoring of the place where the ship was built and where the trees grew, slows down the progress as this study has shown by the small number of cross-correlations between wrecks. Nevertheless, besides significant cross-correlations involving three species and seven sites, a common forest origin has been proved for the Dramont A and Madrague de Giens ship finds. Such a result should encourage underwater archaeologists, naval architectures and dendrochronology experts towards a closer collaboration.

ACKNOWLEDGEMENTS

The project has been carried out with financial support by the French Ministry of Culture and with the assistance of Département des Recherches Archéologiques Subaquatiques et Sous-Marines.

The authors are particularly grateful to all divers and archaeologists, and to the various crews of research vessel L'Archéonaute for help during fieldwork campaigns.

REFERENCES

Baillie, M. G. L., 1982, Tree-Ring Dating and Archaeology. London.

1995, A slice through time. Dendrochronology and precision dating. London.

2002, Future of dendrochronology with respect to archaeology. Dendrochronologia, 20, 69-85.

Bowman, S., 1990, Radiocarbon dating: interpreting the past. London.

Evin, J. & Oberlin, C., 2001, Les développements récents en datation par le radiocarbone pour l'archéologie. In: J.-N. Barrandon, P. Guibert & V. Michel (eds), Datation. Actes des XXIe Rencontres Internationales d'Archéologie et d'Histoire d'Antibes. Antibes, 93-111.

Guibal, F., 1992, Dendrochronologie des épaves de navire en Méditerranée Occidentale. Mediterraneo, 1, 77-87.

1996, Dendrochronological Studies in the French Mediterranean Area. In: J. S. Dean, D. M. Meko & T. W. Swetnam (eds), *Tree Rings, Environment and Humanity*. Proceedings of the International Conference, Tucson, Arizona, 17-21 May, 1994. Radiocarbon. Tucson/Arizona, 505-513.

Guibal, F. & Pomey, P., 2003, Timber Supply and Ancient Naval Architecture. In: *ISBSA 9*, 35-41.

2004, Dendrochronologie et construction navale antique. *Revue d'Archéométrie*, 28, 35-42.

Kaennel, M. & Schweingruber, F. H., 1995, *Multilingual Glossary of Dendrochronology*. Bern.

Rival, M., 1991, *La charpenterie navale romaine. Matériaux, méthodes, moyens*. Travaux du Centre Camille Jullian, 4. Paris.

Wicha, S., 1997, *Analyse dendrochronologique de deux épaves antiques Chrétienne A et C*. Mémoire de D.E.A. Préhistoire, Archéologie, Histoire et Civilisations de l'Antiquité et du Moyen-Age. Université de Provence, Aix-en-Provence.

UFUK KOCABAŞ

ÇAMALTı BURNU I SHIPWRECK: THE ANCHORS

The 13th-c. shipwreck at the Çamaltı Burnu (Cape Çamaltı) on the N.W. coast of Marmara Island in the Sea of Marmara was excavated between 1998 and 2004 under the direction of Prof. Nergis Günsenin, granted by Istanbul University[1]. Resting 22 to 32 m deep, the shipwreck lies to the S. of Çamaltı Burnu, approximately 110 m away from the cape and 45 m away from the coast itself (**Fig. 1**). The finds from the site include amphorae scattered on the sandy sea floor, more than thirty iron anchors and flat based storage jars lying in the area between.

Although it is difficult to imagine the disaster the ship faced at Çamaltı Burnu, it is assumed that it might have sunk due to a strong storm from W. or S.W. W. storms, sometimes called »squalls«, which unexpectedly blow around Marmara Archipelago especially in summer, may have forced the ship dangerously close to the coast, and after pounding onto the rocks, the ship may have been blown into the inlet, where it sank. The fact that the cargo lay in three separate areas suggest that the ship tried to escape from the storm by jettisoning its cargo.

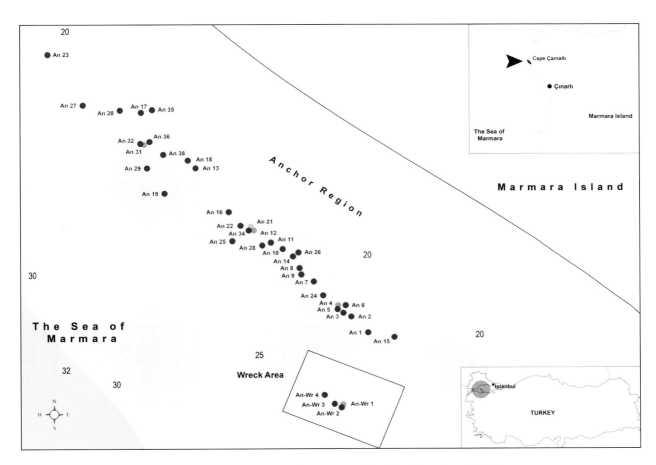

Fig. 1   Location map, wreck area and anchor region (Çamaltı Burnu I wreck archive-Illustration Ç. Çakir).

Fig. 2   Çamaltı Burnu I. – Raising operation of Y-shaped An 3 (Photo R. Dönmez).

Our early observations determined the form and the position of the anchors; they were subsequently added to the plan. Visual documentation work included *in-situ* drawings, black and white photography and slides. Conservation and restoration work, as well as the historical studies on the anchors, has been conducted by the author since 2003 within the scope of a project[2].

UNDERWATER WORK AND RECOVERY

The underwater stage of the project, conducted in 2003 and 2004 through 150 dives totalling 4204 min of work, recovered anchors mostly dating to the 13th c. A.D. After seven years of excavation, the number of iron anchors salvaged reached thirty seven, five from the wreck area (abbreviated as *An-Wr*) and thirty two from the anchor region (abbreviated as *An*), weighing in total approximately 1.5 tons. Thirteen anchors belong to the T-shaped Kapitän type D (Kapitän 1984), eighteen to the Y-shaped Kapitän type E; one matches the half moon-shaped Kapitän type E and one is to be identified as grapnel type. The remaining four finds consist merely of shank parts, so their typology could not be determined. Three pieces of lead stocks, not related to the iron anchors, were also recovered.

After the anchors had been completely detached from the seabed in 2003 and 2004, raising operations took place. A carrier with a steel framework and a lift bag with a capacity of 100 kg were used for this purpose (**Fig. 2**). For land transportation and storing of the anchors, fifteen wooden cases were constructed and their interiors were coated with polyester and fibreglass (Kocabaş 2003).

STORING, PASSIVE PROTECTION AND PACKAGING

Surface cleaning of the finds was done with plastic hammers and sharp-pointed chisel in order to avoid damage to the concretion layer covering them. During the process, the artefacts were kept wet to prevent damage through rapid drying.

In order to prevent rapid drying, water was sprayed on the finds with hand sprays at regular intervals during the day, and the progress was constantly monitored. In the meantime, the anchors in the excavation laboratory on Marmara Island were weighed and documented by means of digital and slide photography and video recordings, and then labels, made of thick polypropylene plates prepared by thermal printing, were attached. In order to prevent damage that might occur during the transportation from Marmara Island to Istanbul, the anchors were wrapped with bubble packs of various sizes. Stryrofoam® pieces were placed between

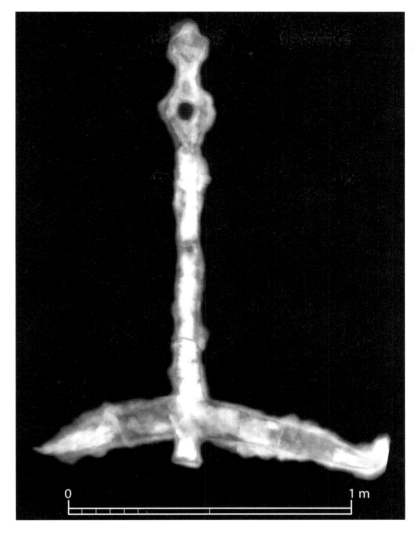

Fig. 3   Çamaltı Burnu I. – X Ray of Y-shaped An 4 (Gammagraphy U. Kocabas, assembled by Ç. Çakir).

these packages, and also fixed on the wooden cases as barriers to prevent slipping. In addition, worn tyres were placed under the cases to minimize shaking.

RADIOGRAPHIC ANALYSIS

Radiographic methods were employed in order to understand the state of corrosion, to get a better idea of manufacturing techniques and to discover the precise areas where un-oxidized iron remained within the concretions. Results of the analyses provided a good reference in determining the mechanical cutting points on the calcareous crust during the replica production. Most importantly, the original appearance and dimensions of the anchors, which were covered with thick concretion, were acquired before the start of five- or six-year conservation and restoration work. Thus, typological studies and computer-generated modelling based on these films were carried out along with the process of conservation and restoration. All gammagraphy films were transferred to digital media and combined into a single picture by using Adobe Photoshop 6.0 (**Fig. 3**). Drawings of these pictures were made on Macromedia FreeHand 8. In this way, the actual dimensions were acquired without awaiting the completion of protection and restoration that would take four to five years (Kocabaş & Ekinci 2006).

During the planning stage of the project, the diving surveys and radiographic analysis revealed that the concretion layer on the anchors was very thin and irregular in thickness, which is a result of environmental factors that directly affect corrosion.

CONSERVATION, RESTORATION AND REPLICA

Conservation, restoration and replica-making processes were undertaken according to the three corrosion categories defined by Robinson (Robinson 1982). Anchor *An5* represents the group of anchors whose metal was completely decomposed inside the concretion and replaced by corrosion; *An4*, the group whose metal parts were preserved relatively well throughout; and *An15*, the largest group that shows both cavities and areas of surviving iron.

Strengthening the concretion, cutting and mechanical cleaning

The first work was done on anchor *An15*. Before the cutting process, weak points on the concretion layer covering *An15* were determined by visual examination and radiographic films. The parts with thin cross sections visible in the films, and cracked, broken or worn-out surfaces were determined by visual examination. These types of surface were strengthened by FC 52 (Huntsman Co.), a fast hardening polyurethane which was also applied to glue together some parts that would have otherwise come off during the cutting process. After the strengthening work, shells were cut. Undamaged iron parts and cavities were noted in the radiography films, and cutting points were accordingly marked on the anchors.

Replication

A method has been employed similar to the examples in the literature given by Katzev & van Doorninck Jr. (1966), Rohner (1970), Frazier (1974), and Hamilton (2001). During the replica manufacture, however, unoxidized iron pieces inside the concretion were put into their original places during casting and used together with epoxy, as described by Muncher (1988), which differs in technique from the traditional processes.

Careful research had to be done in order to choose the epoxy to be used for the moulds, taking into consideration such criteria as density, curing time, viscosity, tension, resistance, maximum thickness to be cast and a suitable balance between quality and price. In the end, CW 2215- HY 5160, a Huntsman Company product, used at a ratio of 5:1 for the casting of parts with a thickness of 9 to 10 cm appeared to be the appropriate solution. For the colouring, Huntsman DW 0131 black paint was added with a ratio of 0.5%.

Once the epoxy material inside hardened, the modelling paste was removed, and the mould opened. In order to detach the mould from the replica, the mould was hammered gently.

All parts of the anchor were cast in the same way with synthetic resin and with the incorporation of any surviving iron. What was important here was to minimize errors in measurement that might occur when assembling a number of separate casts. This was accomplished by the use of the radiography films, drawings, and earlier photographs of the anchor.

After completion of the work on anchor *An15*, which belonged to the most problematic group in terms of protection and restoration, the replication of *An4*, from the group with minimum corrosion, was next

Element	*An15* metal	*An15* concretion	*An4* metal	*An4* concretion
Na	355±30	3102±221	2741±198	–
Fe	63.5±0.8%	31.9±0.6%	30.2±0.6%	–
As	7033±993	4992±705	17±3	1.4±0.2%
Br	–	62±24	120±45	–
La	–	–	2.4±0.9	–
Cr	15.9±2.8	10±1.3	12±2	1.3±0.3%
Sr	–	1103±99	2073±165	–
Sc	–	–	0.5±0.02	–
Co	42±2.3	4.1±0.3	3.6±0.21	–
Eu	–	–	0.2±0.04	–
Sb	46±11	75±17	0.5±0.2	–
Zn	–	–	9.45±4.5	–
Ni	0.3±0.02%	0.33±0.08%	0.21±0.09%	0.21±0.09%
Cu		2.5±0.2%	3.5±0.2%	3.5±0.2%
Ti	–	–	1.96±0.2%	8.8±1.6%

Table 1 Analyses of anchor iron and concretion formations (XRF and NAA).

undertaken. Due to the existence of a metal core inside the concretions, they were opened very carefully by slow hammering to prevent any damage. Eight separate parts of the anchor, all suitable for reassembly, were recovered intact. The parts were mechanically cleaned and underwent chloride decontamination. Following these operations, they were combined in accordance with drawings made from the radiography films of the anchor. The combining of ring and shank parts with the arm (only one arm recovered) was accomplished with FC52 and appropriate fabric pieces used at joints, and epoxy was applied to increase mobility and strength.

The third group consisted of completely oxidized anchors. *An5*, which contained no metal core according to the radiography films, was chosen as an example representing this group. Following the completion of its drawings at 1:1 scale, it was cut at appropriate sections by means of a small angle grinder. This was easily carried out due to the absence of un-oxidized iron inside. Cut into sections at appropriate points, each segment was divided into two longitudinally and mechanically cleaned. An epoxy replica was then made through the procedure already described.

METAL ANALYSIS

Analyses of samples of anchor iron and concretion formations were done through the methods of energy emitting x-ray fluorescence (XRF) and neutron activation analysis (NAA). The elements detected are listed in **Table 1**. Examinations of *An14* and *An4* indicated that the anchors were made of bloomery iron, and the slag inside tends to break easily.

In order to pinpoint the source of iron ore used in the manufacture of the anchors, examinations have benefited from the works of Vryonis (1962), Bryer (1982) and Pitarakis (1998) on mining in the Byzantine period. According to these scholars, one of the areas in which iron deposits were found was Chalybia to the E. of the Black Sea. In Greek mythology, the Chalybes were people who lived in the middle and E. part of the S. shore of the Black Sea and were said to have invented steel. In ancient sources, *khalybs* (steel) is used together with the term *sideros* (iron). It is also known that the iron products of this region were especially exported to the

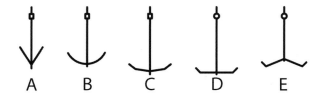

Fig. 4 Kapitän's typological table (Kapitän 1984: 43).

Aegean world through the city of Amisos (Samsun) (Belli 2004: 246). How ironworkers collected the ore near the Granikos River in the 10th c. was described by Niketos Magistos (Bryer 1982: 136).

The settlement on the Anatolian side of the Bosporus, known as Sophianae in the Byzantine period, was renamed as Çengelliköy or Çengelköy (literally »Hook Village«) by the Ottomans due to the discovery of many anchors on the coast there after the conquest of Istanbul (Aysu 1993). It has been stated that the town owes its Turkish name to the fact that in the Byzantine period ship anchors were manufactured here. Due to the lack of any written sources, it is not clear whether the anchors were manufactured in Byzantine buildings or in the monastery, which are said to be located near Kuleli in Çengelköy.

In the light of the available data, it is impossible to locate the anchor workshops or the source of the iron. In order to realize such a study, it would be necessary to determine the trace elements inside the metal and compare these with references from known ore deposits. Unfortunately, the absence of such data makes comparisons impossible[3].

TECHNOLOGY

Each anchor shows a hole under the anchor ring in the top part of the shank to insert a removable stock. We did not recover any stocks. This may indicate that wooden stocks were used instead of iron stocks. Perhaps any iron stocks present on the ship had become entirely decomposed through corrosion or, not being mounted on anchors at the time, had been stacked together in their own separate pile on the deck and somehow remained undetected somewhere on the seabed. However, there is no evidence to support either of these unlikely possibilities.

The thin hank and arms of the T- (Kapitän type D) and Y-shaped (Kapitän type E) types is the common characteristic of early wrought iron anchors. Analysis on *An4*, which has the highest percentage of unoxidized iron, leads us to the conclusion that the anchors were assembled by the forger out of 10 to 15 components.

Kapitän suggests that the Y-shaped anchors were developed because the T-shaped anchors got stuck on the seabed and were easily broken. Van Doorninck, who studied the anchors on the 7th- and 11th-c. shipwrecks of Yassi Ada and Serçelimanl, pointed out that there is no evidence that the Y-shaped design was a product of gradual evolution. Through this design change, the body length was reduced while the distance between the tooth and the stock was obtained by arms sloped downward away from the stock. The aim was to reduce the leverage power of the shank on the tips (van Doorninck 1988[4]).

The necessity for reducing the shank length is the result of the limited technology used by the makers of iron anchors in Graeco-Roman and medieval times. The nature of this technology was clearly understood when the anchors of the CAB I shipwreck were closely examined. The anchors, each with a total weight of 50 to 60 kg, were manufactured by the forging together of 10 to 15 components, each weighing 4 to 5 kg. Either arm consists of four pieces; the shank, six pieces; and the ring, one piece.

TYPOLOGY

The typology of ancient iron anchors referring to dated finds was published in 1984 by Kapitän (Kapitän 1984). It includes five types: A, B, C, D and E, which relate to different periods and objects found in known

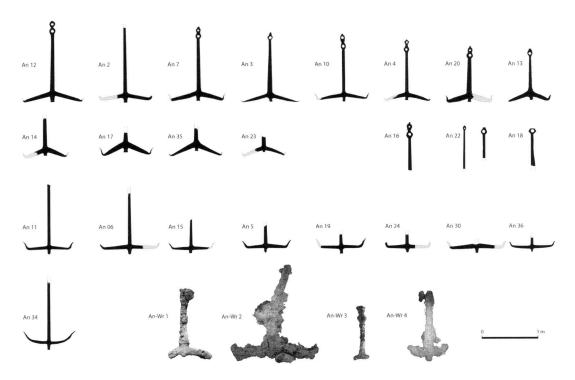

Fig. 5 Typology of Çamaltı Burnu I iron anchors (Drawing Ç. Çakir).

contexts (**Fig. 4**) As there are no instances of contemporaneity in their use or of contact between successive types, this is especially the case for the early middle ages (Riccardi 2003).

Another value conclusion is that T-shaped anchors continued to be used after the appearance of Y-shaped anchors. In the wreck area, the Y-shaped anchor *An-Wr2* were found in square K9, and the T-shaped anchor *An-Wr3* were found in squares J6-J7 (**Fig. 5**). In the anchor area, additional evidence regarding contemporaneous use of T-shaped and Y-shaped anchors has been encountered: the T-shaped *An5* was found *in situ* onto Y-shaped *An4* (**Fig. 6**).

Fig. 6 Çamaltı Burnu I. – Stratigraphy. T-shaped *An 5* on Y-shaped *An 4* (After Günsenin 2001b: 127, fig. 14).

CONCLUSIONS

The relationship between the wreck area and anchor field proved to be one of the most important and problematic aspects of research. Thirty two anchors, which were scattered over a distance of 112 m, lying parallel to the cargo and shore line, were independent from the ship context, i.e. they could not be associated with some other find securely linked to the ship. Therefore, different theories may be suggested regarding their relationship with the wreck. One is that some of the anchors in this area were used on the ship during its voyage, and the remaining were part of the cargo like the amphorae and, if the ship's destination was Constantinople, then they were being transported for repair or as scrap iron.

The number of undamaged anchors recovered, that is nine, is perfectly convenient for a ship as large as indicated by the wreck. It should be mentioned that the 11th-c. Byzantine ship at Serçe Limanı, a ship of a similar small size and with anchors of similar size, carried also nine anchors (van Doorninck 2005)

It is assumed that the scrap anchors and some of the ship's anchors were thrown into the sea to reduce weight in the face of disaster. Thus, the anchors were dropped along the 112 metres-long shoreline, where the ship was blown. In order to test the validity of this hypothesis, the route of the ship has been drawn starting from Çamaltı Burnu to the location of the wreck according to the locations of the anchors. The intention was to determine whether the locations of the anchors on the seabed were consistent with their having been thrown off the ship while she moved along this route. Their positions suggest that they could have been thrown in some cases from the port side and in other cases from the starboard side.

However there are likewise arguments pointing against such a scenario. One would be that the stowing of cargo on ships had some rules that remained unchanged for thousands of years. Heavy cargoes are loaded at the bottom part of the hold, while lighter ones are on the top part, and no cargo is transported on the deck. In the above discussed scenario, if the ship was carrying scrap anchors apart from the *amphorae*, and the crew was able to throw these quickly into the sea, then they most probably have been stowed on the deck. The anchors weighed approximately 1.5 t. Although heavy deck cargo contradicts marine tradition, this might have been disregarded in the present instance in view of the short distance of the voyage, the relative lightness of the total weight of the anchors and the potential for damage to the hull by the sharp edges of the broken anchors.

A second argument would be that the anchors in the anchor area do not belong to the wreck but to other ships which could not raise them. This might well have been the case, if the shore strip were a convenient anchoring place. It is known that some well-protected places and estuaries on sea trade routes were used for anchoring since ancient times. The fact that in ancient times Marmara Island was an important anchoring point for ships sailing from the Mediterranean or Aegean Sea to Constantinople and the Black Sea, or in a E.-W. direction into the Sea of Marmara, seems to support this view along with the fact that the island exported marbles by sea and the anchors are located on the route. Against this second argument, however, it is to confess that Çamaltı Burnu is indeed not suitable for anchoring, since it is open to W. and S.W. winds. The *in situ* examination of the anchors, excluding the arc-shaped *An34*, which may not be contemporaneous with the other ones, did not yield any evidence that they had been stuck to the seabed and could not be raised.

One of the most persuasive reasons to believe that the anchors as a group have not been lost by ships while at anchorage is that they almost all belong to the period in which Y-shaped anchors were in use and not, except for *An34*, to an earlier or later period. The proof of this is the fact that none of the T-shaped anchors have outer arms and tips shaped like those of T-shaped anchors that date before the introduction of Y-shaped anchors. Instead, they are like those of Y-shaped anchors [5].

ACKNOWLEDGEMENTS

The author is most indebted to his consultants Sait Başaran and Oktay Belli, also to Nergis Gunsenin, director of Çamaltı Burnu I underwater excavation, who provided scientific assistance in his doctorate thesis. He is grateful to Frederick H. van Doorninck, Jr. for very kindly editing this paper and providing scientific critique, and to Şinasi Ekinci and Asiye Başsari for radiographic analysis of anchors. To Işil Özsait Kocabaş, Gürkan Ergin and all his colleagues and students, the author wishes to thank for their collaboration by joining underwater and laboratory studies. – This work was supported by the Research Fund of Istanbul University. Project number: T-193/06032003 and UDP 833/19072006.

NOTES

1) Detailed information about the excavation: Günsenin 2001a; 2001b; 2001c; 2003; 2005; www.nautarch.org.

2) For more detailed information about anchors cf. Kocabaş 2005.

3) Personal communication of Ünsal Yalçın in 2005.

4) Personal communication of Frederick H. van Doorninck, Jr., in 2003.

5) Personal communication of Ünsal Yalçın in 2005.

REFERENCES

Aysu, Ç., 1993, Çengelköy, Dünden Bugüne Istanbul Ansiklopedisi. In: S. Eyice (ed.), *Dünden Bugüne İstanbul Ansiklopedisi*, II. İstanbul, 485-487.

Bryer, A. A. M., 1982, The question of Byzantine mines in the Pontos: Chalybian iron, Chaldian silver, Koloneian alum and the mummy of Cheriana. *Anatolian Studies*, 32, 133-150.

Doorninck Jr., F. H. van, 1976, The 4th century wreck at Yassi Ada. An interim report on the hull. *IJNA*, 5, 115-131.

1988, The anchors: A limited technology, a sophisticated design. *INA Newsletter*, 15.3, 24-25.

2005, The anchors. In: G. F. Bass, S. D. Matthews, J. A. Steffy & F. H. van Doorninck Jr. (eds), *Serçe Limanı. An Eleventh-Century Shipwreck*, I. College Station/Texas, 189-240.

Frazier, F., 1974, Production of artifact casts using epoxy resin. *The American Archeologist*, 1, 33-42.

Günsenin, N., 2001a, Byzantine shipwrecks discovered around the Marmara Islands (Prokonnessos): Points of departure and probable destinations. In: *TROPIS VI*, 221-222.

2001b, L'Epave de Çamaltı Burnu I (Ile de Marmara, Proconnèse): Résultats des anneés 1998-2000. *Anatolia Antiqua,* IX, 17-133.

2001c, Çamaltı Burnu I Wreck. In: O. Belli (ed.), *Istanbul University's Contributions to Archaeology in Turkey 1932-2000*. Istanbul, 252-256.

2003, L'Epave de Çamaltı Burnu I (Ile de Marmara, Proconnèse): Résultats des anneés 2001-2002. *Anatolia Antiqua,* XI, 361-376.

2005, A 13th-Century Wine Carrier: Camalti Burnu, Turkey. In: G. Bass (ed.), *Archaeology Beneath the Seven Seas*. London, 118-123.

Hamilton, D. L., 2001, *Basic Methods of Conserving Underwater Archaeological Material Culture*. www.nautarch.tamu.edu/class/ANTH605/File0.htm.

Kapitän, G., 1984, Ancient anchors-technology and classification. *IJNA*, 13.1, 33-44.

Katzev M. L. & Doorninck, F. H., 1966, Replicas of iron tools from a Byzantine shipwreck. *Studies in Conservation*, 2, 133-141.

Kocabaş, U., 2003, Çamaltı Burnu I Batığı demir çapaları üzerinde yapılan 2003 yılı çalışmaları. In: T. Tuglu (ed.), *SBT 2003, 7th Sualtı Bilim ve Teknoloji Toplantısı Bildiriler Kitabı*. Bursa, 89-96.

2005, *The Conservation, restoration and replication study of the iron anchors of Camalti Burnu I shipwreck within their historical context*. Unpublished PhD thesis, Istanbul University.

Kocabaş, U. & Ekinci, Ş., 2006, Çamaltı Burnu I Batığı demir çapalarının radyografi ile incelenmesi. In: M. Egi (ed.), *SBT 2006, 10th Sualtı Bilim ve Teknoloji Toplantısı Bildiriler Kitabı*. Istanbul, 92-98.

Muncher, D. A., 1988, Composite Casting of Partially Degraded Iron Artifacts. *Studies in Conservation,* 33, 94-96.

Pitarakis, B., 1998, Mines Anatoliennes exploitées par les Byzantins: Recherches récentes. *Revue Numismatique*, 153, 141-185.

Riccardi, E., 2003, Anchors, Kapitän's Typological Table Updated to 1996, www.infotech.sirio.it/CSAM/manifesta1i.htm.

Robinson, W. S., 1982, The Corrosion and preservation of ancient metals from marine sites. *IJNA*, 11.3, 221-231.

Rohner, J. R., 1970, Technique of making plastic casts of artefacts from permanent moulds. *American Antiquity*, 35.2, 223-226.

Vryonis, S., 1962, The question of the Byzantine mines. *Speculum*, 37, 1-17.

AOIFE DALY

THE CHRONOLOGY OF COGS AND THEIR TIMBER ORIGIN

THE COG

Results of the determination of the provenance of the earliest cogs are the subject of an article in the proceedings of the 10th ISBSA in Roskilde (Hocker & Daly 2006). Since writing that article, the author has completed a Ph.D. thesis entitled »Timber, Trade and Tree-rings«, submitted to the University of Southern Denmark in February 2007. The thesis is concerned with developing and refining the methodology of the determination of provenance, using dendrochronology, and can be seen as a further development of the concepts introduced in the above mentioned contribution. Several case studies were also carried out where the methodology of provenance determination was applied to the tree-ring data from a number of ship-wrecks. The question of the cogs was pursued, not to analyse new samples but to examine the current status of the dendrochronological analyses of cog wrecks and where ever possible to reassess the prove-nance determination. A short description of the methodology and a summing up of the current status of cog dendrochronology are presented in this paper.

METHODOLOGY

The identification of the origin of oak timber from shipwrecks had been carried out before, in N. Europe, but to a very wide regional level, using a network of large regional master chronologies (e.g. Bonde & Jensen 1995; Crumlin-Pedersen 2002). The aim was to move away from building large regional master chronologies. Learning from the results of the provenance determination of the earliest cogs to a local level, using site chronologies from Denmark (Hocker & Daly 2006), the aim initially was to reach a point where N. Europe would be covered by a dense network of local chronologies. The basic dataset for the study consists of individual measurements for oak, from both living trees (covering the last some 200 years) and from timber from historic buildings and archaeological sites. This data has been accumulated by dendro-chronologists working in N. Europe, and was assembled during the 1990s, through a EU-funded project concerned with the reconstruction of climate from tree-rings (e.g. Kelly et al. 2002). The author was very kindly given permission to use this dataset for her research. In the analysis, it was found that it was useful, not only to have the network of site chronologies, but also to utilise the data of the individual tree-ring measurements. As each site in the dataset is connected, by its geographical coordinates, to a geographic information system, any analysis can be readily plotted on a map, allowing an immediate visual represen-tation of the results. It was found that testing the method using living tree data, where all the geograph-ical parameters are known, gave very positive results, especially because the results could be illustrated on a map. It was concluded that the region of origin of oak could be tested at three levels. The first, widest level uses a network of master chronologies. The second level is where oak is tested with all the site chronologies. The third level test is where the oak tree-ring series is tested with all individual trees in the dataset (Daly 2007a; 2007b; Daly & Nymoen 2008). All these results are mapped, so that for each construc-tion being tested three maps can be produced. The test that is mapped at these three levels is to see how similar the tree-ring curve, e.g. from a ship, is to each chronology or tree in the tree-ring dataset. The simi-

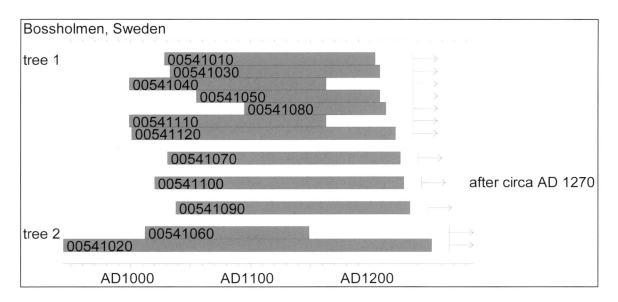

Fig. 1   The Bossholmen cog, Kalmar län. Diagram showing the chronological position of the dated samples, grouped according to Bartholin (1985).

larity is measured by a correlation statistic (t-test) and the higher the result, the more similar the ship's tree-ring curve is to the curve it is being tested against. The map of the results then shows the t-value between the ship and each chronology. The size of the dot on the map represents the t-value achieved.

One of the reasons that it is beneficial to move away from exclusively using the master chronology is that the oaks from historical buildings and archaeological sites also have a history. It is not known how far these structural timbers might have been transported before they ended up in a historical building. The strength of keeping the tree-ring data separate, in site chronologies, is that timber in the dendrochronological dataset remains isolated in small groups, allowing the identification of building timber which is not of local origin.

DENDROCHRONOLOGY OF COGS

The dendrochronological analysis of a great many cogs from N. European finds allows a very detailed description of the ship type, from a precise dating and timber source point of view. When the word cog is used here, it is used as the archaeological term, when describing ship finds which have characteristics similar to the Bremen cog. The terminology and the defining characteristics are discussed in Crumlin-Pedersen (2000), where the archaeological finds of the type are also listed. For the reassessment of the dendrochronological results for the cogs, data was kindly made available by the dendrochronologists who had done the initial datings. Not all cogs were included, as time did not allow it. Tree-ring measurements were reassessed from all except the Darss cog, from N. Germany (Jöns 2002), and the Helgeandsholm cog in Sweden (Varenius 1989). In this paper just two examples will be presented, demonstrating the approaches and methodology. The chosen examples are the Bossholmen ship from Sweden and the Doel ship from Belgium. A summary of the status of the dendrochronological provenance determination of timber from cogs is finally outlined.

	00541090	00541080	00541010	00541120	00541030	00541040	00541110	00541050	00541060	00541020	00541100	00541070
00541090		7.00	8.85	9.37	7.75	8.30	9.00	7.40	3.78	4.94	5.27	6.73
00541080	7.00		12.34	15.99	11.24	9.89	11.61	12.53	4.55	5.39	6.34	7.86
00541010	8.85	12.34		21.27	17.78	16.20	18.03	12.58	6.45	5.38	6.09	8.77
00541120	9.37	15.99	21.27		16.80	16.29	16.78	13.19	6.77	6.57	8.11	9.73
00541030	7.75	11.24	17.78	16.80		19.21	23.04	17.07	6.12	6.28	7.10	10.6
00541040	8.30	9.89	16.20	16.29	19.21		26.93	11.78	7.11	7.28	6.45	8.91
00541110	9.00	11.61	18.03	16.78	23.04	26.93		12.74	7.22	7.72	7.98	9.44
00541050	7.40	12.53	12.58	13.19	17.07	11.78	12.74		3.27	4.70	5.28	8.88
00541060	3.78	4.55	6.45	6.77	6.12	7.11	7.22	3.27		10.89	8.21	6.23
00541020	4.94	5.39	5.38	6.57	6.28	7.28	7.72	4.70	10.89		16.56	9.67
00541100	5.27	6.34	6.09	8.11	7.10	6.45	7.98	5.28	8.21	16.56		10.54
00541070	6.73	7.86	8.77	9.73	10.6	8.91	9.44	8.88	6.23	9.67	10.54	

Fig. 2 The Bossholmen cog, Kalmar län. Matrix of internal correlation.

BOSSHOLMEN

The Bossholmen cog, from near Oskarshamn in S.E. Sweden, was analysed dendrochronologically by Thomas Bartholin (1985). Twelve samples had been analysed from the ship, and the measurements were kindly supplied by Hans Lindersson, Lund University. All samples are dated, and their relative position is shown in **Figure 1**. In several publications the date of the felling of the timbers is quoted as being quite specific; »Dendrochronological analyses showed that the ship timbers had been felled about A.D.1250, with the exception of one plank which had been felled around 1270« (Cederlund 1990: 194) or »the Bossholmen cog from Sweden, was built in A.D.1242 in the W. Baltic« (Crumlin-Pedersen 2000: 239). Actually the conclusion in Bartholin's report is not at all so specific. He states: »12 prøver indleveret hertil har givet en datering af vraget til 1272±5 eller senere« (Bartholin 1985: 1). None of the samples had sapwood preserved so the date is only a terminus post quem. Bartholin does point out that just one sample gives this date, while the others could indicate an earlier date (after A.D.1242), in other words that the later sample is a repair. To confirm this, he argues, would require additional sampling. Whether the dendro dates cited in Cederlund come from a subsequent confirmation archaeologically of the later plank, as a repair, is not explained, but nevertheless the dates are still *termini post quem* and this seems to be ignored in the archaeological publications. Given the very high correlation between the samples, the indications are that a single building phase is represented. The twelve samples in the diagram of the dates for the ship are grouped according to Bartholin's conclusions. He suggested that samples nos 2 and 6 might come from the one tree. It is exactly sample 2 which provides the latest preserved tree-rings in the ship, and if sample 6 comes from the same tree, we have a clear indication of the number of rings which can have been removed in the shaping of the timber for the construction. Overall the evidence from the dendrochronological analysis must conclude that a single phase is represented. Returning to Thomas Bartholin's original conclu-

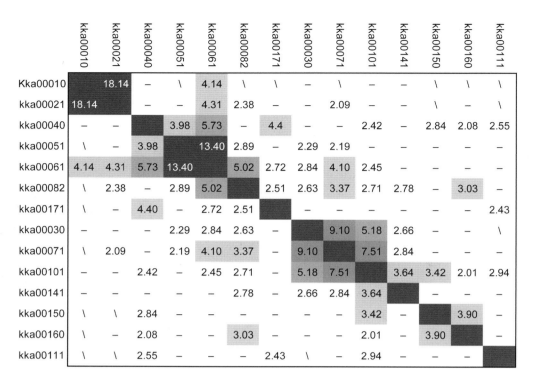

	kka00010	kka00021	kka00040	kka00051	kka00061	kka00082	kka00171	kka00030	kka00071	kka00101	kka00141	kka00150	kka00160	kka00111
Kka00010		18.14	–	\	4.14	\	\	–	\	–	–	\	\	\
kka00021	18.14		–	–	4.31	2.38	–	–	2.09	–	–	\	–	\
kka00040	–	–		3.98	5.73	–	4.4	–	–	2.42	–	2.84	2.08	2.55
kka00051	\	–	3.98		13.40	2.89	–	2.29	2.19	–	–	–	–	–
kka00061	4.14	4.31	5.73	13.40		5.02	2.72	2.84	4.10	2.45	–	–	–	–
kka00082	\	2.38	–	2.89	5.02		2.51	2.63	3.37	2.71	2.78	–	3.03	–
kka00171	\	–	4.40	–	2.72	2.51		–	–	–	–	–	–	2.43
kka00030	–	–	–	2.29	2.84	2.63	–		9.10	5.18	2.66	–	–	\
kka00071	\	2.09	–	2.19	4.10	3.37	–	9.10		7.51	2.84	–	–	–
kka00101	–	–	2.42	–	2.45	2.71	–	5.18	7.51		3.64	3.42	2.01	2.94
kka00141	–	–	–	–	–	2.78	–	2.66	2.84	3.64		–	–	–
kka00150	\	\	2.84	–	–	–	–	–	–	3.42	–		3.90	–
kka00160	\	–	2.08	–	–	3.03	–	–	–	2.01	–	3.90		–
kka00111	\	\	2.55	–	–	–	2.43	\	–	2.94	–	–	–	

Fig. 5 The Doel cog, E. Flanders, Belgium. Matrix of internal correlation.

that the correlation with Ostra Vram is so high, for a small site chronology, then this Ostra Vram correlation can be more significant than the correlation with the larger master chronology. So, Skåne-Blekinge cannot been ruled out as the source of the timber. Neither can Småland be ruled out. The strong match with Ostra Vram points though to the E. Skåne area as the timber source for Bossholmen.

DOEL NEAR ANTWERP, BELGIUM

The Doel wreck was found and excavated in 2000 (Vlierman 2006). It was spectacularly well preserved, found lying with its keel uppermost. Elsemieke Hanraets completed dendrochronological analysis of 17 samples in December 2000 (Hanraets 2000). Three of the samples had very few tree-rings (less than 50) and could not date, but the remaining 14 samples are dated. Two samples with complete sapwood preserved provide a very precise date for the felling of the timber for the ship: that is, between summer A.D. 1325 and spring A.D. 1326 (Hanraets 2000).

The tree-ring measurements from the analysis were kindly made available to the author by Elsemieke Hanraets and Esther Jansma. As can be seen from the matrix of correlation between all the dated samples from the Doel ship (**Fig. 5**) it appears that a very spread group of timber is reflected. Three small groups appear, but otherwise there is low correlation between the samples. When each individual sample is tested against the master chronologies from N. Europe the highest t-values that appear are with German chronologies, especially with one from the Lower Saxony region. The t-values achieved for the individual trees are not high enough for confident provenance determination, only reaching t = 6.5 at the most. Therefore, it has

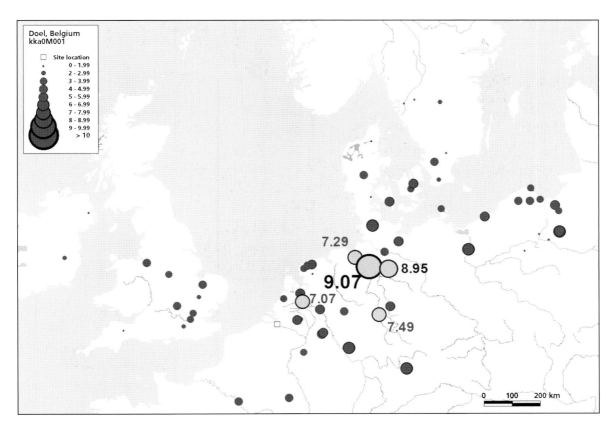

Fig. 6 The Doel cog, E. Flanders, Belgium. Map showing the distribution of correlation values achieved between the mean for Doel and master chronologies from N. Europe (the 1st level test).

been decided to make a ship average using all dated samples, despite the relatively low internal correlation, for the provenance determination test. Hanraets in her original analysis also made an average of all samples, but the ship average used here is modified a little, deleting the first five tree-ring indices, as they had a very extreme dip in ring-width, which is probably due to measurements close to the pith of the tree.

The ship average then, of all dated samples, is tested at the three provenance test levels. The test at the first level, with master chronologies (**Fig. 6**), shows that the highest correlation (t = 9.07) is achieved with a regional chronology from Lower Saxony in N. Germany. The next best (t = 8.95) is with a chronology from Lüneburger Heide, also in the province of Lower Saxony. Although the sizing of the dots highlights the higher t-value, there is not much difference between these two correlations. Hence, the original suggestion by Hanraets can be confirmed, that the timber grew in Lower Saxony. At the test then at the second level (**Fig. 7**), a sharper localisation within the Lower Saxony region might be verified. Here the dots indicate the correlation results, and the highest values are given. The two sites that give the highest correlations are both sites that have been analysed at the University of Göttingen. The site means for these sites are all longer than the ship average so there are no problems of varying overlap. The t-values are very similar to each other. However, the replication of the site chronologies vary. The Truhen site average is made from 35 timbers and gives a t-value t = 8.04, while the Medingen site average is from only six trees and gives a value of t = 8.02. All of this attention to detail is taken because it is relevant to look at the distribution of the highest t-values in relation to the topography of the region. By this it might be possible to make a suggestion as to the shipbuilding site, or at the very least, to suggest along what major river the timber can

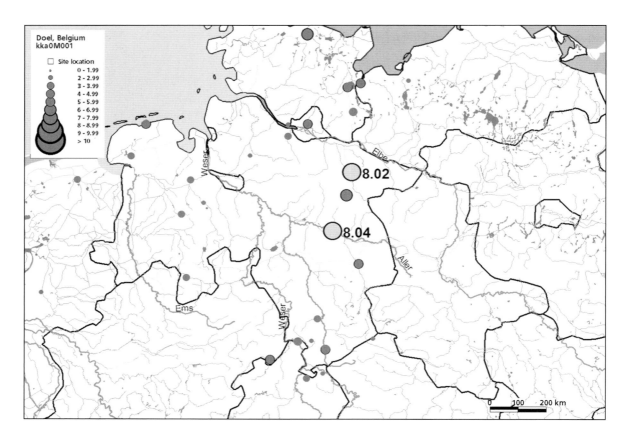

Fig. 7   The Doel cog, E. Flanders, Belgium. Map showing the distribution of correlation values achieved between the mean for Doel and site chronologies from N. Europe (the 2nd level test) in relation to the major drainage of the region.

have been transported. As can be seen from the map, the Truhen site is from the Aller River basin, which drains into the Weser. To confirm the local nature of the timber from this site, the Truhen site chronology has also been tested with the network of site chronologies, and it matches best with another site on the same drainage system, on a tributary to the Aller River further upstream. However the other site, which matches equally well with the Doel ship average, comes from another drainage system, the Ilmenau, which is a tributary of the Elbe River. Would then the test at the third level allow the identification of the timber origin?

In the third level test (**Fig. 8**) the correlation values greater than t = 6.00 are highlighted in light grey, and the two highest are labelled. Again the highest (t = 7.66) is with the site on the Aller River, while the next best (t = 7.04) is with a tree from Lüneburg. Here the problems of varying replication are removed, but one has to look into the varying overlap. The second highest correlation is with an overlap of 165 years, while the highest correlation the overlap is 149 years. The higher correlation must be given a bit more importance than the second highest, pointing indeed to the timber origin for the Doel ship in the Aller River drainage region. Given the non-homogeneity of the tree-ring patterns from the many samples from the Doel ship it can be suggested that the timber is from a relatively wide area, and this indicates the necessity of transport of the timber to the ship-building site. The less clear provenance determination for the timber can also be due to the non-homogeneity of the tree-ring series. When an average is made of these tree-ring series, which individually seem to come from the same general region, but which do not match each other so well, the average might represent a wider regional climate signal, rather than a local signal. It is, one could

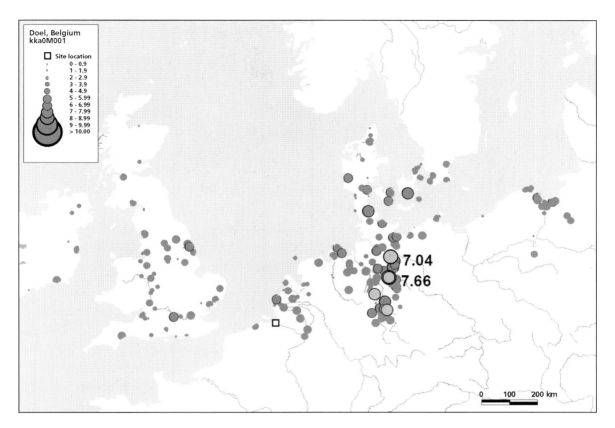

Fig. 8 The Doel cog, E. Flanders, Belgium. Map showing the distribution of correlation values achieved between the mean for Doel and single tree-ring measurements from N. Europe (the 3rd level test).

say, in sharp contrast to the Bossholmen ship discussed above. In its case the tree-ring series are very similar to each other indicating a very limited source area, and the resulting ship average is of a very local nature.

SUMMING UP

These two examples of provenance determination to a local level demonstrate the technique. They are from quite similar periods, Bossholmen dates to after about A.D. 1270 while Doel's timbers were felled in 1325-1326. Firstly the timber used in each ship is assessed as to its homogeneity. This is to try to suggest whether the timber is from a single source, or whether it is from a variety of sources. The matrices give a clear indication of the internal correlation, and it can be seen that the two examples are quite different in terms of the homogeneity of the timber. This ultimately affects the provenance determination, as can be seen in the results for the two examples. The homogeneous timbers from the Bossholmen ship give a very clear provenance determination, while the diffuse source of timbers used in the Doel ship gives a diffuse distribution of t-values in the maps of correlation at the three levels, resulting in a less clear provenance conclusion. The causes of these differences can be suggested. Availability of timber for shipbuilding, in some regions, by the end of the 13th and start of the 14th c., begins to vary. The Doel ship seems to be built from timber from the region of Lower Saxony, but from a diffuse timber source. The Bossholmen ship on the other hand

name	felling date	provenance	group	reference
Lille Kregme	ca. 1358	Baltic	cog	Rieck 1996
Vejby	winter 1372	Baltic	cog	Crumlin-Pedersen 1979; Bonde & Jensen 1995
Kuggmaren I	summer 1215	Danish	cog	Adams & Rönnby 2002
Skagen	ca. 1195	Danish	cog	Dokkedal 1996
Kollerup	ca. 1155	Danish	cog	Andersen 1983
Kolding	winter 1188-89	Danish	cog	Hansen 1944; Hocker 2000
Helgeandsholm 2	1330	not known	cog	Varenius 1989
Skanör	after 1382	Baltic	cog	Hörberg 1995; Nilsson 2004
Bremen	1378	Weser German	cog	Lahn 1992; Bauch 1969
Oskarshamn Bossholmen	after c. 1270	East Skåne Sweden	cog	Cederlund 1990; Dokkedal 1996
Flevol. OZ43 Nijkerk	1275-1300	not known	cog	Luns 1985
NOP M107 Marknesse	1375-1400	not known	cog	Modderman 1945
NOP Q75 Ens	1300-1325	not known	cog	Reinders 1985
Flevol. N5 Dronten	1325-1350	not known	cog	Reinders 1985
Flevol. NZ42 Spakenburg	1350-1400	not known	cog	Reinders 1985
Flevol. NZ43 Spakenburg	1402-1414	Holland/Westfalen	cog	Van de Moortel 1991
Flevol. OZ36 Nijkerk	1336	not known	cog	Luns 1985
NOP A57 Rutten	1265-75	NE Germany?	cog	Oosting 1985; 1987
Flevol. Almere	1410	not known	cog	Hocker & Vlierman 1997
Darss cog	1298-1313	Baltic	cog	Jöns 2002
Doel Belgium	1325-26	Aller/Weser German	cog	Vlierman 2006; Hanraets 2000
Dronten M61	after c. 1296	not known	cog	Vlierman 1996
CZ46 Oostvaarderplassen	after 1327	Holland	cog	Hanraets 1999
Swifterbant OG77	ca. 1305	Holland	cog	Karel Vlierman pers. comm.; Hanraets 2001

Table 1 Table summarising the dating and provenance determination results for the cogs examined in this study.

is built in a region where timber is available in abundance, and therefore the timber can be harvested from a single area, reducing transport costs and logistics.

STATUS

A table summarises the cog finds, updated and revised since Crumlin-Pedersen (2000: 237) to include dendrochronological dates for some ships and where possible, an updated suggestion of the timber origin (**Table 1**). The status of the dendrochronological analysis is given. This is based on the fact that many samples should be analysed from each ship, so that a fuller picture of the timber composition of the ship is possible, and so that a reliable provenance for the timber can be suggested. Only very few cogs are satisfactorily analysed from a dendroprovenance point of view. For many that have been studied dendrochronologically, often only few samples have been analysed or dated. Six of the ships have not been analysed dendrochronologically at all. Therefore, the conclusion that can be drawn is that there is still much that can be done on the chronology and origin of cogs.

Plate 1 shows the distribution of the cog finds in N. Europe. The dating and provenance results are added in this map, for those ships where a reliable provenance result is achieved. An interesting pattern emerges. Firstly, the earliest examples from the second half of the 12th c. and the 13th c. are the Scandinavian finds, with a confirmed (in the case of Kollerup and Kolding) or a suggested (Skagen and Kuggmaren) Danish timber provenance. The Bossholmen ship has a Scandinavian timber provenance also, but this time in the region of Skåne, which was of course part of the Kingdom of Denmark at the time. The cogs made from S. Baltic timber are dated to the 14th c. and these are all finds from the coasts around the mouth of the Baltic Sea. The cog finds from the Low Countries on the other hand are generally made from timber from the region.

Several angles of interpretation have to be incorporated here. Firstly, the provenance determination points towards the region where the trees grew. In many instances the evidence points towards the probability that a ship was built near to the timber source, for example the Bremen cog (Lahn 1992) was not complete when it was wrecked on the Weser River, and its timber appears also to come from up the Weser (Bauch 1969), or the Vejby cog (Crumlin-Pedersen 1979), where both the timber provenance results and the coins in the mast step point towards Gdańsk as the place where the ship was built (Bonde & Jensen 1995). There are, however other examples of ships, where timber from several sources are used in the construction, making the identification of the actual region in which the ship was built difficult[1]. A third angle of interpretation here is that the map shows the distribution of the final resting place of the ships, in relation to the timber provenance. The map combines information about the beginning of the ship's life, with its final wreckage or abandonment. How to interpret the patterns in the distribution? It should in this case then be distinguished between the ships that are wrecks and those that are deliberately abandoned or scuttled. One is an unintentional loss of the ship, the other intentional. The deliberate disposal of a worn out ship was probably a decision made by the owner/s, and this map might give an image of the pattern of ownership of a vessel. That ownership is linked to the place where the ship is built, and therefore the ship is scuttled in the same region that it was built. Wreckage on the other hand, gives an insight into the journeys made in the ship, and how far these cogs ventured from their home ports.

ACKNOWLEDGEMENTS

Thanks to the Danish Research Council for funding the author's Ph.D. studies, to Poul Holm, Mike Baillie and Nils Engberg, her supervisors, and to the Centre for Maritime and Regional Studies, University of Southern Denmark. Thanks to the National Museum of Denmark for access to the dendrochronology archives. Thanks to Thomas Bartholin, Hans Lindersson, Esther Jansma and Else-mieke Hanraets for supplying copies of tree-ring measurements from their analyses. Finally thanks to dendrochronologists in several laboratories for the permission to use their tree-ring data, namely Mike Baillie, Dieter Eckstein, Olafur Eggertsson, Esther Jansma, Hans Hubert Leuschner, Cathy Tyers (was Groves), Ian Tyers and Tomasz Ważny.

NOTE

1) E.g. ship 3 from Dokøen in Copenhagen (Gøthche & Høst Madsen 2001; Bonde & Eriksen 2002) and the Roman barge Woerden 7, The Netherlands (Vorst 2005).

REFERENCES

Adams, J. & Rönnby, J., 2002, Kuggmaren 1: the first cog find in the Stockholm archipelago, Sweden. *IJNA*, 31, 172-181.

Bartholin, T. S., 1985, *Dendrokronologisk datering af Bossholms-vraket*. Report to C. O. Cederlund, 30.01.1985, Lunds Universitet, Dept. of Quaternary Geology.

Bauch, J., 1969, Die Bauzeit der Bremer Kogge. In: *Die Bremer Hanse-Kogge. Ein Schlüssel zur Schiffahrtsgeschichte. Fund,* *Konservierung, Forschung*. Herausgegeben von der Wittheit zu Bremen, Monographien, 8. Bremen, 123-126.

Bonde, N. & Jensen, J. S., 1995, The dating of a Hanseatic cog-find in Denmark. What coins and tree rings can reveal in maritime archaeology. In: O. Olsen, J. S. Madsen & F. Rieck (eds), *Ship-shape. Essays for Ole-Crumlin-Pedersen. On the occasion of his 60th anniversary, February 24th 1995*. Roskilde, 103-121.

Cederlund, C. O., 1990, The Oskarshamm cog. Part I: development of investigations and current research. *IJNA*, 19.3, 193-206.

Crumlin-Pedersen, O., 1979, Danish Cog-finds. In: S. McGrail (ed.), *The Archaeology of Medieval Ships and Harbours in Northern Europe*. BAR Internat. Series, 66. Oxford, 17-34.

Crumlin-Pedersen, O., 2000, To be or not to be a cog. *IJNA*, 29.2, 230-246.

2002, Description and analysis of the ships as found, Skuldelev 2. In: O. Crumlin-Pedersen & O. Olsen (eds), *The Skuldelev Ships I*. Ships and Boats of the North, 4.1. Roskilde, 141-194.

Daly, A., 2007a, The Karschau Ship, Schleswig-Holstein: Dendrochronological Results and Timber Provenance. *IJNA*, 36.1, 155-166.

2007b, *Timber, Trade and Tree-rings. A dendrochronological analysis of structural oak timber in Northern Europe, c. AD 1000 to c. AD 1650*. Unpublished Ph.D. thesis submitted February 2007 to the University of Southern Denmark.

Daly, A. & Nymoen, P., 2008, The Bøle ship, Skien, Norway – Research history, dendrochronology and provenance. *IJNA*, 37.1, 153-170.

Dokkedal, L., 1996, *Koggen i Nordeuropa fra 1150-1450 e. Kr. – Definition af skibstypen og diskussion af en mulig årsag til dens anvendelse i nordeuropæisk skibsfart*. Unpublished thesis submitted to the University of Copenhagen, Institute of Archaeology and Ethnology.

Gøthche, M. & Høst Madsen, L., 2001, Middelalderlige vrag på Dokøen, København. *Marinarkæologisk Nyhedsbrev fra Roskilde*, 17, 28-33.

Hanraets, E., 1999, Kavel: *CZ-46/Oostvaardersplassen, scheepswrak*. Rapportage daterend onderzoek RING/ROB, September 1999.

2000, Antwerpen, *Doel; kogge*. Rapportage daterend onderzoek RING/ROB, November/December 2000.

2001, *Kavel: OG-77; scheepswrak*. Rapportage daterend onderzoek RING/ROB, July 2001.

Hansen, K. E., 1944, Kolding Skibet. Foreløbig Meddelelse om Fund af Middelalderskib. *Handels- og Søfartsmuseet på Kronborg. Årbog* 1944, 119-129.

Hocker, F. & Daly, A, 2006, Early cogs, Jutland boatbuilders, and the connection between East and West before AD 1250. In: *ISBSA 10*, 187-194.

Hocker, F. & Vlierman, K., 1997, *A small cog wrecked on the Zuiderzee in the early fifteenth century*. Nederlands Instituut voor Scheeps- en onderwater Archeologie, excavation report, 19. Lelystad.

Hörberg, P. U., 1995, Nuts, Bricks and Pewter – preliminary notes on three new ship-finds in Scania, Sweden. In: O. Olsen, J. S. Madsen & F. Rieck (eds), *Shipshape. Essays for Ole-Crumlin-Pedersen. On the occasion of his 60th anniversary, February 24th 1995*. Roskilde, 123-126.

Jöns, H., 2002, Presentation of the four wreck sites within the project: Germany. MoSS Newsletter 1/2002, 18-21. www.nba.fi/internat/MoSS/download/moss_newsletter1.pdf.

Kelly, P. M., Leuschner, H. H., Briffa, K. R. & Harris, I. C., 2002, The climatic interpretation of pan- European signature years in oak ring-width series. *Holocene*, 12.6, 689-694.

Kohrtz Andersen, P., 1983, *Kollerupkoggen*. Thisted.

Lahn, W., 1992, *Die Kogge von Bremen*, 1: *Bauteile und Bauablauf*. Hamburg.

Luns, A. F. T., 1985, *De constructie van scheepswrak OZ 36 in Zuidelik Flevoland*. Rijksdienst voor de Ijsselmeerpolders, Werkdocument, 1985-106. Lelystad.

Modderman, P. J. R., 1945, *Over de wording ende beteekenis van het Zuiderzeegebied*. Groningen.

Nilsson, M., 2004, Ett senmedeltida vrak från Falsterbohalvön – Skanörkoggen. *Marinarkeologisk tidskrift*, 3, 12-13. www.marinarkeologi.net

Oosting, R., 1985, Opgravning ven het vlak ven een kogge bij Rutten (Noordoostpolder, kavel A57). *Jaarverslag* (Onderafdeling Scheepsarcheologie, Rijksdienst voor de Ijseelmeer polders, Lelystad), 1985, 7-14.

Oosting, R., 1987, De opgraving van het vlak van een kogge bij Rutten. In: R. H. Reinders (ed.), *Raakvlakken tussen scheepsarcheologie, maritieme geschiedenis en scheepsbouwkunde*. Lelystad, 57-63.

Reinders, H. R., 1985, *Cog finds from the ijsselmeerpolders*. Flevobericht, 248. Ketelhaven.

Rieck, F., 1996, Ll. Kregme koggen. Et middelalderligt skibsforlis i Roskilde Fjord. In: H. Jeppesen (ed.), *Søfart, politik, identitet – tilegnet Ole Feldbæk*. Helsingør, 17-25.

Van de Moortel, A., 1991, *A cog-like vessel from the Netherlands*. Flevobericht, 331. Ketelhaven.

Varenius, B., 1989, *Båtarna från Helgeandsholmen*. Riksantikvarieämbetet och Statens historiska museer, Rapport UV 3/1989. Stockholm.

Vlierman, K., 1996, Van Zintelen, *Van Zintelroeden ende Mossen*. Flevobericht, 386. Lelystad.

2006, The cog finds at Doel: State of affairs of accommodation, documentation and research. In: M. Pieters, G. Gevaert, J. Mees, & J. Seys (eds), *To sea or not to sea – 2nd international colloquium on maritime and fluvial archaeology in the southern North Sea area, Brugge (Belgium), 21-23 September 2006. Book of abstracts*. Vlaams Instituut voor de Zee (VLIZ), Special Publication, 32. Oostende, 29-30.

Vorst, Y., 2005, *De constructie en herkomst van de Romeinse platbodem »Woerden 7«, een studie van jaarringpatronen en bewerkingssporen*. PhD thesis, Universiteit van Amsterdam.

CARLO BELTRAME

THE EXCAVATION OF THE BRIG *MERCURE*
OF THE *REGNO ITALICO* (1812)

WHY TO INVESTIGATE A MILITARY VESSEL FROM THE BEGINNING
OF THE 19TH CENTURY?

The wreck of the brig *Mercure* lies seven miles off the border between the Veneto and the Friuli Venezia-Giulia region in N.E. Italy (**Fig. 1**), at a depth of 17 m.

When, on the night of the 22nd February 1812, the ship exploded struck by the British brig *Weasel*, it was escorting the French 74 guns vessel *Rivoli* on its maiden voyage (James 1847: 64-67; Troude 1868: 155-158). The *Mercure* had been built by the French navy, following the plan of the architect Sané, in the Italian private shipyard of the *Foce* (mouth) in Genoa between 1805 and 1806 (Boudriot & Berti n.d.: 48; Bucci 1916: 14). In 1810, the brig was yielded from the French fleet to that one of the Italic Kingdom (*Regno Italico*) whose capital was Venice (Crociani, Ilari & Paoletti 2004: 441).

The *Mercure* belonged to a family of 50 brigs built between 1800 and 1813. These ships are quite well known thanks to a monographic study by Boudriot and Bertì based on the model of one, Le *Cygne*, hosted in the Naval museum of Paris (**Fig. 2**) (Boudriot & Berti 1981). As well as other Boudriot's excellent studies, the main source for this publication has been the model itself, plans of the architect Pestel and written documents which have been very useful to the French scholar.

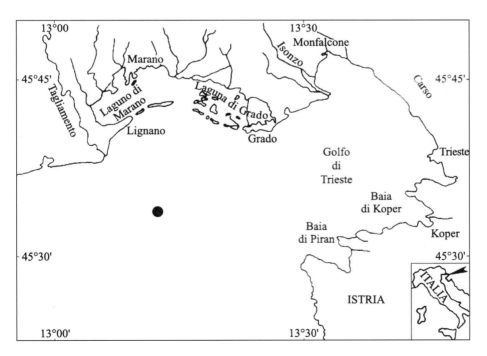

Fig. 1 Site of the wrecking of the *Mercure*.

Fig. 2 Model of the *Cygne*, twin of the *Mercure* (After Boudriot 2006: 109).

The author has directed six small seasons of excavation on the site of the shipwreck[1]. Here, students of both the Ca' Foscari University and of other athenaeums had the opportunity of practical education (Beltrame 2004; 2005; Beltrame & Gaddi 2002; 2004).

The distribution of the findings on the sea bottom shows that, after the explosion of the brig quoted by the historians, the ship lost its stern, but continued its struggle for another 70 m ending its trip at the foot of a dune. Here in fact we have found the prow, with the starboard anchor, and a part of the hull preserved for more than 16 m of the 32 m of the complete ship (**Plate 2**).

During the excavation, hundreds of findings were recovered: components of rigging, nails and others parts of the hull, fire and white arms, and personal belongings. The rigging is composed of fragments of blocks and a variety of pulleys which will need a long study of comparison with the archive documentation relating specifically to these objects (Beltrame 2007).

The artillery, already found, is composed of eight of the 14 original carronades, two cannons and one bronze swivel gun. The finding, on the prow, of the cannons confirms what is known historically: in 1809, all the brigs had to substitute two carronades with two guns (Boudriot & Berti 1981: 46). The swivel gun, probably due to its small size, is neither mentioned in the archives nor represented in the *Cygne*'s model.

Personal belongings show curious presences. In fact, other than the foreseeable findings of jacket buttons, tobacco pipes and glass bottles, objects which have no bearing on the military environment, for example gold jewels, have been found. These findings propose new questions about life aboard a military vessel at the beginning of the 19th c. In 2006, at least four incomplete skeletons had been found.

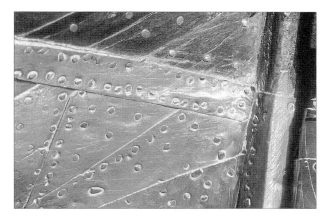

Fig. 3 Detail of the copper sheeting on the hull of the model of the *Cygne* (After Boudriot 2006: 114).

Although didactics for students is an important motivation for the continuation of the excavation, research reasons are not lacking. The quantity and variety of objects found will enable to analyze in detail many aspects of navigation at the beginning of the 19th c. Additionally, interest was dedicated to the knowledge of the construction technique of the hull. While the first motivations commonly find large acceptance, it is not the same for the latter.

Some scholars are thinking that the excavation of a military vessel of this period – especially if it is French – makes no sense in furthering the knowledge of the construction system of the hull. The justification of such a concept would be that a huge amount of non archaeological information and studies about this subject is already available and also a vast quantity of literature about this area has already been published (e.g. Pomey & Rieth 2005: 60-61; 186).

Our knowledge of 18th and 19th c. vessels derives from three major sources: written and graphical documentation and the models built in the period of the construction of the ship. The questions to be put forward here are: are these non archaeological sources completely exhaustive and absolutely reliable for the comprehension of the construction techniques of military vessels belonging to the 18th and 19th c.? Subsequently therefore, may the archaeological excavation and the documentation of a hull of this period add something more to our knowledge?

First of all, the builder drafts of the ships of this period are to be considered. The author but not only (e.g. G. Penzo, pers. comm.) is increasingly more conscious as to the fact that these plans were often not used, as is today, as detailed and executive projects which had to be faithfully followed. Actually, at the beginning of 19th c., in the shipyards, the shipwrights still followed the drafts of the architects in broad outline; often they interpreted the plan and they preferred following their »eye« rather than the drafts. It seems that only a small part of the available plans are proper projects: in fact they are to a certain extent mostly surveys made after the construction of the ship with illustrative aims in mind.

The builder drafts owned of the French brigs represent only their shape and their decorations, but they show very little detail that would be useful for the study of the ships construction. Concerning the models, it must be emphasized that, for definition, they are of a reduced scale. Obviously, this was a limit that let builders to make choices that summarized and interpreted these models often skipping details. For example, on the *Cygnes*' model, both the covering of copper sheets present on a limited area of the hull and the numbers in Latin alphabet for showing the draft marks have been omitted. Due to the great number and of the small size of the original nails used to fix the metal sheets, the model maker had to reduce their number and to make them bigger (Frölich 1985) (**Fig. 3**).

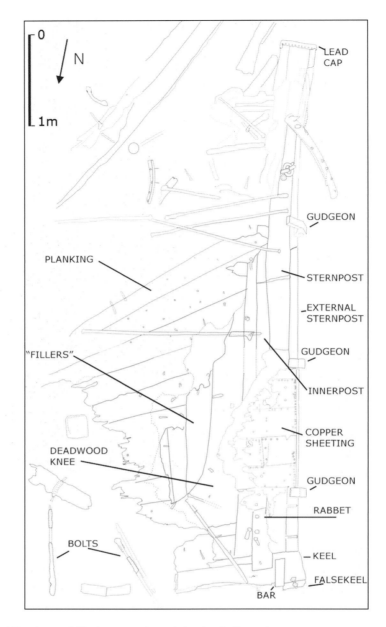

Fig. 4 *Mercure*. – Plan of the sternpost (Photogrammetry and drawing S. Caressa).

Besides, anachronisms in the models must be taken into account: in Boudriot's opinion, e.g., the kitchen on the deck of the model of the *Cygne* is a mistake of the model maker (pers. information J. Boudriot). More than once, technical details of the hulls are omitted, both on the builder drafts and on the models, because of problems of scale and for simplification. This is evident on the *Mercure*. Although executed underwater, the analytical documentation of its stern obliged to complete and to correct the plan executed by Boudriot and Berti on the base of the *Cygne*'s model (**Figs 4-5**).
The stern remains indicate traces of the false keel and a section of the keel. Over these, in vertical position the external oak sternpost, the oak sternpost and the inner oak sternpost are present. On the external sternpost three bronze gudgeons are nailed (**Fig. 6**). Sections of eight strakes of the outboard planking are

connected to the stern where they end. Only a trace of a pair of oak strakes of the left planking are nailed to the rabbet sculptured in the middle of the sternpost. Inside the inner sternpost and between the planking of the two sides, there are many wooden elements: the first one is the deadwood knee: a piece with a curved shape. Inside its curve three »fillers« are present. Between the bottom of the deadwood knee and the keel there are some elements not clearly identifiable. All the components are connected both to each other and to the no longer preserved frames by long bronze bolts. Between these wooden elements, pieces of felt have been interposed probably to avoid wood rot. The entire stern is protected by copper sheeting.

A superficial view of this part of the hull would not bring to light any difference between the archaeological evidence and the drafts obtained by the model, but an analytical observation enables to recognize some interesting details. Over the head of the stern, that is the part of the stern inside the deck, there is a cap of lead sheeting nailed on the wood which is not documented by other sources (**Fig. 7**). Perhaps the metal was used as a protection. The keel has been connected to the stern by a bronze bar (**Fig. 8**). This solution has been noted on the model of the French vessel *Colossus* too, but it is quite rare, not being present on the plans of our

Fig. 5 *Mercure.* – The sternpost from the bottom (Photo S. Caressa).

family of brigs (Boudriot & Berti 1995). The elements between the deadwood knee and the keel could be the extension of the rising wood. On this wreck, unlike the drafts, the element is composed of three pieces, one of which continues till under the rising wood. Finally, the tenon of the sternpost that enters in the step over the keel, shows an asymmetrical shape different from the one documented by Boudriot's drafts.

Portions of both the right and the left sides of the hull, not far from the stem, have been excavated and documented. On either side, external and inner planking are divided by oak frames which are in touch; that is to say that there is no space between them. This disposition could be expected in the extremity of the ship, but not at this level. It may be understood as an attempt to brace the hull protecting it from cannon shots. This constructional solution to strengthen the hull would not have come to light in any non archaeological source.

Analysis has revealed that although the left planking is made of oak wood the right one, either near the prow and on the stern, is of *Quercus cerris*/turkey oak. French specialized literature takes for granted that military vessels of this period were made of *Quercus robur* (e.g. Boudriot 1979: 50-54). In the W., *Cerris* was not considered a wood suitable for shipbuilding probably because underwater, it easily rots (Giordano 1976: 406-407): from the Middle Ages on, written sources testify its use especially as firewood and recommend not to use it for shipbuilding (information F. Ciciliot). Accordingly, the use of that wood species for the planking of the right side is certainly astonishing.

Fig. 6 *Mercure*. – The gudgeons on the sternpost (Photo S. Caressa).

Fig. 7 *Mercure*. – Cap of lead sheeting nailed on the end of the stern (Photo S. Caressa).

There are two possible explanations for this presence. As it is known, in 1811, the *Mercure* was refitted in Trieste (archive of the Musée National de la Marine). Here the shipwright could have used *Cerris*, and probably did so without the knowledge of the navy authorities. This is a reminder that the ship had been built in a private shipyard in Genoa where the shipwright could have cheated the Napoleonic Navy using a very cheap wood.

The stem is completely covered with a brass sheeting. Here one could have expected to find some numbers in Latin alphabet to show the draft-marks nailed to the sheets, as documented on the stern. Curiously here the letters have been obtained in relief on the sheeting with a technique that seems to have no parallel and that, apparently, seems illogical (**Fig. 9**).

If so much and such original information has been gathered during an underwater analysis, how much more data can be revealed by a study in a laboratory, where traces of tools, marks and technical details would became clearer?

All the examples presented here should demonstrate that the common assumption that military vessels, that is to say State ships, were built following standard plans and were mass-produced

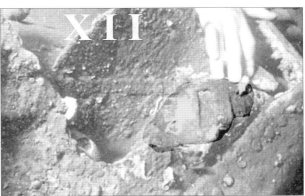

Fig. 8 *Mercure.* – Bronze bar under the keel (Photo S. Caressa).

Fig. 9 *Mercure.* – Numbers in Latin on the copper sheeting of the prow (Photo S. Caressa).

meets at least two exceptions: the free interpretation of the shipwright, especially in the private shipyards, and the refitting during the life of the ship. It should be considered then that, although we know a lot about the French and the British navy of the 18th and 19th c., there is very little knowledge of the navies of the Italian pre-union states. The *Mercure*, in part, belongs to one of these navies.

In conclusion, the author wishes to emphasize archaeology can give opportunity to collect a multitude of information that could not be obtained through the study of traditional sources. In particular, archaeology permits to attain such details that non archaeological sources rarely can reach. Moreover archaeology helps to prove informations obtained by the analysis of other sources. The author is of the opinion that archaeological investigation has got great options in the field of history of military naval construction both of the 18th and 19th c. All these potentials imply that the time in which scholars are enabled to say they know everything about a particular kind of ship is still considerably far off.

NOTE

1) The first season of excavations was organized in 2001 by the Soprintendenza per i Beni Archeologici del Veneto. – From 2004 to 2008, the project continued thanks to a collaboration between the Ca' Foscari University and the Soprintendenza. – The final sponsors have been the Veneto Region and the Friuli Venezia Giulia Region. – The author is indebted to dott. Luigi Fozzati who assigned the project to him, to Mauro Bondioli for scientific informations, and to Mrs. V. Odogwu for proof-reading the English manuscript.

REFERENCES

Beltrame, C., 2004, Lignano, relitto del brick italo-francese Mercure, seconda campagna di scavo sottomarino, 2004. *Archeologia Postmedievale*, 8, 207.

2005, Lignano, relitto del brick del Regno italico *Mercure, 2005. Archeologia Postmedievale*, 9.

2007, Il Mercure. Il relitto del brick del Regno Italico affondato nel 1812 nelle battaglio de Grado. In: L. Fozzati (ed.), Caorle archeologica. Tra mare, fiume e terra. Venezia, 137-146.

Beltrame, C. & Gaddi, D., 2002, Report on the first research campaign at the wreck of the Napoleonic brick, *Mercure*, Lignano, Udine. *IJNA*, 31.1, 60-73.

2004, Resoconto della prima campagna di indagine sul relitto del brick napoleonico *Mercure* (Lignano – UD). In: A. Benini & M. Giacobelli (eds), *Atti del II Convegno nazionale di archeologia subacquea, Castiglioncello, 2001.* Bari,125-134.

Boudriot, J., 1979, *Le vaisseau de 74 canons. La costruction du vaisseau*, I. Paris.

2005, *Modeles historiques. Musée National de la Marine*, II. Paris.

Boudriot, J, & Berti, H., 1981, *Le Cygne (1806-1808)*. Paris.

1995, *Les vaisseaux 74 à 120 canons*. Paris.

Bucci, E., 1916, *Il cantiere navale della Foce*. Turin.

Crociani, P., Ilari, V. & Paoletti, C. 2004, *Storia militare del Regno Italico (1802-1814), II. Il dominio dell'Adriatico*. Rome.

Frölich, B., 1985, Le doublage en cuivre: point de vue d'un modeliste. *Neptunia*, 157, 26-29.

Giordano, G., 1976, *Tecnologia del legno, 3. Le prove ed i legnami di più frequente impiego*. Turin.

James, W., 1847, *The Naval History of Great Britain*. London.

Pomey, P. & Rieth, E., 2005, *L'archéologie navale*. Paris.

Troude, M., 1868, *Batailles navales de la France*. Paris.

INTERACTION INLAND-SEA

ROBERT VAN DE NOORT

TO TRAVEL IS MORE IMPORTANT THAN TO ARRIVE:

SEAFARING BETWEEN BRITAIN AND THE CONTINENT IN THE 2ND MILLENNIUM B.C.

The world is a confusing place. The many natural phenomena, such as the seasons of the year and rising and setting of the sun, demand explanations. Once the local social memory has been exhausted, travel is the only means by which new knowledge and understanding of the world around us could be gained in a prehistoric world without texts. Travellers have the prospect of gaining such knowledge from other peoples, and also the prospect of coming in contact with new materials and artefacts, which raise new questions about the world we live in. Throughout the human past, people have travelled and acquired knowledge in the process, both sacred and profane, and brought objects home that provided a material reflection of these journeys (e.g. Helms 1988).

The archaeological evidence for long-distance trade and exchange of ideas between Britain and the Continent throughout the 2nd millennium B.C. is extensive, and this included bronzes, pottery (e.g. parallel development of Beakers on either side of the North Sea), and jewellery of gold, amber and faience (Clarke *et al.* 1985). Much has been written about the socio-political implications of these long distance exchanges, including the rise of power of a distinct elite (e.g. Shennan 1982; 1986; Bradley 1984; Barrett 1994; Harding 2000). Similarly, much has been written about the craft which would have enabled these journeys to take place and the British sewn-plank boats from Ferriby, Kilnsea, Dover, Caldicot, Testwood Lakes, Goldcliff and Brigg are thought to exemplify this activity (Van de Noort *et al.* 1999; McGrail 2001; Clark 2004; Van de Noort 2006).

What has not been done in any great detail to date is combining the »products« of these long-distance exchanges with the »processes« required to obtain them or, in other words, the study of the material culture and the maritime aspects of archaeology remains largely disjointed (cf. Adams 2001; McGrail 2003: 1). This paper sets out to offer an integrated or contextualised approach to the study of seafaring in the 2nd millennium B.C. The importance of travel and the significance of geographical distance, as argued by the anthropologist Mary Helms in her cross-cultural study of travel *Ulysses Sail* (1988), is central to the arguments presented here: the value placed upon objects and ideas is closely linked to the manner (i.e. distance, dangers and difficulties) in which these were obtained. Thus, the human-centred actions of travelling and undertaking great journeys, rather than the theoretical concepts of diffusion and acculturation, become the means by which cultural change can be explained.

LONG-DISTANCE EXCHANGE IN THE 2ND MILLENNIUM B.C.

From the perspective of the British Isles, the mode of long-distance exchange in the Early Bronze Age (2050 to 1500 cal B.C.) was of a different character that that of the Middle and Late Bronze Age (1500 to 750 cal B.C.), using Stuart Needham's (1996) chronology for the British prehistory. The character of long-distance exchange in the Early Bronze Age has been interpreted as »directional« exchange, whereby goods were acquired directly from the source of manufacture, whilst during the Middle and Late Bronze Age, goods were exchanged »down-the-line«, involving a series of exchanges over relative short distances before reaching their destinations (e.g. Northover 1982; Bradley 1984; Pare 2000). In outline, these differences had already been identified in two seminal works on Bronze Age interaction across the North Sea and the Channel, Butler's (1963) *Bronze Age Connections across the North Sea* and O'Connor's (1980) *Cross-Channel Relations in the later Bronze Age*.

The study of long-distance exchange in the Early Bronze Age in Britain was for a considerable time focused on the Beakers. Beakers in general, and Bell Beakers in particular, have been described as »exotic or high quality items, to indicate differentiation, including prestige, in a way which had not previously occurred« (Shennan 1982: 159). Beakers formed only one part of what has been described as a »toolkit« for the elite. What constituted the full toolkit changed over time, but it could include such items as jewellery made of gold, amber and tin, early copper or bronze artefacts, tools and weapons, flint daggers, archery equipment including flint arrowheads and wrist guards, and buttons with V-shaped perforations (Bradley 1984; Clarke *et al.* 1985). The majority of whole Beakers have been found in funerary contexts, but recent research has clearly shown that the distribution of Beakers extended beyond their use in mortuary practices (e.g. Case 1993).

Recently, Barry Cunliffe (2000) has reminded of the fragmented geographical distribution of regions that engaged in Beaker exchanges. However, even a cursory analysis of the distribution maps show that these regions were connected by water, and were located either along the coast or adjacent major navigable rivers, implying that water transport was the manner by which these goods were transported. Rather than seeing elite groups within all these regions maintaining contact with elite groups in all other regions all the time, further analysis of the long-distance traded goods suggests a more dynamic nature. Thus, it is possible to recognise reasonably well-defined elite networks within Europe, for example one based on the distribution of amber spacer-plates (forming part of amber necklaces) noted some years ago by Anthony Harding (1993) and which linked elite groups in the Wessex region with those in the Aegean and southern Germany, another one based on jet necklaces (concentrated on the British North Sea coast), one on golden *lunulae* (linking Ireland with Britain and Continental Europe: Taylor 1968), and one that linked elite groups on opposite sides of the English Channel and the North Sea, but extended along the course of the River Rhine into Germany and Switzerland, based on drinking cups made from gold, silver, amber and shale (Needham *et al.* 2006). The exact nature of the networks is not completely clear. For example, debate continues on the importance of marriage-partner exchange, or whether the networks included the exchange of skilled craftsmen, as may be inferred from the discovery of the Amesbury Archer (Fitzpatrick 2002). What is not doubted, however, is that the elite networks facilitated the exchange of exotic goods and ideas, and that some sort of common cosmology existed, as shown by the copying of the many changes in Beaker design, or the use of spacer plates in both amber and jet necklaces, as well as their engraved representation on some *lunulae*.

Though the networks were of a dynamic, rather than static, nature, it is a matter of ongoing debate what mechanisms drove these changes in the elite networks. Availability of and access to early metal may have played a significant role in this (cf. Pare 2000). The application of electron probe microanalysis coupled with lead isotope analysis of bronze alloys has offered an as yet unparalleled insight into the distances travelled by raw material, scrap metal and finished products in the 2nd millennium B.C. (Northover 1982). These studies identify Irish copper-arsenic alloys as the first metals in Britain, alongside a gradually increasing importation of metal from the Continent. Bronze-tin alloy bronzes became increasingly important only after 1700 cal. B.C., indicating the growing importance of British tin probably mixed with Continental copper. Chris Pare (2000), in a review of the evidence of the circulation of bronze based on this kind of evidence, concludes that during the Early Bronze Age metal was a scarce commodity in Britain, relative to later

sewn-plank boat	date	period	reference
Ferriby 3	2030 to 1780 cal. B.C.	3	Wright *et al.* 2001
Ferriby 2	1940 to 1720 cal. B.C.	3	Wright *et al.* 2001
Ferriby 1	1880 to 1680 cal. B.C.	3	Wright *et al.* 2001
Caldicot 1	1870 to 1680 cal. B.C.	3	McGrail 1997
Kilnsea	1750 to 1620 cal. B.C.	3/4	Van de Noort *et al.* 1999
Dover	1575 to 1520 cal. B.C.	4	Bayliss *et al.* 2004
Testwood Lakes	c. 1500 cal. B.C.	4/5	Fitzpatrick pers. comm.
Goldcliff	c. 1170 B.C.	5	Bell *et al.* 2000
Caldicot 2	c. 1000 cal. B.C.	6	McGrail 1997
Brigg »raft«	825 to 760 cal. B.C.	7	cf. Switsur in McGrail 1981

Table 1   Dates and periods (After Needham 1996) of sewn-plank boats.

periods, and that the trade in bronze, copper and tin was of a high-level and long-distance nature. The nature of the exchange with continental Europe of tin in particular may have dictated, to a degree, the changing nature of the elite networks.

Pare's (2000) review for British bronze in the Middle and Late Bronze Age points to the increased availability of both scrap bronze and raw materials. As a material, bronze appears to have become more readily available, with regional traditions indicating an ubiquitous distribution and a widespread knowledge of bronze casting amongst regionally based smiths. For the period after 1300 cal. B.C., the archaeological record shows a strong interaction with Continental styles, with weapons in particular becoming much-traded items. This is also illustrated by the 13th c. cal. B.C. Langdon Bay cargo, found in the Channel just east of Dover harbour, containing over 400 bronze tools and weapons, many of French types, and thought to be scrap material destined for Britain where it was to be melted down and remoulded (Muckelroy 1981; Northover 1982; Needham & Dean 1987). This transition would explain the replacement of the directional exchange of the Early Bronze Age by the down-the-line exchange of the Middle and Late Bronze Age.

THE SEWN-PLANK BOAT AS SEAFARING CRAFT

To date, the sometimes fragmentary remains of ten sewn-plank boats have been discovered: the Brigg »raft« (McGrail 1981), three boats from North Ferriby (F1, F2 and F3: Wright & Wright 1939; Wright 1990; Wright *et al.* 2001), and a single boat-plank from Kilnsea (Van de Noort *et al.* 1999) all from the Humber estuary and its tributaries; two boats from the Welsh side of the Severn estuary known as Caldicot 1 (a boat plank of a side strake) and Caldicot 2 (up to three additional fragment of another boat; Nayling & Caseldine 1997), and two pieces of boat planking from Goldcliff (Bell 1992; 1993; Bell *et al.* 2000). The Dover boat was found in 1992 (Clark 2004) and the tenth boat is represented by the fragment of a cleat from the Testwood Lakes excavations, just north of Southampton in the floodplain of the River Test (Fitzpatrick *et al.* 1996; A. Fitzpatrick pers. comm.). The most up-to-date ages for the boats, taking into account the recent re-dating of the Ferriby boats, is provided in **Table 1**.

It seems probable that the type of craft used for maintaining the elite networks in the 2nd millennium B.C. were the sewn-plank boats. Undoubtedly, the discussion about the seafaring capabilities of this type of craft will continue until a full-scale model with a design widely supported by the maritime archaeological community will have been comprehensively tested. Also, alternative types of craft, especially hide-boats, will continue to be considered as having played a role in prehistoric seafaring. In the meantime, there are four good reasons for stating that the sewn-plank boat was the most probable candidate for enabling prehistoric seafaring:

First, the seafaring capabilities of prehistoric craft should be defined in their context, rather than in a modern one. From the discussion on long-distance exchange presented above, it can be inferred that prehistoric craft did not provide a daily, weekly or even monthly ferry service, rather their use on the sea may have been an annual, decadal or even a generational event. Therefore, it was not the prevailing but the exceptionally favourable conditions that determined the seafaring capability of prehistoric craft.

Second, the remains of all Bronze Age sewn-plank boats have been discovered in locations that are either on major estuaries (Ferriby, Kilnsea and Goldcliff) or on navigable rivers, which offer direct access to the sea[1]. This contrasts quite clearly with the distribution of dated prehistoric logboats, which are usually found on inland rivers or lakes (Van de Noort 2006).

Third, recognising the simple fact that sewn-plank boats were built over a period of 1000 years, with considerable effort and drawing on increasingly rare resources (i.e. very large oak trees), suggests that they offered certain advantages in terms of use or navigation over alternative craft such as hide-boats. In the pastoral economy of the British Isles, there can not have been a shortage of suitable hides, and the sewn-plank boat was not designed out of necessity, but out of a desire for craft that could be used more often, for longer journeys or carrying greater crews and cargos than alternative boats. That the 1000 year period of sewn-plank boat building is paralleled by a period during which long-distance exchanged goods were of great importance (especially when compared with long-distance exchange during the Neolithic or Iron Age), is surely no coincidence.

Fourth, recent experiments with a half-size model of Ferriby 1 and a full-size reconstruction of the Hjortspring sewn-plank boat suggest that the seafaring capabilities of such boats have been greatly underrated in the past, and that even quite rough seas can be mastered by these craft (Crumlin-Pedersen & Trakadas 2003; Gifford & Gifford 2004; Kaul 2004). In the light of these recent experiments, the suggestion that their »shape, lack of sheer, and their structure were such that that they would have insufficient stability, freeboard and sea-kindliness qualities« (McGrail 2001: 194), requires urgent revision.

CONTEXTUALISING THE SEWN-PLANK BOATS

On the basis of her cross-cultural studies, Helms (1988) argues that when undertaking long-distance journeys that were dedicated to obtaining esoteric knowledge and goods, the departure from the home territory was frequently marked in early societies by ritual or ritualised activities. Similar activities may have signalled the homecoming too. These may have included transient activities which left no archaeological information, such as offering a glass of wine to the god(s) of the sea, the decoration of boats with flags, or bodily adornments for the travellers. However, specific locales would have been selected as departure and arrival points, namely those that linked the travellers to the ideological concepts represented in the landscape that gave meaning to long-distance travel.

This understanding of the significance of travel and geographical distance provides a basic archaeological tool. Through the analysis of the landscape context of the sewn-plank boat locations, we can ascertain something of the »ritual of travel«. For the Bronze Age we may expect to see, for example, a reference to ancestors such as burial places, the presence of »territorial« markers such as barrows or cairns, or votive/ structured depositions, especially of esoteric objects.

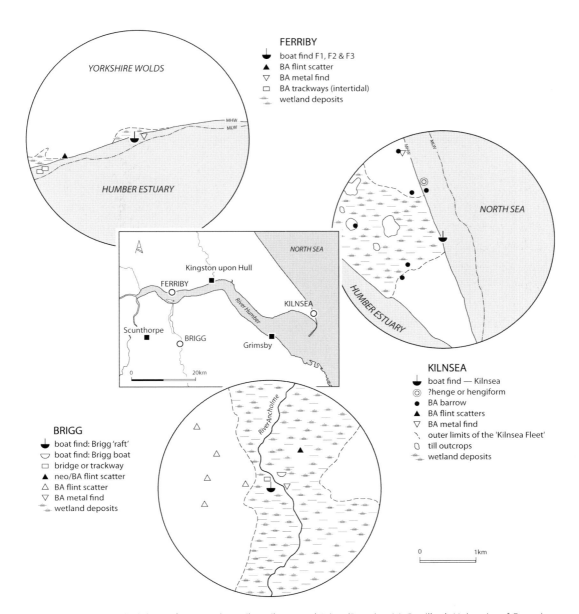

Fig. 1 Contextualised sewn-plank boats from North Ferriby, Kilnsea and Brigg (Drawing M. Rouillard, University of Exeter).

The author has undertaken such an analysis for all the ten sewn plank boats (**Fig. 1** shows the contextual analysis of the Ferriby, Kilnsea and Brigg boats as an example of this), and the results are summarised in **Table 2** with four trends emerging: first, none of the craft dated to 2000 to 1500 cal. B.C. was associated with ritual deposits, but the contexts of all the sewn-plank boats dated to 1500 to 1000 cal. B.C. included deposits that have been described as ritual; second, the sewn-plank boat fragments dated to 1500 to 1000 cal. B.C., had all been reused in structures that have been interpreted by the excavators as used for crossing rivers, but none of those dated between 2000 and 1500 cal. B.C. had been reused in this way. The strakes which had been removed from the Dover boat may, or may not, have been reused elsewhere, whereas the Brigg »raft« appears to have sunk, and reuse was not an option; third, with the exception of Caldicot 2 which shares the cultural landscape of Caldicot 1, only boats of Early Bronze Age date had earlier »ances-

sewn plank-boat	immediate context		landscape setting (2 km radius)	
	associated ritual deposits?	re-use of boat timbers in river crossings?	nearby ancestral monuments?	nearby contemporary monuments?
period 3				
Ferriby 3	none	no	none	none
Ferriby 2	none	no	none	none
Ferriby 1	none	no	none	none
Caldicot 1	none	no	Neolithic long barrow at Portskewett	large EBA barrow
period 3/4				
Kilnsea	none	no	Neolithic houses and hengiform monument or circular structure	several EBA barrows containing beaker pottery
period 4				
Dover	none	no	none known	possible EBA burials represented by whole Beaker
period 4/5				
Testwood Lakes	bronze Acton 2 rapier	bridge	none	none
period 5				
Goldcliff	human skulls	trackway	none	none
period 6				
Caldicot 2	Wilburton-type chape, two vessels, an amber bead, wooden objects and a dog skeleton	trackway or bridge	as Caldicot 1	as Caldicot 1
period 7				
Brigg »raft«	bronze axe, spearhead and pin, human and animal bones, pottery	no, but nearby bridge or jetty	none	none

Table 2   The context of sewn-plank boats: archaeological evidence (periods according to Needham 1996).

tral« monuments within their immediate landscape setting; and fourth, only the Early Bronze Age craft were associated with contemporary monuments (i.e. burial mounds) within their landscape settings, again with the exception of Caldicot 2. The North Ferriby boats were an exception here too; this may well be explained by the interpretation that North Ferriby was a place for boatbuilding, rather than one from where long journeys commenced.

On the basis of these trends, one may discern that the socio-political significance of seafaring in the Early Bronze Age was quite different from that of the Middle and Late Bronze Age. In the Early Bronze Age, seafaring was associated directly to the monuments of the ancestors. Long-distance journeys offered opportunities to link the importance of the ancestors in social reproduction with an enhanced status for certain individuals, even deification, by linking the horizontal and vertical dimensions of the seafarers' cosmology (Helms 1988: 66; Needham 2000). The evidence for this period does not suggest any »special« treatment of the craft themselves. In the Middle and Late Bronze Age, the role of seafaring boats can be interpreted within a context of transition and regeneration. The evidence does suggest special treatment of the craft themselves – their fragmentation and reuse in structures which were used for crossing small bodies of water referred to the long distance journeys of their ancestors, and the special nature of crossing rivers and wetlands was reinforced by the use of other votive depositions, including bronze artefacts and human remains.

CONCLUSION

Through the contextualisation of the sewn-plank craft, and through the detailed analysis of their archaeological contexts and cultural landscape settings, we can begin to understand the significance of the transfer of ideas and exchange between Britain and the Continent in the 2nd millennium B.C., and thus integrate maritime aspects of archaeology with its parent discipline (cf. McGrail 2003:1). The result of this study indicates that seafarers in the Early Bronze Age equated geographical (»horizontal«) distance with time and the ancestors (»vertical distance«), thus the farther one travelled, the closer one would get to the ancestors. In this way of thinking, the knowledge and objects obtained during these journeys was believed to have been imbued with a special quality. In the Middle and Late Bronze Age, the need for long journeys diminished with the greater availability of bronze, but the reuse of fragments of sewn-plank boats indicates that the crossing of certain water bodies imitated the extended journeys of their ancestors, and thus by proxy retained something of the significance of travel and geographical distance. The journeys themselves were, in effect, more important than the acquisition of certain goods.

NOTE

1) Brigg, Caldicot 1 and 2, and Testwood Lakes; the debate whether the River Dour where the Dover boat was found was navigable in the Bronze Age, is ongoing.

REFERENCES

Adams, J., 2001, Ships and boats as archaeological source material. *World Archaeology*, 32, 292-310.

Barrett, J. C., 1994, *Fragment of Antiquity. An Archaeology of Social Life in Britain, 2900-1200 BC*. Oxford (UK), Cambridge (USA).

Bayliss, A., Groves, C., McCormac, C., Bronk Ramsey, C., Baillie, M. Brown, D., Cook, G. & Swisur, R., 2004, Dating. In: Clark 2004, 250-255.

Bell, M., 1992, Field survey and excavation at Goldcliff, 1992. In: M. Bell (ed.), *Severn Estuary Levels Research Committee Annual Report*, 15-29.

1993, Intertidal Archaeology at Goldcliff in the Severn Estuary. In: J. Coles, V. Fenwick & G. Hutchinson (eds), *A Spirit of Enquiry. Essays for Ted Wright*. Exeter, 9-13.

Bell, M., Caseldine, A. & Neumann, H., 2000, *Prehistoric Intertidal Archaeology in the Welsh Severn Estuary*. CBA, Res. Report, no. 120. York.

Bradley, R. 1984, *The social foundations of prehistoric Britain*. London

Butler, J. J., 1963, Bronze Age Connections across the North Sea. *Palaeohistoria*, 9, 1-286.

Case, H., 1993, Beakers: deconstruction and after. *PPS*, 33, 241-268.

Clark, P. (ed.), 2004, *The Dover Bronze Age Boat*. London.

Clarke, D. V., Cowie, T. G. & Foxon, A., 1985, *Symbols of Power at the Time of Stonehenge*. Edinburgh.

Crumlin-Pedersen, O. & Trakadas, A. (eds), 2003, *Hjortspring: a pre-Roman Iron-Age warship in context*. Ships and Boats of the North, vol. 5. Roskilde.

Cunliffe, B., 2000, *Facing the Ocean*. Oxford.

Fitzpatrick, A. P., 2002, »The Amesbury Archer«: a well-furnished Early Bronze Age burial in southern England. *Antiquity*, 76, 629-630.

Fitzpatrick, A. P., Ellis, C. & Allen, M. J., 1996, Bronze Age »jetties« or causeways at Testwood lakes, Hampshire, Great Britain. *Newsletter of the Wetland Archaeology Research Project*, 20, 19-22.

Gifford, E. & Gifford, J., 2004, The use of half-scale model ships in archaeological research with particular reference to the Graveney, Sutton Hoo and Ferriby ships. In: P. Clark (ed.), *The Dover Bronze Age Boat in Context. Society and Water Transport in Prehistoric Europe.* Oxford, 67-81.

Harding, A. F., 1993, British amber spacer-plate necklaces and their relatives in gold and stone. In: C. W. Beck & J. Bouzek, with D. Dreslerová (eds), *Amber in Archaeology.* Prague, 53-58.

2000, *European Societies in the Bronze Age.* Cambridge.

Helms, M. W., 1988, *Ulysses' Sail. An Ethnographic Odyssey of Power, Knowledge, and Geographical Distance.* Princeton.

Kaul, F., 2004, Social and religious perceptions of the ship in Bronze Age Europe. In: P. Clark (ed.), *The Dover Bronze Age Boat in Context. Society and Water Transport in Prehistoric Europe.* Oxford, 122-137.

McGrail, S., 1981, *The Brigg »raft« and her prehistoric environment.* BAR, British Series, no. 89. Oxford, and National Maritime Museum, Archaeological Series, no. 6. Greenwich.

1997, The boat fragments. In: N. Nayling & A. Caseldine, *Excavations at Caldicot, Gwent: Bronze Age palaeochannels in the Lower Nedern Valley.* CBA, Res. Report, no. 108. York, 210-217.

2001, *Boats of the World.* Oxford.

2003, The sea and archaeology. *Historical Research*, 76, 1-17.

Muckelroy, K., 1981, Middle Bronze Age trade between Britain and Europe. *PPS*, 47, 275-297.

Nayling, N. & Caseldine, A., 1997, *Excavations at Caldicot, Gwent: Bronze Age Palaeochannels in the Lower Nedern Valley.* CBA, Res. Report, no. 108. York.

Needham, S., Parfitt, K. & Varndell, G., 2006, *The Ringlemere Cup: Precious Cups and the Beginning of the Channel Bronze Age.* British Museum Research Publication, no. 163. London.

Needham, S. P. & Dean, M., 1987, La gargaison de Langdon Bay à Douvres: la signification pour les échanges à travers la manche. In: C. Mordant & A. Richard (eds), *Les relations entre le continent et les Iles Britanniques à l'Age du Bronze. Actes du colloque de Lille dans le cadre du 22ème Congrès Préhistorique de France; 2-7 septembre 1984.* Amiens, 119-124.

Needham, S. P., 1996, Chronology and periodisation in the British Bronze Age. *Acta Arch.*, 67, 121-140.

2000, Power pulses across a cultural divide: Armorica & Wessex. *PPS*, 66, 151-194.

Northover, J. P., 1982, The exploration of the long-distance movement of bronze in Bronze and Early Iron Age Europe. *Bulletin of the University of London Institute of Archaeology*, 19, 45-72.

O'Connor, B., 1980, *Cross-Channel Relations in the later Bronze Age. Relations between Britain, North-Eastern France and the Low Countries during the later Bronze Age and the Early Iron Age, with particular reference to the metalwork.* BAR, Internat. Series, no. 91. Oxford.

Pare, C., 2000, Bronze and the Bronze Age. In: C. Pare (ed.) *Metals Make the World Go Rounds. The Supply and Circulation of metals in Bronze Age Europe. Proceedings of a Conference held at the University of Birmingham in June 1997.* Oxford, 1-38.

Shennan, S. J., 1982, Ideology, change and the European Early Bronze Age. In: I. Hodder (ed.), *Symbolic and Structural Archaeology.* Cambridge, 155-161.

1986, Interaction and change in the third millennium BC western and central Europe. In: C. Renfrew & J. F. Cherry (eds), *Peer Polity Interaction and Socio-Political Change.* Cambridge, 137-48.

Taylor, J. J., 1986, Early Bronze Age gold neck-rings in Western Europe. *PPS*, 34, 259 -265.

Van de Noort, R., 2006, Argonauts of the North Sea: a social maritime archaeology for the 2nd millennium BC. *PPS*, 72, 267-287.

Van de Noort, R., Middleton, R., Foxon, A. & Bayliss, A., 1999, The »Kilnsea-boat«, and some implications from the discovery of England's oldest plank boat. *Antiquity*, 73, 131-135.

Wright, C. W. & Wright, E. V., 1939, Submerged boat at North Ferriby. *Antiquity*, 13, 349-354.

Wright, E. V., 1990, *The Ferriby boats. Seacraft of the Bronze Age.* London.

Wright, E. V., Hedges, R., Bayliss, A. & Van de Noort, R., 2001, New AMS dates for the Ferriby boats; a contribution to the origin of seafaring. *Antiquity*, 75, 726-734.

PATRICE POMEY

A NEW APPROACH
TO MEDITERRANEAN NAUTICAL ARCHAEOLOGY

HARBOUR, RIVER AND RIVER-SEA BOATS

Following the development of underwater archaeology, research in ancient nautical archaeology from the Mediterranean area for a long time addressed the issue of maritime wrecks found in open sea, along the coast or off shore[1] (Gianfrotta & Pomey 1981; Parker 1992). Excavations of the Yassi Ada Byzantine wreck in Turkey (Bass & van Doorninck 1982), the Kyrenia greek ship in Cyprus (Swiny & Katzev 1973; Steffy 1985) or that of the Roman wreck of La Madrague de Giens on the French coast (Tchernia, Pomey & Hesnard 1978; Pomey 1982) are among the most famous examples. On one hand, that resulted in a revival of our knowledge on ancient Mediterranean shipbuilding especially on merchant boats and ships, from the little coaster to the big merchantman (Steffy 1994; Pomey & Rieth 2005). On the other hand, despite evidence supplied by ancient iconographical and literary evidence (Casson 1971; Basch 1987; Pomey 1997), river and inland boats, river-sea and harbour boats remained for a long time largely unknown from an archaeological point of view. In the Mediterranean such boats were rare contrary to N. Europe where archaeological discoveries involving the Celtic and Gallo-Roman periods were particularly numerous, especially in the Swiss lakes, in the Rhine valley, and in the Channel and North Sea areas[2]. That favoured the development of the »Romano-Celtic« nautical archaeology and led to the theory about a specific »Romano-Celtic« ship construction (McGrail 1995; Arnold 1998). Nevertheless curiously, this theory did not concern S. Gaul as if there was no specific ship construction in this area. In fact, for a long time, there were no archaeological discoveries concerning such boats and especially river boats in S. Gaul.

An obvious reason can be found in the great difference between the conditions of navigation in each area (Pomey & Rieth 2005: 38-41). In N. Europe, the rivers network is dense, with rivers largely opened to the sea by wide estuaries (**Fig. 1**). The result is a continuous system of inland and coastal navigation areas where the different zones are directly connected. It is the opposite in the Mediterranean area where the rivers network is not very dense and there is often a discontinuity between rivers and sea or between the different river areas (**Fig. 2**). That does not mean that there was no river traffic, but only that conditions for archaeological finds are different.

However, things are changing. During the last 25 years excavations of ancient harbour zones in Toulon, Marseilles, Pisa and Naples for the maritime area, or in Lyon, Arles and Chalon-sur-Saône in the river area have supplied several wrecks that come to be added to the rare discoveries known. All these wrecks firmly inversed the former trend. Several types of ships and boats, hitherto unknown, are discovered and studied: inshore fishing boats, harbour boats, lagoon boats, river and fluvio-maritime boats.

DISCOVERIES

The first well-known example goes back to the end of the fifties and the early sixties with the discovery of the Fiumicino wrecks, in the harbour of the Emperor Claudius, when the Rome international airport was constructed (**Fig. 3**). Seven wrecks address harbour boats and a fishing craft, from the 2nd to the

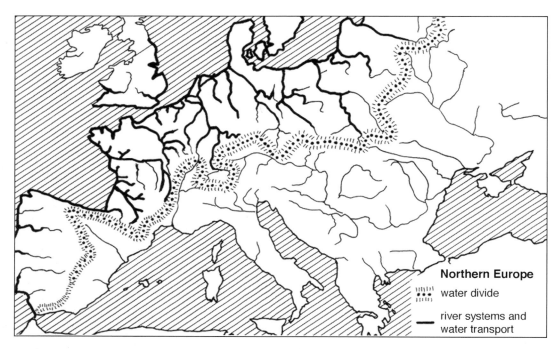

Fig. 1 North European rivers network (After Beaudouin 1994).

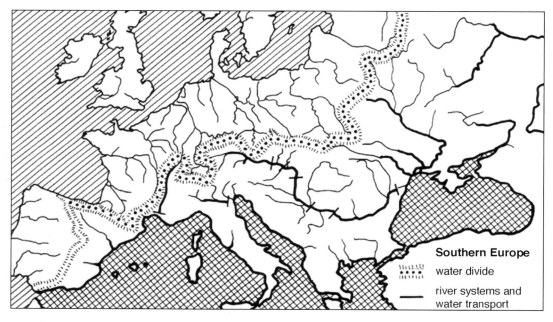

Fig. 2 South European rivers network (After Beaudouin 1994).

5th c. A.D.[3]. The three main wrecks, Fiumicino 1, 2 and 3, according to Boetto`s classification, belong to the late Roman Empire and are of the *navis caudicaria* type (Boetto 2000; 2002; 2003; 2006a).

The Fiumicino discovery was an example of what was to ocur later. In fact, since the beginning of the 1980s, infrastructural works investigated by rescue archaeology in salvage operations have provided, both in urban, harbour areas and rivers, new evidence for nautical archaeology:

- 1980. In Comacchio, in the area of the Po delta, a large sea-river barge (still 20 m long and 5.7 m wide) from the Augustean period (end of 1st c. B.C.) was found (Berti 1990) (**Fig. 4**). The boat is partly sewn and partly assembled with a classical mortise-and-tenon system.

- 1987. In Toulon, a part of the ancient harbour was excavated. Six wrecks from the 1st to the 3rd c. A.D. were discovered of which two (Toulon 1 and 2) are typical harbour boats of *horeia* type characterized by a transom bow. The boats, of the 1st c. A.D., are respectively 6 and 8 m long (Brun 1999: 800; Boetto, this volume pp. 290-295).

- 1990. In Lyon, place Tolozan, along the Rhône River, was found a part of a river barge from the 1st c. A.D. with some mortise-and-tenon joints (Rieth 1999). It was the first discovery of a »Gallo-Roman« river barge in conjunction with the Mediterranean rivers network.

- 1993. In Marseilles, place Jules-Verne, during excavations at the site of the ancient harbour, seven wrecks were found (Pomey 1995). Two of them (Jules-Verne 7 and 9) are the famous Greek archaic boats – a merchant ship and a coastal boat – from the 6th c. B.C. (Pomey 1998). Five other wrecks belong to the Roman period. Three of them (Jules-Verne 3, 4 and 5; 1st and 2nd c. A.D.) are working harbour boats, possibly dredge boats (Pomey 1999) (**Fig. 5**). They are characterized each by a central well which surrounds an opening in the ship's bottom. Another wreck (Jules-Verne 8) comes from a little harbour craft.

- 1996. In Chalon-sur-Saône, in the River Saône, in the extreme N. part of the Mediterranean rivers network, two Gallo-Roman river barges from the 1st c. A.D. were found (Lonchambon 2000; Bonnamour 2002).

- 1998. At La-Conque-des-Salins, near Sète, in the Étang de Thau, an inland lagoon open to the sea, a little wreck dated from the Gallo-Roman period was found. The boat, probably a lagoon boat, is characterized by a flat bottom section with a central keel plank and by a typical mortise-and-tenon system (Rouquette, Jézégou and Wicha 1999).

Fig. 3 Fiumicino, wreck 5 under excavation (Photo Soprintendenza per i Beni Archeologici di Ostia).

Fig. 4 Comacchio, Ferrara province. – Shipwreck. Lower part with floor-timbers removed (After Berti 1990).

Fig. 5 Marseilles, Place de Jules-Verne wrecks 3 and 4 *in situ* (Photo Centre Camille Jullian, CNRS).

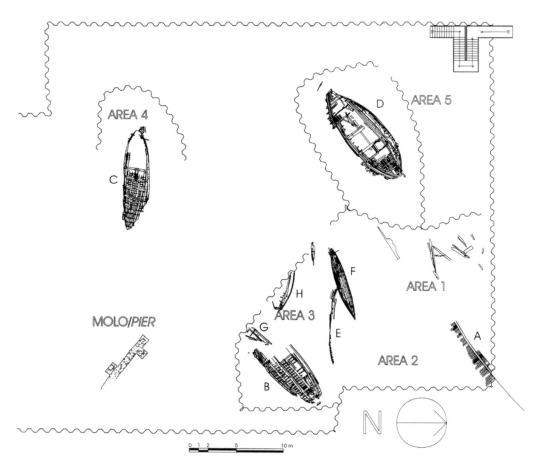

Fig. 6 Pisa, San Rossore. – Site plan with shipwrecks uncovered (After Bruni 2000).

– 1998 to 1999. In Pisa, San Rossore, a famous series of a dozen of ancient wrecks from the 2nd c. B.C. to the 5th c. A.D. was found. Boats were discovered inland, in the area of a paleo-channel of the River Auser (Bruni 2000; Camilli 2004). Among the wrecks are probably some characteristic river boats of which a rowing one with a cutwater (boat C, 14 m long), a long craft looking like a sort of pirogue but made of assembled planks (wreck F, about 9 m long) (Bockius 2002) and a late Roman vessel (wreck D, 5th c. A.D.) (**Fig. 6**). The wrecks are well conserved, but, ten years after the excavation, unfortunately, they are still not fully documented nor analysed from a nautical point of view.

– 2003. In Lyon, parc Saint-Georges, at the Saône river bank, a series of six Gallo-Roman barges of the 1st to the 3rd c. A.D. was discovered. The largest one is preserved near 20 m long (**Fig. 7**). They are the largest river barges ever found in the Mediterranean rivers network (cf. Guyon & Rieth, this volume pp. 157–165).

– 1998 to 2003. Near Les-Saintes-Maries-de-la-Mer, off the coast of Camargue, another fluvio-maritime boat was found in 1998, dated to the 1st c. A.D. The Saintes-Maries-de-la-Mer 24 (SM 24) wreck was excavated in 2003. Identified as remains of a large boat with a flat bottom section and a flat keel, according to the technical features which include mortise-and-tenon construction of the planking, and frames fastened by treenails and lashings (Long, Marlier & Rival, this volume pp. 277–287), the vessel belongs to the »lashed frames family« of ancient Mediterranean ships and boats (Pomey 2002).

– 2004. The rescue excavation opened during the subway public works of Napoli (Italy) found the Ancient harbour with three well-preserved wrecks from the 1st to the 3rd c. A.D. (Boetto 2005). One wreck (Napoli C, end of the 1st c.) is a harbour boat, similar to the *horeiae* type boats from Toulon, with a transom stem (Boetto, this volume pp. 289–296).

– 2004 to 2006. In the Rhône River, at Arles, a Gallo-Roman barge approx. dated to the 1st c. A.D. was found in 2004. It is still under excavation. The wreck shares similarities and characteristics of the Gallo-Roman barges found in Lyon (Long, Rival & Marlier, this volume pp. 303–331).

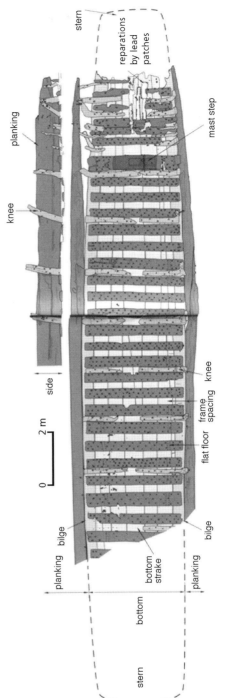

Fig. 7 Lyon, Parc Saint-Georges. – Wreck 4 (Drawing INRAP; after Ayala 2004).

CLASSIFICATIONS

This compilation of the most important discoveries made over the last 25 years, of river, river-sea and harbour boats from the Mediterranean network, shows how such matters has been advancing. All these

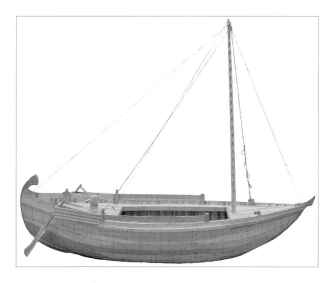

Fig. 8 Reconstruction model of Fiumicino 1 (Photo G. Boetto, Centre Camille Jullian, CNRS; model built in scale 1:10 by the Museum für Antike Schiffahrt, Mainz).

discoveries shed new light on types of boats and systems of shipbuilding with mixed influence of sea and river traditions. They contribute to address new topics, particularly the issue of a peculiar »Romano-Celtic« shipbuilding tradition of S. Gaul besides a N. one. According to their characteristics, their functional use and their area of navigation these different types of boats can be classified into three main categories: 1. harbour and fishing boats; 2. fluvio-maritime boats; 3. river boats.

The 1st category, »harbour and fishing boats«, is the most diversified and can be subdivided into four groups:

– Group 1 consists of the Fiumicino 1, 2 and 3 wrecks (Boetto 2000; 2003; 2006a). They belong

Fig. 9 Marseilles, Place de Jules-Verne, wreck 3. – Ship bottom with central well (Photo Centre Camille Jullian, CNRS).

to same type, well-documented by documentary and iconography evidences: *navis caudicaria* (**Fig. 8**), a lighter used for transhipping and unloading the cargo of big merchant vessels which were unable to enter the Tiber River. Such vessels were towed upstream transporting goods from the *Portus* of Ostia to the urban harbour of Rome. Sharing the same structural and technical characteristics which proceed either from a maritime and river boat construction influence, the type was a functional part of the supply system of Rome.

– Group 2 comprises of wrecks Toulon 1and 2 and Napoli C. These vessels are characterized by transoms located at each one of their extremities which can be identified, according to iconography, as stems. On the Althiburus mosaic from Tunisia (Duval 1949), this type of boat is called *horeia*. It is interpreted as a harbour and fishing boat (cf. Boetto, this volume pp. 289-296).

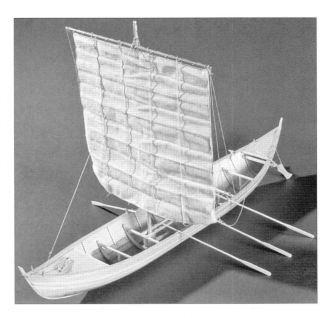

Fig. 10   Reconstruction model of Marseilles, Place de Jules-Verne 9 (Model and photo Centre Camille Jullian, CNRS).

– Group 3 includes Roman working boats, the wrecks Jules-Verne 3, 4, and 5. As can be traced back from an opening in the central part of the ship bottom (**Fig. 9**), such craft were provided with a well construction. The latter is supposed to be an element of a dredging device presumably made of a bucket wheel. Consequently, such boats had to be identified as floating dredgers (Pomey 1995; 1999)[4].

– Group 4 boats which are linked to sea-harbours, were used for fishing. In fact, apart from the very specific boat construction as revealed by Fiumicino 5, it might be hard to distinguish a fishing boat functionally from a small vessel in general. However, the Greek Late-Archaic wreck Jules-Verne 9 from Marseilles which was a coastal craft used for coral fishing, belongs to this group (Pomey 1998; 2000; 2003) (**Fig. 10**). As its most characteristic representative, the Fiumicino 5 wreck can be identified as a *navis vivaria*, a fishing boat equipped with a central container wherein caught fishes were kept (Boetto 2006b) (**Fig. 3**). According to G. Boetto, Fiumicino 4 wreck also comes into question as the relict of a fishing boat (Boetto 2006a). The same could be true for the wreck Jules-Verne 8 dated to the 3rd c. A.D. (Pomey 1995). Although without functional particularity, its size suggests a usage either as a multi-purpose harbour craft or a merchant ship tender.

The 2nd category, fluvio-maritime or river-sea boats, in the Mediterranean area may be defined by the Comacchio and the Saintes-Maries-de-la-Mer 24 (SM 24) wrecks. Both show structural features of inland vessels as a flat bottom, but also elements of seagoing craft maritime, i.e. the frame pattern combined with a flat keel, and with stem and stern post (**Fig. 11**). Apparently those boats sailed on maritime waters and rivers. The La-Conque-des-Salins ship with her specific structural keel plank resembles a »Romano-Celtic boat« (Arnold 1998), though she was built in the Mediterranean mortise-and-tenon system.

The 3rd category, river boats, comprises different types of boats. However, from a cultural and technical point of view it can be subdivided into two groups:

– The 1st one can be considered as belonging to the Greco-Roman tradition according to the structural system and their mortise-and-tenon construction. The wrecks from Pisa seem to belong to this group. The wreck Pisa C, characterized by a reverse stem with cutwater is a mixed river boat for sailing and rowing,

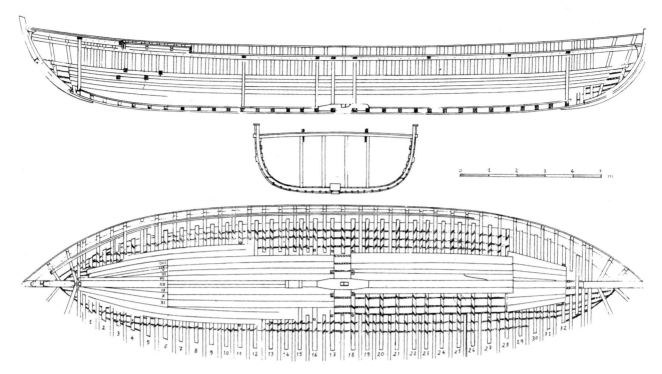

Fig. 11 Graphical reconstruction of the Comacchio wreck (Drawings M. Bonino; after Berti 1990).

Fig. 12 Pisa, San Rossore. – Plan-drawing of wreck F *in situ* (After Bruni 2000).

with a mast hole and oar ports. Pisa F due to its proportions resembles a dugout canoe, but it is made of planks (**Fig. 12**). This boat type may be considered as typical of inland waters.

– The 2nd group consists of the Gallo-Roman barges from the rivers Rhône and Saône: the wrecks from Arles, Lyon (place Tolozan and parc Saint-Georges) and Chalon-sur-Saône. These barges belong to the Romano-Celtic »bottom based« shipbuilding tradition. But they have several specific characteristics of which some indicate a Mediterranean influence like the use of mortise-and-tenon joints, pitched cloth for luting or lead sheets for repairs (**Fig. 7**).

Therefore the so-called »Romano-Celtic« shipbuilding tradition must be reconsidered according to the distribution of the rivers network. This tradition cannot be reduced to a monolithic whole as was done up until the discoveries of wrecks from the rivers in S. Gaul. According to regional characteristics, we can subdivide this tradition into regional groups like a N. one and a S. one or, to take into account the geographical fluvial basins, a »Rhenish group«, an »Alpine group« and a »Rhône-Saône group« (Guyon & Rieth, this volume pp. 163-165, fig. 8).

CONCLUSIONS

The discovery of several wrecks in new geographical situations, like harbours, rivers and inland waters, yields new data for the nautical archaeology of S. Gaul and in the Mediterranean. Accordingly, new research topics are being raised that make it possible to reconsider some wrecks previously studied, like the Fiumicino ship finds, and to address new issues. Among them, harbour and fishing boats, fluvio-maritime boats and river boats. All of which appears as a rich body of new knowledge, such as:
– new type of boats of which many of them were quite unknown before, from an archaeological point of view;
– new evidence about mutual influence between maritime and river shipbuilding tradition;
– new discoveries of Gallo-Roman river barges with Mediterranean influence.
This last issue is particularly important because it sheds new light on the »Romano-Celtic« shipbuilding which appears now to be subdivided into different geographical groups (N. and S.) according to the wreck origins. On the whole, these recent wrecks discoveries contribute towards instigating and renewing Mediterranean nautical archaeology.

NOTES

1) Cf. the introduction paper of H. Tzalas (2002) about a century of underwater archaeology in the Mediterranean, and the related papers about Bulgaria, Egypt, France, Greece, Israel, Italy, Syria, Lebanon, and Turkey in: *Tropis VII*, vol. II, part B, 875-1005.

2) To a general view on the main boat discoveries in N. Europe cf. Arnold 1992: 57-104.

3) The first publication by V. Scrinari (1979) is quite obsolete. It has been revised after detailed analyses of the wrecks by G. Boetto (2006a). Also cf. Boetto 2000; 2002; 2003; 2006b.

4) The excavation has provided evidences about harbour dredging during the 1st c. A.D. (Hesnard 1994: 198). Recently, during the excavation of the ancient harbour of Napoli, evidence about the dredging of the harbour have been also found with the marks of the dredge buckets (Giampaola 2005: 54-57). However, the hypothesis of sludge boats is not to be excluded.

REFERENCES

Arnold, B., 1992, *Batellerie gallo-romaine sur le lac de Neuchâtel*, vol. 2. Archéologie Neuchâteloise, no. 13. Saint-Blaise.

Arnold, B., 1998, Embarcations romano-celtiques et construction sur sole. In: É. Rieth (ed.), *Concevoir et construire les navires. De la trière au picoteux*. Ramonville Saint-Agne, 73-90.

Ayala, G. (ed.), 2004, *Romains d'eau douce. Les bateaux de Saint-Georges*. Catalogue exposition. Lyon.

Basch, L., 1987, *Le musée imaginaire de la marine antique*. Athens.

Bass, G. F. & van Doorninck, F. H., 1982, *Yassi Ada*, vol. I. *A Seventh-Century Byzantine Shipwreck*. College Station/Texas.

Beaudouin, F., 1994, L'économie motrice pré-mécanique. Les chemins qui marchent. *Neptunia*, 193, 1-13.

Berti, F. (ed.), 1990, *Fortuna Maris. La nave romana di Comacchio*. Bologna.

Bockius, R., 2002, On the reconstruction of Pisa, nave F, by the Museum für Antike Schiffahrt, Mainz. In: *The Ancient Ships of Pisa. A European laboratory for research and preservation. »Culture 2000« programme*. Bruxelles, 23-29; 101-104.

Boetto, G., 2000, New technological and historical observations on the *Fiumicino 1* wreck from *Portus Claudius* (Fiumicino, Rome). In: *ISBSA 8*, 99-102.

Boetto, G., 2002, Fiumicino 1, 2, 3, 4, 5. In: A. Mees & B. Pferdehirt (eds), *Römerzeitliche Schiffsfunde in der Datenbank »Navis I«*. Kataloge Vor- und Frühgeschichtlicher Altertümer, no. 29. Mainz, 134-159.

Boetto, G., 2003, The late Roman Fiumicino 1 wreck: reconstructing the hull. In: *ISBSA 9*, 66-70.

Boetto, G., 2005, Le navi romane di Napoli. In: Giampaola *et al.* 2005, 63-76.

Boetto, G., 2006a, *Les navires de Fiumicino (Italie): architecture, matériaux, types et fonctions. Contribution à l'étude du système portuaire de Rome à l'époque impériale*. Unpubl. PhD thesis, Université de Provence, Aix-Marseille 1, directed by P. Pomey.

Boetto, G., 2006b, Roman techniques for the transport and conservation of fish: the case of the Fiumicino 5 wreck. In: *ISBSA 10*, 123-129.

Bonnamour, L., 2002, Saône-et-Loire, Chalon-sur-Saône. Le pont Saint-Laurent. *Bilan scientifique du DRASSM 2000*. Paris, 100-101.

Brun, J.-P., 1999, *Le Var*. Carte archéologique de la Gaule, no. 83.2. Académie des Inscriptions & Belles-Lettres. Paris.

Bruni, S. (ed.), 2000, *Le navi antiche di Pisa. Ad un anno dall'inizio delle reicerche*. Firenze.

Camilli, A., 2004, Il Cantiere delle navi antiche di Pisa: note sull'ambiente e sulla periodizzazione del deposito. *Archeologia Maritima Mediterranea*, 1, 53-75.

Casson, L., 1971, *Ships and Seamanship in the Ancient World*. Princeton/New Jersey (reprint 1986).

Duval, P.-M., 1949, La forme des navires romains d'après la mosaïque d'Althiburus. *Mélanges Ecole Française de Rome*, 61, 119-149.

Giampaola, D., *et al.*, 2005, La scoperta del porto di *Neapolis*: dalla ricostruzione topografica allo scavo e al recupero dei relitti. *Archeologia Maritima Mediterranea*, 2, 47-91.

Gianfrotta, P. & Pomey, P., 1981, *Archeologia subacquea. Storia, tecniche, scoperte e relitti*. Milano.

Hesnard, A., 1994, Une nouvelle fouille du port de Marseille, place Jules-Verne. *Comptes Rendus Académie Inscriptions & Belles-Lettres*, janvier-mars, 195-217.

Lonchambon, C., 2000, Un bateau monoxyle assemblé à Chalon-sur-Saône (Ier siècle ap. J.-C.). In: L. Bonnamour (ed.), *Archéologie des fleuves et des rivières*. Paris, 174-178.

McGrail, S., 1995, Romano-Celtic boats and ships: characteristic features. *IJNA*, 24.2, 139-145.

Parker, A. J., 1992, *Ancient Shipwrecks of the Mediterranean and the Roman Provinces*. BAR, Internat. Series, no. 580. Oxford.

Pomey, P., 1982, Le navire romain de la Madrague de Giens. *Comptes Rendus Académie Inscriptions & Belles-Lettres*, janvier-mars, 133-154.

1995, Les épaves grecques et romaines de la place Jules-Verne à Marseille. *Comptes Rendus Académie Inscriptions & Belles-Lettres*, avril-juin, 459-484.

1998, Les épaves grecques du VIe siècle av. J.-C. de la place Jules-Verne à Marseille. In: *ISBSA 7*, 147-154.

1999, Les épaves romaines de la place Jules-Verne à Marseille: des bateaux dragues? In: *TROPIS V*, 321-328.

2000, Un témoignage récent sur la pêche au corail à Marseille à l'époque archaïque. In: J.-P. Morel, C. Rondi-Costanso & D. Ugolini (eds), *Carallo di ieri. Corallo di oggi. Atti del Convegno di Ravello, 1996*. Bari, 37-39.

2002, Une nouvelle tradition technique d'assemblage antique: l'assemblage de la membrure par ligatures et chevilles. In: *TROPIS VII*, vol. II, part B, 597-604.

2003, Reconstruction of Marseilles 6th century BC Greek ships. In: *ISBSA 9*, 57-65.

Pomey, P. (ed.), 1997, *La navigation dans l'Antiquité*. Aix-en-Provence.

Pomey, P. & Rieth, É., 2005, *L'archéologie navale*. Paris.

Rieth, R., 1999, L'épave gallo-romaine de la place Tolozan à Lyon (France). In: *TROPIS V*, 339-348.

Rouquette, D., Jézégou, M.-P., Wicha, S., 2004, Epave Conque des Salins (étang de Thau). *Bilan scientifique du DRASSM 1999*. Paris, 35-38.

Scrinari, V., 1979, *Le navi del porto di Claudio*. Roma.

Steffy, J. R., 1985, The Kyrenia Ship. An Interim Report on its Hull Construction. *American Journal of Archaeology*, 89.1, 71-101.

1994, *Wooden Ship Building and the Interpretation of Shipwrecks*. College Station/Texas.

Swiny, H. W. & Katzev, M. L., 1973, The Kyrenia shipwreck: a fourth century B.C. Greek merchant ship. In: D. J. Blackman (ed.), *Marine archaeology*. Colston Paper, no. 23. London.

Tchernia, A., Pomey, P. & Hesnard, A., 1978, *L'épave romaine de la Madrague de Giens (Var)*. Gallia, suppl. XXXIV. Paris.

Tzalas, H., 2002, Introduction: A century of Underwater Archaeology in the Mediterranean. In: *TROPIS VII*, vol. II, part B, 875-878.

LUC LONG · SABRINA MARLIER · MICHEL RIVAL

THE SAINTES-MARIES-DE-LA-MER 24 (SM24) SHIPWRECK (FRANCE, A.D. 40 TO 75)

A SEA-RIVER CARGO VESSEL WITH STITCHED FRAMES

The Saintes-Maries-de-la-Mer 24 shipwreck, called more commonly SM24, is situated to the W. of the Small Rhône, in the S. of France (Bouches-du-Rhône, côtes de Camargue) (**Fig. 1**). It lay 10 m deep and was discovered in 1998 by a local fisherman. A short survey, carried out by L. Long, of the Department of Sub-aquatic and Sub-marine Archaeological Research (DRASSM) in 2002, within the framework of the Archae-ological Map of Camargue Project, revealed that the wreck was a Roman trading ship loaded with iron bar-shaped ingots (**Fig. 2**). Thus, this shipwreck fits into a series of Roman shipwrecks, also loaded with iron, which were lost in front of the mouth of the Rhône River, between the second half of the 1st c. B.C. and the 1st c. A.D. (Long 1997: 65-68, fig. 1). The investigations allowed to highlight some architectural compo-nents, frames in particular. The observation of three of these frames showed a very particular fastening system, by means of single treenails, nails and internal stitches blocked by treenails, already known from twelve other shipwrecks (Pomey 2002: 604, figs 1-2). This technique was also recorded on another ship-wreck loaded with iron bars, the SM2 shipwreck, localised to 500 m S.E. of the SM24 shipwreck (Long 2000: fig. 2). Nonetheless, only a small part of the hull, entirely concretionnated and metallized, was preserved of the ship.

Regarding the importance of the preserved part of its hull, which has mysteriously escaped the trawlers' nets, and the importance of the iron ingots, a more elaborated exploration, was carried out under the direc-tion of Luc Long, in August 2003.

MATERIAL AND DATING

The important concretion »A«, situated in the centre of the site, the concretions »B«and »C«situated in the S.E., and others scattered, belong to the principal cargo of iron ingots (**Fig. 3**). The only weight of the concretion »A«was estimated at about 5 tons. A series of whitewood logs, laid out under the ingots of concretion »C«, probably represented an extra load.

It has been noticed that, like the other shipwrecks of this area, SM24 beached in 1.5 to 2 m water[1] and thus its cargo was partly salvaged in antiquity[2].

Included to the lifted concretion »B«, a human jaw, associated to a small fragment of a human vertebra, was discovered. The preliminary analyses done by Pierre Giustiniani and Olivier Dutour (laboratoire d'An-thropologie-Biologie, Marseille, CNRS) suggest a young man, probably a prisoner or a slave. Indeed, an iron half-collar (incomplete)[3], indicating a chain (Halbout *et al.* 1987: 111, fig. 207.), was discovered very close to the human remains.

The shipwreck is dated between A.D. 40 and 75. This date is based on the radiocarbon analyses done on a frame and the comparative study of a fragment of S. Gaulish Samian ware belonging to the type Dragen-dorff 29b (**Fig. 4**).

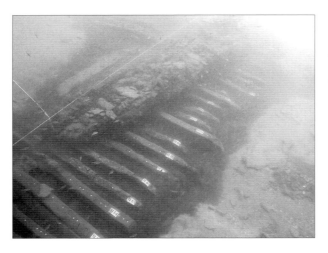

Fig. 1 View of the N.-E. zone of the SM24 shipwreck taken in 2003 with part of its cargo of iron ingots in the centre of the shipwreck (Photo Ch. Durand, CCJ/CNRS).

PRESERVATION AND ARCHITECTURE

The wreck was not entirely uncovered, but a trench of 10.2 m long to 5 m wide was open, however. The remains correspond to the central part of the ship including the keel, a part of the planking with eight strakes in the N. part of the site, nine strakes preserved in the S., and 26 frames in place (**Fig. 3**). Protected by a sand layer and by compact mud as well as some slabs of stones formed by the agglomeration of sand, the timbers are relatively well preserved. However, the keel has several fractures and breakings along its N. lateral face, at the level of the mortises. This has led to the pulling out of the upper part of the keel in its E. end. Also, the N. and

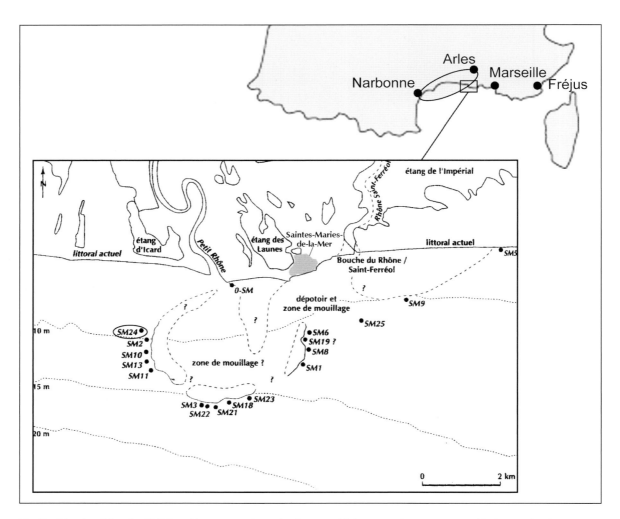

Fig. 2 Map localising the SM24 and its »espace de navigation« combining coastal-sea transport with river navigation.

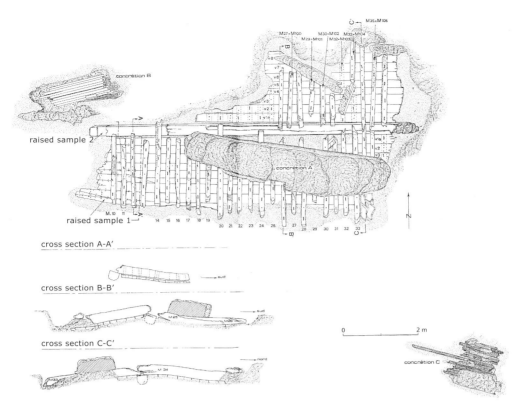

Fig. 3 Plan of the SM24 shipwreck (Drawing M. Rival).

S. planking is detached from the keel. Finally, some frames, in the N. part of the site, were not preserved (**Fig. 3**). The architectural investigations and documentation were done by S. Marlier[4] and M. Rival, directed by L. Long. In addition to the exploration *in-situ*, two significant hull sections were raised. The first sample was picked up on the W. end of the hull comprising of frames M10, M11 and M12, and planking connected to them; the second sample was picked up on the W. end of the keel (**Fig. 3**). The keel was preserved at 8.60 m length and presents, in its W. part, a hook scarf intended fasten a stem or sternpost not being preserved (**Fig. 5**). With a quadrangular section in its upper part and a round section in the lower, the keel is 26 cm moulded and 22 cm sided. Its lateral faces are neither chamfered nor rabbeted. Assembled to the garboard strake by

Fig. 4 S. Gaulish Samian ware (*terra sigillata*) rim of a bowl Dragendorff type 29b (Photo L. Long).

mortise-and-tenon joints which are blocked by wooden pegs, the mortises alternated on both sides of the keel in order to not weaken the construction. The mortises are 3.5 cm wide and 3.3 cm deep. Average space between the pegs is 5.8 cm. The garboard (V1S), on sample no. 1, is 20 cm wide for a constant thickness of 7.5 cm (**Fig. 6**). It has a quadrangular section without chamfer or bevel, and it abuts upon the plane keel

Fig. 5 W. extremity of the keel at the hook scarf (Photo Ch. Chary, 2ASM).

edges, determining thus a hull of horizontal angle. The second strake (V2S) is 22 cm wide and shows a narrowing profile which is reduced from 7.5 cm thickness next to the garboard to 6 cm at the third strake (V3S), caused by a slight chamfer made on its external face (**Fig. 6**). The third strake narrows down from 6 cm to 5 cm at the fourth strake where the planking thickness becomes finally constant (**Fig. 6**). The strakes are fastened edge to edge also with pegged tenons. As with the keel and garboard assemblage, the mortises are placed in alternation (**Fig. 7**). The tenons are 16 to 19 cm long, 6 to 7 cm wide and 7 to 8 mm thick. The small pegs are bevelled, and according to their internal diameter of 15 to 16 mm and their external diameter of 13 to 15 mm they were inserted from inside. Their average

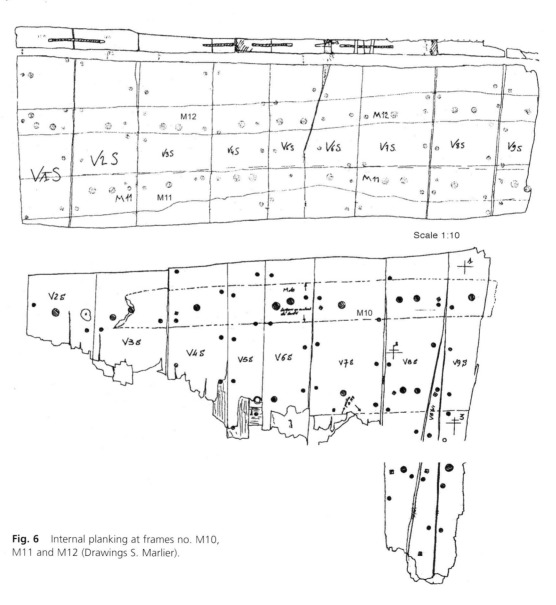

Scale 1:10

Fig. 6 Internal planking at frames no. M10, M11 and M12 (Drawings S. Marlier).

space is 16.35 cm, almost the threefold distance of pegs in the keel-garboard-area. On the hull section that could be studied, planks are joint with a classical diagonal scarfs which also were fastened by tenons (**Figs 3; 6**).

The framing system is difficult to determine because the frames S. of the keel were covered from concretion (from M17 to M26) and to the N. frames were not preserved (**Fig. 3**). Nonetheless, at the W. end of the hull, a sequence of two half-frames (M10 and M11), one floor-timber (M12), one half-frame (M13) and one floor-timber (M14) was recorded. At the E. part of the wreck, from M26 to M31, a small series of floor-timbers grouped with half-frames was observed, from M32 to M36, followed by a sequence of floor-timbers. If an average frame width of 12.23 cm (from 9 to 16 cm individually) is considered, the frame spacing is close, about 15.5 cm. The frames are much solid: they measure from 14 to 18 cm thick and reach 23 to 26 cm at the keel (**Fig. 3**). By their rectangular profile thicker than wide, the frames appear light, and they look rectilinear over the entire width of the uncovered hull (**Fig. 8**). At the centre of the lower surface of the floor-timbers, there are some rectangular limber holes nicely cut out with slight chamfers at the edges.

The frames are fastened to the planking by means of three different techniques: single treenails, nails and internal stitches blocked by treenails. They are laid out in a general pattern arranged in a *quincunx* with an alternation of single treenails and of stitches in transversal and in longitudinal directions (**fig. 3**). At the level of each plank, there is an assembly point (single treenail or stitch) almost systematically sourrounded by nails.

However, none of these three types of fastening attach the frames to the keel. The single treenails are 18 to 30 mm in diameter. They are without bevel, and were driven from outside. Stitches were carried out in the following way (**Fig. 9**): lashings, made of vegetable braids[5], were passed in loops in a couple of channels drilled through the frames and the corresponding strakes. Between the channels, some little grooves are notched in the frames' back

Fig. 7   Tenons exposed on the outer planking (Photo Ch. Durand).

Fig. 8   Perspective view of frames no. M11 and M12 (Photo Ch. Durand).

Fig. 9   Assembly of frames to the planking by means of vegetal plaits which were fixed by treenails inserted in the ligature's direction. Notch cut into frame no. M101 (Photo Ch. Durand).

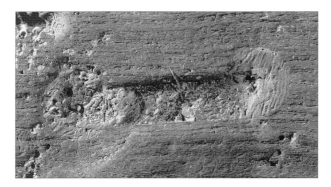

Fig. 10 View of the back of frame no. M101: remains of ligature fixed by two bevelled treenails visible in a groove sealed by pitch (Photo Ch. Durand).

Fig. 11 Vine sprouts between the frames (Photo Ch. Chary).

and in the outer part of the shell in order to connect the channels[6]. This system allows avoiding that the ligatures protrude of the assembled timbers. After two or three loops of each ligature, treenails block it in their channels and warrant watertightness. For each pair of channel, bevelled treenails[7] were inserted on both sides of the hull in the direction of the ligature in order to not only to block it but also to increase its tension. Finally, a thick layer of pitch is internally cast on the back of the frames and outside on the planking, thus coming to seal the grooves in order to improve the sealing of these fastenings (**Fig. 10**). Nails, probably made of iron, of square shaft sections of about 17 mm, were driven from outside into the planking and frames without passing through the frames' back.

No mast step was found, but the sequence of floortimbers, observed in the E. part of the site, showing an interruption of frame alternation suggests that area to be its position[8]. Besides, rabbets were recorded on the frames' back of M26 and M34.

No traces of ceiling were found. On the other hand, some planks, observed under the iron bars of concretion »B«, removed on land, correspond to ceiling planks. Their thickness is about 7 cm and they are 40 cm wide. Traces of square nails also point to girders. These planks supported the weight of the iron burden, which explains, on one hand their great thickness and the presence, of a »vegetable mattress« of protection, between these planks and the ingots, on the other hand. In absence of ceiling planks, dunnage, apparently made from vine sprouts was found on the hull in large quantities between the frames (**Fig. 11**). The interior surface of the planking was also coated with a thick layer of pitch mixed with vegetable chips.

WOOD SELECTION

F. Guibal, from the Mediterranean Institute of Ecology and Paleoecology (IMEP, Université Aix-Marseille III-CNRS), in collaboration with S. Wicha, carried out the analysis of wood samples taken from the hull. The results reveal the use of the oak (*Quercus sp.*) for the keel and for the whole of the strakes uncovered. Planking made of oak is very unusual in ancient Mediterranean shipbuilding for which resinous species are preferably used (Rival 1991: 53-56; Guibal & Pomey 2003: 36-38). Only a few exceptions are known: the Greek late Archaic César 1 wreck (Marseille; end of the 6th c. B.C.) the oak planks of which correspond very likely to repairs (Pomey 2001); the Fiumicino 1 sea-river boat (Ostia; 4th to 5th c. A.D.) the planking of which was partially made of oak (Boetto 2001: 125); the Giraglia ship (Cap Corse; around A.D. 20) with a few of the preserved planks made of oak (Sciallano & Marlier in press); and the Baie de l'Amitié ship (Agde; 2nd half of the 1st c. A.D.) with keel and planking entirely of oak (Wicha, Guibal & Médail 2003: 235). Whilst the usage of oak in Gallo-Roman shipbuilding is a strong characteristic (Arnold 1998: 49-72), for the manufacture of the planking of Mediterranean vessels it is exceptional. In the case of the SM24 and Baie de l'Amitié ships, and probably with the Giraglia wreck, the use of oak for the bottom-construction may have been linked to the heavy loads that the ships carried (iron ingots for SM24, lead ingots for Baie de l'Amitié and *dolia* filled with wine for La Giraglia). All of these ships and boats, except César 1 which presents only repairs in oak, very likely represent sea-river boats[9]. Consequently, the use of oak in planking, partly or entirely, in sea-river boats was perhaps, as for the Gallo-Roman barges, a characteristic of construction.

Unlike planking, the frames of SM24 present a remarkable diversity of wood species: oak (*Quercus sp.*), elm (*Ulmus campestris*), ash (*Fraxinus sp.*), Bosnia pine (*Pinus leucodermis*), poplar (*Populus sp.*) and fir (*Abies alba*). Although ancient shipbuilding is characterized by a relative heterogeneity for the frames, this great diversity with six different species is rare. Along the French Mediterranean coast, just six wrecks with four or five species as well as one with ten species used for frames are known (Guibal, Pomey 2003: 38-39). In the case of SM24, the six species used include hardwoods with good mechanical qualities (oak; elm), easily available (Bosnia pine; fir) and mediocre species (poplar).

The treenails – beveled and single ones – were analysed as fir (*Abies alba*). The use of a resinous species might be singular insofar as treenails are generaly made of hardwoods, preferentially of evergreen oak (*Quercus ilex*), even of olive tree (*Olea Europaea*), in ancient shipbuilding (Guibal & Pomey 2003: 38, 41). Nevertheless, all the beveled treenails used to tighten stitches as far as analyzed in sewn ships were made of fir but also the treenails crossed by iron nails (Guibal & Pomey 2003: 38; 41). Thus, the usage of softwood for treenails refers to secondary function in this sort of mixed assemblies (Guibal & Pomey 2003: 38). Associated with stitches, treenails of softwood are easy to insert in bore holes already occupied by the ligatures; associated with nails, soft treenails allow an easier insertion of the nails crossing them. For the single treenails found in SM24, it is likely that the shipbuilders prefered to use the same species for all types.

Finaly, the analysed tenons were made of evergreen oak (*Quercus ilex*), the analysed pegs of elm (*Ulmus campestris*). Evergreen oak is a hardwood preferentially used in joinery whereas elm is rarely used for this function (Guibal & Pomey 2003: 38; 41)

As far as the selection of woods is concerned, the construction of SM24 reflects a contrast between a homogeneity of the shell (keel and planking) and diversity of the frames. The use of various species and the opposition of shell and frames is classic in ancient shipbuilding despite of the fact that use of oak for planking in the Mediterranean shipbuilding tradition is exceptional. Moreover, all the species used for the construction of the ship, except the fir which is an Alpine species, grew at low altitude so that they could be found close to the coast. That means that the ship could be built in the »espace de navigation« defined for it[10], between Narbonne and Arles (see below).

ARCHITECTURAL SYSTEM AND TYPE, PRINCIPLES AND CONSTRUCTION METHODS OF SM24

The keel associated to the planking of SM24 is perfectly fastened in all its parts and indicates homogeneity. Thus, the shell provided structural strength of the hull, whilst the heterogeneous frames, assembled to the planking, only serve as transversal reinforcement. In so far, this architectural system corresponds to the traditional principles of »shell first« construction, and the same is true for the examined construction methods (Pomey 1988; 1998; 2004).

as well as the same architectural system, the study of their architectural type shows that we cannot classify them within the same architectural family. Therefore the SM24 shipwreck, associated with the SM2 shipwreck, seems to be characteristic of a particular type of ship, sailing in a particular »espace de navigation«.

CONCLUSIONS

By its cargo, SM24 belongs to a group of eleven Roman contemporary ships loaded with iron that were trying to make the Rhône to reach Arles. Among these ships, only SM24 has permitted, until now, the examination of a hull thanks to the exceptional state of conservation of its bottom. This preliminary study shows that the SM24 shipwreck could be characteristic of a particular type of ship linked to a specific »espace de navigation« of sea-river type. It would even belong to a precise socio-economic organisation (the *navicularii marini Arelatenses*), known by texts. Nevertheless, this is just, for the moment, a working hypothesis that will be confirmed by a systematic excavation, especially with an attempt to find the ends of the ship. In any case, this is all the more necessary because SM24 is the best preserved ancient shipwreck at the Camargue coast, thus allowing an original architectural analysis well deserving an extensive study.

NOTES

1) To the evolutions of the shores of this part of Camargue since the Antiquity cf. Long 1997; in press; Long & Illouze 2004.

2) The recovery of cargoes of beached ships in Camargue was a rather frequent phenomenon attested in the archives. Cf. Illouze 1988.

3) The dimensions of this half-collar are: 2 cm wide and 2,5 cm thick at the external edge; internal diameter about 14 cm.

4) Study conducted in the framework of her PhD dissertation, cf. Marlier 2005.

5) Braids are made of nine strands of 1 mm diameter; width of of the braids about 5 to 9 mm. The material was analysed as sapwood of a deciduous tree species by Brigitte Talon (Institut Méditerranéen d'Écologie et de Paléoécologie, CNRS), unpublished. Cf. Wicha 2005.

6) Grooves are 2 to 7 cm long, 1 to 3.1 cm wide and 1.3 to 4 cm deep on the frames' back.

7) Bevelled treenails taper from 23 to 31 mm diameter to 22 to 26 mm diameter.

8) E.g. on the Dramont A wreck (France, around 50 B.C.), where at least eight sucessive floor-timbers were recorded under the

mast step (cf. Santamaria 1975: 194). Cf. generally Gianfrotta & Pomey 1981: 246.

9) Concerning the hypothesis of the dolia ships as belonging to a sea-river ships type, cf. Marlier in press b; for the Baie de l'Amitié shipwreck, cf. Marlier 2005: 361-362.

10) There is 6 m of planking between the end of the keel and the presumed position of the mast step to which it could be added a further 3 m for the missing end (stem).

11) To the meaning of »espace de navigation« cf. Beaudouin 1975: 4-11; Pomey & Rieth 2005; Marlier in press a.

12) To cross the Rhône sandbar a small draught of about 1.50 m was required (cf. Marlier in press b). However, in modern times, the draught had to be reduced, according to the conditions, to 1.30 m. Cf. Rambert 1966: 7, note 1.

13) Caesar, in his war against Pompey, constructed twelve galleys in thirty days in the Arlesian *navalia* (*De Bello Gallico*, I 36).

14) c.f. the La Tour Fondue, La Roche Fouras, Cavalière, Dramont C, Plane 1, Cap Béar 3, Cap del Vol, SM2, Barthélemy B, SM24, Baie de l'Amitié and Port La Nautique shipwrecks: Pomey 2002; Marlier 2005; Wicha 2005.

REFERENCES

Arnold, B., 1998, Embarcations romano-celtiques et construction sur sole. In: É. Rieth (ed.), *Concevoir et construire les navires. De la trière au picoteux*, T.I.P. Revue d'anthropologie des connaissances. Ramonville, 49-72.

Beaudouin, F., 1975, *Bateaux des côtes de France*. Grenoble.

Boetto, G., 2001, Les navires de Fiumicino. In: J.-P. Descoeudres (ed.), *Ostia – port et porte de la Rome antique*. Musée Rath, catalogue d'exposition. Genève, 121-130.

Coustures, M.-P., Rico, Ch., Béziat, D., Djaoui, D., Long, L., Domergue, Cl. & Tollon, F., 2006, La provenance des barres de fer romaines des Saintes-Maries-de-la-Mer (Bouches-du-Rhône). Étude archéologique et archéométrique. *Gallia*, 63, 243-261.

Gianfrotta, P. A. & Pomey, P., 1981, *Archeologia Subaquea, storia, tecniche, scoperte e relitti*. Milano.

Guibal, F. & Pomey, P., 2003, Timber Supply and Ancient Naval Architecture. In: *ISBSA 9*, 35-41.

Halbout, P., Pilet, C. & Vaudour, C., 1987, *Corpus des objets domestiques et des armes en fer de Normandie, du Ier au XVe siècle*. Cahier des Annales de Normandie, no. 20. Caen.

Illouze, A., 1988, *Épaves de Camargue d'Aigues-Mortes à Fos-sur-Mer du XVe au XIXe siècle*. Nîmes.

Long, L., 1997, Inventaire des épaves de Camargue, de l'Espiguette au Grand Rhône. Des cargaisons de fer antiques aux gisements du XIXe s. Leur contribution à l'étude du paléorivage. In: M. Baudat (ed.), *Crau, Alpilles, Camargue. Histoire et archéologie, Actes du colloque des 18-19 nov. 1995, Groupe archéologique arlésien*. Arles, 65-68.

2000, Saintes-Maries-de-la-Mer, Étude d'ensemble des épaves antiques chargées de barres et de lingots de fer (SM2, SM6, SM9, SM10). *Gallia Informations, 1998-1999. DRASSM 1991-1995*, support CD-Rom. Paris.

2003, Carte Archéologique. Au large de la Camargue. *Bilan Scientifique DRASSM 2000*. Paris, 53-57.

in press, »Duplex Arelas«, Port fluvial et maritime. *Société d'Archéologie française, Actes du colloque de Paris, 2005*.

Long, L. & Illouze, A., 2004, Nouvelles épaves de Camargue. Les gisements antiques, modernes et contemporains. In: *Delta du Rhône. Camargue antique et médiévale. Bulletin Archéologique de Provence*, suppl. 2. Aix-en-Provenvce, 291-330.

Marlier, S., 2005, *Systèmes et techniques d'assemblage par ligatures dans la construction navale antique méditerranéenne*. Unpublished PhD thesis, Université de Provence, Aix-en-Provence.

2006, An example of experimental archaeology and the construction of the full-scale research-model of the Cavalière ship's bottom. In: *ISBSA 10*, 43-49.

in press a, »Espace de navigation« and the survival of traditional shipbuilding techniques: examples of the Adriatic Sewn Boats (from the Po delta to the Dalmatian coast). In: *TROPIS VIII*.

in press b, Architecture et espace de navigation des navires à dolia. *Archaeonautica*, no.15. Paris.

in press c, Les modèles d'étude Jules-Verne 9, Cavalière, Comacchio et Nin: données et résultats d'un programme d'archéologie expérimentale portant sur la restitution de systèmes d'assemblage par ligatures différents. In: *TROPIS IX*.

Pomey, P. & Rieth, É., 2005, *Archéologie Navale*. Paris.

Pomey, P., 1988, Principes et méthodes de construction en architecture navale antique. In: *Navires et commerces de la Méditerranée antique: hommage à Jean Rougé*. Cahiers d'Histoire, XXXIII, 3-4. Lyon, 397-412.

1998, Conception et réalisation des navires de l'Antiquité méditerranéenne, In: É. Rieth (ed.), *Concevoir et construire les navires. De la trière au picoteux, T.I.P.* Revue d'anthropologie des connaissances. Ramonville, 49-72.

2001, Les épaves grecques archaïques du VIe siècle av. J.-C. de Marseille: épaves Jules-Verne 7 et 9 et César 1. In: *TROPIS VI*, 425-437.

2002, Une nouvelle tradition technique d'assemblage antique: l'assemblage de la membrure par ligatures et chevilles. In: *TROPIS VII*, vol. 2, part B, 597-604.

2004, Principles and Methods of construction in ancient naval architecture. In: F. M. Hocker & C. A. Ward (eds), *The Philosophy of shipbuilding. Conceptual approaches to the study of wooden ships*. College Station/Texas, 25-36.

Rambert, G., 1966, *Histoire du commerce de Marseille,* vol. VII. *De 1660 à 1789*. Paris.

Rigaud, Ph., 2001, La marine d'Arles. Une histoire deux fois millénaire. *Chasse-Marée*, 146, 16-27.

Rival, M., 1991, *La Charpenterie navale romaine. Matériaux, méthodes, moyens*. Paris.

Santamaria, C., 1975, L'épave A du Cap Dramont (Saint-Raphaël). Fouilles 1971-1974. *Revue Archéologique de Narbonnaise*, 8, 185-198.

Sciallano, M. & Marlier, S., in press, L'épave à dolia de l'île de la Giraglia. *Archaeonautica*, no.15. Paris.

Wicha, S., 2005, *Caractérisation d'un groupe d'épaves antiques de Méditerranée présentant un assemblage des membrures par ligatures végétales: approche architecturale et paléobotanique*. Unpublished PhD thesis, Université de Provence. Aix-en-Provence.

Wicha, S., Guibal, F. & Médail, F., 2003, Archaeobotanical characterisation of three ancient Mediterranean shipwrecks. In: É. Fouache (ed.), *The Mediterranean World. Environment and History, Paris, 24-26 avril 2002*. Paris, 233-237.

GIULIA BOETTO

NEW ARCHAEOLOGICAL EVIDENCE OF THE *HOREIA*-TYPE VESSELS

THE ROMAN NAPOLI C SHIPWRECK FROM NAPLES (ITALY) AND THE BOATS OF TOULON (FRANCE) COMPARED

The *Horeia*-type vessels are well known from iconographic sources that portray these Roman craft curved at one end and flat at the other. These iconographic documents raise basically two questions: Is the flat end the stern or the bow? Is it possible to identify the function of these vessels?

THE PROBLEM OF THE *HOREIA*-TYPE VESSELS

Paul-Marie Duval in his fundamental article »La forme des navires romains d'après la mosaïque d'Althiburus« presents an excellent description of the small boat named *horeia*, which figured in the 3rd c. A.D. Tunisian mosaic of Althiburus (Duval 1949: 140). Duval disagreed with the first publisher of the mosaic, Paul Gauckler (1905), and demonstrated that in the *Horeia*-type vessel the curved end was the stern and the flat end the bow. Moreover, he stressed that the boat carried two bundles of merchandise and not, as previously thought, bundled fishing nets.

Since Duval's study in 1949, the theory of the transom bow has found in Lionel Casson (1964; 1995: 331, fig. 144; 2006) one of its more convinced supporters. As he pointed out, since the steering oars are always placed near the curved end, this might have been the stern. L. Casson argued that the transom bow had been developed in order to facilitate the loading of cargo in harbours as to have enabled these boats to make fast flush to a dock or quay. In spite of that, Peter Marsden (1963) and Marco Bonino (1963) recently followed by Lucien Basch (1987: 471; in press) and Zaraza Friedman (in press), reaffirmed the opposite theory: the flat end is identified again with the stern. Finally, Deborah Carlson (2002) noted that the problem of transom stern versus transom bow would not be relevant since the *Horeia*-type vessels were double-ended[1].

Concerning the function of the *Horeiae*-type vessels, written sources associate them with fishing (Plautus, *Rudens*, IV, 820)[2]. The same can partly be traced back from ancient iconography according to which *Horeiae*-type vessels show different dimensions from small boats propelled by oars used as fishing boat, or as tender of maritime cargo vessels (Casson 1995: 330-331; 2006; Carlson 2002), to the more larger craft rigged with sails[3]. Such boats could be used as cargo vessels too[4].

Iconographic analysis has raised several issues and, surely, will raise more in future. However, as the author agrees with Duval's and Casson's identification of the bow with the flat end, she will focus her attention on fresh archaeological evidence concerning this type of craft. In future, a reconstruction of the hull shape from the archaeological remains might shed light on the problem of the identification of the flat end.

The recent discovery of a *Horeia*-type ship in Naples (Italy)[5], and the option to examine unpublished documentation of two wrecks discovered in 1980 in Toulon (France)[6], may contribute to the definition of the *Horeia*-type. Hence, the principal aim of this paper is to present a preliminary comparative study of the available archaeological sources.

Fig. 1 Three shipwrecks and structures of the ancient harbour of Naples (Photo F. Avallone, Archaeological Superintendence of Naples).

NAPLES AND TOULON: THE CONTEXT

A few years ago, the construction of a new subway line in Naples (Italy) allowed archaeologists to explore the waterfront of the ancient town, from the Greek times onwards (De Caro & Giampaola 2004; Giampaola 2004; Giampaola & Carsana 2004; 2005; Giampaola, Carsana & Boetto 2004; Giampaola *et al.* 2005; Carsana *et al.* 2007). In particular, on Piazza Municipio, near the modern Stazione Marittima and the Aragonese Castle known as »Castel Nuovo«, a section of the Roman harbour of *Neapolis* has been investigated in 2004. Under almost 17 m of sediment, three Roman shipwrecks were uncovered (**Fig. 1**) (Giampaola, Carsana & Boetto 2004; Boetto 2005; in press)[7]. These ship finds were related to other structures and scattered artefacts. The harbour of *Neapolis* was established around the late 4th c. B.C. and remained in active use until the end of the 5th c. A.D. when the basin definitely silted up. This range of activity is documented by a 4 m deep of stratigraphic sequence.

The floor of the harbour basin had been dredged from the late 4th c. until the 2nd c. B.C., a difficult and costly activity carried out to improve its functionality. The 3 to 5 m long and on average 1.8 m wide trails of a dredging machine, presumably a dredging ship, were observed on both the sandy layers and the rocky eruptive sediment (*cinerite*).

Stratigraphic analysis indicated that two of the ships, named »Napoli A« and »Napoli C«, were abandoned at the end of the 1st c. A.D. near a mole facing E.-W. (**Fig. 1**). The latter, dated to the 1st c. A.D., was made of wooden posts and blocks of limestone. Napoli A was identified as a maritime cargo vessel, preserved at a length of 11.77 m, a width of 3.32 m and a depth of 0.88 m. The ship rested on her port side where she

Fig. 2 *Horeia*-type boat Toulon 2 (After Brun 1999).

is preserved to her upper side. During the 2nd c. A.D., several wooden posts, belonging to at least three wharves were driven into the sediments, and these structures perforated the hulls of Napoli A and Napoli C wrecks.

The third shipwreck, »Napoli B«, sank at the turn of the 2nd to the 3rd c. A.D. Lime and fragments of calcareous stones seem to be remains of cargo. The hull was preserved on a length of 7.3 m and a width of 2 m.

Napoli B was dismantled at the end of May 2004, then recovered in pieces and stored in water tanks. The two larger ships, Napoli A and Napoli C, were raised each in a single piece on September 7th-8th, 2004 after being secured by a steel frame and an external fibreglass shell[8]. The ships are stored still under water, in a deposit of the Archaeological Superintendence of Naples.

The construction of a modern commercial centre in 1987, presented the opportunity to investigate a section of the Roman harbour of Toulon (France), the ancient town of *Telus Martius*. Here, two *Horeia*-type boats dated to the end of the 1st c. A.D. were uncovered which had been re-used within the construction of a quay (**Fig. 2**). In the 3rd c. A.D. this area of the harbour basin started to silt up, and three cargo vessels were abandoned (Borréani, Brun, Lecacheur & Pasqualini 1987: 18-22; 1988; Brun 1999: 797-803). The latter shipwrecks, named »Toulon 3-4«, were dismantled and only few parts have been conserved, whilst the *Horeia*-type boats, named »Toulon 1« and »Toulon 2«, were raised to be treated with PEG[9].

NAPLES AND TOULON: PRELIMINARY COMPARATIVE STUDY

Napoli C is preserved at a length of about 13 m, a width of 3.7 m and a depth of 0.8 m (**Fig. 3**). It is composed of a chamfered keel which had been assembled to a rabbeted stern gripe and to a transom bow; of two internal posts related to the transom bow; each ten strakes per side; 50 frames and 45 futtocks; four strakes of ceiling planks on each side, and some internal boards lying parallel to the keel.

Toulon 1 is preserved on a length of 8.5 m, a width of 3.1 m and a depth of 0.35 to 0.45 m, whilst the Toulon 2 wreck is still 6.3 m long, a 2.2 m wide and 0.32 to 0.45 m deep (**Fig. 4**). Their hulls, preserved as high as to the gunwale, are composed of: a chamfered keel assembled to a rabbeted stern gripe, and to a

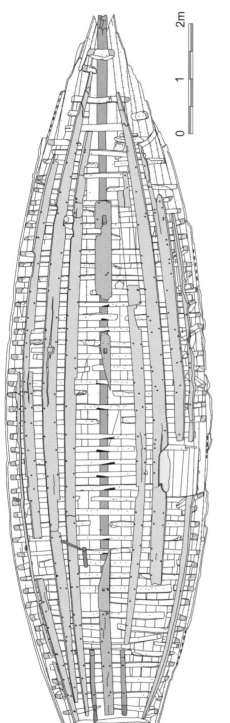

Fig. 3 Plan of Napoli C shipwreck. End of the 1st c. A.D.

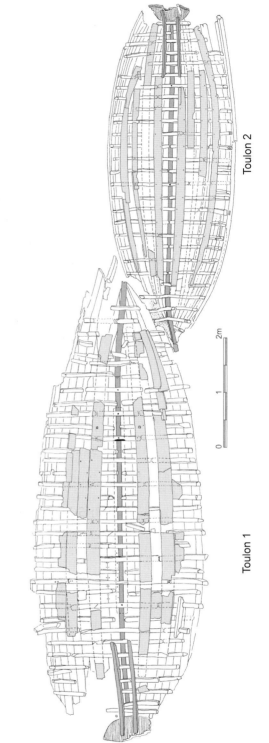

Toulon 1

Toulon 2

Fig. 4 Plan of Toulon 1 and Toulon 2 shipwrecks (Drawing after photogrammetry, J.-M. Gassend, IRAA/CNRS).

transom bow[10]; two internal posts related to the transom; 35 timbers in Toulon 1, and 27 timbers in Toulon 2; four strakes of ceiling planks on each side. Napoli C shows a flat bottom amidships, and a gently rounded bilge. This shape continues forward, whereas the cross sections aft presents are V-shaped (**Fig. 5**). Toulon 1 proves similar shape but the sides are much more leant out caused by post-depositional deformation. However, Toulon 2 presents a more rounded bottom forward (**Fig. 5**).

The keels of the three vessels longitudinally curve aft at the level of the stern gripe. This curve is more accentuated in Toulon 2. On the other direction, the keel of Napoli C rises gradually and forms with the transom bow an angle of 120°. It sticks out of 6 cm (**Figs 6-7**). In Toulon 1, the keel is very flat but originally raised forward, and could have been initially more curved in shape, forming an angle of 145° with the transom bow. In Toulon 2, the longitudinal section shows a curved stem; the angle formed by the keel and the transom measures 140° (**Fig. 6**).

In Napoli C, a very thick timber semi-circular in cross-section forms the base of the transom bow. This element had originally an L-shaped cross-section, and it was assembled, by means of mortise-and-tenon joints, with another type of timber which had not been preserved (**Figs 3; 6-7**). The transom was connected to two parallel shaped posts seated atop the frames. In Toulon 1, as in Toulon 2, the same feature was noted (**Figs 4; 6**). In the latter cases, only the base component of the transom bow is preserved, and in Toulon 2 the traces of tenons could be observed, which proved the assembly of an upper element which had been lost.

In Toulon 1 and 2, the transom was connected to the keel by metal nails driven from inside, with their

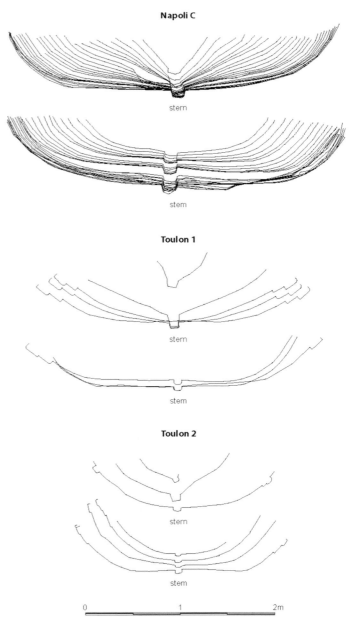

Fig. 5 Transversal sections of the *Horeia*-type vessels of Naples and Toulon.

heads countersunk in triangular recesses. Whether the assembly between the keel and the transom of Napoli C had the same feature, could not be examined due to the thick layer of caulking (resin) found inside the hull. The extremities of the strakes of the three shipwrecks were fastened to the transom by means of metal nails driven from outside. Strakes were edge-joined, with tenons pegged in their mortises. In Napoli C planking is 3.6 cm thick opposed to just about 2 cm in both Toulon boats. In the former wreck, the average spacing between pegs is 12 cm, and the planking system proved to be symmetrical with alternate stealers.

In Napoli C, the frame system appears strong and massive. Space between frames is on average 14 cm, and the frames are not arranged in the standard alternation of floor-timbers and paired half-frames. Instead,

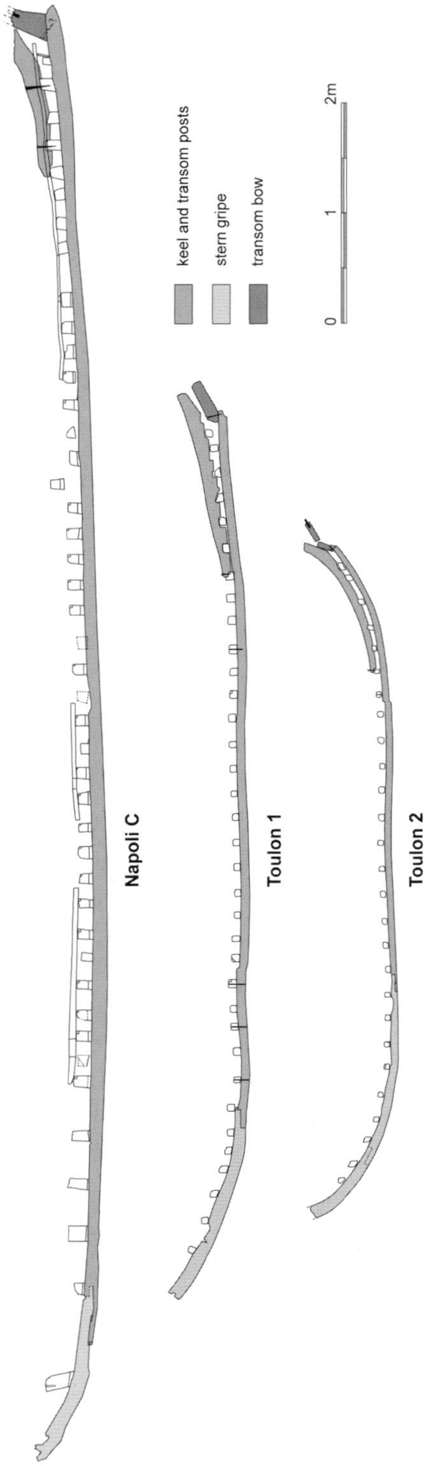

Fig. 6 Longitudinal sections of the *Horeia*-type vessels of Naples and Toulon.

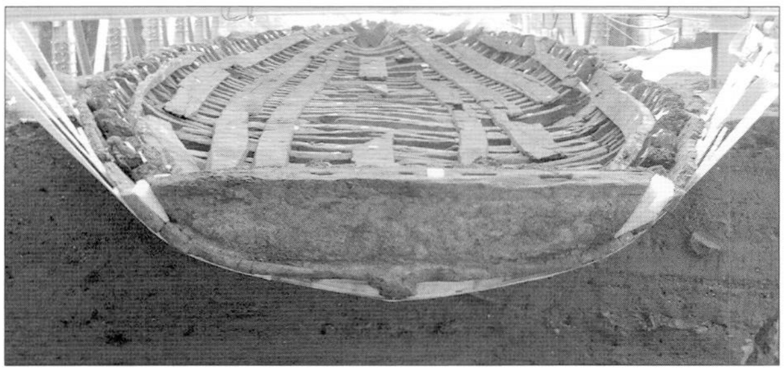

Fig. 7 Transom bow of the Napoli C shipwreck (Photo G. Boetto, CCJ/CNRS).

crossed half-frames could be observed also[11]. Four very short (average length 1.1 m) floor-timbers showed a very unusual shape, looking like ribs, with trapezoidal longitudinal section. The heel of the futtocks fits below the ribs without joint, as usual in Graeco-Roman naval construction (**Fig. 8**)[12]. In Toulon 1 and Toulon 2, the frame system is lighter with intervals of 15 and 20 cm respectively.

Napoli C bears vague traces of its propulsion system: triangular recesses on top of the frames (**Fig. 3**) originally fitted a keelson of approx. 6 m length and 13 to 30 cm width. In principle the latter could had been provided with a mast step. The same is indicated in Toulon 1 by two recesses on the top of frames and a sequence of floor-timbers, though the boat was rowed. On the other hand, no traces of a mast step were found in the Toulon 2 boat which was probably propelled by oars since on the top of the gunwale recesses for thole-pins are preserved.

All the three vessels attract attention for their ancient repairs: in the planking several »patch-tenons« have been identified[13]. Furthermore, Napoli C shows planks without mortise-and-tenon joints simply nailed to frames, and fothering means or wooden patches inserted into damaged or rotted planks.

CONCLUSIONS

This study offers new archaeological data to characterise architectural features of *Horeia*-type vessels. It underlines the importance and widespread use of this kind of craft in the W. Mediterranean during the

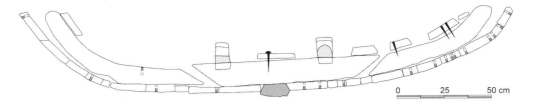

Fig. 8 Napoli C. Transversal section at floor-timber M5.

1st c. A.D. Furthermore, it was noted that these vessels could vary in dimensions, but some basically identical structural features define the architectural type[14].

In the author's opinion, the *Horeia*-type vessels were working boats. Probably, the bigger ones, such as the *Horeia*-type ship Napoli C, carried cargo, whereas boats like Toulon 1 and Toulon 2 may have been used as service port boats (tenders) or for fishing.

NOTES

1) Also Olaf Höckmann, this volume pp. 297-302.

2) Further references to *horeia* in Aulus Gellius, *Noctes Atticae*, X 25, 5; Nonnius Marcellus, s.v. *horeia*.

3) Cf. the Uadi ez Zgaia mosaic in Carlson 2002: fig. 2.

4) A wall painting from Pompei shows a *Horeia*-type craft loaded with amphoras (Carlson 2002: fig. 8).

5) The wreck was excavated in 2004, from April to the first week of August, by a team directed by Daniela Giampaola (Archaeological Superintendence of Naples), under the field coordination of Vittoria Carsana (Istituto Universitario Suor Orsola Benincasa, Napoli). The author has been responsible for the analysis and documentation of the ship within the Research Programme of Naval Archaeology of the Centre Camille Jullian of Aix-en-Provence (France).

6) Special thanks is owed to J.-M. Gassend (IRAA/CNRS) for the permission to utilize his field documentation (photogrammetric plan, longitudinal and transversal sections). The author also had the opportunity to examine the documentation of the restoration and the preserved fragments of the Toulon boats in Grenoble, restoration laboratory of ARC-Nucléart, thanks to the friendship of H. Bernard-Maugiron.

7) Napoli A and B were identified in December 2003, and Napoli C at the end of February 2004. Two 3D scanner lasers were used to record these shipwrecks. The plans were interpreted *in-situ* and constructional details recorded and added to the plans. In addition, a classical method of manual survey (transversal and longitudinal sections, scale 1:1 tracings) provided the necessary complement of the graphical documentation. To documentation in naval archaeology cf. e.g. Pomey & Rieth 2005: 122-130.

8) The fibreglass shell was first implemented by the Istituto Centrale del Restauro (ICR, Rome) during the excavation of the Comacchio shipwreck (Meucci & Berti 1997). Later, it was used to protect the shipwrecks Pisa C and F (Camilli 2002), and the Late Roman shipwreck of Ravenna (Medas 2001; Maioli & Medas 2001: 126).

9) Cf. the note »Deux épaves romaines à Toulon« published in *Le Chasse-marée. Histoire et ethnologie maritime,* 33, 1988: 60-62. – The conservation process, carried out by the conservation laboratory ARC-Nucléart of Grenoble, was currently completed. – The boats are still waiting for restoration and display.

10) In Toulon 2 it seems the stern gripe had been joined to the sternpost by a hook scarf.

11) The crossed half-frames, known as »demi-couples outrepassés«, have been observed at some Mediterranean wrecks (Bourse de Marseille, Laurons 2, Luque B, Saint Gervais 3, Port Vendres 1) representing the Roman Imperial architectural type: Pomey & Rieth 2005: 166-167.

12) Similar features recorded above the keel of the County Hall ship by P. Marsden (1974: 6, fig. 6H; 1994: 117, fig. 105 & 107J) are interpreted as ancient repairs. Moreover, he noted also overlapped joints in frames. Unlike the example of Napoli C, scarfs were held by a single treenail and apparently used to join lengths of timbers.

13) Observed on the Greek vessel of Kyrenia, Cyprus (4th c. B.C., Steffy 1985; 1999), they are also well-known from Roman ship finds.

14) For definition cf. Pomey & Rieth 2005.

REFERENCES

Basch, L., 1987, *Le musée imaginaire de la marine antique.* Athèns.

in press, Un modèle de bateau à poupe à tableau (transom stern) au Musée Gréco-Romain d'Alexandrie. In: *TROPIS IX.*

Boetto, G., 2005, Le navi romane di Napoli. In: Giampaola *et al.* 2005, 63-76.

in press, Naples, Piazza Municipio (Italy): first observations on the Roman ships. In: *TROPIS IX.*

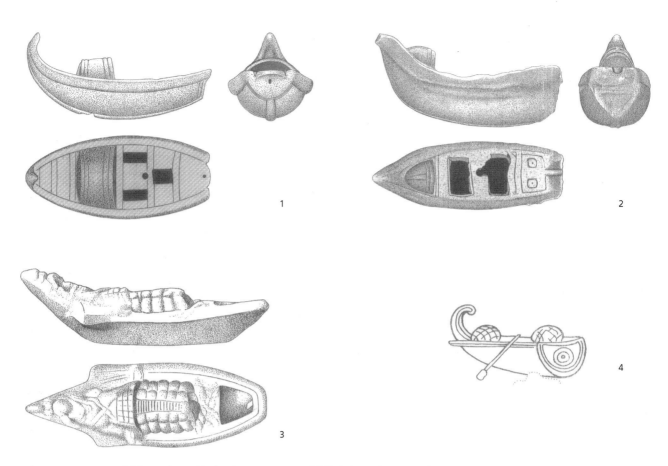

Fig. 1 **1** Type B model from Alexandria (A 3). – **2** Type B model likely from the Fayum (A 14). – **3** Type A model from Alexandria (A 4). – **4** *Horeia* in the Althiburus mosaic, Tunisia (B 1). – No scale.

type B: all four). In restricted numbers also the renderings of one mast-step (A 14) and some keels (A 1.3.14) are confined to type B.

As opposed to these features diagnostic of one type or the other, closed decks are the rule in both, as are fewer occurrences of beams impressed across them (A 1.3.8.10.[13].14.16 to 17), cabins (A 2 to 7.10-18), and open (A 1 to 3.5-10.[13].14-17.[19]) or closed hatches (A 13 to 14.17).

A review of the individual features of both types points out conspicuous differences not only in their outward appearance (**Fig. 1**) but also in their functions and spiritual background. Only type A boats are shown carrying one or the other kind of cargo, as might oblige to interpret them as small merchantmen. However, most of their helmsmen are shown as children or rather »child-gods« (cf. below).

In type B the absence of cargo, rudder bearings and helmsmen and the singular presence of a mast-step hint at a different function of the boats, whereas the models of both types are as similar in size and state of preservation as to make one think that they are to be seen in the same general context.

THE FUNCTION OF THE BOATS

Type A boats, no doubt, were meant for carrying small loads of cargoes of amphoras or enigmatic flat trapezoidal objects stacked amidships in front of the cabin, in calm river (and inshore?) waters. »Children«

sleeping with one hand at their mouths in the position of helmsmen cannot be understood as realistic, however, and call for a different explanation.

Sandra Sandri's identifying the »helmsmen« of the models A 13 and A 18 to which can be added A 4.12.15(?) and A 16(?), as reposing »child-gods« connects the models with a motif in Egypt's Graeco-Roman religion that is concerned with supplying food and drink[9].

The type B models do not give any hint as to their function by themselves, but a considerable number of Roman mosaics and frescoes show such boats. A 3rd c. mosaic from Althiburus in Tunisia even quotes the Roman type name: *horeia* (**Fig. 1, 4**)[10]. The word meaning a fishing boat originated in the Messapian language of S. Italy[11], and likely was adopted into Latin not too long after the Roman conquest of Messapia in 266 B.C. Since bow-transom models are unknown from that country but exclusively from Egypt, it is to be thought that the Romans gave type B boats, when they were introduced to Italy, a name with which they had been familiar for long, leaving open how the boats were called in their home country on the Nile.

There is no reason for thinking that type B originates from Messapia. On the one hand no source whatsoever hints at its existence in that country, whereas on the other, some Roman two-dimensional representations place such boats in an ambience that by such elements as pygmy crewmen or hippopotamuses is characterised as *Nilotic*. When details are shown the boats mostly serve for fishing. Since open or closed hatches on some models (A 1 to 3.6.10. [13].14-17.[19]) seem too small for giving access to holds, they can be considered to have served fish wells as are known from Roman wrecks[12].

Few boats of a version combining features of both types suggest that they have been utilised as sea freighters' launches[13], unspecific »water taxis« or harbour boats[14], or horse transports on the Danube in Trajan's Dacian wars[15]. A representation from Pompei, of something like a type B boat carrying amphoras likewise falls in this category[16].

The prevalent characterisation of type B boats in two-dimensional representations, of serving fishermen coincides with the Roman meaning of the type name, *horeia*. Two dugouts, each with one original end cut off and replaced by a transom, re-used as floating fish wells, from the Roman camp of Zwammerdam in The Netherlands demonstrate that the general concept of type B was spread as far as to a remote border province of the Empire[17].

THE CONSTRUCTION OF THE BOATS

Constructional features can be identified only on type B models, if at all. They might seem to suggest at a first glance that the hulls incorporate some traces of papyrus construction, as are the thick shell protruding beyond the transoms of A 1.3 (?), the rockered keels of them all, and on both types, narrow beams running athwart the decks of A (1).3.8.10.14.(16).17.

Nothing is known about hollow shells consisting of papyrus. A reference to Aeneas disabling the boat of Charon ferrying him to the Underworld by fiercely stomping on its floor (Virgil, *Aeneis* VI, 413 sq.) is not conclusive for establishing that Virgil imagined Charon's boat as a hollow shell of papyrus. From a technical point of view, such a hull hardly could have been waterproofed by any other material as asphalt. That substance was used on Mesopotamia's round »basket boats« woven from reeds[18], but it was not available in Egypt as a cheap commodity.

As to keels, A 1 and A 3 (**Fig. 1, 2**) have massive rockered keels with rounded edges protruding from their bottoms, and A 14 (**Fig. 1, 3**) has two thin rounded »keels« side by side. The former would form perfect backbones for any kind of hull but the latter rather look like runners for taking the boat ashore, below a hull the lengthwise stability of which had been achieved by the strong sheer strakes.

16) Pekáry 1999: 176, no. I-N 21; Carlson 2002: 218, fig. 2; Sandri 2006: 298, fig. 12.

17) See note 12.

18) Basch 1987: 442, fig. 969B.

19) Goddio & Clauss 2006: 198, no. 336; 440, no. 336.

20) Landström 1970: 22.

21) See note 16.

22) Cf. 2nd c. B.C. representations from Pantikapaion / Kerch, Crimea (Košelenko et al. 1984: 275 tab. 85:7) and Carthage (Harden 1962: 171, fig. 49:1).

23) The earliest coin of this kind known to the author has been struck for Pompeius in 44/43 B.C. (Crawford 1974, no. 483/2). Coins of Marcus Antonius, as ruler of Egypt, from itinerary mints on his campaign in 32 B.C. against Octavian: Crawford 1974, no. 544/11.15.29.30.

24) BMC: Nero 176.

25) Hellmann 1987: 61. If the low cabin with a roof sloping down

26) aft is a late feature, also A11, A12, A14, [A14a], and A18 can be dated to the later Imperial period.

26) For Peruvian caballitos cf. Johnstone 1980: 14-15.

27) Landström 1970: 19.

28) Casson 1971: 167 dates the latest mention to the 1st c. A.D.

29) Shaw & Nicholson 2002: 48.

30) See note 2.

31) Beaudouin 1985: 35-37; 99.

32) Schenk & Hartlieb 2005: cover.

33) Cf. the transfer of the Roman caudicaria type of river cargo-boats to the Upper Rhine (Höckmann 1995), for leaving aside the river-warship type lusoria. The latter's introduction on the Rhine and Danube will have been commanded by central authorities. As opposed to the latter model, the transfer of such inconspicuous types of small private boats as the caudicaria and the horeia, should have gone back to »individuals« who came to distant provinces of the Empire on their own.

REFERENCES

Basch, L., 1987, Le musée imaginaire de la marine antique. Athens.

Beaudouin, F., 1985, Bateaux des Fleuves de France. Douarnenez.

BMC: The British Museum Catalogue of Coins. London.

Boetto, G., 2006, Roman techniques for the transport and conservation of fish: the case of the Fiumicino 5 wreck. In: ISBSA 10, 123-129.

Bonino, M., 1963, The Roman transom stern. MM, 49. 4, 302-303.

Carlson, D. N., 2002: Roman fishing boats and the transom bow. In: TROPIS VII, vol. 1, 211-218.

Crawford, C.R., 1974, Roman Republican Coinage. Cambridge.

De Weerd, M.D., 1988: Schepen voor Zwammerdam. Academisch Proefschrift Universiteit van Amsterdam. Haarlem.

Foucher, L., 1965, Les mosaiques nilotiques africaines. In: La Mosaique Gréco-Romaine. Colloque International 1963. Paris, 137-145.

Goddio, F. & Clauss, M. (eds), 2006, Ägyptens versunkene Schätze. Katalog zur Ausstellung im Martin-Gropius-Bau Berlin. Berlin.

Göttlicher, A., 1978, Vorarbeiten zu einem Corpus der antiken Schiffsmodelle. Mainz.

Göttlicher, A. & Werner, W. 1971, Schiffsmodelle im alten Ägypten. Wiesbaden.

Hamburg 1991, Götter, Gräber und Grotesken. Bilderheft des Museums für Kunst und Gewerbe Hamburg, no. 25. Hamburg.

Harden, D., 1962, The Phoenicians. London.

Höckmann, O., 1995, Bemerkungen zur Caudicaria. Arch. Korrbl., 24, 425-439.

in press, Jahrb. RGZM.

Johnes, D., 1990, Model boats from the tomb of Tut 'Ankhamun. Tut 'Ankhamun Tomb Series, vol. IX. Oxford.

Johnstone, P., 1980, The Sea-craft of Prehistory. London, Henley.

Kaufmann, C. M., 1915, Graeco-ägyptische Koroplastik. Leipzig, Kairo (2nd edition).

Košelenko et al., 1984, Košelenko, G. A., Kruglikoval, T. & Dolgorukov, V. S., Antičnye gosudarstva Severnogo Pričernomor'ja. Arheologija SSSR. Moskv).

Landström, P., 1970, Die Schiffe der Pharaonen. München, Gütersloh, Wien.

Lehmann-Hartleben, K., 1926, Die Trajanssäule. Ein römisches Kunstwerk zu Beginn der Spätantike. Berlin, Leipzig.

Marsden, P., 1963, A Roman Transom Stern. IJNA, 49, 2, 143-144.

Pekáry, I., 1999, Repertorium der hellenistischen und römischen Schiffsdarstellungen. Boreas, suppl. 8. Münster.

Ponsich, M., 1961, Note sur une lampe en forme de bateau. Saitabi, 11, 221-223.

Sandri, S., 2006, Der Kindgott im Boot. Zu einem Motiv in der gräko-ägyptischen Koroplastik. Chronique d'Égypte, LXXXI, Fasc. 161-162, 287-310.

Santa Maria Scrinari, V. (ed.), 1979, Le navi del porto di Claudio. Rome.

Schenk, P. & Hartlieb, J., 2005, Elsass. Marco Polo Führer. Ostfildern (10th edition).

Shaw, I. & Nicholson, P., 2002, The British Museum Dictionary of Ancient Egypt. London (pocket edition).

Throckmorton, P., 1973, The Roman wreck at Pantano Longarini. IJNA, 2, 243-266.

TLL: Thesaurus linguae Latinae VI. (Leipzig 1934 [3rd edition]).

Wachsmann, S., 2002, The Moulid of Abu el-Haggar: a contemporary boat festival in Egypt. In: TROPIS VII, vol. 2, part A, 821-835.

Weber, W., 1915, Die ägyptisch-griechischen Terrakotten. Königliche Museen zu Berlin, Mitteilungen aus der ägyptischen Sammlung, no. II. Berlin.

LUC LONG · MICHEL RIVAL · SABRINA MARLIER

THE GALLO-ROMAN WRECK ARLES-RHÔNE 3

A FLAT-BOTTOMED RIVERBOAT IN THE RHÔNE RIVER, IN ARLES (FRANCE) – A PRELIMINARY REPORT

In the autumn of 2004, a relatively well preserved shipwreck was discovered during an archaeological survey in the River Rhône in Arles (S.-E. of France), which was directed by Luc Long of the DRASSM (Département des Recherches Archéologiques Subaquatiques et Sous-Marines). The wreck is situated at approx. 50 m upstream of the motorway bridge, almost parallel to the right river side (**Fig. 1**). Investigations were focused on the remains of an important Roman site with waste material, amphoras and ceramics dated to the 1st c. A.D., indicating harbour activities to which the wreck also belongs (**Fig. 2**). The peak period of the harbour's economic activities can be estimated between 40 and 80 A.D. Wood samples of the wreck, taken from the wreck in 2005, were dated by radiocarbon between 15 B.C. and A.D. 130. This ship find should not be confused with the badly preserved wreck Arles-Rhône 2, the remains of a capsized vessel (Long 1994: 54-55), which was discovered some 500 m downstream from Arles-Rhône 3 in 1990. As for the complex Arles-Rhône 1 which was initially identified to be a wreck and its cargo (Long 1994: 52-54), it was in fact, like Arles-Rhône 2, a waterfront structure of the river bank in Roman times. Consequently, Arles-Rhône 3 represents the first well-preserved physical evidence of a flat-bottomed river barge

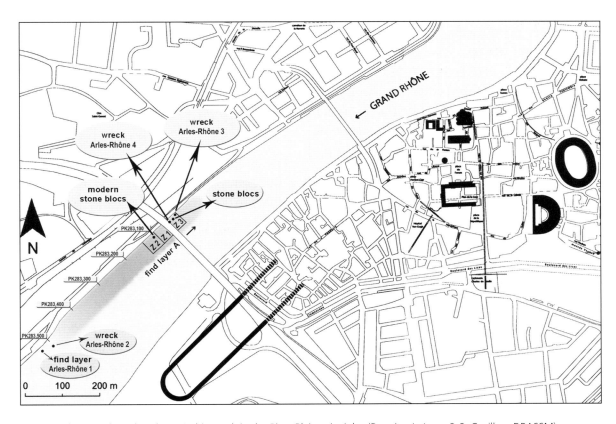

Fig. 1 Map showing the Arles-Rhône 3 shipwreck in the River Rhône, in Arles (Drawing L. Long & S. Cavillon, DRASSM).

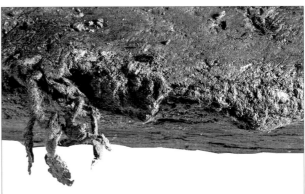

Fig. 15 Arles-Rhône 3. – Detail of the pitched cloth used for making the boat watertight placed on the edges of the strakes (Photo Ch. Durand, CCJ/CNRS).

Fig. 16 Arles-Rhône 3. – Detail of the pitched rope used for making the boat watertight placed between the side and the bilge of the boat (Photo Ch. Durand, CCJ/CNRS).

was exposed above the waterline, where it has been quickly destroyed, whereas the wreck was deeply silted up on the sloping river bed. The other extremity was located below 1.40 m of sediment. Taking in account those observations, the minimum lenghth of the boat might have been 24 to 25 m.

LUTING

The edges of the strakes show rough and irregular cutting which seems to follow the graining of the wood; they are rather rounded than flattened. That was apparently intended by the application of luting material which is particularly thick, more than 1 cm, extruding from the interior face of the planking (**Fig. 15**). On the external face, the mixture of fabric and pitch or bitumen constitutes a regular outgrowth comparable with a »roll«. Organic traces observed between fabric and wood might be confirmed as tar by analysis. The luting material found between chine-girder and bottom planking apparently consists also of vegetable substance and pitch or bitumen (**Fig. 7**). In contrast, the seam to the rounded side wale contained a mixture of vegetable substance of 1.5 cm thick, made of pitch or pitch and a rope (**Fig. 16**). The lower edge of the side element was roughly bevelled (**Fig. 7**). As the material was put between the planks without using force, it seems plausible that the technique is related rather to the luting than caulking.

PRINCIPLES OF CONSTRUCTION

Arles-Rhône 3 was built according to the »bottom-based shipbuilding« Romano-Celtic tradition (Rieth 1981). However, the barge reveals some »archaeological fingerprints«, in particular plank seams luted with pitched fabric and low hull planking with a half tree trunk at the side. These characteristics indicate Mediterranean influence which has already been recorded from other shipwrecks recently discovered in the Rhône (Lyon, place Tolozan wreck: Becker & Rieth 1995; Rieth 1999; six wrecks found in Lyon, Parc Saint-Georges: Guyon & Rieth, this volume pp. 157-165) and Saône region (Chalon-sur-Saône wreck 1: Lonchambon 2000). According to É. Rieth, these shipwrecks may constitute a regional sub-group of the »bottom-based« Romano-Celtic shipbuilding tradition, called »Rhône-Saône group« which he distinguishes from the »Rhineland«, »Alpine« and »Atlantic« types of river barges (Rieth 2006; Guyon & Rieth, this volume pp. 157-165).

CONCLUSIONS

The Arles-Rhône 3 barge proves evident relations with the construction principles of flat-bottomed barges found in W. Europe. However, this vessel shows peculiarities by some structural details and by its luting technique which might refer to Mediterranean influence. Arles-Rhône 3 probably carried white limestone originating from the neighbouring quarries of Beaucaire (*Ugernum*) or Saint Gabriel (*Ernaginum*). Perhaps, the barge was used within the framework of a local or even a regional trade. Equally it might have been also assigned as a ferry or used for consolidation works on riverbanks.

However, Arles-Rhône 3 is the first evidence of such a type found in the Rhône, in the vicinity of Arles, which could be studied. It contributes to a better understanding of river shipping on the lower Rhône at the beginning of the Roman Empiral period, and affirms its own characteristics. It may be premature today to link Arles-Rhône 3 to other kind of boats. Nevertheless, the complete excavation and examination of the wreck would benefit the understanding of inland vessels.

ACKNOWLEDGEMENTS

The authors would like to thank all the divers, technicians and all the people of the 2ASM association for their hard work and dedication during these campaigns. Gratitude is also owed to Mohamed Abd el Maguid (DUA, Egypt) and David Bouman (The Netherlands) for reading this paper.

REFERENCES

Arnold, B., 1992, *Batellerie gallo-romaine sur le lac de Neuchâtel*, vols. 1-2. Archéologie neuchâteloise, no. 12-13. Saint-Blaise.

Becker, C. & Rieth, É., 1995, L'épave gallo-romaine de la place Tolozan, à Lyon: un chaland à coque monoxyle assemblée. In: J.-Cl. Béal (ed.), *L'arbre et la forêt, le bois dans l'Antiquité*. Publications de la bibliothèque Salomon Reinach. Paris, 77-91.

Lonchambon, L., 2000, Un bateau monoxyle-assemblé à Chalon-sur-Saône (1er siècle ap. J.-C.). In: L. Bonnamour (ed.), *Archéologie des fleuves et des rivières*. Catalogue d'exposition. Paris, 174-178.

Long, L., 1994, Prospections et sondages archéologiques dans le Rhône à Arles et ses environs. In: *Histoire du Rhône en pays d'Arles*. Actes du colloque du 7 nov. 1992, Arles, Groupe archéologique arlésien. Arles, 45-71.

Long, L., Rival M., Marlier S. & Greck S., in press, L'épave gallo-romaine Arles-Rhône 3: un chaland à fond plat de type monoxyle assemblé. *Bilan Scientifique du DRASSM 2006*. Paris.

Rieth, É., 1981, La construction navale à fond plat en Europe de l'Ouest. *Ethnologie française*, XI, 47-62.

1999, L'épave gallo-romain de la place Tolozan à Lyon (France). In: *TROPIS V*, 339-348.

2006, *Archéologie et architecture nautique monoxyle-assem-blée et assemblée. Archéologie de la batellerie. Architecture nautique fluviale*. Les cahiers du Musée de la Batellerie, no. 56. Conflans-Sainte-Honorine, 49-88.

PATRICIA SIBELLA · JOHN ATKIN

PORTS AND NAVIGATION
IN THE GIRONDE ESTUARY (FRANCE)
FROM ANTIQUITY TO MIDDLE AGES

BRION, THE REYSSON MARSH AND THE GIRONDE ESTUARY

The Gironde estuary, outlet to the Atlantic of the Narbonne-Toulouse-Bordeaux route, has no ancient instal-lations characteristic of ports. This is surprising as the estuary was a main centre for commerce and naviga-tion during Antiquity and the Middle Ages.

The last post-glaciation transgression was the principal cause of the flooding of paleo-valleys and the formation of Rias, notably the Gironde and its small affluent valleys on both banks. The silting of the Gironde still continues but its small tributary streams rapidly evolved to form first tidal mud-flats and then marshes drained by an *estey*, a natural channel, which canalises flood- and ebb-tides. The mouth and upstream end of an *estey* are often trans-shipment points for maritime and terrestrial routes, places where ports may have existed.

In this paleogeographic context, interest concentrated on the only ancient agglomeration known in the Médoc – most probably the *Noviomagus* of Ptolemy – because this major archaeological site – which most likely functioned as a port – is not situated on the bank, but 5 km inland on the edge of the Reysson marsh. Thus, the objective of the work, which combines some fourteen specialists from several universities, is to locate and investigate ancient port sites through a comprehensive study of the Reysson marsh by surveys, core borings, soundings and excavations (Sibella 2006). The aim is to propose a progressive reconstruction, in 3D, of the Reysson marsh and the conditions of navigation, and will allow a new reflection on the rela-tions between man and environment in an original context.

The objective of this note is to resume the available historical, toponymic and epigraphic data from a maritime point-of-view.

GEOGRAPHICAL SETTING

The archaeological site belongs to the municipality of Saint-Germain d'Esteuil (Gironde, France) and is situated about halfway between the modern towns of Lesparre and Pauillac in the Médoc area. It occu-pies a central position in the ancient territory of the *Medulli* tribe, whose *pagus* was part of the territory controlled by the *Bituriges Vivisques*.

Implanted on a rocky spur of about 12 hectares, Brion is located to the N.-W. of the Reysson marsh through which passes an »estey«, the Caloupeyre, a channel canalising ebb and flood. The site is about 5 km inland from the left bank of the Gironde Estuary and about halfway between Royan at the

Fig. 1   Aerial view of the Brion (Gironde) site (Photo F. Didier-jean, Ausonius Archaeological Research Center).

Fig. 2 Early 18th c. map of the Reysson marsh (C. Masse [ca. 1710], Bibliothèque Municipal de Bordeaux) before clearing (Photo J. Atkin).

mouth of the estuary (24 miles) and the port of Bordeaux (26 miles). Reclaimed at the end of the 18th c. the Reysson marsh is now largely used for the cultivation of maize. On the aerial photo (**Fig. 1**) one can discern to the N. (the estuary out of sight and about 5 km to the E. on the right):

– the overall contours of the site,

– the temple, theatre and uncovered habitations. The earliest known map of the Reysson marsh before reclamation was made in about 1710 by C. Masse on order of Louis XIV (**Fig. 2**).

The marsh has been dated as existing to before the Roman period and therefore boats would have entered the river from the estuary at low-tide or during the rising tide and then sailed to Brion on the flood. Such use of tides to reach inland river harbours has been well documented notably in the U.K. (Fryer 1973: 264). The name of the village and port of Mapon (now silted-up) has to be highlighted. It lies on the estuary which permitted access to Brion via a channel through the marsh (**Fig. 2**). Although width and depth of this channel is unknown, a geographical reconstruction shows that it probably passed very near the Brion archaeological site[1]. The authors believe that Mapon is related to the Celtic god Maponus, rather similar to Apollo, and associated with the sun, health and youth. This would point to a native town or market near the Brion site.

THE TOPOLOGY OF THE BRION SITE

A topographic plan of the Brion site is shown in **Figure 3** (Provost 1994: 185). This plan shows the principal features of the site:

– Roman theatre and a fortified 14th-c. house re-incorporating Roman elements;
– Roman dwellings;
– base of an ancient edifice;
– remnants of Roman dwellings;
– the temple.

Archaeological excavations have revealed several pre-Roman occupation layers ranging from the middle of the 1st Iron Age to the beginning of the 2nd Iron Age. A quasi-sterile layer indicating re-structuring of the local habitat separates the two periods (Garmy 1988: 37-38). The site was abandoned until the 3rd c. B.C. when it was progressively re-occupied to become a secondary agglomeration, without doubt in the middle of the 1st c. A.D., with the construction of blocks of habitation during the Claudian era. After a short period of prosperity, probably during the Flavian era, during which the main public buildings – theatre and temple – were constructed, the population started to decline and from the second half of the 2nd c. the town struggled to exist. The temple area, abandoned at the beginning of the 3rd c., saw its ruins temporarily occupied by settlements during the next two centuries and by the 5th c., the Brion agglomeration had totally disappeared. A study was made of the geographical and chronological distributions of 109 coins from the various archaeological excavations (except the medieval period) (Genevièvre 2004: 284-

Fig. 3   Topographic plan of the Brion site showing temple (F), theatre (A) and dwellings (After Provost 1994: 185, fig. 109).

305). It showed that 81 coins had been minted between the Gaulish period and A.D. 92; of the 28 remaining coins, minted from 19 to 353 A.D., 23 came from the temple area and only four from others (the fifth had an unknown origin). In the 14th c. a fortified dwelling was built over the site of the theatre and its underground vaults (Faravel & Garmy 1989: 169-184); Brion again fell into decline until the middle of the 18th c. [2].

THE SITE OF *NOVIOMAGUS*?

Only one known text refers to the existence of *Noviomagus*: there is a reference made by Ptolemy in the chapter on Aquitaine in his »Geography«, probably written towards the middle of the 2nd c. A.D. (Müller, 1883: 203). This chapter starts by giving the geographical positions of the most notable features along the coast of Aquitaine such as the main ports: *Noviomagus* is not cited. However, in his list of peoples and the localisation of their principal towns starting from the River Loire, in chapter 8 he writes: »[...] below these, the Bituriges Vivisques, of which (the) towns (are)«[3] *Noviomagus* 17° 8/12, 46° 3/12, *Burdigala* 18°, 45° 6/12«. The well-known problem with the co-ordinates given by Ptolomy is that they are often misleading.

Fig. 4   Photo of the temple ruins taken from the E. (Photo J. Atkin).

Various locations have been proposed for *Noviomagus*: the first to have evoked Brion seem to have been Léo Drouyn in his »Guyenne Militaire« published in 1865 (Drouyn 1865: 92-96).

MODERN ARCHAEOLOGICAL FINDINGS

From the middle of the 1960's, Brion has been subject of archaeological soundings and excavations; from 1966 to 1968, archaeologists studied the Roman theatre and the associated remains including coins and pottery dating from the 1st and 2nd c. A.D.[4]. From 1985-1989, archaeological excavations revealed two housing blocks constructed in the middle of the 1st c. A.D. and abandoned at the end of the first or the beginning of the 2nd c. A.D., as well as a *fanum* – a Gaulish temple – located at the most exposed point of the site. A fire destroyed the temple and part of the *peribolos* at the end of the 2nd c. Between 1988 and 1991 their remains were archaeologically excavated under the supervision of the Aquitaine Regional Archaeological Service (P. Garmy and, later D. Barraud) (Barraud & Pichonneau 1992) in collaboration with the Centre d'Études des Peintres Murales Romaines (CEPMR) du CNRS (Soissons)[5]. The aim of the current Research Programme which is directed by P. Sibella and supported by the Ausonius Archaeological Research Center, is to locate and to study the Roman harbour.

THE TEMPLE

The plan of the temple, which is of the indigenous Gallo-Roman type known as a *fanum*, is square with a gallery for circulation that opens to the E.: the *cella* measures about 11.4 m by 11.4 m. **Figure 4** shows the ruins of the temple which was placed on the highest point of the site at more than seven metres above datum. A recent reconstitution of the structure calculated that its height was more than 6 m. This means that the total height would have been some 13 m and easily visible from the estuary during Roman times: it may therefore have been a landmark for shipping in the estuary. The general layout of the *fanum* was

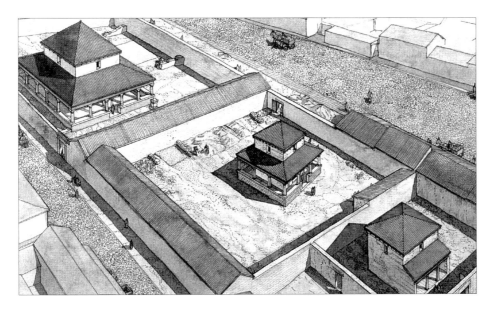

Fig. 5 Sanctuary with two fana and a »chapel« at the Gallo-Roman site of Argentomagus (Indre). Reconstruction drawing (After Coulon & Golvin 2006).

probably similar to those of the reconstructed Gallo-Roman site of *Argentomagus* (Indre) which included two *fana* and a small »chapel« with a *pronaos* (**Fig. 5**).

THE FRESCOS

The archaeological excavations carried out from 1988 to 1991 revealed a number of frescos. The 200 fragments which were recovered from the temple's *cella*, represented less than 10% of the total painted surface. They indicated the quality of the frescos as to a very high level of workmanship, design and decoration. This level was identical for the four walls according to a statistical analysis of the decorated motifs. Certain of the frescos seemed to have a maritime signification. The first to consider is a diademed head associated with a crescent moon and stars (**Fig. 6**).

Navigation in the Gironde estuary is difficult, because the tides can exceed 6 knots and the tidal range can be over 5 m. To reach the estuary from the S. means a long sail across the S. Bay of Biscay often with bad weather; or a difficult coastal journey along the Landes with only the Arcachon bay for shelter but with a difficult access.

When approaching the estuary from the N., the coast can be followed but the entrance to the estuary must be timed right, especially in the case of large W. swells (at the present time a boat must approach from way off the shore to avoid dangerous sand-banks but these probably did not exist in Roman times).

Knowledge of tides and star navigation was therefore important, and it is suggested here that this fresco may have had a maritime background:

– the diademed head could be that of a local maritime divinity perhaps related to the Roman goddess Luna and perhaps the sanctuary's protector;

– the crescent moon related to knowledge of tides;

– the stars related to navigation.

Fig. 6 Restored section of a fresco showing a diademed head, moon and stars displayed in the Municipal Museum in St.-Germain-d'Esteuil (Photo J. Atkin; drawing after Barbet & Becq 1994, 113, fig.10a).

The second fresco shows the stern of a ship with a well-designed steering oar (**Fig. 7**). This is obviously a maritime scene and contributes a maritime context to the mythological nature of the frescos (Barbet & Bech 1994: 108). The steering oar has two shoulders characteristic of the oar associated with the statue of Isis found in Ostia and preserved in the Naples National Museum. The end of the oar and the base of the hull are surrounded by white paint marks that disappear into the dark blue water. Contrary to the suggestion put forward in the preliminary study of the frescos (Barbet & Bech 1994: 107), these whitish forms do not seem to correspond to foam caused by the movement of the ship. In fact, if one examines the displacement of water around a hull, the wave shape depends on speed and hull form: in this case, the wave is missing. The authors wonder if the structures visible in the water could be marine animals because:

– numerous historical references refer to marine animals and the use of birds in navigation (Plinius, *nat. hist*, 6, 24);

– however, very few illustrations showing ships and aquatic animals exist, and these are partly much earlier: the ship procession at Thera (Minoan); the Sennacherib Palace (Phoenician); the Okeanos mosaic at Bad Kreuznach, Germany (2nd to 3rd c. A.D.); Lod, Israel (3rd to 4th c. A.D.).

The Brion mosaic resembles some of the paintings from Pompeii of mythological scenes such as Ariadne abandoned by Theseus or Ulysses with the Lestragons. This would suggest a conception in the representation such has been attested in the E. Mediterranean[6]. In addition, the use of birds as navigational aids is known from the beginning of recorded time (Plinius, op. cit). Whether it is the story of Jason and the Argonauts in which Euphemus frees a dove that guides them through the reefs in the Bosporus (Apollonius Rhodius, *Argonautes,* 2, 560-573), or the well-known story of Noah and his dove (*Genesis*, 8, 6-12).

In the case of the fresco from the temple in Brion, the authors are tempted to identify the white forms to the right of the oar as sea birds frequently seen at the Atlantic littoral; in this case, forms could suggest a grebe and a puffin.

THE INSCRIPTIONS

The frescos also contain inscriptions that were most certainly in Gaulish and may have had maritime connections. These were *APOVNV*, *ABOVNV* or *APLOVNV* (set below the foot of a kneeling figure offering

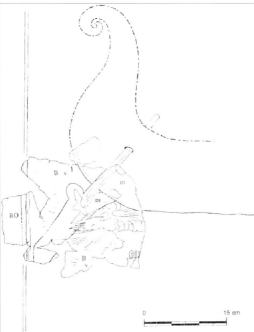

Fig. 7 Restored section of a fresco showing a ship's stern and steering oar displayed in the Municipal Museum in St.-Germain-d'Esteuil (Photo J. Atkin; drawing after Barbet & Becq 1994, 113, fig. 10b).

(a gift?), and *INLETIL* (found on an isolated fragment forming *TVS, INLETIL*). As no references to the meanings of these words were found in the available works on Gaulish language, interpretions based on the available literature and dictionaries were made.

– *APOVNV*. A simple analysis of *APOVNV, APLOVNV* or *ABOVNV* was made (Delamarre 2001). This shows that – *AP*- or – *AB* – which may signify »water« or »the waters« as natural forces (of a religious character?). *OVNV* may signify »fear« or »respect«. Could this be related to a mythical maritime episode based on the respect of the sea or the estuary in a religious context?

– *INLETIL*. No correspondence was found in the literature for this word in Gaulish (although it must be remembered that only very few Gaulish words are known). Could this word be related to the modern English word »inlet« and therefore to the position of Brion which is set in an inlet on the largest European estuary?

CONCLUSIONS

The Brion Gallo-Roman site is set on the largest W. European estuary. The available historical, toponymic and epigraphic data on the temple reveals that this may have been related to maritime activities and raises the following questions:

– Was the temple designed as a landmark to be seen from the Gironde?
– Can the attribute of the Divinity be related to navigation by the Moon (tides) and by the Stars (route)?
– Do the designs underneath the stern of the ship represent marine animals such as birds?
– Are *APOVNV* and *INLETIL* related to the sea?

Hopefully future archaeological study will give the answer to some, if not all, of these problems.

ACKNOWLEDGEMENTS

The authors particularly wish to thank Francis Tassaux, Professor of Roman Archaeology, Université de Bordeaux 3, for his collaboration and encouragement, and also to Danny Barraud, Service Régional d'Archéologie Aquitaine, for his support.

NOTES

1) Laboratoire de Géographie Physique Appliquée, Université Michel de Montaigne – Bordeaux 3 (report to be published).

2) Raby 1911: 71: in 1786, Baurein (an abbot) noted the existence of a 14th c. fortified dwelling; 74: in 1865, Léo Drouyn made a plan of the site showing the location of archaeological remains and dwellings.

3) These numbers indicate, in order, longitude and latitude: the longitudes start at the Canary Islands, the extreme west of the known world, the latitudes start at the equator.

4) Provost 1994: 183: archaeological remains and coins found during first »modern« excavations are described.

5) Barbet & Becq 1994: 107-108; CEPMR, CNRS-ENS UMR 8546, Abbaye Saint-Jean-des-Vignes 02200 Soissons France.

6) Morgan 1988: 124, fig. 70: the first known representations are those of the ship procession at Akrotiri where a bird (dove?) is shown at the stem and stern.

REFERENCES

Barbet, A. & Becq, G.,1994, La peinture à sujets figurés dans le temples de tradition indigène en Gaule. In: Goudineau *et al.* 1994.

Barraud, D. & Pichonneau, J.-F., 1992, St.-Germain-d'Esteuil – Brion. *Bilan scientifique de la Direction Régionale des Affaires Culturelles Aquitaine – Service Régionale d'Archéologie, Bordeaux*

Becq, G., 1991, *Le fanum de Saint Germain d'Esteuil (Gironde) 1991: Enduits peints de la Cella et Fouille partielle de l'Enclos* (CEPM). Soissons.

Coulon, G. & Golvin, J.-C., 2006, *Voyage en Gaule Romaine*. Paris.

Delamarre, X., 2001, *Dictionnaire de la Langue Gauloise*. Paris.

Drouyn, L., 1865, La ville de Brion (Noviomagus). *Guyenne Militaire*, vol. 3. Paris, 92-96.

Faravel, S. & Garmy, P., 1989, Le site de Brion à Saint-Germain d'Esteuil (Gironde), problématique de recherche, état des questions en 1987. In: Faravel, S. (ed.), *Soulac et les pays médocains*. Actes du XLe Congrès de la Fédération Historique du Sud-Ouest, Soulac-Pauillac-Saint-Germain-d'Esteuil, 16-17 avril 1988. Bordeaux, 27-35.

Fryer, J., 1973, The harbour installations of Roman Britain. In: D. J. Blackman (ed.), *Marine Archeology. Colston Papers, no. 23*. London, 261-273.

Garmy, P., 1989, *Archéologie en Aquitaine*, 7, 47-50.

Garmy, P. *et al.*, 1990, *Brion – St Germain d'Esteuil*. Bordeaux.

Genevièvre, V., 2004, Les monnaies antiques de Brion-Saint-Germain-d'Esteuil. *Aquitania*, 20, 283-305.

Goudineau, C. *et al.*, 1994, *Les sanctuaires à tradition indigène en Gaule Romaine*. Paris.

Morgan, L., 1988, *The Miniature Wall Paintings of Thera*. Cambridge.

Müller, C., 1883, *Claudii Ptolemaei Geographia*. Paris.

Provost, M., 1994, *La Gironde, 33*. Carte Archéologique de la Gaule (C.A.G.). Paris.

Raby, L., 1911, *Saint Germain D'Esteuil*. Bordeaux.

Sibella, P., 2006, *Projet Collectif de Recherche – Rapport 2006, Port et navigation en Gironde de l'Antiquité au Moyen-Âge: le cas du marais de Reysson*, S., Bordeaux.

ALEYDIS VAN DE MOORTEL

THE UTRECHT TYPE

ADAPTATION OF AN INLAND BOATBUILDING TRADITION
TO URBANIZATION AND GROWING MARITIME CONTACTS
IN MEDIEVAL NORTHERN EUROPE

The Utrecht I ship is the first excavated and best known example of a small group of five ship and boat finds with similar characteristics, labelled the »Utrecht type« by Peter Marsden (Marsden 1976; Van de Moortel 2003: figs 28.1, 28.2; Van de Moortel, this volume pp. 329-336)[1]. Three vessels of this type have been found in the city of Utrecht itself: the Utrecht I ship (Vlek 1987; Van de Moortel 2003), the Waterstraat boat (Hoekstra 1975; de Groot 1997: 35-36; Vlek 1987: 89-103), and the Lange Lauwerstraat boat (Vlierman 1996: 88-91). A fourth wreck was excavated at Velsen in N.-Holland (Vlek 1987: 140-143; de Weerd 1987); and fragments of a seagoing Utrecht-type vessel were found reused as sheathing in a wharf frontage of the medieval port of London (Goodburn 2000). These five wrecks date from the late 10th c. to some time in the 12th c., and are at home in the Rhine Delta, as is indicated by their geographic distribution as well as by dendro-provenancing.

Various studies have concluded that Utrecht-type vessels are in fact expanded and extended oak logboats (Van de Moortel 2003; Goodburn 2000: 222; Crumlin-Pedersen 1997: 27-28; de Weerd 1987: 266). The expansion process gave the logboat a pronounced curve in a transverse as well as fore-and-aft direction (cf. Vlek 1987: fig. 1.2.1). The discovery of the existence of a logboat tradition along the Lower Rhine in this rather late period of the Middle Ages caused considerable surprise among marine archaeologists and historians. Its importance in the history of N. European shipbuilding is still very much in debate. Vlek and other scholars believe that the Utrecht type was the terminal product of a long line of logboats (Vlek 1987: 143-145; Reinders & Oosting 1989). In contrast, Ole Crumlin-Pedersen (1983; 1984) and Detlev Ellmers (1985: 67; 2000) see it as a transitional stage between logboats and fully planked boats; more specifically they believe that this humble inland craft with its sweepingly curved profile was developed into a plank-built boat type with similar profile known in historical documents as the hulk. Crumlin-Pedersen (1983; 1984) considers the Utrecht type to be one of the four basic ship types of N. Europe in the Middle Ages. If the Utrecht type was indeed an early form of the hulk, it would have played a very important role in European shipbuilding, since the hulk at the end of the Middle Ages became the largest seagoing vessel of N. Europe.

In the following it will be argued that the Utrecht type was not an outmoded tradition and can indeed be understood as transitional between small inland logboats and fully planked large seagoing ships. Plausible reasons for this development will be suggested. Detailed comparisons of the characteristics of the hulk and the Utrecht type lead to the conclusion that they are very close, allowing the possibility of an overlap between the two, though this does not necessarily imply a one-to-one correspondence.

Contrary to Vlek's opinion, the Utrecht type is now known to represent a versatile tradition of expanded logboats, including small (Velsen boat) as well as large river-going cargo vessels (Waterstraat boat and Utrecht I ship) and even a seagoing ship (Queenhithe fragments), which had at least three superimposed strakes and is likely to have had higher sides than the other craft (Van de Moortel 2003: 187-188; Goodburn 2000). The origin of this tradition must have predated the late 10th c. by some time, since the largest

Utrecht-type ships – the Waterstraat boat and the Queenhithe and Utrecht I ships – are also the earliest (Van de Moortel, this volume pp. 330-332, Table 1. The Utrecht I ship in particular is so massive and outsized that it can only be seen as an extreme version of the type. Its logboat base was cut from an oak trunk at least 14 m tall with a diameter of perhaps 1.2 to 1.5 m. Its planks were ca. 8 to 10 m long, 50 to 60 cm wide, and 2 to 3 cm thick, and its wales had been cut from half tree-trunks 19 m long and ca. 60 cm in diameter. A vessel with such heavy scantling must have strained the capabilities of this building tradition, let alone the available timber supplies.

What would have driven the builder to produce such an outsized extended logboat in the early 11th c.? Part of the answer seems to lie in the economic developments that took place in the Rhine Delta in the 10th and 11th c. Historical documents and archaeological finds indicate that with the waning of the Viking attacks in the early 10th c. the area revived and local as well as international trade flourished. Utrecht, for one, experienced rapid urbanisation and became the most important political, religious, and commercial centre of the Lower Rhine area, its markets attracting local as well as foreign goods (van Vliet 2000). It had busy trade connections via the Rhine with Central Germany, and via the river Vecht and the Almere (the predecessor of the Zuyderzee) with the Frisian coast, Saxony and Scandinavia. Utrecht merchants also sailed to England via a more S. branch of the Rhine. Other towns of the Lower Rhine area, such as Tiel and Deventer, were very active in trade as well.

The economic revival had its effect on river transport. Harbour facilities at Tiel were expanded in the early 10th c., and at Utrecht and Deventer around A.D. 1000 (de Groot 1992: 23-27; 1997: 20-29). Whilst the older harbours had sloping river embankments where boats were pulled up to be unloaded, the new harbours had wooden wharf fronts allowing larger boats to be moored and unloaded. Particularly in the early part of the 11th c. Utrecht must have had a great need for heavy river-going cargo carriers. In that period as many as three churches, an abbey, and a small palace were built (de Bruin et al. 1999: 16-17). The tufa stone and probably also the wood for these buildings were transported by boat from the Middle Rhine area. It is possible that the Utrecht I ship was built so outsized so as to meet the large demand for imported building stone at that time.

In spite of its spacious hold, the Utrecht I ship was an inefficient cargo carrier. With a design waterline at 60% of the midship height, its cargo capacity would have been only about 6.5 tons, or less than 0.5 tons/m length of the immersed hull (Van de Moortel 2000). This is quite inefficient, especially when compared to the almost 2.5 tons cargo capacity per meter length of the 14th-c. Falsterbo VI Barge of comparable length (18 m: Nilsson et al. 2004), the 1.05 tons cargo capacity per meter keel length of the smaller 15th-c. Zuydersee cog NZ 43 (Van der Moortel 1991), the 1.79 tons/m keel length of the more box-like 15th-c. Almere cog (Hocker & Vlierman 1996: 38) or the 4.1 tons/m keel length of the seagoing 14th-c. Bremen cog. Why would one have preferred an Utrecht-type vessel for heavy transport over the contemporary Rhine barge which had a more efficient cargo design and would not have required such massive timbers?

It is proposed here that the Utrecht type was preferred precisely because of its logboat base, which was much stronger than a planked bottom and much more suitable for crossing rough waters. The Rhine at that time was not the peaceful river it is now. Until the 19th c., the Middle Rhine between Mainz and Koblenz was notorious for its rocky rapids, which were hazardous to any passing vessel (Lebecq 1983: 118-122). Since the weakest parts of the hull are the plank joins, it is likely that the Utrecht type with its one-piece logboat bottom was desired for braving those rapids. This would also explain why the builder used very wide and long planks and one-piece wales, reducing the number of joins in the hull planking as much as possible. Thus rather than being inferior or backward, as Vlek (1987) thought, the Utrecht type appears to have been considered superior in strength to the plank-built bottom, and for this reason it was adapted for ever larger cargoes in this late period of the Middle Ages. Their trust in the strength of the one-piece bottom and the hull with minimal joins prompted medieval owners and builders to produce also seagoing vessels in the Utrecht-type tradition.

If the Utrecht type was so well-functioning and the expanded logboat base considered superior to the plank-built bottom, what would then have caused its disappearance? Since sailing conditions remained the same, it is proposed here that the likely causes are changes in wood supply and demands of transportation. Due to the massive timber sizes required for Utrecht-type vessels, this method of construction must have caused considerable strain on the available wood reserves. The situation must have been aggravated by the further growth of riverborne and maritime commerce in the later Middle Ages, which demanded increasingly larger cargo vessels. Under these pressures it seems that at some point boatbuilders must have run out of suitable trees and were forced to abandon their trusted expanded logboats.

Ellmers and Crumlin-Pedersen argue that at this point the Utrecht-type vessels began to be built with fully planked bottoms, and the Utrecht type evolved into the hulk. Vlek, in contrast, denies any link between the Utrecht type and the hulk. Some of Vlek's arguments, however, have been invalidated by later finds, and others are not as strong as they once seemed. Vlek considers the Utrecht type unseaworthy because of its open hull and lack of a strong mast and keel (Vlek 1987: 87-88; 139-140). However, the Queenhithe fragments have demonstrated once and for all that the Utrecht type was indeed capable of producing seagoing ships. Vlek also believed that the Utrecht type was much older than the large seagoing hulks depicted on 13th and 14th-c. seals, and that it lacked the internal framing needed to support the broad extremities and castles of those late-medieval hulks (Vlek 1987: 144-145). To take the last argument first, a full documentation of the Utrecht I ship carried out in 1998 to 2000 under the present author's direction has revealed evidence for a much stronger internal support structure than Vlek described, including futtocks and deck beams carrying at least partial decks fore and aft (Van de Moortel 2000; 2003). Contrary to Vlek's findings, the builders were obviously concerned with internal reinforcement. They seem to have been capable of developing a large fully planked vessel from the Utrecht type and creating an internal stiffening system for it.

A closer look at the iconographic evidence reveals, furthermore, that the chronological gap between Utrecht-type vessels and hulk depictions seen by Vlek no longer exists. Ships with rounded hulls commonly accepted as being hulks appear already from the early 12th c. onwards, e.g. on the well-known baptismal fonts from Winchester and Zedelgem, and the ship type is first attested in a text of ca. A.D. 991 to 1002 (Fliedner 1969: 54, figs 6-7). This earliest record occurs in an English tax document of King Aethelred II and refers to Billingsgate in the harbour of London, only ca. 800 m E. of where the Queenhithe ship fragments were found (Liebermann 1903: 232; Fliedner 1969: 54)[2]. Thus the Utrecht type and the hulk indeed overlapped in time – and in space as well, and it is conceivable that in the 10th to 12th c. they belonged to the same boatbuilding tradition.

At the core of the problem of linking the Utrecht type to the hulk is the discrepancy between an archaeologically known ship type and a historical type (cf. Maarleveld 1991). Two epistemologically different categories are compared, in that the Utrecht type is a classification imposed by scholars on archaeological data (»etic« type), whereas the hulk is known from historical records, and so was a type recognized by medieval people themselves (»emic« type). When one ponders whether the Utrecht type was an early hulk, the question one really asks is: do the characteristics of the Utrecht type as they have been selected correspond to criteria that for medieval people were diagnostic of the hulk? The answer can never be known entirely, because historical documentation is not sufficiently detailed. It remains unknown how many undocumented ship and boat types there were, nor do we know how strictly the criteria of the historical hulk were defined or how much they varied regionally or chronologically. However, considering that hulk, cog, and keel were the three main seagoing ship types mentioned in 10th- to 12th-c. texts, and that the 12th- to 14th-c. hulk iconography (as identified by the A.D. 1295 New Shoreham seal) was extremely consistent and different from that of cogs and keels, it seems justifiable to apply the term »hulk« broadly as a heuristic or analytical category, as long as one is aware of that it does not necessarily correspond entirely to the »emic« hull type. In the following, the relationship of the archaeologically attested Utrecht type to the analytical hulk will be investigated more closely in an effort to determine whether this expanded logboat may indeed have been a proto-hulk that later developed into a fully planked boat.

The etymology of the word hulk is uncertain and hence of little use to establish a relationship with the Utrecht type (Fliedner 1969: 56-57). Ellmers (2000: 119) believes that it is derived from the Germanic root *hul-*, and means »something hollowed out«, thus referring to the hollowed-out logboat base of the Utrecht type. However, as Fliedner pointed out, the name hulk could also have its origin in the more neutral derivative meaning of *hul-* as »cover, shell«, or it could come from the ancient Greek ship type *holkas* or »towed vessel«, a large merchantman which had to be towed in and out of harbours. The problem with the last interpretation is that the Greek word *holkas* was not widespread in ancient Latin, and it is never attested in Medieval Latin. Given the uncertainties surrounding its etymology, it is better to focus on whatever hulk characteristics are clearly given by medieval texts and depictions. These relate to size, hull profile, some external hull characteristics, method of propulsion, and geographic distribution.

With respect to size, late 10th- through 12th-c. hulks may have been comparable to the largest Utrecht-type vessels. Aethelred II's tax document of ca. A.D. 1000 lists the hulk as a large sailing ship of similar size as the keel (Fliedner 1969: 54). The largest known archaeological finds of contemporary keels are the Hedeby 3 ship of 22.1 m length and the Skuldelev I ship of 16.5 m length, both built in the early 11th c. (Crumlin-Pedersen 1997: 103-104). Hulks may not have been larger, and thus would have been comparable in size to the ca. 18 m long Utrecht I and Queenhithe ships. Likewise indicative of the rather modest size of the hulk is the fact that in a 10th- or 11th-c. Anglo-Saxon glossary it is equated with the *liburna*, a light Roman warship, and in an early 11th-c. Old High German text (*Heinrici Summarium*) it is compared to the *actuaria navis*, a Roman merchant galley which could be sailed and oared (Fliedner 1969: 54-55). It is only in the 13th and 14th c. that the hulk gradually increases in size, and it is then that it appears as an emblem on city seals and coins.

When the hulk finally surpassed the cog in size, in the 15th c., it had borrowed a number of characteristics from the cog, and had effectively become a hybrid (Fliedner 1969: 67-68). A comparison of hull shapes of hulks and Utrecht-type vessels should therefore focus on earlier sources. The hulk is commonly depicted in 12th- through 14th-c. images as a symmetrically crescent-shaped ship with extremely curved plank runs and no visible stem or sternpost (e.g. Fliedner, 1969: 55, figs 1. 6-9, 13; Hutchinson 1994: figs 1.5, 1.6, 3.2). The hood ends do not run horizontally into the hull extremities, but curve upwards in a bizarre way, ending into animal heads or, later, castles that close off the bow and stern.

If these later depictions are compared to the hull profile of the Utrecht I ship – the only Utrecht-type profile published thus far – some differences can be noticed. The Utrecht I ship as currently restored has a much less curving hull than the 12th- to 14th-c. hulk, and its curvature is asymmetrical, the bow showing a more relaxed curve than the stern (**Fig. 1, 1**). The author believes that this asymmetry derives from its expanded logboat base, and is caused by the fact that the bow was made from the bottom of the tree, which was the widest part of the trunk. Plank runs of the upper hull follow the logboat's curvature. A second difference relates to the sheerline of the Utrecht I ship, which has been reconstructed in its museum display with a slight countercurve toward both hull extremities. This countercurve looks quite Art Deco and appears to be the result of a mistaken reconstruction in the 1930s. Close observation of the restored ship extremities reveals that treenails or treenail holes are missing from the last meter or so of the strakes and wale. It is highly unlikely that the medieval builder would have omitted these treenails, for in the Waterstraat boat the plank edges

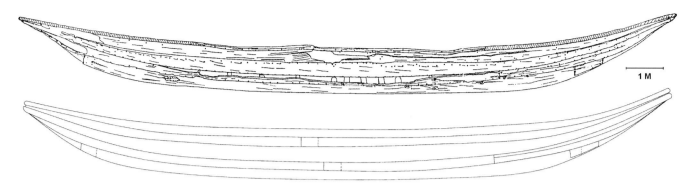

Fig. 1 **1** Starboard profile of the Utrecht I ship in its present condition. – **2** Schematic reconstruction of the same profile; hatched lines indicate the sheerline as it is currently restored (Drawings A. Van de Moortel, inked by L. Dokkedal).

are connected throughout. Rather, workers in the 1930s must have cut away the much deteriorated edges and treenail holes of those planks, visible on a work photo, and connected them by other, now hidden fasteners rather than restoring the planks to their full widths. It is reasonable to assume that at least 5 cm of each plank and wale edge have been cut away. If one restores those missing edges, the hull extremities rise 15 to 20 cm higher than in the present reconstruction, and the plank runs in sheer view make a simple curve, resembling more closely the plank runs on depictions of late medieval hulks (**Fig. 1, 2**).

It remains to be seen whether the seemingly unrealistic plank runs of most 12th- to 14th-c. hulk depictions have a base in reality, as Greenhill (2000) has argued, or whether they are the result of artistic exaggeration. It is argued here that these very rounded symmetrical hulls may be overly stylized representations of slightly asymmetrically curving hulls such as that of the Utrecht I ship. Trying to fit this hull shape onto the round medieval city seals, seal carvers may well have simplified and exaggerated the real curvature of the plank runs. A similar phenomenon can be demonstrated for Minoan seals from ca. 1700 to 1450 B.C., which show hulls with a comparably strong symmetrical curvature (Basch 1987: 100-101), whereas contemporary representations on much larger surfaces of a different shape, such as the miniature ship fresco from Akrotiri, depict the same ships with slightly asymmetrical, softly curving hulls not unlike that of the Utrecht I ship (Basch 1987: 119-122; Sakellarakis & Sapouna-Sakellaraki 1991: fig. 128; Siedentopf 1991: pls 35-36). A very different and arguably more realistic depiction of a hulk may be seen in a 12th-c. miniature from Winchester showing Thomas Becket returning from France (Heinsius 1956, pl. I.6; Hutchinson 1994: 13). With her gently curving hull and strakes ending horizontally against the hull extremities rather than bending up as in most hulk representations, the Winchester ship closely resembles the Utrecht I vessel in profile.

More correspondences can be seen between the Utrecht type and the hulk in details of their construction. The overlapping side-planking and apparent lack of stem and sternpost of hulks are also features of Utrecht-type hulks. Likewise, a 14th-c. lead badge depicting Becket's return from exile in a hulk shows hull planking marked by small circles with central dashes; these may well represent the wedged treenails connecting the strakes of Utrecht-type vessels (Hutchinson 1994: frontispiece; Goodburn 1991: fig. 14.2). In contrast, the reverse lapstrake planking seen in about one-third of the hulk depictions is not found in the Utrecht type. It is possible that this curious feature represents a mistake by the seal carver, and was inspired by the reverse overlap of the upper strake and wale on Utrecht-type ships.

Also in terms of propulsion there are striking correspondences between hulks and Utrecht-type ships. Comparisons in 10th- to 12th-c. texts of hulks with light Roman warships and merchant galleys indicate that they were oared as well as sailed. The Winchester miniature in addition shows a hulk being towed, which would fit the *holkas* etymology of the term hulk. A similar versatility of propulsion is seen in Utrecht-type vessels. The Queenhithe ship is too fragmentary to provide reliable clues, but the Utrecht I ship and Velsen boat have small mast steps located in a frame close to the bow at ca. 2/7 to 1/3 of the hull length, respectively. Such location would have been ideal for towing from a river bank (Rieth 1998: 106-107), a practice known in the Rhine Delta (Lebecq 1983: 218-219). Vlek, estimating the size of the masts from mast hole dimensions, believes that they were too small to have carried a sail. However, if one estimates the mast diameter from the frame width instead, one arrives at 17 cm for the Utrecht I ship and ca. 10 cm for the Velsen boat, or even thicker if they tapered towards the base. Such masts would have been strong enough to carry a small sail, although the absence of a keel would have made the hull prone to lateral drift. Sailing does not seem have been their primary mode of propulsion, but it is certainly possible that Utrecht-type vessels did it when conditions were favourable.

In shallow water the Utrecht I ship was probably punted as well. There is some evidence that it also carried a few oars. A pair of vertical blind holes recently discovered in the rubbing strake on the starboard side may have carried a double thole-pin or rowlock (Van de Moortel 2000). To judge by its treenail pattern, this rubbing strake fragment appears to have been originally located 4.7 m further aft, and the thole 2.3 m aft of amidships. It may have held an oar used to keep course during towing, as is shown on the Winchester miniature. However, it may also have been part of a set of oars used for propulsion. A matching thole-pin may have been located in the missing rubbing strake on the port side, and a second pair of oars may have been mounted further forward, where the rubbing strake has equally disappeared. Two pairs of oars would have sufficed to propel the ship in any direction on the river Vecht, which did not have tidal currents (de Groot 1997: 17-19).

From the previous comparisons it appears that the archaeological Utrecht ship-type and the hulk known from historical documents of the 10th- to 12th c. are indeed related in size, hull profile, construction details, and modes of propulsion. They also correspond in terms of provenance, although not entirely. Whilst the Utrecht type thus far is restricted to the Lower Rhine, the hulk had strong connections not only with the Netherlands, but also with Belgium, France, and Germany (Hutchinson 1994: 12-13; Fliedner 1969: 54-56; 63-66). This discrepancy may be a result of archaeological serendipity, however, since no other wrecks of possible hulks dating to this period have been found in these areas either.

In conclusion, the author believes that there are sufficient similarities between the Utrecht-type and the hulk to state that the Utrecht type is a good candidate to have been a forerunner of the seagoing hulk. But it need not have been the only forerunner. It is conceivable that in the future contemporary wrecks of inland crafts will be found in Belgium, France or Germany that are somewhat different from the Utrecht type, but still show convincing correspondences with the hulk. The expanded logboat of the Utrecht type, being eminently suited for the rapids of the Middle Rhine, may well have been retained on that river longer than elsewhere, and other areas may have developed crescent-shaped fully planked hulls with hulk features earlier. Even so, it is predicted that their hull curvature will be similar to that of the Utrecht-type boats, and that the common origin of all these vessels was the expanded logboat.

NOTES

1) This manuscript was originally submitted for the ISBSA 10 proceedings.
2) Contra Goodburn (2000) who had stated that the tax regulations refer to Queenhithe itself. The present author thanks Katrin Thier for alerting her to the correct reading and for sending her a copy of the original text.

REFERENCES

Basch, L., 1987, *Le musée imaginaire de la marine antique*. Athens.

Crumlin-Pedersen, O., 1983, Schiffe und Seehandelsrouten im Ostseeraum 1050-1350. In: *Lübecker Schriften zur Archäologie und Kulturgeschichte*, 7, 229-237.

1984, Der Seetransport: Die Schiffe von Haithabu. In: H. Jankuhn, K. Schietzel & H. Reichstein (eds), *Archäologische und naturwissenschaftliche Untersuchungen an Siedlungen im deutschen Küstengebiet*, vol. 2. Weinheim, 241-250.

1997, *Viking-Age Ships and Shipbuilding in Hedeby/Haithabu and Schleswig*. Ships and Boats of the North, vol. 2. Roskilde.

de Bruin, R., Hoekstra, T. J. & Pietersma, A., 1999, *The City of Utrecht through Twenty Centuries*. Utrecht.

de Groot, H., 1992, *Traces at Traiectum. An Archaeological Survey*. Utrecht.

1997, De haven die verdween. In: G. Bakker & T. Hoekstra (eds), *Het stenen geheugen. 25 jaar archeologie en bouwhistorie in Utrecht*. Utrecht, 12-39.

de Weerd, M. D., 1987, Velsen: The Mediaeval Logboat. In: R. W. Brandt, W. Groenman-van Waateringe & S. E. van der Leeuw (eds), *The Assendelver Polder Papers*, vol. I. Amsterdam, 265-283.

Ellmers, D., 1985, The History of the Cog as a Ship Type. In: K.-P. Kiedel & U. Schnall (eds), *The Hanse Cog of 1380*. Bremerhaven, 60-68.

2000, Zur Herkunft des spätmittelalterlichen Schiffstyps Holk. *Zeitschrift für Archäologie des Mittelalters*, 28, 119-128.

Fliedner, S., 1969, »Kogge« und »Hulk«. Ein Beitrag zur Schiffstypengeschichte. In: *Die Bremer Hansekogge. Fund, Konservierung, Forschung*. Monographien der Wittheit zu Bremen, no. 8. Bremen, 54-75.

Goodburn, D. M., 1991, New Light on Early Ship- and Boatbuilding in the London Area. In: G. L. Good, R. H. Jones & M. W. Ponsford (eds), *Waterfront Archaeology*. London, 105-115.

2000, New Light on the Construction of Early Medieval »Frisian« Sea-going Vessels. In: *ISBSA 8*, 219-224.

Greenhill, B., 2000, The Mysterious Hulc. *MM, 86*, 3-18.

Heinsius, P., 1956, *Das Schiff der hansischen Frühzeit*. Weimar.

Hocker, F. M. & Vlierman, K., 1996, *A Small Cog Wrecked on the Zuyderzee in the Early 15th Century*. Flevobericht, no. 408. Lelystad.

Hoekstra, T. J., 1975, Note on an Ancient Ship Found at Utrecht. *IJNA*, 4, 390-392.

Hutchinson, G., 1994, *Medieval Ships and Shipping*. London.

Lebecq, S., 1983, *Marchands et navigateurs frisons du Haut Moyen Âge*. Lille.

Liebermann, F., 1903, *Die Gesetze der Angelsachsen*. Halle (reprint Aalen 1960).

Maarleveld, T., 1991, Classificeren van schepen. Nut en risico's, theorie en praktijk. In: H. R. Reinders (ed.), *Bouwtraditie en scheepstype. Inleidingen gehouden tijdens het vierde Glavimans symposion*. Groningen, 94-103.

Marsden, P., 1976, A Boat of the Roman Period Found at Bruges, Belgium, in 1899, and Related Types. *IJNA, 5*, 23-55.

Nilsson, M., Krąpiec, M. & Ossowski, W., 2004, *Medieval Barges from Falsterbo, Sweden*. In: Brandt & Kühn, Haithabu, 71-81.

Reinders, H. R. & Oosting, R., 1991, Mittelalterliche Schiffsfunde in den IJsselmeerpoldern. In: W. H. Zimmermann & L. Spath (eds), *Ländliche und städtische Küstensiedlungen im 1. und 2. Jahrtausend*, Dokumentation des Vortragszyklus 23.-25. Oktober 1987. Wilhelmshavener Tage 2. Wilhelmshaven, 106-122.

Rieth, E., 1998, *Des bateaux et des fleuves. Archeologie de la batellerie du Neolithique aux Temps modernes en France*. Paris.

Sakellarakis, I. & Sapouna-Sakellaraki, E., 1991, *Archanes*. Athens.

Siedentopf, H .B., 1991, *Alt-Ägina*, vol. IV. *2: Mattbemalte Keramik der mittleren Bronzezeit*. Mainz.

Van de Moortel, A., 1991, *A Cog-like Vessel from the Netherlands*. Flevobericht, no. 331. Lelystad.

2000, *The Archaeological Study of the Utrecht Ship*. www.natmus.dk/nmf/maresUK/maresuk.htm. Project Report for the European Commission.

2003, A New Look at the Utrecht Ship. In: *ISBSA 9*, 183-189.

Van Vliet, K., 2000, De stad van de bisschop (ca. 925-1122). In: R. E. de Bruin, P. D. 't Hart, A. J. van den Hoven van Genderen, A. Pietersma, & J. E. A. L. Struick (eds), *Een paradijs vol weelde. Geschiedenis van de stad Utrecht*. Utrecht, 45-71.

Vlek, R., 1987, *The Mediaeval Utrecht Boat. The history and evaluation of one of the first nautical archaeological excavations and reconstructions in The Low Countries*. BAR, Internat. Series, no. 382. Oxford.

Vlierman, K., 1996, *Kleine bootjes en middeleeuws scheepshout met constructiedetails. Scheepsarcheologie II*. Flevobericht, no. 404. Lelystad.

1997, A caulking method used as an aid to dating shipwrecks from the Hanseatic period. In: G. de Boe & F. Verhaeghe (eds), *Travel Technology and Organisation in Medieval Europe. Papers of the »Medieval Europe Brugge 1997« Conference*, vol. 8. Zellik, 41-52.

ALEYDIS VAN DE MOORTEL

THE UTRECHT SHIP TYPE

AN EXPANDED LOGBOAT TRADITION IN ITS HISTORICAL CONTEXT

The following is a third interim report on the author's ongoing research into the Utrecht ship type. At the 9th ISBSA conference she reported on the archaeological documentation of the Utrecht I ship and presented evidence for the expansion of its logboat section (Van de Moortel 2003). At the 10th ISBSA conference she discussed the characteristics of five wrecks of the Utrecht type and argued for their close correspondence with the historical hulk type[1]. The present article is subdivided into three parts: first, it reports on three more identified members of the Utrecht type. Then, some results of the recent documentation of the Utrecht-type wreck from the Waterstraat at Utrecht will be reviewed, including more evidence for the expansion of the logboat base. Finally, links between the Utrecht type and the hulk will be considered in greater detail, and the historical context in which both operated will be discussed. In this context it will be proposed that economic and political conditions rather than purely ship-technical factors were the principal reasons for why not the hulk, but the cog became the first dominant large seagoing cargo vessel of N. Europe in the late Middle Ages.

THREE ADDITIONAL VESSELS OF THE UTRECHT TYPE

Whilst previously only five wrecks of the Utrecht type have been attributed, now three more are added, bringing the total to eight (**Figs 1-2**; **Table 1**). In his catalogue of small boat finds from the Netherlands, Vlierman had suggested the possibility that a hull fragment excavated by him in 1989 at lot ZP 49[2] in the former Zuyderzee at Zeewolde, 6 km W.S.W. of the harbour of Harderwijk, belonged to the Utrecht type (Vlierman 1996A: 91, 135). Vlierman did not provide a description or illustrations. After examining photos and drawings of this wreck as well as two small surviving hull fragments kept at the Rijksdienst voor Archeologie, Cultuurlandschap en Monumenten Lelystad (RACM), formerly Netherlands Institute of Ship and boat Archaeology (NISA), the author is able to confirm Vlierman's tentative identification. The excavators found only part of a logboat in lot ZP 49, preserved over a length of ca. 5.5 m and a width of ca. 60 cm. The walls of the dugout were only 2.2 to 2.8 cm thick. They showed treenails and treenail holes, 2.0 to 2.4 cm in diameter, for the attachment of frames. Treenails were spaced 41 to 48 cm apart, reflecting distances between frames. It is remarkable that no thickness gauges were recorded in the logboat of lot ZP 49, whereas they have been found on all other sufficiently preserved log-

Fig. 1 Distribution of the eight presently identified Utrecht-type vessels (Completed after Vlek 1987: fig. 1.1.1).

wreck	date	function	pres. l (m)	rec. l (m)	rec. b (m)	midship h (m)	logboat th (cm)
Utrecht, Waterstraat	late 10ᵗʰ c.	river-going cargo carrier	ca. 12	12.80	ca. 3		3.5-4
London, Queenhithe	end 10ᵗʰ c.	seagoing cargo carrier		ca. 18			ca. 4-5
Utrecht I	early 11ᵗʰ c.	large river-going cargo carrier		17.45	3.84	1.36	4-6
Antwerp, Steenborger-weertpolder	11ᵗʰ c.	small river-going boat		5.5	1.5	0.70	»thin«
Antwerp, Steenborger-weertpolder	11ᵗʰ c.	small river-going boat					
Velsen	late 11ᵗʰ to late 12ᵗʰ c.	river-going cargo carrier	5.78	ca. 6.50	1.45	0.38	3-5
Utrecht, Lange Lauwerstraat	early 12ᵗʰ c.	river-going cargo carrier	ca. 3				3.5
Zeewolde ZP49	not dated	small lake boat	ca. 5.5				2.2-2.8

Table 1 Eight presently identified wrecks of the Utrecht type in chronological order.

boat bases of the Utrecht type (Utrecht I ship, Waterstraat boat, Velsen boat, Lange Lauwerstraat boat). Only two small fragments of the logboat of lot ZP 49 have been saved and treated with PEG. Fragment C has a preserved length of 1.35 m and width of 22.5 cm, and fragment E – with sculpted curvature indicating that it belonged near one of the logboat's extremities – is preserved over a length of 80 cm and width of 35 cm. The extreme thinness of the logboat as well as the multitude of small cracks seen on its surface is strongly suggestive of expansion.

Wreck ZP 49 cannot be dated closely, but its identification is important as it expands the current understanding of the versatility as well as the geographical range of the Utrecht type. Most of the known Utrecht-type vessels were river craft and the fragments found at Queenhithe in the harbour of London must have belonged to a seagoing ship (cf. below). Because of its location wreck ZP 49 must have been of a boat that was used either in the Zuyderzee or in its predecessor, Lake Almere (Modderman 1945: 27-28; Van de Moortel 1991: note 1). This is the first time that an Utrecht-type wreck has been identified in this open body of water which at that time served as an important passageway for ships sailing from Utrecht and the Rhine area to the Frisian Wadden Zee and the Baltic (van Vliet 2000: 70).

Two more vessels of the Utrecht type have been identified by Detlev Ellmers in his monumental work on early Medieval shipping in Central and N. Europe (Ellmers 1984: 54, 287-288, nos 35g-h, fig. 35a-f). The remains of these now-lost boats were discovered in 1905 during the excavation of dock A at Steenborger-weertpolder in the harbour of Antwerp (Antwerpen). One was a largely intact oak logboat, 5.5 m long, 1.5 m wide, and 70 cm high (Ellmers 1984: no. 35g). Sketches made by the Belgian antiquarian Georges Hasse show characteristics closely resembling those of the Utrecht type. The logboat is drawn as very thin and displaying a smooth parabolic curve in cross-section, in a manner typical of expanded logboats (**Fig. 2**; Crumlin-Pedersen 1991: 254). Heavy frames were set symmetrically about the centre-line and were fastened with treenails to the shell. Caulking was done with moss, battens, and *sintelnagels* – iron staples holding the caulking into the seams. Of the second vessel (Ellmers 1984: no. 35h) only two frames of unspecified size were preserved; no details were recorded.

An unusual feature of the sketched boat from Antwerp is the reported raising of the hull by the addition of two strakes that did not overlap as on the other Utrecht-type boats, but were lying flush, and were connected not to each other but to small planks nailed and treenailed on the outside. Since similar small planks were used to repair cracks in the logboat of the Waterstraat boat (cf. below), Hasse might have misunderstood this feature of the Antwerp hull. Rather than having strakes, the vessel may have consisted solely of a deep logboat, and the thin planks may be repair planks covering longitudinal cracks in the

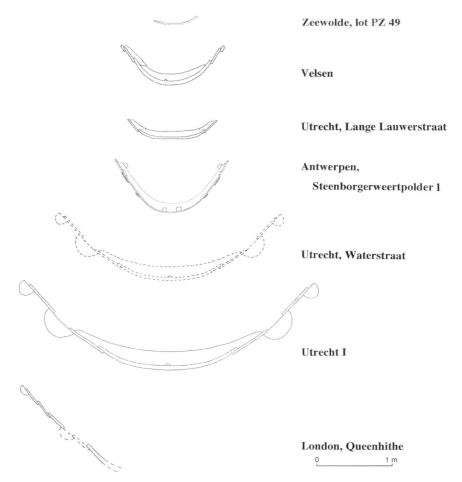

Fig. 2 Schematic cross-sections of seven Utrecht-type vessels, shown roughly to scale (Velsen boat: after de Weerd 1987: fig. 12.5a; Lange Lauwerstraat boat: after Vlierman 1996A: fig. 61F; Steenborgerweerdpolder I logboat from Antwerp: after Ellmers 1984: fig. 35c; Queenhithe ship: hypothetical reconstruction after Goodburn 2000: fig. 5B). – The second Antwerp logboat is too poorly known to be drawn.

logboat. A second unusual feature is the reportedly angular longitudinal bottom profile of the Antwerp hull, which does not agree well with an expanded logboat. In view of the poor conditions of documentation and Hasse's limited understanding of early vessels, it is conceivable that he misinterpreted also this part of the hull.

The two Utrecht-type vessels from the Antwerp harbour were found in an old bed of the River Scheldt (Schelde) and must have been river craft. The better documented boat Steenborgerweerdpolder I has been fairly securely dated to the 11th c. by the discovery of black pottery in the same stratum close to the vessel. A piercing of the hull near one extremity is thought by Ellmers to be related to the rudder attachment, in which case the rudder would have been located on the port side, as it may have been on the Utrecht I ship (Van de Moortel 2003). A small spade-shaped wooden object found with the Antwerp boat is interpreted by Ellmers as a handheld secondary steering oar for going downstream. A similar auxiliary rudder is used on a towed ship depicted in the illumination of a 12th-c. manuscript from Winchester which shows remarkable resemblances to the Utrecht type (Heinsius 1956, pl. I.6; Van de Moortel, this volume p. 325).

The finds from Antwerp expand the geographical distribution of the Utrecht type further to the S. and for the first time into the area of a continental river other than the Rhine. Archaeological find spots of the Utrecht type now range from the Zuyderzee to Antwerp and London, corresponding even more closely to the distribution area of the historical hulk (**Fig. 1**; **Table 1**; Van de Moortel, this volume pp. 321-327).

THE WATERSTRAAT BOAT: NEW EVIDENCE

In the winter of 2005 the author was given the opportunity to document the surviving remains of one of the larger wrecks of the Utrecht type, excavated in 1974 at the Waterstraat in Utrecht and stored in water tanks of the former NISA at Lelystad (Vlek 1987: 89-103)[3]. She planned to document also the much smaller, and very fragmentary, boat found at the Lange Lauwerstraat in Utrecht, but it appears to have been lost (Vlierman 1996A: 88-91; 135).

During its excavation, the Waterstraat boat had been dismantled. Nearly all pieces survived in the water tanks except for one or two hull planks. It was the first time since the excavation that these pieces were accessible for study. A first goal of the present project was to settle the dispute surrounding its date. Vlek had proposed an early 12th-c. date based on the style of pottery found below the wreck (Vlek 1987: 103). In contrast, Utrecht archaeologist Huib de Groot had argued for a 10th-c. date because the Waterstraat boat had been found in an older stratum than a barge of ca. A.D. 1000 discovered nearby (de Groot 1997: 36). Dendrochronological analysis carried out in December 2005 by Aoife Daly and Esther Jansma established that de Groot was right: the wood of the Waterstraat boat had been cut in the late 10th c. and is of roughly the same date as the Utrecht-type ship fragments from Queenhithe in the harbour of London (Goodburn 2000). Like the Utrecht I ship, the Waterstraat boat was built with wood from the Netherlands. Daly and Jansma were able to compare also the Queenhithe data with the recently improved Dutch dendrochronological curve, and determine that also this ship had been built with Dutch wood. Previous analysis of this wood by Tyers had shown weaker correspondences with E. England and N.W. Germany (Goodburn 2000: 223)[4].

The 2005 documentation of the Waterstraat boat has given valuable new evidence about the characteristics of the Utrecht type. The study is not finished, but it is possible to report already some observations on the logboat base and on one unusual feature of the hull. At the 9th ISBSA conference it was argued that the logboat base of the Utrecht I ship, the largest known vessel of the Utrecht type, had been expanded because of the unnatural distortion of the wood structure observed in core samples taken from several places in the logboat (Van de Moortel 2003). It was much easier to study the wood structure of the Waterstraat logboat because during its excavation it had been cut transversely into five pieces of roughly similar length. Moreover, its surfaces were visible, whereas those of the Utrecht I logboat had been covered by a thick layer of creosote and linseed oil.

The logboat base of the Waterstraat boat is preserved over a length of about 12 m; its reconstructed length is 12.80 m, and its width ca. 1.5 m. Already its feeble thickness, only 3.5 to 4 cm, is suggestive of expansion since expanded logboats as a rule are thin (Crumlin-Pedersen 1991: 254). Moreover, like the Utrecht I ship the Waterstraat boat has transverse rows of thickness gauges. With a diameter of 1.5 cm and a distance of 15 cm between holes and ca. 48 cm between rows, these are a little smaller and spaced slightly further apart than in the Utrecht I ship, but they are otherwise comparable. These thickness gauges helped the builder to hollow out the logboat to an even thickness – a necessary condition for expansion. Another criterion indicative of expansion – the presence of multiple small cracks on the interior surface – did not yield clear results. The Waterstraat logboat indeed has multiple surface cracks, but having been submerged in a water tank for thirty-two years, it is now entirely flat, and it is unclear whether the surface cracks are the results of an expansion or of this recent flattening.

Much stronger evidence was derived from a study of the tree-rings in the cross sections and on the surfaces of the Waterstraat logboat. This showed beyond a doubt that most of the logboat had been hollowed out following the wood grain of the parent tree; the rings had been cut through only at the very edges of the logboat on the port and starboard side, and over the last 2.5 m or so at either extremity of the logboat, where the profile had been sculpted so as to curve sharply upwards towards the bow and stern. In its central part, where the builder had followed the wood grain, the shape of the floor-timbers and the position of their plank fasteners show that the logboat displayed a continuous curvature in profile and plan view, tapering from amidships towards both extremities. This shape must have been obtained through expansion, because tree trunks naturally do not have such double taper.

Furthermore, to judge by the shape of the floor timbers, which had kept their original curvature, the interior surface of the logboat amidships had curved very gently, indicating that if it had not been expanded, the parent tree would have had a diameter of more than 3 m at a height of about 6.50 m above the ground. A similar midship diameter has been noted for the Utrecht I ship (Van de Moortel 2003). As it has been argued already for the Utrecht I ship, even if such a huge oak tree existed, it is highly unlikely that its inner texture would have been still sufficiently sound to allow the carving of the up-curving logboat extremities. It is possible to estimate the original thickness of the parent tree, because at the one completely preserved extremity of the Waterstraat logboat the heart of the tree had been cut through, suggesting an original diameter of about 1.50 m. This means that the diameter of the logboat had been expanded to about twice its original dimension.

The Waterstraat boat closely resembles the Utrecht I ship also in the remainder of its hull construction. On both vessels the logboat was extended with heavy overlapping planking, a half-round wale, and a half-round rubbing strake. Floor timbers are heavy and laid symmetrically about the centre-line. Many floor timbers only cover the width of the logboat and do no extend over its sides; ostensibly their function was to hold the logboat in shape after its expansion. Ship parts were fastened with treenails.

A major difference between the Waterstraat boat and other Utrecht-type vessels is its nearly complete lack of *sintelnagels*, the small iron strips that hold moss caulking and moss laths in place. In his excavation report Vlierman already noted that *sintelnagels* occur only to hold moss caulking in repairs but not in the seams of the hull planking. The only other iron fasteners found in the Waterstraat boat are short nails attaching long thin repair planks over cracks in the logboat. The significance of this scarcity of *sintelnagels* is unclear. They have been attested in this area since at least the late 9th c., but may have been used very sparingly in ship's hulls until ca. A.D. 1000 (cf. Vlierman 1996b: 50-51; 58-62). Alternatively, there may have been a temporary shortage of iron at the end of the 10th c. because of declining iron production in the Rhine Delta before iron was imported from Germany in the 11th c. (Joosten 2004: 96; 109).

THE UTRECHT TYPE AND THE HULK IN THEIR HISTORICAL CONTEXT

The possible link between the archaeological Utrecht type and the historical ship type called the hulk is not accepted by everyone, and the problem will remain unsolved until the actual relicts of a fully planked seagoing hulk will be found. However, the author agrees with Ellmers, Crumlin-Pedersen and other scholars that the Utrecht type and the hulk show remarkable similarities in their hull shape and planking configuration, and she has already argued for similarities in modes of propulsion, range of functions, cargo capacity, and chronological as well as geographic distribution (Van de Moortel, this volume pp. 321-327). It is conceivable that economic conditions and more specifically the growing need for heavy river transport in the Rhine Delta from the late 10th c. onwards, pushed boat builders to construct increasingly more and larger Utrecht-type vessels. This in turn may have led to the exhaustion of large oak trees needed to build these craft, prompting boat builders to replace the logboats with fully planked bottoms while retaining the characteristically deep curvature typical of Utrecht-type hulls.

Two late-medieval boats from the harbour of Antwerp show remarkable similarities with the Utrecht type and may be early examples of such fully planked hulks. They were found in a stack of five wrecks during the construction of the Lefèbvre dock in 1884. The boats are now lost, and only a short report and sketches of their plan view and section remain, again made by Hasse (Ellmers 1984: 284-286, figs 182a-b, nos 35a-b). The two boats have been dated to the 13th c. on the basis of their geological stratum. They closely resemble Utrecht-type vessels in size (20 m by 4 m by 1.20 m; 15 m by 3 m by 1 m) and length-to-beam proportions (5:1) as well as in many other aspects: they have a similar shape in plan view with the hull tapering to blunt extremities; lacking stem and sternpost, the extremities are formed by the up-curving or up-sloping bottom planking; floor timbers as a rule have been laid symmetrically along the centre-line of the hull, and many are short, covering only the bottom; there is a fairly regular alternation between short and long floor timbers; planking and frames have been joined with treenails; plank seams have been caulked with moss, and those of the bottom planking have been covered on the interior with moss laths and *sintels* or *sintelnagels*, and on the exterior by thin planks fastened with iron nails resembling the repair planks on the Waterstraat boat. The flush-laid bottom planking and overlapping side planking of the Antwerp boats likewise are reminiscent of the smooth logboat bottom element and the overlapping side planking of Utrecht-type vessels.

The greatest differences between the 13th-c. Antwerp boats and the Utrecht ship type relate to their reportedly flat bottoms and the curious fastening of their overlapping planking with short iron nails inserted from inboard and outboard. Hasse did not draw the Antwerp boats in profile, but only in cross section. One wonders whether the flat bottom he drew is the result of hull distortion or of misinterpretation, since he would not have been aware of the very gentle rise typical of Utrecht-type hulls. Alternatively, it is possible that these 13th-c. boats indeed had flat bottoms, as do traditional wooden *Nachen* of the Middle Rhine, which likewise show close similarities in shape and planking configuration with Utrecht-type hulls. The use of short iron nails for joining the overlapping side-planking of the 13th-c. Antwerp boats is thus far unique, and may represent a local feature. The fact that iron is used for hull fasteners rather than treenails as on Utrecht-type vessels may not be significant but merely reflect the increased use of iron in late 12th- and 13th-c. shipbuilding in this region. It is now waiting for the discovery and more thorough documentation of late-medieval vessels with similar characteristics as the Antwerp boats to confirm whether they indeed form the missing link between the logboat-based Utrecht type and the fully planked seagoing hulk.

Whether or not the Utrecht-type vessels and the 13th-c. planked boats from Antwerp were early hulks, from written evidence it is known that the hulk underwent a gradual increase in scale throughout the later Middle Ages and became the dominant cargo carrier N. Europe in the 15th c. (Fliedner 1969: 66-68). For about 250 years, however, from the mid-12th c. through the end of the 14th c., the hulk was overshadowed by the cog, which during that period became the largest seagoing cargo vessel of this area. Scholars long have wondered about the reason for this set-back. It has been speculated that the technological capabilities of the hulk created obstacles for its growth, and only when these were resolved through the adoption of certain cog features the hulk would have been ready to surpass the cog in size and take the lead in maritime transport. Although the adoption of cog features by the 15th-c. hulk cannot be denied, one may wonder why this did not happen earlier. The author's research into the historical context of the Utrecht type and the hulk from the 10th through 14th c. leads to the supposition that not ship-technical but geopolitical and economic reasons slowed the development of the hulk and favored the rise of the cog from the mid-12th c. onwards.

As it has been argued before, Utrecht-type ships with their single-piece bottom elements must have been ideally suited for transport between the Rhine Delta and the Middle Rhine, because they were stronger than planked bottoms for braving the dangerous rocky rapids between Koblenz and Mainz (Van de Moortel, this volume p. 322). As historical documents relate, the Rhine trade experienced slower growth from the mid-12th c. onwards because local lords increasingly imposed tolls and forced merchants to put their wares on the market in specific towns (German: *Stapelrecht*; cf. Gönnenwein 1939: 16). The imposition of these tolls and obligations was in fact an act of rebellion on the part of the local lords against the German emperor who had decreed that the Rhine must be free. This rebellious attitude can be situated within the general erosion of the central imperial power in favour of local lords' power in the wake of the Viking attacks (Irsigler 1989: 75)[5].

Increased regulation of shipping on the Rhine appears to have made land transport a more attractive alternative. Already in the 12th c. the land route between Bruges (Brugge) – the Flemish maritime harbour – and Cologne (Köln) had become very important, allowing merchants to circumvent Rhine tolls and impositions. Here and further S., waggons were able to use the old Roman road network, which was still in operation (Stoob 1998). Land transport was made even more attractive by a number of inventions including the horse collar, which was widely adopted by the 12th c., improving the pulling power of horses and making them an increasingly preferred alternative to the slower oxen (Langdon 1986: 9-21). Remains of an 11th-c. cart found at *Haithabu* near Schleswig, N. Germany, show that they were of considerable size; this cart is estimated by the thickness of its axle to have carried up to 1 ton (Hayen 1984: 253). Considering that the cargo capacity of the Utrecht I ship was about 6.5 tons, one may conclude that only seven such carts were needed to carry the same load as the Utrecht I ship, the largest known Utrecht-type vessel. These advances in land transport together with the increased Rhine tolls must have made it a very attractive alternative to waterborne transport. These developments slowed the growth of the river transport on the Rhine and are likely to have been the main reasons that hulk sizes increased but slowly throughout the 13th and 14th c.

Unlike the feeble growth in Rhine transport, maritime trade increased rapidly from the 11th c. onwards, and the creation of the Hanseatic league in the late 12th c. soon caused the cities on the North Sea coast of Germany and the Netherlands to flourish (Fliedner 1969: 83). The archaeological ship type of these coastal regions was not the hulk but the cog. Thus one may conclude that it was for these political and economic reasons, rather than for purely technical reasons, that the cog and not the hulk grew into the first large seagoing cargo vessel of the later Middle Ages.

NOTES

1) This article inadvertently did not appear in the proceedings of that conference (ISBSA 10). Thanks to the kindness of Dr. R. Bockius it is published in the present volume. Cf. pp. 321-327.

2) Zuyderzee wrecks formerly referred to with »PZ« have now been relabelled with »ZP.«

3) The author is very grateful to the people of the RACM Lelystad for allowing her to study these boat remains and for their co-operation in her research. The recording was done with a digital drafting arm by Frank Dallmeijer, Esther Martens, Gert Schreurs, and the author. Frank Dallmeijer converted the digital data into drawings. Jaap Morel sorted and reassembled the surviving ship parts of the Waterstraat boat, and provided valuable help and advice throughout.

4) The author is much obliged to Damian Goodburn and Ian Tyers for making the Queenhithe data available to Aoife Daly and Esther Jansma.

5) Historian Bas van Bavel of the University of Utrecht drew the author's attention to the economic and political changes in this period, and gave her valuable help with bibliographical references. She is most grateful for his kindness.

REFERENCES

Crumlin-Pedersen, O., 1991, Bådgrave og gravbåde. In: S. H. Andersen, B. Lind, & O. Crumlin-Pedersen (eds), *Slusegaard-gravpladsen, III. Gravfromer or gravskikke. Bådgravene*. Aarhus, 93-263.

de Groot, H., 1997, De haven die verdween. In: G. Bakker & T. Hoekstra (eds), *Het stenen geheugen. 25 jaar archeologie en bouwhistorie in Utrecht*. Utrecht, 12-39.

de Weerd, M. D., 1987, Velsen: The Mediaeval Logboat. In: R. W. Brandt, W. Groenman-van Waateringe & S. E. van der Leeuw (eds), *The Assendelver Polder Papers*, vol. I. Amsterdam, 265-283.

Ellmers, D., 1984, *Frümittelalterliche Handelsschiffahrt in Mittel- und Nordeuropa*. Offa-Bücher, no. 28. Neumünster.

Fliedner, S., 1969, »Kogge« und »Hulk«. Ein Beitrag zur Schiffs-typengeschichte. In: *Die Bremer Hansekogge. Fund, Konservie-rung, Forschung*. Monographien der Wittheit zu Bremen, no. 8. Bremen, 54-75.

Gönnenwein, O., 1939, *Das Stapel- und Niederlagsrecht*. Weimar.

Goodburn, D. M., 2000, New Light on the Construction of Early Medieval »Frisian« Sea-going Vessels. In: *ISBSA 8*, 219-224.

Hayen, H., 1984. Der Landtransport: Wagenreste aus Haithabu. In: H. Jankuhn, K. Schietzel, & H. Reichstein (eds), *Archäologische und naturwissenschaftliche Untersuchungen an ländlichen und frühstädtischen Siedlungen im deutschen Küstengebiet vom 5. Jahrhundert v. Chr. bis zum 11. Jahrhundert n. Chr., 2: Handels-plätze des frühen und hohen Mittelalters*. Weinheim, 251-253.

Heinsius, P., 1956, *Das Schiff der hansischen Frühzeit*. Weimar.

Irsigler, F., 1989, Grundherrschaft, Handel und Märkte zwischen Maas und Rhein im frühen und hohen Mittelalter. In: K. Flink & W. Janssen (eds), *Grundherrschaft und Stadtentstehung am Nie-derrhein*. Kleve, 52-78.

Joosten, I., 2004, *Technology of Early Historical Iron Production in the Netherlands*. Amsterdam.

Langdon, J., 1986, *Horses, Oxen and Technological Invention*. Cambridge.

Modderman, P. J. R., 1945, *Over de wording en de beteekenis van het Zuiderzeegebied*. Groningen.

Stoob, H., 1998, Über den Aufbruch zur Städtebildung in Mittel-europa. In: J. Jarnut & P. Johanek (eds), *Die Frühgeschichte der europäischen Stadt im 11. Jahrhundert*. Köln, 1-20.

Van de Moortel, A., 1991, *A Cog-like Vessel from the Netherlands*. Flevobericht, no. 331. Lelystad.

2003, A New Look at the Utrecht Ship. In: *ISBSA 9*, 183-189.

Van Vliet, K., 2000, De stad van de bisschop (ca. 925-1122). In: R. E. de Bruin, P. D. 't Hart, A. J. van den Hoven van Genderen, A. Pietersma, & J. E. A. L. Struick (eds), *Een paradijs vol weelde. Geschiedenis van de stad Utrecht*. Utrecht, 45-71.

Vlek, R., 1987, *The Mediaeval Utrecht Boat. The history and eval-uation of one of the first nautical archaeological excavations and reconstructions in The Low Countries*. BAR, Internat. Series, no. 382. Oxford.

Vlierman, K., 1996a, *Kleine bootjes en middeleeuws scheepshout met constructiedetails. Scheepsarcheologie II*. Flevobericht, no. 404. Lelystad.

1996b, *Van Zintelen, van Zintelroeden ende Mossen. Een breeuwmethode als hulpmiddel bij het dateren van scheeps-wrakken uit de Hanzetijd*. Flevobericht, no. 386. Lelystad.

H. REINDER REINDERS

THE SAILING ROUTE FROM UFFELTE TO UTRECHT

Over the last decade, the Utrecht ship excavated in the 1930s has attracted a great deal of attention from scholars who relate the Utrecht-type ship finds to shipping on the Rhine and even to overseas trade. In this contribution attention shall be drawn to the district of Drenthe in the N. part of the Netherlands, where the Bishop of Utrecht and many churches in Utrecht held property. The distribution of farmsteads and manors in Drenthe belonging to the bishop and the church of Sint Pieter (Saint Peter) will be examined, as well as the yields from their property. The question arises of how they managed to transport the goods from Drenthe to Utrecht and whether perhaps boats of the Utrecht type were used for transport.

UTRECHT-TYPE SHIPS

So far, at least seven ships or ship fragments of the Utrecht type of varying dimensions have been excavated in Utrecht, Velsen and London. In cross section, the Utrecht ship has a rather thin hollowed-out and expanded tree trunk as base, and it is extended with upper planking and provided with frames and longitudinal wales (**Fig. 1**). Van de Moortel (2004: 47-48) has related the Utrecht-type ship finds of the 10th to 12th c. to shipping on the Rhine, and Goodburn (2000) even to overseas trade through the fragments of a ship of the Utrecht type found in London. The felling date of the trees used for the vessel from London is between A.D. 966 and 990 and the sequence of the annual rings matches the E. England and N. German chronologies, and more closely the latter, thus the Low Countries region.

In Goodburn's opinion the London ship came from overseas (Goodburn 2000). In his hypothetical reconstruction of the fragments, the London vessel is even more seaworthy than its sister from Utrecht (**Fig. 1**). Van de Moortel (2004: Tab. 1) also classified the London find as a seagoing carrier, but classified the other finds of Utrecht-type boats as large and small riverine cargo vessels because, in spite of its large size, the cargo capacity of the Utrecht ship was relatively modest, 6.5 tons according to an analysis by Kenn Jensen (Van de Moortel 2004: 47).

When the location of Utrecht in the Lower Rhine area is considered (**Fig. 2**), it is obvious to relate the ships of the Utrecht type to shipping and trade on the River Rhine, but the present author wants to explore other possibilities.

FOREESTRECHT AND SCHULDMUDDEN

The Bishop of Utrecht combined the sacred and the secular. Between A.D. 800 and 1000 six mother churches were founded in the district of Drenthe, and the Bishop of Utrecht held the *seendrecht,* jurisdiction in ecclesiastical matters (Blok 1985: 150). His influence increased considerably when in 944 Emperor Otto I endowed the bishop with the *ius forestensis* in the *pagus forestensis* and in Drenthe. The *pagus forestensis* was a large area of wasteland in the S.W. of Drenthe. The *ius forestensis* was not restricted to the game laws, but also included the rights over wasteland in Drenthe. After 944 the owners of the farms had to pay *schuldmudden* to the bishop, an annual tax of 1 *mud* of rye, for using wood for the construc-

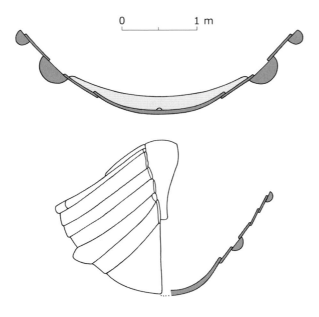

Fig. 1 Cross sections of the Utrecht and London (Queenhithe) ships (After Van de Moortel 2003: 184, fig. 28.2d-e).

tion of farms, collecting firewood, and the pasture of cattle, pigs and sheep, etc.

Written sources about Drenthe for the period 800 to 1000 are almost entirely lacking, but the situation is reflected in the written sources of a later period. The amount of *schuldmudden* for each *buerschap* (community of farmers, village) was not registered before ca. 1545, but although the number of farms in Drenthe increased considerably between 944 and 1545, the number of *schuldmudden* remained the same. The village of Uffelte, for instance, numbered 18 farms in 1300, but only six of them paid one *schultmudde* each. This number is not mentioned in the register of 1545, because the bishop donated the revenues from the *schuldmudden* of Uffelte to the chapter of Sint Pieter.

Blok (1985: 164-170) concluded that the number of *schuldmudden* registered in 1545 reflects the number

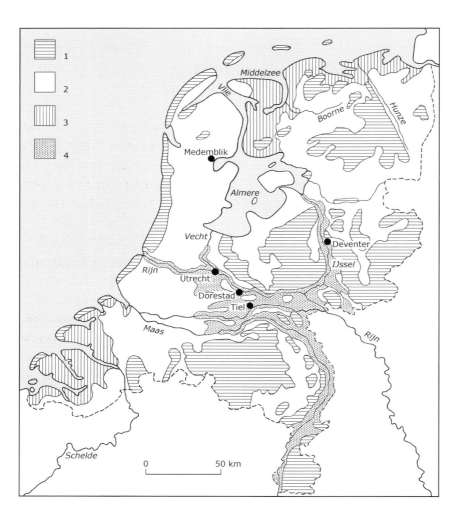

Fig. 2 The Netherlands around 800 with the location of Dorestad, Utrecht and Tiel: 1 Dunes along the coast and pleistocene sandy regions in the eastern part of the Netherlands. – 2 Peat bog. – 3 Salt marsh areas in the N. part of the Netherlands and in the S.W. – 4 River sediments.

of farms in 944. Although his hypothesis is criticized and has not yet been supported conclusively by the results of excavations of medieval farms and villages in Drenthe, it allows to estimate the number of farms and the revenues of the bishop. Blok (1985: 170) calculated the total number of farms in Drenthe in 944 to be 610, thus an under-populated area. Consequently, the bishop's revenues from the *ius forensis* came to 610 *mud* of rye. One *mud* of rye measures 90 litres and weighs ca. 70 kg, so the revenues of the bishop from the *schuldmudden* amounted to more than 42 tons of rye.

The Bishop of Utrecht also became secular leader of Drenthe after the donation of the district of Drenthe to Bishop Bertold in 1046. The bishop's properties in Drenthe had in the meantime already been increased by the donation of the manors of Uffelte, Wittelte, Peelo and Groningen to Bishop Bertold in 1040 (**Fig. 3**), who in his turn donated this property to the chapter of Sint Pieter in Utrecht, on the occasion of its foundation in 1048 (Blok 1985: 150-151).

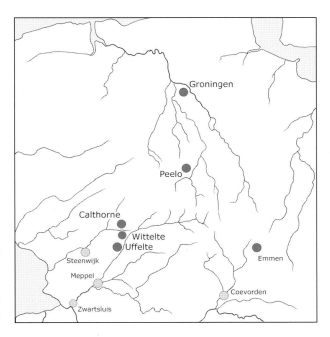

Fig. 3 Location of the manors of Uffelte, Wittelte, Peelo and Groningen donated to Bishop Bertold in 1040.

ARCHAEOLOGICAL EVIDENCE

Farmsteads and manors of the Bishop of Utrecht and the chapter of Sint Pieter dating to the 11th to 14th c. are known from excavations. As already mentioned the manor at Peelo, donated to the Bishop of Utrecht in 1040 and granted by him in fief to the chapter of Sint Pieter in 1048. Large-scale excavations by the Groningen Institute of Archaeology have resulted in the location of three late medieval yards with farmsteads, granaries and wells in Peelo (Kooi 1993/1994: 169-306; 1999/2000: 417-480). The study of archives and toponyms has resulted in the names of three late medieval yards: *Huisinge* (0.45 ha), *Derkinge* (0.53 ha) and *Hovinge* (0.75 ha).

The name *Hovinge* refers to the *Hof* of Peelo, the manor where the Bishop of Utrecht, and later the chapter of Sint Pieter after its foundation in 1048, collected taxes and the yield from their property (Bardet *et al.* 1983: 7-9). In the 9th to 10th c. the village was perhaps larger and numbered four or five houses.

In 2004, a medieval site was uncovered in Kalteren at the edge of the stream valley of the Kwasloot, the headwaters of the River Wapserveense A (Hielkema & De Wit 2005: 196-208). A farmyard of 2 ha, enclosed by a ditch, was found to contain the remains of a farmstead that was 50 m long and 17 m wide, a large barn, granaries and a well (**Fig. 4**). Tree-ring analysis of the posts that supported the roof revealed that the farmstead was built shortly after 1150. The size of the site and the dimensions of the farmstead suggest that this was the Episcopal manor of Calthorne mentioned in a deed from 1209 (OGD 48; Reinders 2005: 193; 2006). Apart from the *curia* Calthorne, which was held in fief by Wouter Sturms, the deed also mentions a nearby *mansus*, a farmstead belonging to the bishopric.

The bishop also possessed manors in Emmen, Loon and Noordbarge. The exact location of these manors is unknown, but they were probably also situated near small rivers. The unusual position of the manor of

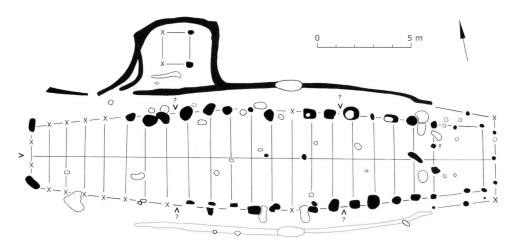

Fig. 4 Plan of the bishopric manor of Calthorne, built around 1150.

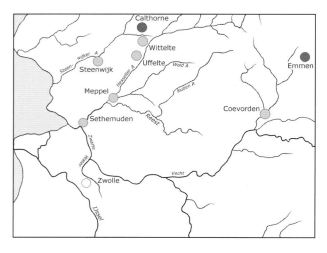

Fig. 5 Map of the S. part of the province of Drenthe, showing the location of the manors of Calthorne and Emmen.

Calthorne on the edge of the Kwasloot stream valley near the Kalterbroeken meadowlands might suggest that livestock farming – and in particular cattle raising – was an important activity at the site. It is also possible that the position of Calthorne at the headwaters of the Wapserveense A would have made it easy to transport agricultural products by water to the city of Steenwijk, a stronghold of the Bishop of Utrecht (**Fig. 5**). The Wapserveense A was navigable up until the junction with the Kwasloot (Coert 1991: fig. 13). Likewise, goods from Emmen and Noordbarge could have been transported via the River Vecht and the large Almere lake (later the Zuiderzee) to Utrecht.

The archaeological features of medieval farmsteads in the Netherlands of the Gasselte type were not recognized until the 1970s (Waterbolk 1990: 154-160). They can be identified as rows of roughly square, grey-coloured discolorations in the yellowish sand: an indication of the post holes which supported the roof of the farmstead. The walls of the farmstead were slightly curved, resulting in boat-shaped houses which are also common in other countries during this period (Hamerow 2002). The late medieval farmsteads of the Gasselte B type, dated between 1100 and 1400, have an average length of 24 to 36 m and a width of 13 to 15 m (Huyts 1992: 183). The 50 m length of the *curia* of Calthorne is exceptional and underlines its position as a bishopric manor.

LARGE LANDOWNERSHIP

Although Drenthe generally consisted of free peasant communities, large-scale landownership and serfdom are also known. The Bishop of Utrecht and the churches had administrative rights and private property, and

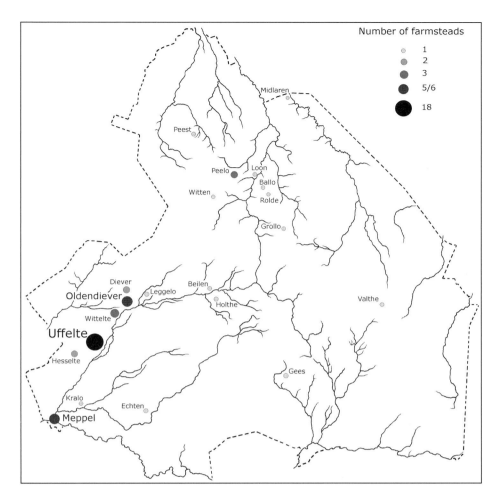

Fig. 6 Map of the province of Drenthe, showing the location of the property of the manor of Sint Pieter.

enjoyed large yields and revenues from their possessions in Drenthe and elsewhere. Archival sources inform about these yields. The property of the bishop and the chapter of Sint Pieter were recorded in the 13th c., in 1235 and between 1296 and 1304 (OGD 199), respectively. The records of the bishopric property do not mention the names of the farmyards and the villages where they were located, but the list of Sint Pieter's property gives detailed information about names of villages, farmyards and yields. Ribertinc in Oldendene (Oldendiever), for instance, had to produce eight *mud* of rye and eight *mud* of barley annually (OGD 199). In 1296 to 1304 Sint Pieter owned no less than 54 farmsteads in the district of Drenthe (**Fig. 6**), which had to produce 294 *mud* of rye, 266 *mud* of barley, 4.5 *mud* of oats, barrels of butter, barrels of honey and cash (OGD 199). There are also records from 1435 with the following yields: 325 *mud* of rye and 4.5 *mud* of barley or oats (Spek 2004: 513). In the 15th c., Sint Pieter drew up contracts with farmers to deliver additional amounts of wheat.

The large-scale landownership of Sint Pieter in Drenthe resulted from endowments of bishopric property to the chapter of Sint Pieter after its foundation in 1048. Much of its property was located in the S.W. part of Drenthe. In the village of Uffelte alone it owned 17 farmsteads and a manor in ca. 1300 (OGD 199).

Around 1438 the chapter changed serfdom into long lease and the tenants had to deliver their annual rent of rye *(roggepacht)* to the *spieker* (granary) of the manor of Uffelte. It is generally accepted that before 1439 the granary was situated in the centre of Uffelte, but afterwards it was removed to the Leemgraven

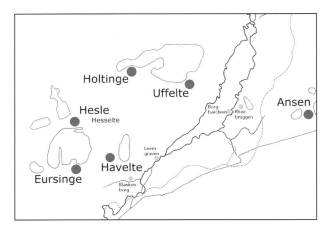

Fig. 7 Map of the area of Uffelte, showing the location of Borgbarchien and Leemgraven.

on the W. bank of the Oude Vaart (Van Kalveen 1985: 227), about 2.5 km S.W. of Uffelte in an area with the toponym Ettelte (**Fig. 7**). The prefix *Leem-* indicates a location in an area with loamy sand *(leem)* and the suffix *-graven* refers to the improvement of the waterway by canalizing shallow parts of the river. The exact location is not known, but stone fragments were found in the 1930s along the shore of the Oude Vaart (Havelter A), close to the borderline between the *marken* of Uffelte and Havelte (Lonsain 1927: 82; Dorenbos 1930: 117-118).

The tenants, not only of Uffelte but also from other villages in the S.W. of Drenthe, had to deliver their rent, mainly rye and barley, to the Leemgraven granary, when the ship of the provost (*prost*) arrived. Some farms around Meppel paid in barrels of honey and others in butter. Apart from products *in natura*, remote farms paid their rent in cash at the manor. Apparently around 1435 the chapter of Sint Pieter had reorganized the collection of its revenues, and the ship of the *prost* could reach Uffelte after improvement of the sailing route.

Even after the transition to Protestantism at the end of the 16th c., farmers had to pay annual revenues to the chapter of Sint Pieter. Under Napoleon the property was confiscated and transformed into domain lands in 1811, but the farmers still had to pay rent. In 1835 a farmer of Uffelte refused in vain to pay.

TRANSPORTATION OF REVENUES IN THE 15TH C.

How was the transportation of its revenues organized by the chapter of Sint Pieter? Nowadays, the Oude Vaart river, canalized in the 1640s, and the Drentse Hoofdvaart canal, dug in the 1780s, are all that remain of the connection between S.W. Drenthe via Meppel and Zwartsluis, the first part of the sailing route to the former Zuiderzee and via the Vecht to Utrecht. The Oude Vaart was a river that originated E. of Beilen. Successive parts of the river were called Beilerstroom, Dwingelderstroom and Havelter A. Near Meppel, the Ruiner A, Echtenerstroom and Reest emptied into the Oude Vaart and the water route between Meppel and Zwartsluis was called the *Aa* or *Sethe* and after canalization *Meppelerdiep*. Due to successive re-allotment, levelling and canalization, the medieval riverine landscape was completely destroyed by the 20th c.

N. of the Leemgraven the Havelter A followed two separate courses through a peat area which served as meadowland for the farmers of Uffelte (**Fig. 7**). The E. course, called *Scheidgruppe*, followed the border between the *marken* of Uffelte and Ansen. A small, artificial mound along the Scheidgruppe is called *Borgbargchien*, i.e. »castle mound«. On a map of the *marke* of Uffelte, made by order of the chapter of Sint Pieter in 1760 by the surveyor Meursinge (RAU, Sint Pieter 989), the site is called *Burgberg* with the following explanation: »[...] en men zegt dat er een Burg of Spijker op gestaan heeft [...]« (a mound with a *burg* or a granary). A 10th- to 12th-c. axe was found in a test trench through the mound (Van Doesburg 2003: 179-183); the lack of other finds suggests that the mound was not permanently occupied; a granary? On the same map the following information near the Leemgraven is given: »[...] alwaar de Rogge wort betaald [...]« (where the rye is paid).

Although nowadays the riverine landscape is completely gone, the sailing route from the granary at Leemgraven to Meppel in the 1440s can be reconstructed with the help of cadastral maps of 1830, pre-cadastral maps of the 1640s and toponyms in late medieval contracts. The late medieval Hesselter A was a small river with a winding course through a large peat area that served as meadowland and hayfields for the farmers of Hesselte, in the *marke* of Westerhesselen (**Fig. 8**). The nature of the riverine landscape is known from toponyms mentioned in the registers of the pre-cadastral maps of the 1640s and by numerous acts of the chapter of Sint Pieter ca. 1440 for the delivery of additional supplies of rye by the farmers of Westerhesselen (RAU, Sint Pieter 996).

These toponyms indicate the existence of *horsten* – Zegelhorst, Tenningehorst and Eeckerst – uninhabited sandy elevations used as meadowland along the course of the river (**Fig. 9**). Other toponyms indicate the winding course of the river and obstacles for the sailors: *kleine en grote reigerhals* (small and large heron's neck). Maps of the 1640s show many sandy shallows (*sandplaeten*) which also hindered water transportation (Gerding 2006).

The sailing route from Meppel to Zwartsluis, a small harbour at the outlet of the Vecht into the Zuiderzee, had the same winding course through a large peat area with hamlets on the sandy elevations: Olde Staphorst, De Gaste, Dingstede, Hamingen, Byl and Baarlo. Dingstede was an important site for two reasons. Firstly, because before the 15th c. it was here that the Bishop of Utrecht enforced the jurisdiction in ecclesiastical matters, and secondly because it was a transit point in the sailing route. Products from S.W. Drenthe, supplied by small ships, went along the rivers Aa or Sethe as far as Dingstede, where they were trans-shipped (**Fig. 10**). The winding course of the Sethe between Dingstede

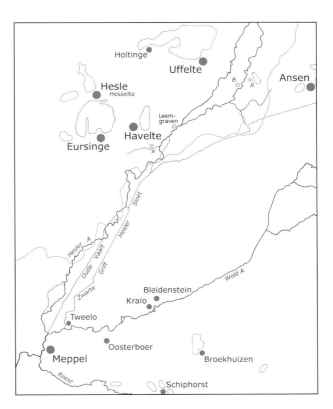

Fig. 8 The sailing route from the granary at Leemgraven (Uffelte) to Meppel.

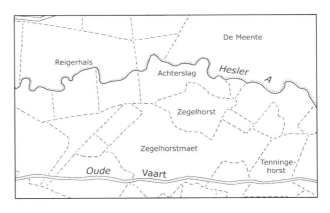

Fig. 9 Part of the sailing route between Uffelte and Meppel, showing the winding course of the Hesselter A river, *horsten* and *Reigerhals*.

and Meppel was subdivided into three reaches – Korterak, Langerak and Vrouwenrak – and was difficult to sail (Coert 1991: 37). The passage from Dingstede to Meppel was improved in the beginning of the 15th c. by digging the *Richte Graven*, a straight canal from Dingstede to Hesselingen, which was already out of use by the early 17th c. (Coert 1991: 37; 125; Gerding 2006).

Obviously the chapter of Sint Pieter had improved the water route between Dingstede and Uffelte by digging the Richte Graven and the Leemgraven and the *prost's* ship could reach the granary at the Leem-

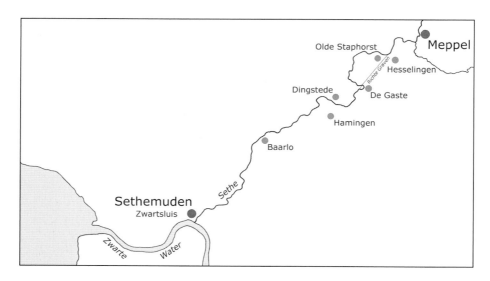

Fig. 10   The sailing route between Meppel and Zwartsluis.

graven after autumn rainfall, when the water level was high. It is not quite clear whether the *prost's* ship transported the revenues all the way from the Leemgraven to Utrecht, because in the 15th c. products had to be transshipped in Zwartsluis, where a dam had been constructed at the outlet of the Sethe before 1398 (Top 1991: 39).

TRANSPORTATION OF RYE AND BARLEY RENTS AROUND 1300

What was the situation in the 1290s, before the transition from serfdom to long lease? An inventory of farms and revenues of the chapter of Sint Pieter (OGD 199) also provides information about delivery and transportation around A.D.1300. The water route had not yet been improved and the serfs had to deliver their products to the large ship of the *prost* of Sint Pieter: »[…] *solvent annonam, quam ad navem magnam apud Mappele in festis Omnium sanctorum et Palmarum suis laboris et expensis presentabunt*«.

The serfs had to transport rye and barley at their own expense twice a year in boats along the Hesselter A to the *prost's* ship, and this large vessel was used for transportation to Utrecht via the Zuiderzee. It is generally accepted that the serfs had to deliver their products to Meppel (*apud Mappele*), the present-day town with the same name (Top 1991: 38). A translation of »in the neighbourhood of Meppel« is also possible, or more obviously it means the *marke* of Meppel because the farmsteads of Meppel lay dispersed and were not concentrated in a village, like for instance in Uffelte and Hesselte. It was only in the 16th c. that Meppel developed into an important centre for shipping (Coert 1991: 39). In the present author's opinion it is plausible that the *prost's navis magna* went as far as Dingstede where the revenues from S.W. Drenthe were trans-shipped.

An immense change took place in the 13th c.; large floods destroyed the peat belt in the central parts of the Netherlands, and gradually the freshwater lake was transformed into the inland Zuiderzee (**Fig. 11**). The chapter of Sint Pieter used a *navis magna* for the shipment of its revenues via the Zuiderzee and River Vecht to Utrecht. It is tempting to refer to written sources mentioning the translation of the word cog in Latin, *coggo sive navis magna*, but it is of course doubtful whether a *magna navis* is a cog (Ellmers 2002; Weski 2002; 2006).

Fig. 11 The Netherlands around 1250.

Sint Pieter's property was not restricted to the district of Drenthe. The chapter also owned farms in the E. part of the Netherlands, where the serfs and later the tenants had to deliver their rent to the chapter's manors at Brummen, Zeelbeke and Espelo (**Fig. 12**). The tenants of Brummen had to deliver their products *ad navem* (to the ship) in Deventer, a city along the River IJssel. Tenants of the *curtis* of Espelo also delivered their products *ad navem*, but a place of delivery is not mentioned; perhaps it was in Espelo itself? For the delivery of products to the *curtis* of Zeelbeke, no particular mention is made of the place of delivery or the way of transportation, but Zeelbeke was situated along the Rhine. Transportation by boat was obvious and possibly required no further explanation. The logboat, perhaps a *drubbort,* excavated E. of Zeelbeke in Meinerswijk

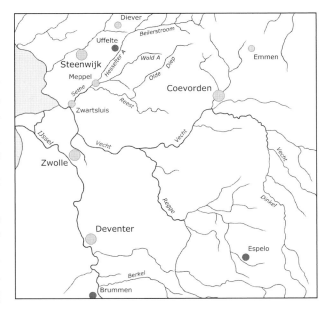

Fig. 12 Location of the manors of the chapter of Sint Pieter in the E. part of the Netherlands.

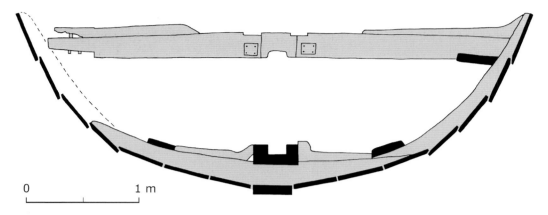

Fig. 13 Cross section of a small »cog« (IJsselmeer-type vessel), excavated in 1945 in the Noordoostpolder.

could be a suitable candidate for the down-river transportation of products from Zeelbeke to Utrecht (Reinders 1983: 21-43). The felling date of the trees used for the Meinderswijk logboat was 1216.

Unfortunately, there are no written sources for the period covering the 10th to 12th c. In that period the central part of the Netherlands was still covered by a large peat belt surrounding the freshwater lake Almere (**Fig. 2**). Presumably manors and granaries in the 10th to 12th c. were situated at the same locations as in the following period, and that transportation by water was the only way to bring the products from Drenthe via small rivers through the vast peat bog across lake Almere to Muiden, at the outlet of the Vecht, and down the Vecht to Utrecht.

The bishopric manor of Calthorne, built in around 1150, was already mentioned. It is likely that revenues from the farms in the Diever area – Diever, Oldendiever, Wittelte, Dwingelo, and Lhee – were collected at the manor and transported via the Wapserveense A and the Vledder A to Steenwijk, a stronghold of the bishop, and via the Steenwijker A and lake Almere to Utrecht. Thus, they could avoid the peat barrier in front of the outlet of the River IJssel.

SHIPMENT OF REVENUES FROM DRENTHE TO UTRECHT

Instead of presenting a new, exciting wreck find, this paper focused on large land ownership, yields and revenues resulting in annual rent and taxes: barley and rye to be transported by boat and ship from Drenthe to Utrecht. Apart from the Mesolithic logboat of Pesse and two Iron Age logboats found near an abandoned course of the Hesselter A (Lanting 2000: 636), the district of Drenthe has virtually nothing to offer maritime archaeologists, although Hoogeveen was an important centre in the 19th c. for the transportation of peat as fuel from Drenthe to other parts of the Netherlands for private and industrial use.

What kind of boats and ships were used in the Late Middle Ages by the Bishop of Utrecht and the chapter of Sint Pieter for the transportation of their revenues? One can assume that the small cog-like vessels excavated from the seabed of the former Zuiderzee were used in the period of the 13th to 14th c. for the transportation of the annual rent in rye and barley and taxes like the *schuldmudden*. **Figure 13** gives the cross section of an example of such a vessel excavated in 1945 and identified by Modderman (1945) as a cog (Van Holk 2006). For the discussion of whether this wreckfind and comparable ones may be called cogs or should be indicated as IJsselmeer-type ships, one may refer to the articles by Weski (1999; 2002; 2006).

They certainly could sail across the Zuiderzee and up the River Sethe as far as Dingstede, but it seems doubtful whether they could sail all the way to Uffelte along the winding course of the Hesselter A.

Logboats of various types were presumably used for the transport of local products to a central assembly point for trans-shipment. In the toll registers of Bremen at the end of the 14th c., for instance, small craft like *enbomene schepe* (*Einbäume*, logboats) and *eke* (a twin logboat) are mentioned alongside *schuten* and *kogghen*. *Eken* were used for the transportation of all kinds of products: peat and building materials but also grain (Pohl-Weber 1969: 10-11).

In the author's opinion, boats and ships of the Utrecht type are suitable candidates for the transportation of products along rivers like the Hesselter A and Sethe, across the Almere and down the Vecht to Utrecht in the 10th to 12th c. Flat-bottomed barges, also known from excavations in the city of Utrecht, could perhaps transport a larger cargo of rye, but were not quite suitable for rivers with a winding course. The location of the Utrecht ship in the fossil bed of the Vecht, N. of Utrecht, and the location of the Velsen boat in a large peat bog area under marine influence in the W. part of Holland, more or less comparable to the environment of the area between Zwartsluis and Meppel, might also plead for the proposed hypothesis. Little is known about the cargo transported by the Utrecht-type ships, but the excavation report on the Velsen boat at least mentions remains of grain or straw (De Weerdt 1987: 263; 272).

To date, with the exception of a few logboats, no other boats or ships have been excavated in Drenthe. Thus, the proposed view has to necessarily remain a hypothesis.

REFERENCES

OGD: *Oorkondenboek Groningen en Drenthe* (= Blok *et al.* 1896).

RAU: Rijksarchief Utrecht (now the »Utrechts Archief«).

Bardet, A. C., Kooi, P. B., Waterbolk, H. T. & Wieringa, J., 1983, *Peelo, Historisch-geografisch en archeologisch onderzoek naar de ouderdom van een Drents dorp*. Mededelingen der Koninklijke Nederlandse Academie van Wetenschappen, Afd. Letterkunde, Nieuwe reeks, no. 46.1. Amsterdam.

Blok, D. P., 1985, De vroege Middeleeuwen, tot ca. 1150. In: J. Heringa *et al.* (eds), *Geschiedenis van* Drenthe. Meppel, 141-170.

Blok, P. J., Feith, J. A., Gratama, S., Reitsma J. & Rutgers, C. P. L., 1896, *Oorkondenboek van Groningen en Drenthe*. Groningen.

Coert, G.A., 1991, *Stromen en schutten, vaarten en voorden. Geschiedenis van de natte waterstaat in Drenthe 1291-1988*. Meppel, Amsterdam.

De Weerd, M. D., 1987, Velsen: The Mediaeval Logboat. In: R. W. Brandt, W. Groenman-van Waateringe & S. E. van der Leeuw (eds), *The Assendelver Polder Papers,* vol. I. Amsterdam, 265-283.

Doesburg, J. van, 2003, Roofridders, boze boeren en bronzen kanonnen. Archeologisch onderzoek naar de mysterieuze kasteelheuvels Borgbarchien te Rheebruggen en de Klinkenberg bij Gees. *Nieuwe Drentse Volksalmanak*, 120, 172-195.

Dorenbos, H. D., 1930, De Spijker te Uffelte. *Maandblad Drenthe*, 1.8, 116-118.

Ellmers, D., 2002, Mittelalterliche Koggesiegel: Ein Diskussionsbeitrag. In: K. Elmshäuser (ed.), *Häfen – Schiffe – Wasserwege. Zur Schiffahrt des Mittelalters*. Schriften des Deutschen Schiffahrtsmuseums, no. 58. Hamburg, 97-106.

Gerding, M. A. W., 2006, De topografische waarde van de kaarten van Vingboons. *Nieuwe Drentse Volksalmanak*, 123, 16-24.

Goodburn, D. M., 2000, New light on the construction of early medieval »Frisian« sea-going vessels. In: *ISBSA 8*, 219-224.

Hamerow, H., 2002, *Early medieval settlement: the archaeology of rural communities in Northwest Europe, 400-900*. Oxford.

Heringa, J., *et al.* (eds) 1985, *Geschiedenis van Drenthe*. Meppel.

Hielkema, J. & de Wit, M. J. M., 2005, De »Hof van Kalteren« te Diever – een archeologisch onderzoek. *Nieuwe Drentse Volksalmanak*, 122, 196-208.

Huyts, C. S. T. J., 1992, *De voor-historische boerderijbouw in Drenthe*. PhD thesis, University of Groningen.

Kalveen, C. A. van, 1985, Late Middeleeuwen, 1395-1522. In: J. Heringa *et al.* (eds), *Geschiedenis van Drenthe*. Meppel, 197-240.

Kooi, P. B., 1993/1994, Het project Peelo: Het onderzoek in de jaren 1981, 1982, 1986, 1987 en 1988. *Palaeohistoria*, 35-36, 169-306.

1999/2000, Het project Peelo: Het onderzoek van het erf Huisinge (1995-1996). *Palaeohistoria*, 41-42, 447-471.

Lanting, J. N., 2000, Dates for origin and diffusion of the European logboat. *Palaeohistoria*, 39-40, 627-650.

Lonsain, B., 1927, De voormalige korenspiekers van Drente. *Nieuwe Drentse Volksalmanak*, 45, 71-82.

Modderman, P. J. R., 1945, *Over de wording en de beteekenis van het Zuiderzeegebied*. PhD thesis, University of Groningen.

Pohl-Weber, R., 1969, Die Bremer Eke. Fund eines mittelalterlichen Binnenschiffs. *Bremisches Jahrbuch*, 51, 9-11.

Reinders, H. R., 1983, *Drie middeleeuwse rivierschepen, gevonden bij Meinerswijk (Arnhem), opgravingsverslagen 5, 6 en 7*. Flevobericht, no. 221. Lelystad.

2005, De bisschoppelijke hof Calthorne en de kluft Kalteren, bij Diever. *Nieuwe Drentse Volksalmanak*, 122, 168-195.

Spek, T., 2004, *Het Drentse esdorpenlandschap. Een historisch-geografische studie*. Utrecht.

Top, M., 1991, Meppel in de Middeleeuwen. In: M. A. W. Gerding *et al.* (eds), *Geschiedenis van Meppel*. Meppel, Amsterdam, 23-59.

Van Holk, A., 2006, Een verloren gewaand scheepswrak en de »Flevoland-Groningen Connection«. *Cultuurhistorisch Jaarboek voor Flevoland*, 16, 74-91.

Van de Moortel, A., 2003, A new look at the Utrecht Ship. In: *ISBSA 9*, 183-189.

2004, Shipbuilding and Navigation in the Rhine Delta during the late Viking Age. In: R. Simek & U. Engel (eds), *Vikings on the Rhine. Recent Research on Early Medieval Relations between the Rhineland and Scandinavia*. Studia Medievalia Septentrionalia, no. 11. Vienna, 39-50.

Vlek, R., 1987, *The Mediaeval Utrecht Boat*. BAR, Internat. Series, no. 282. Oxford.

Waterbolk, H. T., 1990, Zeventig jaar archeologisch nederzettingsonderzoek in Drenthe. *Nieuwe Drentse Volksalmanak*, 107, 137-168.

Weski, T., 1999, The IJsselmeer type: Some Thoughts on Hanseatic Cogs. *IJNA*, 28, 360-379.

2002, Anmerkungen zur spätmittelalterlichen Schiffahrt auf Nord- und Ostsee. In: K. Elmshäuser (ed.), *Häfen – Schiffe – Wasserwege. Zur Schiffahrt des Mittelalters*. Schriften des Deutschen Schiffahrtsmuseums, no. 58. Hamburg, 143-159.

2006, Wurde wirklich eine Kogge gefunden? *Antike Welt*, 37.1, 91-96.

THOMAS FÖRSTER

DUTCH-GERMAN TRADING RELATIONSHIPS
IN THE BALTIC SEA BETWEEN THE 14TH TO 18TH CENTURIES

Maritime relationships have existed between the S.W. Baltic Sea and the region between the mouths of the rivers Weser and Rhine since the 13th c. In the Late Middle Ages, shipping and maritime trade was controlled by the Hanse League. However, Dutch traders gained increasing influence in Baltic Sea trade by the end of the 15th c.

Important evidence of the maritime relations of both regions was found through investigations of various underwater and terrestrial archaeological sites along the coasts of Mecklenburg-Vorpommern and the Netherlands, with finds including shipwrecks and associated cargo along with imported goods. Different phases in the development and transfer of ship technology can be traced back from the construction of flat-bottomed cogs and coastal ships, and of early carvel vessels.

Due to its topographic position the Baltic Sea is and always has played an important role in the inter-European sea trade, especially in the exchange of goods from W. to N. or E. Europe. Between the 14th and the 18th c. many archaeological and historical sources provide a good basis for exemplary research of the trade connections between the area of the Weser and up to the estuary of the Rhine, Maas and Schelde and the S.W. Baltic coast. The close relation is indicated by sources dealing with cargo transport, and by a consistent technology transfer in shipbuilding.

Based on trade connections of Frisian merchants a close exchange between the Lower Rhine area and the Baltic Sea can be traced back as early as to the 9th c. With the rise of the trade alliance of the Hanseatic League a continuous development of these exchange connections can be observed up to the 14th c.

The major river systems of W. Europe played a magnificent role for the efficient transport of products from inland to the coastal cities. Traded goods were clothes, metal works, pottery and wine which were imported to the Baltic Sea by Hanseatic merchants. For exchange, agricultural products were carried to W. Europe, such as furs, fish and wood.

After the 15th-c. decline of the German Hanse it has been Dutch merchants who more and more were involved in the trade of the Baltic Sea region. Among the traditional cargoes were herring from the North Sea and increasingly goods from overseas played an important role for the sea transport from the W. to the E. Wood for ships and cereals were urgently required by the Dutch and the arising colonial powers of Spain and Portugal.

The major importance of the Baltic Sea trade for the Dutch in the beginning of the 17th c. can be seen e.g. at the straits of the Oeresund. In 1607 the Dutch had around 2000 ships involved in Baltic seafaring, which in total crossed 2561 times the Oeresund whilst only seven Dutch ships sailed to India and 15 to Brazil in the same year. In 1608 the Dutch increased the number of passages even up to 4362, a number which continued during the course of the 17th c. Thus Dutch merchants provided 4316 ship passages in 1618, which means in total 72.8% of all the Oeresund transits. On the other hand, with the foundation of the East India Company in 1622, only 77 ships were engaged in the overseas routes.

These numbers demonstrate the outstanding role of the Baltic Sea trade, which was not a minor setting in the scope of colonial expansion, but an important pillar of the European economic system (Olechnowitz 1965).

Fig. 1   Fore body of the Darss Cog (Photo R. Obst, Mühlhausen).

THE »FRISIAN – W. EUROPEAN TRADITION«

A wreck discovered in the Weser near Bremen in 1962 provided important evidence for the research into the sea trade of the Hanseatic League. Due to its appearance in comparison with contemporary depictions the ship was identified as a cog, and her construction thoroughly examined. Typical characteristics of the vessel were the steep and straight stems, the flat carvel bottom and the clinker-built sides. Planks were joined with clenched iron nails. Moss caulking was protected by caulking lathes fastened with iron clamps, known as *sintels* (Lahn 1992). Components of this construction can be traced back to Romano-Celtic ship finds.

Several medieval shipwrecks reflecting such a »Frisian – W. European tradition« (Förster 2006: 230-235; 2007) were located especially in the Ijssel Sea during the 1980s and 1990s. Among river and coastal vessels, ships of higher capacity – as was described for cogs in Mediaeval times – came up to light. According to historic sources, only ships with a capacity of 70 to 330 tons were called cogs (Weski 1999a: 96-106; 2000: 9-22). Consequently, the Bremen ship 85t only was identified as a smaller cog type.

The close trade relation between the Lower Rhine area and the Baltic Sea region is also reflected in the exchange of shipbuilding technology. 12th-c. wrecks mostly found at the entrance to the Baltic Sea in the area of the Danish Isles reveal the expansion of the »Frisian-W. European tradition«. Recent research shows that the majority of the vessels were already built in the coastal area of the North and Baltic Sea[1].

THE DARSS COG

Especially important turned out to be a wreck from the Darss (**Fig. 1**) which demonstrates technology transfer from the Lower Rhine region to the Baltic Sea. The wreck was thoroughly examined in the frame of the EU-funded MoSS-project from 2000 to 2005[2].

The ship was built around 1303 in the »Frisian.W. European tradition« with timbers from the Weichsel area at Elbląg (Elbing). Her hull construction inclusively mast position is almost identical with the Bremen cog. She was built mostly from oak and is characterized by a flat bottom carvel-built up to the fourth strake, with planks 45 to 50 cm wide. The seams of the bottom planks were caulked with animal hair. The clinker-built sides consist of another 15 strakes of 30 cm width each which were joined with clenched nails. Side planking shows moss caulking covered by caulking laths and fastened by *sintels*. Due to the wreck's position the keel can hardly be recognized. It has a width of 30 cm and a thickness of 10 cm. The stem post is joined to the keel plank and carries a rabbet to accommodate the planks. A beam found lying near the stem is supposedly one of the two side stems. The construction of the frames combining floor timbers and futtocks can be well observed in the exposed inner ship. The first five floor timbers are made of v-shaped crooked wood and are supported by beams that run from portside to starboard. This possibly created a small cargo space since the sulphur barrel, reindeer antler, two pairs of shoes, ropes and textiles were found there. The keelson starts at the fifth floor timber and has a maximum width of 70 cm at the thickened section of the mast step. The mast step itself is 70 cm long and 30 cm wide. An incorporated ledge in the mast step served for wedging the mast tight. Three crossbeams penetrate the hull at the twelfth and thirteenth strake. They are supported by standing knee-shaped crooks to achieve a high grade of cross stability. Deck elements were fastened to the top of the knees. Its edge is still to be found at the bulwark. A circular and a square opening in the hull were probably scuppers to allow water to drain off overboard. The ship's interior is lined with ceiling planks which are either nailed to the floor timbers or in case of the pine planks were loosely put on. Stringers are attached to the side boards to increase the cross stability. Treenails of 3.0 to 4.5 cm diameter were used to fasten the frames, keelson, knees, ceiling planks and stringers. Traces of a pitch-like coat could be detected at the inner and the outer side of the hull. A second method of wood preservation was identified on the inner sides of the ceiling planks and stringers. These had deliberately been burnt on the surface. Particular areas show only a partial charring caused by covering with textile. Numerous timbers carry working traces of saw and adze as well as cut-in marks. The preservation of the wreck is similar to that of the Bremen cog which makes it ideal for comparison. Interpreting the parts of the Darss cog that are documented until now several parallels to the Bremen cog from 1380 can be drawn. The flat carvel-built bottom, the lapstrake sides and the steep alignment of the stem indicate that along with the German E. colonization and the foundation of many Hanse towns at the end of the 13th c. the technology of the well established building traditions of the North Sea were transferred to the Baltic Sea.

Also the dimensions of the ships are similar with a length of 21 to 23 m and a width of 7 to 7.50 m. The capacity of the wreck from Darss is calculated to 70 to 80 tons which classifies it as a smaller cog. Already the first underwater-archaeological investigations at the Darss cog indicated that the wreck was very well preserved (Förster 2003a: 13; 2003b: 87-93).

The excavated parts were documented *in situ* using photogrammetry. Currently the 3D data is put into a reconstruction and animation of the wreck. First results can be seen in **Figure 2**. Besides the findings about the ship's construction the excavation also revealed important information on the cargo of Hanse ships.

Since the Darss cog sank approximately 800 m off the coast in 6 m depth it was hard to reach for salvage. The wreck does likewise lie off the reach of breakers and ice which often remove objects from wrecks.

The finds that have been recovered and examined so far deliver a unique insight into the life on board cogs. The following remains of the cargo were found in the wreck: reindeer antler, fish-bones, roofing tiles, whetstones and sulphur.

Parts of the reindeer antler were roughly broken up and used as raw material for combs, gaming pieces or beads. The large amount of fish-bones stems from cod which in the form of dried fish was one of Norway's main export products. According to the finds of whole fish skeletons the dried fish was shipped without

Fig. 2   Animation of the Darss Cog (O. Hofmann, Hamburg).

head. Wooden skewers with a length of up to 30 cm were stuck through the upper part of the fish bodies to hang them up for drying. The dried fish was presumably shipped in bundles considering the position of the finds. The whetstones of mica schist came from quarries at Eidsborg, Norway. They were roughly worked and shipped as bars of up to 60 cm length. These bars were bound by plant climbers to bundles of about 20 kg.

The sulphur from the fore ship of the cog came probably via Bergen from Iceland, as so-called *brennistein*. It was shipped in an oak barrel which was marked with seven carved owner's marks and one burnt-in coat of arms. The barrel has a height of 75 cm and a diameter of 50 cm. The oak staves are split from a tree cut in 1335 in the Vistula region near Danzig. The barrel thereby provides evidence that the cog had been in use for more than 30 years. A wooden skewer carrying numerous notches might have been used for counting purposes in the trade. These notched pieces, so-called tallies, served for the registration of goods. The remains of the cargo indicate that the cog was one of those vessels sailing from Norway round Skagen into the Baltic, called *Umlandfahrer*. The ship wrecked off the Darss coast.

As part of the navigational equipment of the Hansetime a sailors a sounding line made of lead was discovered in the cog. An opening on its bottom filled with wax facilitates the examination of the nature of the sediment. Frequent use had heavily squashed the bottom of the lead.

A small bronze disc might have been the centre piece of an hour-glass. These came into use in the 14th c. and served as navigational instruments on ships until the 18th c. One example for lighting the ship is given by a ship lamp found in the cog. It is made of an almost rectangular piece of leather, which was wrapped around a wooden disc. The lantern, which was open at the top is reinforced by a metal sheet on the inside and rings on the outside, both made of a copper alloy. Light was emitted through the top and the door; a thin horn plate, which was mounted to copper alloy strips on its four sides. The door was attached via two hinges to the main body of the lantern[3].

Ropes of tree bast and hemp were used aboard. One hemp-rope fragment has a diameter of 4 cm. Preserved pieces of fabric are now being examined in order to assign them to either the cargo, sail or clothing of the crew. Two pairs of shoes with traces of use were personal belongings of the crew. The uppers of one pair are artistically perforated displaying a wheel-like pattern. The shoes were laced up on the foot using leather welts. During the excavation of the wreck a water bottle and a *Hanse can,* both of pewter, were recovered. A leather stopper was still sitting on the bottle neck. The *Hanse can,* so-called after the distribution area, carries a depiction of the crucifixion on the inner side of its lid and the inscription *AVE REG(ina)* on the handle. Both of them show carved marks of their original owners. An owner's mark is also shown on a wooden handle which could have belonged to a drill or an awl.

It cannot be determined; whether four bronze pots, a bronze can and the fragments of a cauldron were part of the cargo or the ship's equipment. These objects were recovered from the aft ship. Maybe future investigations shed light on a stove; where the use of these things for the preparation of food could be assumed.

On board ships pots and cans were preferably made of metal since pottery, due to its fragility, does not withstand rough seas as well as crockery made of metal and wood. Metal crockery provides evidence of its origin and thereby information about the distribution of high-quality products on ships. One of the three-footed bronze pots was made in Lübeck and another one in Greifswald which is proven by the town mark with the two-part shield

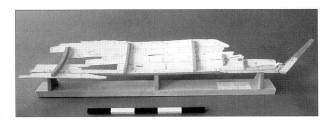

Fig. 3 Cardboard model of the wreck of Wismar-Wendorf (O. Schmidt, Stralsund).

and the caster's mark. The bronze can with its three feet has a Welsh origin according to its shape, similar finds and an analysis of the metal.

A small pewter disc found in the wreck is presumably a gaming piece of a board game that was played on the ship.

A number of lead weights in the find layer might have belonged to a fish net. It is obvious that the sailors would try to supplement their diet with fresh fish if there was opportunity for fishing. Apart from the dried fish, mammal bones and hazelnut shells delivered indications of the provisions.

Information on the stock turn is given by a 4.30 m long gangway, which had an eye for a rope. The pine plank was worked with an adze and was stored next to the keelson during the journey, where it was found. A large number of ballast stones in the keelson section increased the ship's stability in the sea. Samples of the stone shall be examined to determine the stone's origin.

The variety of finds from the Darss cog extends our knowledge about the trade of the Hanse and the daily life aboard late medieval ships (Förster 2002a: 232-236).

THE WISMAR-WENDORF WRECK OF 1476

Another wreck in the »Frisian – W. European tradition« was able to be located and salvaged in 1998 in the port of Wismar. The vessel is dated to around 1476 and shows the long continuity of this construction type in the Baltic Sea. The logs for the ship were knocked in the area of Duena near Riga. The dimension of the ship was reconstructed to a length of 18 m and a width of 7 m (**Fig. 3**). The capacity of this vessel was between 50 and 60 tons, so it possibly was not called a cog anymore.

The vessel was built in the shell-first method using 45 to 50 cm wide, sawn planks. The first three strakes are carvel built. From the stems upwards the planking changes to clinker. A contineous clinker planking can be observed from the fourth strake onwards. The up to 8 m long and 3.5 cm thick clinker planks were connected by double-bent iron nails. The bottom planking was caulked with inner bark, additionally protected with 7 cm wide and 1.5 cm thick lathes whilst neither lathes nor *sintels* were found on the side-planking. The frames 20 cm wide and 15 cm thick are connected to the planks using conical poplar and willow treenails. The plank keel is 9.20 m long, 35 cm wide and 12 cm thick. It is connected to the 2.95 m long sternpost-knee via a horizontal scarf. Rebates for the first two strakes are visible in the steeply shaped sternpost. Attached to the sternpost is the gudgeon with its eye for the rudder. The rudder was still in its original position and is 95 cm long, 40 cm wide and 15 cm thick.

Numerous remains of the ships inventory were found inside the wreck. Three plates, bowls and spoons as well as knifes and skewers are amongst the inventory. Three tin plates, exceptionally well preserved, a brass tap and fragments of a bronze tripod were found in the after part of the vessel. Marks on these plates indicate the tin caster and previous owners. Apart fom fragments of two pots and glazed, red earthenware, no ceramic crockery was found. Repeatedly burnt bricks found in the after body point to the position of hearth construction. Information on the organisation of the sea trade can be given by a lead seal and a tax sign with an imprinted crown. It is not quite clear whether numerous animal bones, peat sods and birch bast were cargo or provision and fuel on the ship. However, they give some insight into the diet on board. Sorted, according to their amount, the bones came from cow, pig, sheep, goat and horse. Furthermore, bones from poultry, such as chicken, goose and bones from red deer, roe deer, otter, hare and waterfoul were found. Fishbones proof that zander, carp and salmon supplemented the diet. Cod, and in the North Sea, ling and blue ling, were probably made into stockfish and could be part of the cargo as well as of the provision. These remains indicate that the ship sailed as far as the North Sea.

Shoe and clothes fragments of leather, parts of a triple layerd horn comb, bone dices and turned gaming pieces made of antler were personal belongings of the crew or passengers. The same goes for beads made of bone from a rosary and a pilgrimage badge depicting the three miraculous hosts from Wilsnack.

Of a maritime character is a grease horn made of tin to store the needles for the repair of sails, two signalling horns made of glazed stoneware and brass and a turned wooden rod to wind up sea charts, which were still in use in the 19th c. Furthermore, 320 ballast stones, weighing 347.90 kg were recovered.

THE POEL WRECK OF 1369 – A HYBRID CONSTRUCTION

Beside the dominant »Frisian – W. European tradition« also other technological solutions were used for bigger vessels. The originally Baltic Sea area coast dominating Nordic clinker tradition was combined with few elements of the »Frisian – W. European tradition«. In 1999/2000 a wreck was salvaged, near the island of Poel, which had a continuing clinkered hull, an emphasized keel but still rather

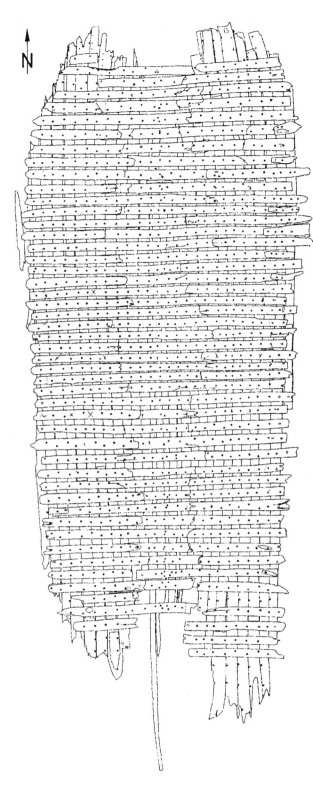

Fig. 4 Plan drawing of the Poel Cog from 1369 (Drawing R. Bleile, Schleswig).

flat and steep uprising stems. The connection between the planks was made by double-bent nails. The vessel was built using split pine planks and frames and dates back to 1369.

The whole construction of the Poel Wreck is 20.20 m long and 7.80 m wide (**Fig. 4**). The ship fragment consists of the starboard and portside of a clinker hull. Parts of the keel construction can be found in the centre. The ship was built in the shell-first method. 13 strakes are preserved on the starboard and portside. The planks were split tangentially. Rebates on the futtocks indicate four more strakes. The caulking material was made of animal and plant fibre. Remains of 54 frames were found in the hull, which were connected with treenails. From outboard the treenails were secured with wooden pegs and from the inside with wooden wedges.

The stern post with an iron gudgeon for the rudder, a V-shaped double frame from the aft or fore body and a fragment of the rising board were found in the vicinity of the wreck. The vessel was reconstructed to test the sailing abilities and is being tested at the moment (**Fig. 5**). The hybrid construction allows a major enlargement of the ship dimension and thus of the capacity (**Fig. 6**). With a length of 31.50 m and a width of 8.5 m, this vessel could load 230 tons. Compared to historic sources; it is a cog of medium size (Förster 2007).

THE GELLEN WRECK OF A.D. 1378

The above mentioned hybrid form of the Poel Cog was not a ship technological experiment, as it could also be examined at a different wreck, which was salvaged in 1997 on the W. coast of Hiddensee near Gellen. The ship was dated to 1378 and shows the same construction as the Poel Cog.

The Gellen wreck is a 15.90 m long and 3.60 m wide clinker-built fragment of the port side of a stranded ship. It is entirely constructed of pine wood. The preserved port side fragment

Fig. 5 The replica of the Poel Cog under sail (Photo K. Andrews, Hamburg).

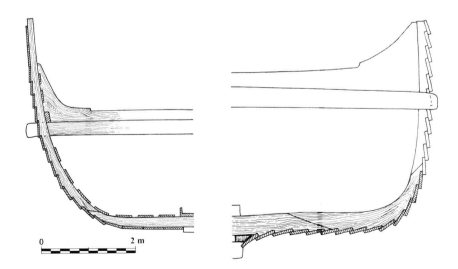

0   2 m

Fig. 6 Reconstructed cross section of the Darss Cog from 1303 and the Poel Cog from 1369 (Drawings D. Hinz, Berlin, & Th. Förster, Stralsund).

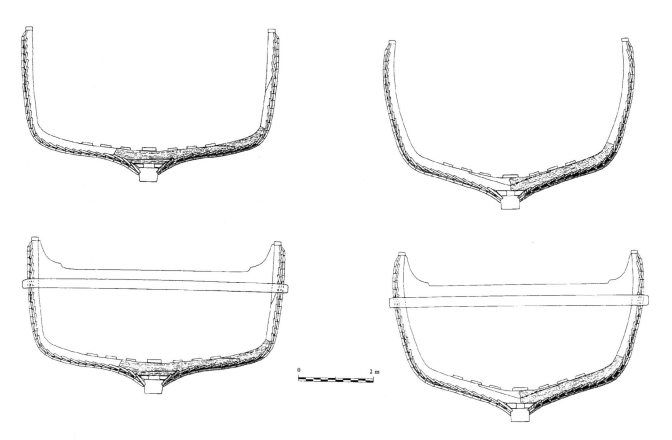

Fig. 7 Reconstructed cross-section of the Gellen Wreck from 1378 at amidships and aft. The drawing shows the multiple planking and the construction with and without cross beams (Drawings D. Hinz, Berlin, & Th. Förster, Stralsund).

allows a mirror reconstruction of the starboard side. The wreck was constructed in the shell first method and consists of 15 strakes. The planks were tangentially split, just like the planks on the Poel Cog. 33 frame elements were found inside the preserved hull fragment. The connection between the planks was made by double bent iron nails and between the hull and the frames with treenails. As on the Poel Cog *sintels* and caulking lathes are missing.

The preserved hull fragment shows multiple planking. Beside the regular clinker planks, a secondary layer of planks was attached to the first one as a means of repair. To level out the step like clinker planks, triangularly shaped lathes were applied. Finally a smooth – carvel layer of planks was attached. The analysis of the timbers revealed that the repair was carried out at around 1394 with pine wood from the S.W. Baltic Sea coast (**Fig. 7**).

The Gellen Wreck is reconstructed to a length of 28 m, a width of 7 m and a capacity of 150 tons. Both vessels were optimal for transporting outsized goods. Cargo inside the wreck were polished limestone slabs from the Swedish island Öland. Furthermore a stone tong for the transport of the slabs, an iron stove fragments with bricks and a pan, parts of four bronze tripods, a lead weight, a spoon drill and a caulking iron were found.

Different kinds of wood inside the Poel Cog indicate that this ship was also used to deliver logs. In the Late Medieval Ages the scarcity of timbers reached the Lower Rhine region. Logs were transported over the river systems but also increasingly imported from areas around Weichsel and Duena. With ships like those from Poel and Gellen big quantities of the required raw material were transported into the Dutch coastal regions.

HARBOUR INVESTIGATIONS

Due to the location and preservation of the wrecks it is often very difficult to detect cargo. Often the cargo was completely unloaded from stranded ships or current and waves washed the load away. To gain evidence about the trade relations between the Dutch coastal cities and the cities of the Hanse League of the S.W. Baltic, finds of excavations in city centres play an important role. Various ceramic pieces, clothes seals and metal pots are proof of an extensive trading volume. In this context underwater archaeological research about the trans-shipment processes in the harbours is of an immense importance. Outside the Hanseatic cities of Wismar and Stralsund roadsteads were discovered, at which the cargos from big ships were loaded onto smaller vessels. In both places the major contingent of imported ceramics was stoneware from the Rhineland or the so-called »Weserware«. The material dates from the 14th to the 17th c.

Outside Wismar a 9 m long vessel was found with pieces of the »Weserware«. It dates to 1591. The vessel is probably a lighter (a smaller vessel into which a ship is unloaded). According to its consruction the boat resembles the nordic clinker tradition.

CARVEL CONSTRUCTION

An important level of development in shipbuilding in N. and W. Europe was the spread of the carvel design from the 15th c. on. The distinctiveness of this style is that the planks lie on their longitudinal side plain together. This construction has the advantage of effective utilisation of the wood and is easier to repair. However, a significant factor for the dominance of the carvel design is due to the higher stiffness of the ship's body so that the size of the ship could be elevated. The sources of the carvel design lie in the Mediterranean, from where it reached the Baltic Sea area, over the Netherlands and the Atlantic coast. The »entire-carvel design« was initially built as the hull first construction. The plank connections were primarily assembled with the help of little connection boards and then they were stiffened with ribs. This technology was already used for the flat carvel hull of the »Frisian – W. European tradition« and can be proven on the »entire caravel design« until the 17th c.

The spread of the carvel design was carried out over the trading contacts and thus often at the purchase of ships. In 1462 the caravel *Peter von La Rochelle* with a cargo of Baien salt entered the port of Gdańsk. With a reconstructed length of 43 m and a load capacity of 800 tons this ship was also called *Dat Grote Kraweel* (The Great carvel). Due to a lightning strike the vessel was so heavily damaged that the city acquired it. In 1466 Hamburg purchased a caravel from Flanders, which was used as a model to build more vessels.

Increasingly the skeleton-first style took over in the construction of caravels. The vertical frame was erected first and then the planking was attached. Nearly identical built caravels can be seen all over the European coast in the 16th c. More essential improvements in that period were the increasing number of masts with a combination of square sail and lateen sail. These innovative changes were leading to an increase in output of the ships and they were the beginning of the era of discoveries at the coasts of America, Africa and Asia.

THE STONE WRECK OF 1523

The mentioned development can also be seen on several early carvel constructions of the S.W. Baltic Sea. In 2002 a carvel was detected near the Darss between the seaports Rostock and Stralsund. According to

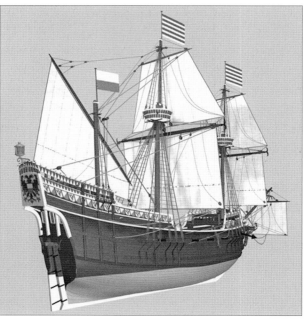

Fig. 8 Exposed carvel construction of the Stone Wreck from 1523 with the cargo of »Wangen stones« (Photo Th. Förster, Stralsund).

Fig. 9 Computer based reconstruction of the Mukran Wreck from 1565 based on the archaeological findings (O. Hofmann, Hamburg).

dendrochronological analysis the vessel was built between 1476 and 1523 with oak from the Elbe area near Hamburg. The ship had a reconstructed length of 18 m and a width of 6 m. Relatively thin planks and the usage of a few caulking lathes lead to the assumption that the vessel was built as a »shell-first« construction. The wreck was completely covered with cargo identified as limestone from Gotland or the area around Paernu. Among large slabs which were possibly used as tombstones or for footpaths, »Wangen stones« and other semi-finished products were found (**Fig. 8**).

THE MUKRAN WRECK OF 1535

A nearly identical construction was demonstrated by the Mukran Wreck discovered at the E. coast of the island of Ruegen. The vessel has a length of at least 25 m and a width of 8 m (**Fig. 9**). It was built from oak trees cut in the Elbe area between A.D. 1499 and 1535. The carvel-planked hull was built in the shell first method. This wreck also had only a few *sintel* laths which were fixed to the plank joints.

Based on this and the preserved ship's fragment the following unusual construction can be reconstructed: the stem with its rising curvature was attached to the keel, which has a cross section of 35 cm. The fragment of the stem was found in the N. part of the wreck. The stern, to the S. of the wreck, consists of four individual pieces of timber. It was attached to the keel at right angles and rises steeply.

The keel shows a little step and a rebate just forward of the stern to receive the garboards. The planks are 45 cm wide and 3 to 5 cm thick. The second strake was attached to the garboard with the help of clamps and little connective lathes. The remaining strakes were attached in the same manner. The wreck fragments indicate a flat bottom, which turns into a rounded shape near the futtocks. Due to the archaeological nature of the find the shaping with templates could not be detected.

The hull now could receive the caulking lathes and frames. The clamps between the planks were removed during the insertion of 40 cm wide and 20 cm thick frames and small nail-holes were closed with dowels. First the floor timbers were inserted over the keel and planks with a distance of 20 cm between one another. The futtocks were attached, so that they lay flush on the floor timbers and, together with the entire construction, improved the stability of the sides of the ship. The sealing of the plank joints with caulking lathes happened during the insertion of the frames. The lathes were attached to the plank joints in the frame interspaces. Furthermore the frames had little rebates to accommodate the lathes. The connection between planks and frames was made by 3.5 cm thick conical hardwood treenails, which were driven into the frames from the outside. This kind of technology for the construction of a carvel hull can be found in a description of ship construction in the 17th c. by Nicolaes Witsen. The keelson was bolted to the keel above the floor timbers. The keelson had a length of 10 m, a width of 30 cm and was 25 cm thick. It had three rebates, 20 to 40 cm long, which could hold the masts or possibly deck constructions. On top of the floor timbers were the stringers. Midships the stringers are made of alternating 12 to 20 cm wide pine timbers and 35 to 45 cm wide oak timbers. One stringer towards aft shows two semi circular holes, which eventually accomodated a pump.

A large amount of fragments from a bronze tripod with a volume of approximately 20 l was found in the wreck. Several bronze cuboids were found amidships; they were used as bearings for wodden blocks. Many cannon balls made of lead and cast iron were located in the fore-ship. The diameters of 3.5 cm, 4.0 cm, 7.0 cm and 8.0 cm of the ammunition indicate that there were at least four cannons on board with different calibres. One blasted gun made of copper was found in the wreck. It bears the inscription *CHRISTIAN VON GOTES / GENAD KON / IG CH THO DE / NEMARCKEN / NORWEGEN / UND DER GO / TEN ANNO / DOMINI 1551* as well as the Danish royal coat of arms depicting the three jumping lions. More fragments of a blasted bronze canon and an iron stave gun were found in the vicinity of the site. The smaller cannon has a length of 1.30 m and the longer one of 2.50 m. This one also has remains of the wooden gun carriage. The wreck is one of the vessels of the contingent of Denmark and Lübeck which were scuttled on 21 May 1565.

THE DARSS CARVEL OF 1679

The typical flat bottom hull construction with a rounded bilge was able to be investigated on a ship fragment which was washed up and salvaged in 2005 on the W. coast of Darss. The building of the Darss Carvel could be dated to 1679. The oak timbers for the ship were partly from the area around Hamburg and from different sites. Clues to the »shell-first« construction are given by the nail holes which were closed with oak pegs. Z-shaped plank joints are an additional characteristic for the Dutch shipbuilding technology. The planks are average 11.37 m long, 54 cm wide and 8 cm thick. The caulking is made of hemp fibres, with no twist, which was pressed into the joints. Branch holes and other damages were sealed with little lathes during the construction of the ship. These areas were made watertight with a mixture of moss and pitch.

Frames inside the hull consist of floor timbers and futtocks. Unusual is the fact that even in the area of the bilges sapwood was not completely removed and sometimes even bark was found on the framing timbers. Shipwrights made use of naturally curved timbers or branches for the frames in the area of the turn of the bilge. The floor timbers, which provide stability to the ship's bottom are approximately 4 m long and extend over the keel. The original position of the keel is clearly indicated by remains of iron bolts with a cross section of 2.50 cm inside the floor timbers. The futtocks have a length of 2.80 m near the turn of the bilge. The width of the frames varies between 18 to 38 cm and the thickness from 13 to 28 cm. The floor timbers and the futtocks were put edge to edge on top of each other without scarfs or any other joint, another indication of shell first technique. Planks and frames are connected with treenails. Stringers inside the ship fragment indicate that the whole inner area was covered with them. The stringers resemble the dimensions of the planks and are connected edge to edge with Z-shaped ends or scarfs.

The salvaged wreck parts were recorded thoroughly with an industrial scanner. The three dimensional data could be used in comparison with contemporary drawings for a reconstruction. Based on the measured data the shape of the frames and the attached planks could be reconstructed. Due to this method the length between stern and bow could be estimated to approximately 30 m and the maximum width to 7.5 m.

Contemporary publications on shipbuilding, such as »Aelounde en heddendaegsche Scheeps-Bouw en Bestier« by Nicolaes Witsen from 1671 or »Architectura Navalis Mercatoria« by Frederik Chapman from 1768, with its line-drawings and information on dimensions, provided valuable comparison. The major resemblance could be detected at a flute or flyboat, the typical Dutch trade ship of the 17th and 18th c. (**Fig. 10**).

THE SHIP BARRIER OF 1715

Another source for the study of the migration of ship types originating in the Netherlands in the beginning of the 18th c. is provided by the sea barrier in the Greifswalder Bodden, which was created be the Swedish in 1715 during the Greta Nordic War by scuttling local ships. Within the so far analyzed 17 wrecks of the barrier four carvel vessels were detected with a flat bottom and the »shell-first« construction which are the characteristics of the Dutch shipbuilding.

The influence of the Dutch shipbuilding increased in the Baltic Sea area in the 16th c. and can be observed on some of the wrecks from the barrier. A somewhat new technology transfer into the Baltic Sea region occurred due to the dominance of the Dutch in seafaring, shipwrights coming from the Netherlands and the replicating of Dutch ships. In the 17th c. the Dutch ship building was particularly impressive due to its practicality. This means, that vessels were not only seaworthy but also suitable to be used on rivers. These ships had a flat bottom and were relatively small. These characteristics were proven useful in the Baltic Sea and hence the method of construction was adopted. Investigations on three wrecks with a flat bottom supply evidence for the carvel technique and the influence of the Dutch shipbuilding technology. According to dendrochronological analysis these ships were built in the near vicinity. This is supported by the fact that local and proven construction methods were integrated, such as the significantly shaped keel and stern elements on one of the wrecks. The position of the mast step in the keelson points to one or one and a half mast on the ships. These three ships have a reconstructed length of 22 m, 18 m and respectively 16 m. That also aligns with written sources, because in connection to the barrier two skippers complain about the loss of their »Galioten«. This name points to vessels in the Dutch building tradition, which were sunk in the barrier. The »Galiot« is also a flat bottom ship type which can be frequently seen in the North and Baltic Sea from the 16th c. onwards.

THE SCHMACK-SHIP *REGENT DOOR ZEE* OF 1783

Beside the Galiot the ship type Schmack has its roots in the Lower Rhine area and belonged to the most common ship types of the inner European trade navigation. Near the island of Hiddensee the well preserved hull of a 21.50 m long and 5.60 m wide flat bottomed sailing ship could be detected.

The carvel hull is made of oak timbers. The wreck fragments clearly show a nearly rectangular shape with a slight curvature towards the ship's ends. 60 frames are visible on both sides with an average distance of 20 cm, which is reduced to 5 cm at the bow and stern. The frames are 8 cm thick and ca. 12 cm wide. The planks are 6 m long, 30 cm wide and 3.5 cm thick. The two strakes protruding from the seabed have a double layer of planks, increasing the strake's thickness to 7 cm. The multiple planking in this area is presumably the so-called wale, a stiffening of the planking on the last few strakes. The caulking is made of animal hair and pitch. On the inside, stringers are attached to the frames with nails. The stringers are 6 m long, 30 cm wide and 4 cm thick.

Based on the investigations it can be said that the ship was a flat bottomed vessel with curved fore and aft stem. According to the size of the hull the find could be a vessel built in the Dutch tradition, which may be identified as Galiot, Tjalk or Schmack.

Several items were found in the afterbody which help to date the ship. In the vicinity of an iron chest the following small finds were made: a tin spoon from the late 18th c., a pair of scissors made of iron, a tap made of brass and a collection of ceramic vessels. An ear bowl, a folding bowl and a warm beer bowl can also be dated to the second half of the 18th c. Ceramic finds from the vessel indicate that the ship originates from the Lower Rhine area in the late 18th c. Further information about the identity of the wreck can be found in a file of the city archive in Stralsund. It is noted that the Schmack *Regent Door Zee* owned by Jan Albert Venster, and originating from Emden, run aground on 8 August 1783.

The wreck finds from the S.W. Baltic Sea show, that an influence of Dutch shipbuilding traditions existed in the Baltic Sea for more than 500 years. Beside the origin of vessels, that were built at the Dutch coast, also a technology transfer took place which not only influenced Baltic ship building by certain elements but also by vessel types.

NOTES

1) The use of ship terminology handed down from historic sources for the archaeological typology of ship finds have led, especially concerning medieval wrecks, to academic differences in the past. Particularly the term cog was heavily debated. Cf. Weski 1999a: 96-106; 1999b: 360-379; 2002: 143-159; Crumlin-Pedersen 1979: 17-34; 2000: 230-246; 2003: 256-271. – The author recommends a typology of wreck finds according to the construction. A complete description can be found at Förster 2007.

2) The Darss Cog was examined within the scope of the EU-funded MoSS Project – Monitoring, Safeguarding and Visualizing North-European Shipwreck Sites.

3) Karsten 2005.

REFERENCES

Chapman, F., 1768, *Architectura Navalis Mercatoria* (reprint Rostock 1984).

Crumlin-Pedersen, O., 1979, Danish Cog-Finds. In: S. McGrail (ed.), *The Archaeology of Medival Ships and Harbours in Northern Europe*. BAR, Internat. Series, no. 66. Oxford, 17-34.

2000, To be or not to be a cog: the Bremen Cog in perspective. *IJNA*, 29.2, 230-246.

2003, Die Bremer Kogge – ein Schlüssel zur Geschichte des Schiffbaus. In: G. Hoffmann & U. Schnall (eds), *Die Kogge – Sternstunden der deutschen Schiffsarchäologie*. Schriften des Deutschen Schiffahrtsmuseums, no. 60. Bremerhaven, 256-271.

Förster, T., 1999, Das Mukranwrack – Ein ungewöhnlicher Schiffsfund aus dem 16. Jahrhundert. *NAU*, 5, 12-21.

2002a, Alltagsleben auf spätmittelalterlichen Schiffen – Neue archäologische Untersuchungen an Wrackfunden vor der Küste von Mecklenburg-Vorpommern. In: C. O. Cederlund & K. Krüger (eds), *Maritime Archäologie heute. Internationale Tagung der Maritimen Archäologie im Osteeraum*. Rostock, 232-236.

2002b, Schiffswracks, Hafenanlagen, Sperrwerke. Untersuchungen zur maritimen Kulturlandschaft in der Wismarbucht. *Jahrb. BMV*, 50, 207-230.

2002c, Das Wrack vom Harten Ort vor der Insel Hiddensee – Ein Plattbodenschiff des 18. Jahrhunderts. *NAU*, 9, 105-110.

2003, The construction of the Darss Cog. The Darss Cog Site. *MoSS Newsletter*, 2003, no. 2, 13.

2006, An den Strand gespült – Das »Darsser Kraweel«. *NAU*, 13, 21-26.

2008, *Große Handelsschiffe des Spätmittelalters – Untersuchungen an zwei Wrackfunden des 14. Jahrhunderts vor der Insel*

Hiddensee und der Insel Poel. Schriften des Deutschen Schifffahrtsmuseums, no. 67. Bremerhaven.

Förster, T., *et al.* 2002, Die schwedische Schiffssperre von 1715 – Taucharchäologische Untersuchungen im Greifswalder Bodden. In: U. Masemann (ed.), *Forschungen zur Archäologie und Geschichte in Norddeutschland. Festschrift W. D. Tempel*. Rotenburg, 371-388.

Karsten, A., 2005, Die Lederlaterne der Darsser Kogge – Konservierung und Präsentation. *NAU*, 11-12, 89 – 97.

Lahn, W., 1992, *Die Kogge von Bremen*. Schriften des Deutschen Schiffahrtsmuseums, no. 30. Bremerhaven.

Olechnowitz, K.-Fr., 1965, *Handel und Seeschiffahrt der späten Hanse. Abhandlungen zur Handels- und Sozialgeschichte, vol. VI.* Weimar.

Weski, T., 1999a, Fiktion oder Realität? Anmerkungen zum archäologischen Nachweis spätmittelalterlicher Schiffsbezeichnungen. *Skyllis. Zeitschrift für Unterwasserarchäologie* 2, 96-106.

1999b, The Ijsselmeer type: some thoughts on Hanseatic cogs. *IJNA*, 28.4, 360-379.

1999c, Archäologische Anmerkungen zum Schiff der hansischen Frühzeit. *Deutsches Schiffahrtsarchiv*, 22, 9-22.

Witsen, N., 1671, *Aeloude en hedendaegsche Scheeps-Bouw en Bestier. Waer in wijtloopigh wert verhandelt, de wijze van Sheeps-timmeren, by Grieken en Romeynen: sheepsoeffeningen, Strijden, Tucht, Straffe, Wetten en gewonnten.* Amsterdam (reprint Alphen a.d. Rijn, 1994).

MAIK-JENS SPRINGMANN

THE SHIPS OF THE CRUSADERS

EXCHANGE OF NAUTICAL PRINCIPLES
BETWEEN THE MEDITERRANEAN AND THE BALTIC IN MEDIEVAL TIME

CONCEPT AND OBJECTIVES

The time of the crusades (A.D. 1095 to 1291) and of the occupation of the Holy Land can be considered to be one of the biggest »take offs« in medieval times with widespread influences all over Europe (von Stromer 1999: 2). Apart from the periods of the Great Discoveries in the Early Modern era and the industrial revolution in the 19th c., the time of the crusades can be regarded as a period of great cultural and economic exchange, joining Orient and Occident. Exchange has always been related to and connected with transport by land over sea. As much as we know about the land expeditions today, especially from interpretations of the written sources, such as Friedrich Barbarossa's travelling (A.D. 1189 to 1192) from Regensburg, via Belgrade and the Bosporus to the Kingdom of Armenia, voyages have not been much in the scientific focus so far. Research on those expeditions – not at least on the level of seafaring and shipbuilding – and the technological, economic, political, legal, organisational-logistic and socio-cultural determinations of this important cultural exchange through transport is the fundament and one part of the CRUSSHIP project which is under preparation to date.

SHIPS AND THEIR FEATURES

Therefore the Crusaders' presence in the Mediterranean can be understood as a big, presumably even the biggest transport effort in medieval history. Based on the sources it is obvious that the crusaders did not only travel on board of Mediterranean ship types (mostly known as galleys) but also on board ships that were larger than those usually existed in this region, as it was evidently the case on the crusade of Richard the Lionhearted who reached Cyprus on 10 April A.D. 1189. In the Baltic region the ideas of special crusaders' vessels have been supported by Heinrich von Livland who distinguished large crusaders' ships from smaller trading vessels by establishing the order state of Livonia (Stoob 1995: 130-133). Wolfram von Eschenbach around A.D. 1200 has mentioned *kocken* as big transport vessels, exspecially built for the crusaders' travels and military operations. In the N. European context warships are distinguished from merchantmen first at the beginning of the 16th c. (Springmann 1997: 461). Most of the ships involved in Hanseatic struggles were merchantmen, which had soldiers on board (Springmann, 2001: 334). They served as traders for the Hanseatic towns and were hired by the administration during war. It can be traced back from this that the classification into warships – more precisely troop transporters – and merchantmen must be remarkably earlier[1]. Consequently one can assume that cogs sailing from Bayonne, from Cornwall and from the Rhine delta were not equipped for such long voyages to the Mediterranean; probably they were built exspecially for military purposes, because they certainly took risk of sea battles[2].
It is still not dealt with what specific ergologic features were symptomatically for those ship types[3] and how they influenced building procedure and shape of »crusaders' vessels« in peculiar and the developments in

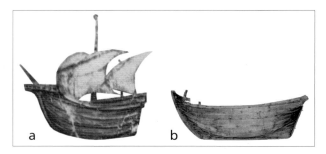

Fig. 1 Medieval ship models. – (a) Three-masted *cocha* shown on the Portolan of Battista Becharius from Genuova (A.D. 1426) – (b) Cog donated by a knight to a church in Ebersdorf, Germany (Yale University, database [a]; photo Springmann [b]).

medieval ship building in general[4]. As the sea raid of Richard the Lionheart revealed the galleys' tactics – to sink enemy ships with their »ram« – did not work in practice, and that Richard's fleet consisted of cog-like ships and galleys as well. The sources are telling about a galley of his fleet attacking an vessel; soldiers tried to board the enemy but failed due to the circumstance that the Muslim ship's freeboard was too high (Pryor 1988: 120), and that she used weapons operated by fire – an example of one of the earliest fire-arms on ships[5].

HULL AND PROPULSION

Some scholars characterize ships from the North Sea sailing to the Mediterranean as two-masted cogs (Quijada 2001: 2-12). However, the earliest multi-masted cog-like ship from N. Europe one can find with a depiction of a manuscript from 1409 (Mott 1994: 39-40)[6]. Other images connected with the Mediterranean show also multi-masted cog-like ships (**Figs 1-3**). It is not sure if these ships were already equipped with more then one mast, and if so, where they were equipped with fore and mizzen masts. It is also a problem whether some of hundred cog-like ships mentioned in written records of the period sailed back to N. waters after their »mission« came to an end, and if they included also some with more than one mast[7] – if so one may ask how these crusaders' vessels stimulated ship and harbour construction in N. Europe. Have they been constructed then with one mast only? According the iconographical evidences one can assume that the multi-masted hybrid vessels were equipped not only with square sails[8]. Usually the first airfoil propulsion on wind curses opposite of the wind pressure principle is connected with the development of the sprit sail. However apart from earlier evidences as a 3rd c. depiction of a Roman sarcophagus in the Copenhagen Glyptothek (Gifford 1984: 177) imlying the ancient use of sprit-sails, this rig type was adopted in the North apparently not before the beginning of the 16th century (Anderson 1927: 58). Impacts are evident on the depictions of the crusaders' period,

Fig. 2 Ship image on Genova map, A.D. 1457. – Three-masted ship, presumably of clinker construction (After Ewe 1978).

Fig. 3 Satopy near Olstyn (Allenstein), Poland. – Altar-piece showing a two-masted ship connected with the State of the Teutonic Order (After Greenhill 1995).

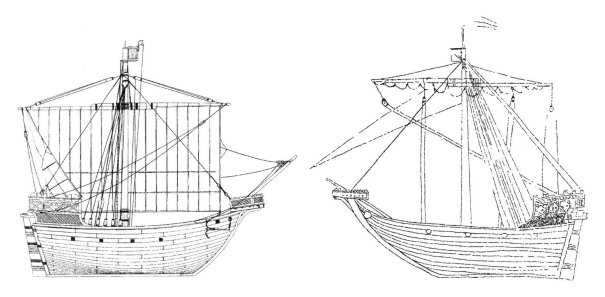

Fig. 4   Reproduction of a ship image in codex *Analecta hymnica medii aevi* (AH3) from A.D. 1343 (right) and reconstruction drawing (left) (After Quiijada 2001).

showing two-masted lateen rigged cogs with the extension of a top sail (Adam 1976: 560-567). The purpose of the lateen mizzen sail might have been to improve steering performance rather than propulsion (Springmann 2003: 170).

If written sources on Richard's the Lionhearted voyage are considered, speed can be estimated: Richard sailed from Messina to Limassol via Crete and Rhodes within 30 days. To pass these 1075 nautical miles he ought to have sailed an average speed of some 1.36 knots. The voyage of Roger of Lauria's Catalan–Sicilian galley that went over 1120 miles took about 30 days (Pryor 1983: 179-216). In future the author aims to verify the above mentioned data by investigating sea capabilities by wind canal and a water tank analyses, as R. Bastard de Pere, J. E. Dotson and J. Pryor already investigated the improvement of Mediterranean *cochas*, cogs and »round ships« ordered by Louis IX. in Marseille, Genoa and Venice through model tests (Bastard de Pere 1972: 327-356; Dotson 1973: 161-170; Pryor 1994: 64 [Fig. 6]). Wilfried Stecher provided computer simulations of those voyages revealing that cogs have been sailing faster than Mediterranean vessels[9].

Scholars are aware of the principle correlation of propulsion and hull construction. If crusaders were using ships with more than one mast, partly rigged with lateen sails, which means air foil propulsion on wind courses, it is to ask whether such cog-like ships were shell or frame first constructions. Quijada in his studies to build a model based on the single mast cog depiction from the AH3 manuscript, interpreted the image as depicting a carvel planked ship from the Mediterranean – built frame first, with a special after castle implemented in the hull construction (Quijada 2001: 6) (**Fig. 4**). Quijadas reconstruction of the after castle resembles that of the Ebersdorf cog model, which besides the Mataró Model belongs to the earliest cog-like models known to date (Steussloff 1983: 189-207; Christensen 1987: 69-70; Springmann 2003: 1-55) (**Fig. 5**). According written records the Ebersdorf church model has been donated by an knight who survived sinking of his ship when sailing from Acre (Akkon) to Messina. Thus – from a historical point of view – the Ebersdorf model is much more connected with Mediterranean seafaring as with previously supposed Baltic traditions (Steusloff 1983: 189-207).

Records of Louis' IX crusade from A.D. 1248 to 1254 mention ships longer than 30 m, with special after castles carrying around 100 heavy horse men and up to 1000(!) passengers (Bastard de Pere 1972: 327-328; Pryor 1994: 63-64; Stoob 1995: 130-133) (**Fig. 6**). Those castles could be used also as fighting plat-

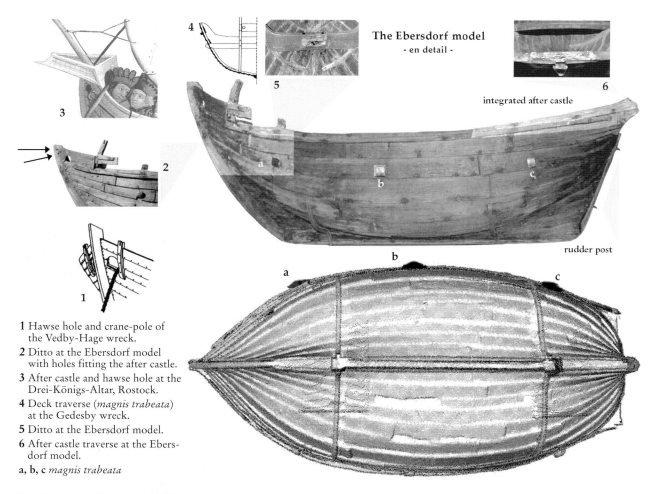

The Ebersdorf model
- en detail -

integrated after castle

rudder post

1 Hawse hole and crane-pole of the Vedby-Hage wreck.
2 Ditto at the Ebersdorf model with holes fitting the after castle.
3 After castle and hawse hole at the Drei-Königs-Altar, Rostock.
4 Deck traverse (*magnis trabeata*) at the Gedesby wreck.
5 Ditto at the Ebersdorf model.
6 After castle traverse at the Ebersdorf model.

a, b, c *magnis trabeata*

Fig. 5 Ebersdorf cog model (cf. fig. 1b). – Constructional details.

Fig. 6 Model reconstruction of one of Louis´ IX crusaders' ships (After Pryor 1994).

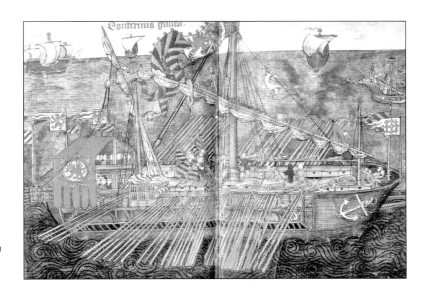

Fig. 7 Galleys and hulk-shaped ships in Conrad Grünemberg, *Reise von Konstanz nach Jerusalem* (publ. 1487) (After Ganz-Blättler 1990).

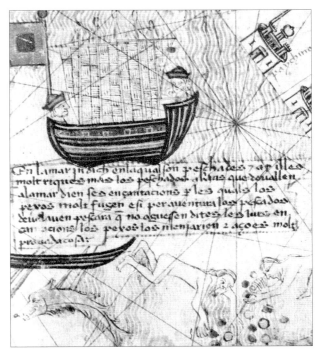

Fig. 8 Ship images shown on a Catalan portolan from A.D. 1375. – The large vessel probably shows a blunt stern known from N. ships, especially inland craft (After Ewe 1978).

Fig. 9 Borgia iron plate, Italia, A.D. 1410. – Section showing a »banana shaped« *hulk/holk* (www.henry-davis.com/maps).

forms. Accordingly, such ships might be called the first »floating castles« as *e.g. Mary ROSE* and *ADLER von Lübeck* (Springmann 2000: 75-85). From a nautical point of view, such bulky castles might have caused problems when sailing in stormy waters (Bill 1996: 50) as it was also realized during trials on *Lisa von Lübeck*. Those ships have used so-called »firrer« which are identified as side rudders (**Figs 6; 10b**), a steering type also accepted for the hulk (Pryor 1994: 64; Ellmers 1999/2000: 121; Waskönig 1969: 139-166; Springmann 2003: 157-185). Taking into account the shape of the Mediterranean »cog-like« depictions most of which are considered here, one can see a relationship to the »banana« ship shape of the hulk (**Fig. 7**) (Ellmers 1999/2000: 120). The same seems true for altar-pieces from Central Europe, especially

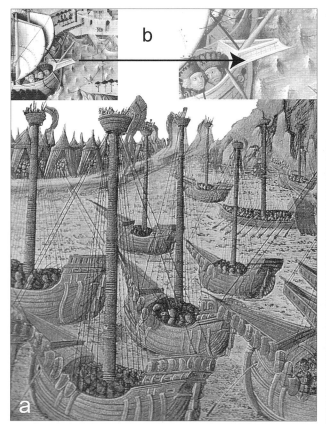

Fig. 13   (a) Ship depictions showing cochas, cogs, naós or carracks(?) published with Jean Froissarts chronicle, around A.D. 1400. – (b) Altar-pieces of the »Dreikönigsaltar« in Rostock, Germany (After Ewe 1978 [a]; Ellmers 1981 [b])

Fig. 14   Planking of a N. European river boat showing transversal nailing, also known from Zwammerdam type barges (cf. Fig. 12) (Photo Springmann).

storm and perfectly capable of open sea crossings. Their increased hull capacity was not given over to loading more passengers of cargo« (Pryor 1988: 44). It can be assumed that the time of the crusaders contributed to these developments (Pryor 1984: 171-219; 275-292; 363-386). According the written sources, it can be presumed that the N. European cog because of her small crew, her remarkable tonnage, her characteristic freeboard and ship body's flexibility produced an impression, and thus influenced Mediterranean shipbuilding. This brings us to the general question of shape and construction of those crusaders' ships, and to the problems of adaption and change of their construction, last but not least to the question of cog building of by the Order's States.

THE MEDIEVAL HARBOUR AND THE SHIPBUILDING OF THE CRUSADERS IN THE ORDER'S STATES

As an important criterion to estimate ships and their capabilities the medieval harbour deserves attraction: its infrastructural elements provided the place for repair and maintenance of ships what could result in alterations of ship construction in the area. This has been proven e.g. for Viking-Age ship constructions

(Herfert 1968: 211-222), whilst geographical circumstances could cause individual measures, e.g. by Vasco da Gama who changed his square sails into lateens when he entered the Indian Ocean. Those suggested technical changes of crusaders' ships (**Fig.13**), determined by cultural landscape interactions and vice versa, had their impact on the cultural region itself because especially such nautical impacts influenced and developed the harbour structure, e.g. in Venice and at the islands of Malta and Cyprus. Activities of more than 120 so-called Hanseatic cogs operating from Akko to defend Damiette demonstrate a more extended action radius for this kind of undertaking than for such of galleys (Pryor 1988: 42). In the Mediterranean, these fleets apparently operated from harbours. However, we do not know much about the medieval infrastructure of those harbours. Akko had an outer and an inner harbour (Desimoni 1886: 321-356), but those harbours still have to be found. According Marino Sanudo's plan (Sanudo 1972: 11), Akkon's arsenal was situated in the N.W. corner of the big outer harbour (Flinder *et al.* 1966: 199-225; Linder *et al.* 180-194).

One of the CRUSSHIPS project's aims is to localise the medieval harbour of Akko by using geo-radar and side scan sonar. Results would shed new light on the problems of shipbuilding and the technological infrastructure of ships as well (Mollat 1967: 345-359). The recently investigated tunnel of the Templer's Order could be an indication to the inner harbour which had to be cleaned from sand[11]. Similar situations are reflected in Venice and Istanbul (Constantinople), where recently discovered shipwrecks gave clues on the extension of medieval harbours. The same was aimed in Lisbon and at places along Vistula Lagoon where efforts concentrate on the extension of the early harbours and their facilities by using geo-morphological investigation methods.

The N. European fleets had to fight against a special enemy: the *teredo navalis*, which were much more aggressive in destroying the oak ship hull as the skippers were accustomed in N. waters.

Such aspects provide the question of shipbuilding of the crusader states Antiochia, Tyros and Jerusalem, and of the usage of Mediterranean wood for shipbuiling. We know about the existence of arsenals in Akko, Tyros and Tripolis. That implies the existence of crusader fleets. However, according to Assises de la Cour de Bourgeois the kings built their own ships since Balduin III. (A.D. 1143 to 1163). During the years 1187 to 1191 the arsenal in Akko did not only repair and equip ships but also built and wrecked ships (Favreau-Lille 1989: 22). A legal claim to stranded wrecks mentioned in the same document is not quite clear because »mizzen-mast« and »rudder« of stranded ships belonged to the crown of the crusader states, which also could point to a reuse of this technical equipment. As indicated by the diploma of Conrad Mont Ferrat dedicated to the citizens of Pisa in October A.D. 1187, king Balduin IV. equipped a fleet in Akko and Tyros (Huygens XXII 19, p.1098). Furthermore, the diploma tells about an organized immigration of foreign ship carpenters. They arrived in A.D. 1183 aboard a ship, which carried wood to Akko. This reveals that wood has been transported over-seas and had not been cut from the rather poor local forests. One of the reasons for local shipbuilding might have been the monopolisation of shipbuilding and seafaring, which combined repair and maintenance of ships from the towns of Marseille, Genoa, Pisa and Venice, and also in the Baltic, e.g. in Królewiec, the later Königsberg, Malbork/Marienburg, and to some extend in Gdańsk. When German settlers arrived at the lower Vistula, their boatbuilding techniques had already been developed. Truso, Gdańsk and Zantyr (between Nogat and Vistula) can be identified as harbour and shipbuilding centres.

To build up the »Order's« land in the Baltic, skilled settlers from W. Europe were invited, among them shipbuilders from towns in Lower Germany, but also shipbuilders from Venice. Teutonic knights did not build ships by themselves. Therefore it was crucial to have shipbuilders and ships, which allowed them to trade and contact the rest of Europe. Soon, they became one of the most important ship owners of ships, especially of cogs and hulks in Prussia and N. Europe. Sarnowsky concludes that the Order worked with ships which were not all in their possession (Sarnowsky 1990, notes 33 index 93). Some ships were hired, others were built for them, e.g. in Królewiec, Gdańsk and Elbląg. The only known riverside shipyard, which belonged to Teutonic knights, was located in Malbork castle in the 15th c. (Domzal 2006; in print).

Images of St. Marco in Venice and from the tower of Pisa enable to compare harbour facilities, in addition to archaeological investigations in Venice harbour which are aimed by the CRUSSHIP project. These images of the crusaders' period and the history of the »Order« in the Baltic have not been discussed from a holistic point of view yet.

A lot of iconographic evidence, recorded far distant from the Mediterranean[12], indicates essential paradigms (Pryor 1988: 25-53). This should be an important research field of this proposed project. Iconography reveals a picture of the organization of fleets, of life aboard, the accommodation of soldiers and pilgrims, even of such specific features as the transport of horses (**Fig. 13**). Single depictions reflect a distinguished intention of the painter, so that the number of ship images statistically analyzed could reveal its essential directions. Therefore, a statistical analysis of all the features of the investigated pictures should be done through a counter management system, which will be developed by the Institute of Computer Science at the University of Rostock having substantial experiences in this field[13].

ACKNOWLEDGEMENT

The author is grateful to his friend and colleague Robert Domzal who assisted him much with informations on ship building of the Teutonic knights, as well as to Yacov Kahanov and his colleagues from Akko for discussing their research. The author also wishs to thank all of those colleagues from Israel, Poland, Italy, Portugal, Turkey and Germany who contributed to the *crusship network* so far.

NOTES

1) With regard to the *Revaler Zoll-Listen* and the study of Wolf (1986) the ships connected with Orders' shipping in the Baltic were vessels around 200 *last* und much bigger than ships of the Hanseatic league which carried around 100 to150 *last* (Vogelsang 1992; Wolf 1986).

2) In this context the maritime warfare of knights from the Lower Rhine area against the Moors should be considered (Kurth 1919: 131-252). Written evidence by Giovanni Villani, a Florentine chronicler from the end of the crusaders' time mentioned in A.D. 1304: »Certain people from Bayonne in Gascony with their ships which are called »cocche«, passed through the straits of Seville (Gibraltar) and came into our sea as pirates and did a great deal of damage. Immediately afterwards the Genoese, the Venetians and the Catalans began to sail with cocche and left off sailing with great navi to be able to sail more safely, and less expensively, and this was a great change in our shipping« (Spufford 2003: 398, cf. also Carbonell 1986: 56).

3) Selection of contributions dealing with the so-called »Mediterranean cog«: Hocquet 1979; Landstrom 1961: 90-91; van der Merwe 1981: 121-129; Scandurra 1972: 205-24; 214; Unger 1980: 129; 183-188; 216-217; Unger 1981: 243-247.

4) General comments on the period: Ayalon 1965: 1-12; Ehrenkreutz 1955: 100-116; Fahmy 1966: 98-106; Lev 1984: 251.

5) On the first »fire arms« onboard ships, developed from the engineer Kallinikos (A.D. 671), cf. Berckenhagen 1994: 25.

6) The first multi-masted ships from the Baltic are proven by stone engravings in the monastery of Helsingör dated to around A.D. 1430, by tomb stones of the church in Prohn near Stralsund dated to A.D. 1482 and in the Bernhardiner monastery in Vilnius, and from an altar-piece in Tallinn (Reval) of A.D. 1482 (Springmann 2001: 350, note 1; 2003: 157-184).

7) Of 787 knights travelling during the first crusade to Palestine, 683 returned home (Stoob 1995: 187).

8) During Vasco da Gamas second voyage (A.D. 1502) on some of his square sail rigged ships – reaching the Indian ocean – he set lateen sails (cf. p. 371).

9) Email from October 2007; cf. also his dissertation in preparation.

10) Discussions with Dr. Ufuk Kocabas and Prof. Nergis Günsenin.

11) Discussion of the working group to prepare the project, Acre, in October 2007.

12) Iconographic evidence of Muslim ships dated before the 13th c. is missing. (cf. Udovicht n.y. 516). To written sources, naval documents by Qudama and Leo VI cf. Christides 1982: 51-103.

13) (www.lagomar/lagoDATAmar.de). The information system to be developed should not only contain references to written sources, archives, iconographic data as images, historical maps but should also allow for a basic spatial-temporal management of information on archaeological finds, on land and sailing routes, and adequate navigation, browsing, and search mechanisms. The technical basis will be a Geographical Information System (GIS) and a web-based Content Management System.

REFERENCES

Adam, P., 1976, Conclusion sur les developments des techniques nautiques médiévales. In: *Revue d'histoire economique et sociale, 54,* 560-567,

Airaldi, G., 1988, Da Genova Siviglia – l'avventura dell'occidente. In: *Genova e Sivilgia.* Genua.

Anderson, R. C., 1927, *The Rigging of Ships in the Days of the Spritsail Topmast, 1600-1720.* Salem/Massachusetts.

Ayalon, D., 1965, Mamluks and naval power: a phase of the struggle between Islam and Christian Europe. In: *Proceedings of the Israel Academy of Science and Humanities, vol. I.* Tel Aviv, 1-12.

Bastard de Pere, R., 1972, Navires mediterrannéens du temps de Saint Louis. *Revue d'histoire economique et sociale,* 50, 327-56.

Berckenhagen, E., 1994, Mediterrane Schiffahrt im Mittelalter. *Deutsches Schifffahrtsarchiv, 17,* 23-50.

Bill, J., 2002, Castles at sea. The warship of the High Middle Ages. In: Jørgensen *et al.* (eds), *Maritime Warfare in Northern Europe.* Copenhagen, 47-56.

Bockius, R., 2002, Abdichten, Beschichten, Kalfatern. *Jahrb. RGZM,* 49, 189-234.

Christiansen, E., 1997, *The Northern Crusaders.* London.

Christides, V., 1982, Two parallel naval guides of the tenth century: Qudama's document and Leo VI's Naumachica: a study on Byzantine and Moslem naval preparedness. *Graeco-Arabica, 1,* 51-103.

Desimoni, C., 1886, I Marches di Monferrato Guglielmo il vecchio e la sua famiglia secondo gli dtu recent con una appendice sui trovatori genovesi. *Giornale ligustico di archeologia, storia e belle arti, 13,* 321-356.

Domżal, R., 2006, Häfen, Schiffahrt und Schiffbau von Marienburg (Malbork) im Mittelalter. *Deutsches Schiffsarchiv, 29,* 115-136.

in print, *Harbours and shipping in low vistula river from XIII.-XVth century.*

Doornick, van F. H., 1969, Did thenth-century dromons have a waterline ram? Another look at Leo Tactica, XIX. *MM, 79,* 387-392.

Dotson, J. E., 1973, Jal's Nef X and Genoese Naval Architecture in the Thirteenth Century. *MM, 59,* 161-70.

Ehrenkreutz, A., 1955, The Place of Saladin in the naval history of the Mediterranean Sea in the middle Ages. *Journal of the American Oriental Society, 75,* 100-116.

Ellmers, D., 1999/2000, Zur Herkunft des spätmittelalterlichen Schiffstyps Holk. *Zeitschrift für Archäologie des Mittelalters, 27/28,* 119-128.

2001, Hansische Umschau, Schiffahrt und Schiffbau. *Hansische Geschichtsblätter, 119,* 236.

Ewe, H., 1978, *Abbild oder Phantasie. Schiffe auf historischen Karten.* Rostock.

Fahmy, A. M., 1966, *Muslim naval organization in the Eastern Mediterranean.* Cairo.

Favreau-Lille, M., 1989, *Die Italiener im Heiligen Land vom ersten Kreuzzug bis zum Tode des Grafen Heinrich von Champagne (1098-1197)* Amsterdam.

Flinder, A., Linder, E. & Hall, E. T., 1966, The Survey of the Ancient Harbour of Akko 1964-1966. In: Heltzer *et al.* (eds), *Studies in the Archaeology and History of Ancient Israel.* Haifa, 199-225.

Ganz-Blättler, U., 1990, *Andacht und Abenteuer: Berichte Europäischer Jerusalem- und Santiago-Pilger.* Tübingen.

Gifford, E., 1984, Sailing into the Past. *Proceedings of the International Seminar on Replicas of Ancient and Medieval Time.* Roskilde, 177.

Herfert, P., 1968, Frühmittelalterliche Bootsfunde in Ralswiek, Krs. Rügen. *Ausgrabungen und Funde, 13,* 211-222.

Hocquet, J.-C., 1979, Le sel et la fortune de Venise. In: *Voiliers et commerce en Méditerranée 1200-1650,* vol. 2. Lille.

Kahanov, Y. & Stern, E., 2008, The ship grafitti from Akko (Acre). *MM, 94.1,* 21-35.

Kurth, F., 1919, Der Anteil niederdeutscher Kreuzfahrer an den Kämpfen gegen die Mauren. *Mitteilung d. Inst. f. Österrr. Gesch. Wien,* 8, 131-252.

Landstrom, B., 1961, *The ship: an illustrated history.* New York.

Lev, Y., 1984, The Fatimid navy, Byzantium and the Mediterranean Sea 909-1036. *Byzantion 54,* 220-252.

Lewis, A. R., 1951, *Naval power and trade in the Mediterranean A.D. 500-1100.* Princeton, 64-75.

1976, Northern European sea power and the Straits of Gibraltar, 1031-1350 A.D. In: W. C. Jordan *et al. (eds), Order and innovation in the Middle ages: essays in honour of Joseph R. Strayer.* Princeton/New Jersey, 139-164.

Linder, E. & Raban, L., 1965, An Underwater Survey in the Akko Harbour. In: *Western Galilee and the Coast of Galilee. The 19th Archaeologicial Convention October 1963.* Jerusalem, 180-194.

Lombard, M., 1958, Arsenauy et bois de marne dans la Mediterranee musulmane (VIIe-XI siècles). In: *La nire et l'economie maritime du moyen age au XVIII siecle, prinispalment en Mediterranée.* Paris, 53-99.

1959, Un probleme cartographie: le bois dans la Mediterranee muslumae, VIIe-YI^{e} siècles, Annales. *Economies – Societes – Civilsation, 14,* 234-254.

Mayer, H. E., 1985, *Geschichte der Kreuzzüge.* Stuttgart.

Mayer, H. E. (ed.), 1997, *Die Kreuzfahrerstaaten als multikulturelle Gesellschaft*. Oldenburg.

de Meer, S., 2009, The Nao of Mataró: a medieval ship model. In: E. Gueda *et al.* (eds), Mediterraneum: splendour of the medieval Mediterranean (13th-15th centuries). Barcelona.

Mollat, M., 1967, Problémes navals de l'histoire des croisades *Cahiers de civilisation médiévale, 10,* 345-359.

Mott, L. V., 1994, The three-masted ship depiction from 1409. *IJNA, 23,* 39-40.

1997, *The Development of the Rudder – A Technical Tale.* London.

Ossowski, W., 2004, Medieval large river craft from the Vistula River, Poland, In: Brandt & Kühn, *Haithabu,* 83-94.

Prawer, J., 1980, *Crusaders Institutions.* Oxford.

Pryor, J. H., 1983, The naval battles of Roger of Lauria. *Journal of medieval history, 9,* 179-216.

1984, The naval architecture of Crusader transport ships: a reconstruction of some archetypes for round-hulled sailing ships. *MM, 70,* 171-219; 275-292; 363-386.

1988, Geography, technology and war. In: *Studies in the maritime history of the Mediterranean.* Cambridge.

1994, The Mediterranean Round Ship. In: R. Gardiner (ed.), Cogs, Caravells and Galleons. Conway's History of the Ship Series. London, 59-76.

Quijada, X. P., 2001, Mediterranean Cog from 1343. *Model Shipwright, 113,* 2-12.

Röhricht, R., 1898, *Geschichte des Königreichs Jerusalem.* Innsbruck.

Sanudo the Elder, M., 1972, Liber Secretorum. Jerusalem (reprint).

Sarnowsky, J., 1990, *Die Wirtschaft des Deutschen Ordens.* Berlin.

Scandurra, E., 1972, The maritime republics: medieval and Renaissance ships in Italy. In: Bass, G., *A History of Seafaring,* London, 205-224.

Schaube, A., 1880, Das Konsulat des Meeres in Pisa. Ein Beitrag zur Geschichte des Seewesens, der Handelsgilden und des Handelsrechtes im Mittelalter. In: *Staats- und sozialwissenschaftliche Forschungen 8,* vol. 2, Leipzig.

1906, *Handelsgeschichte der romanischen Völker des Mittelmeergebietes bis zum Ende der Kreuzzüge.* München, Berlin.

von Schlözer, K., 1966, *Die Hansa und der deutsche Ritter-Orden in den Ostseeländern.* Wiesbaden (reprint).

Schreier, S., *Zur Leistungsfähigkeit einer Hansekogge aus dem 15. Jahrhundert.* Unpubl. thesis, Rostock university; www.lagomar. de/URCCog.

Solver, K.,n. y., *Danske Skibstekningar frå det 15. Aarhundrede.* Copenhagen.

Springmann, M.-J., 1997, Ein Wrack des 16. Jahrhunderts bei Mukran, Rügen. *Deutsches Schifffahrtsarchiv, 20,* 459-487.

2000, Archaeological and Archival Indicators of Socio-Cultural Change on Board Ship in the 16th Century. In: *ISBSA VIII,* 75-85.

2001, Archäologische, archivalische und bildliche Indikatoren für den sozio-kulturellen Wandel des Lebens an Bord von Schiffen des 16. Jahrhunderts. *Deutsches Schifffahrtsarchiv, 24,* 333-354.

2003, Neue spätmittelalterliche und frühneuzeitliche Schiffsabbildungen. Ein Beitrag zur ergologischen Merkmalsanalyse in der Schiffstypologie. Deutsches Schiffahrtsarchiv, 26, 157-184.

2003, *Uecker-Randow-Kogge. Bau- und Konstruktionsunterlagen sowie historio-archäologische Expertise.* www.lagomar.de/pilotprojects/URCCog/PDF-file.

2005, Der frühe Schiffbau und die Schiffahrt in Kur- und Prussenland. In: *Praeities Puslapiai: archeologija, kultûra, visuomenà.* Klaipeda, 145-191.

Steusloff, W., 1983, Das Ebersdorfer Koggenmodell von 1400. Ein Beitrag zum nordeuropäischen Schiffbau des späten Mittelalters. In: *Deutsches Schiffahrtsarchiv, 6,* 189-207.

Stoob, H., 1995, *Die Hanse.* Graz, Köln, Wien.

von Stromer, W., 1999, *Venedig und die Weltwirtschaft um 1200.* Stuttgart.

Sturtzel, W. *et al.*, 1966, *Untersuchung über den Einfluss des Modellmaßstabes und der Kennzahl auf die Versuchsergebnisse von Schiffsrudern.* Köln.

Tangheroni, M., 2004, Pisa e il Regno Crociato di Gerulsalemme. In: *I comuni Italiani,* 497-521.

Udovicht, A., n. y., Time, the sea and society: duration of commercial voyages on the southern shores of the Mediterranean during the High Middle Ages. In: *La navigazione mediterranea nell'alto medioevo, vol. 2,* 503-46.

Unger, W., 1980, *The ship in the medieval economy 600-1600.* London.

1981, Warships and Cargo Ships in Medieval Europe. In: *Technology and Culture, 22,* 233-252.

van der Merwe, P., 1981, Towards a three-mastered ship. In: *Proceedings of the Forth international congress of Maritime Museums.* Paris, 121-129.

Vaughn, R., 1993, *The illustrated chronicles of Matthew Paris. Observations of 13th life.* Gloucestershire.

Vogelsang, R., 1992, Revaler Schiffslisten. In: *Quellen und Studien zur baltischen Geschichte, vol. 13.* Köln.

Waskönig, D., 1969, Bildliche Dastellung des Holk im 15. und 16. Jahrhundert. *Jahrbuch des Altonaer Museums in Hamburg, 7,* 139-165.

Wieczorek, A., Fansa, M. & Meller, H., 1999, *Saladin und die Kreuzfahrer.* Oldenburg.

Wilhelm of Tyros XXII. 18 (edited by Huygens XXII) 19, 1098.

Wolf, T., 1986, *Tragfähigkeiten, Ladungen und Maße im Schiffsverkehr der Hanse.* Quellen und Darstellungen zur hansischen Geschichte, *N.F. 31,* Köln, Wien.

SHIP CONSTRUCTION

BART BOON · EELCO VAN RIETBERGEN

ASPECTS OF THE ANALYSIS OF STRUCTURE AND STRENGTH OF PRE-HISTORIC WATERCRAFT

Any ship or boat has to comply with a variety of requirements. Some of these come from the owner, such as those related to the cargo capacity. Other requirements are physical in nature such as stability: a boat should not capsize. The strength of the ship belongs to the latter group: a boat should be strong enough to reliably operate in its intended conditions. Some of the few publications in this respect are Hausen (1979), Coates (1985; 1994), Jensen (1999) and Fenger & Valbjørn (2003). Owain Roberts (2004) followed similar lines when he used naval architecture to interpret the Dover boat find and thus set a clear course on how naval architectural knowledge may assist the interpretation of archaeological finds. The present paper continues on the basis laid by Roberts. The rather small number of publications on the subject may be the result of an assumption that when remains of a boat are found, probably the vessel was strong enough when in existence, thus denying the relevance of any further analysis of the structure. The present paper will present some of the principles of structural analysis and show how this may assist in interpreting boat remains and may indicate open questions. Two subjects are used for illustration: the longitudinal strength of the Dover boat and the transverse strength of dug-outs.

SOME ASPECTS OF SHIP STRENGTH IN GENERAL

A ship during her life is subjected to a large variety of different loads. Some are simple such as the weight of the vessel and its cargo. Others are more complex such as the load from slamming waves. Some loads effect the ship as a whole. For example those, that keep the vessel in an upright position or those, that lead to ship motions. Simultaneously, these loads cause straining of the vessel leading to deformations of the structure and concomitant internal stresses. The ship structure should remain intact under such loads and not fail or leak. It is this latter type of loads and responses that are the subject of the present paper.
In ancient wooden ships the connection between individual structural elements, such as shell planks and frames whether sewn, nailed, pegged or otherwise, is rather loose. The vessel may be analysed in its entirety acting as one unit, just as any modern steel ship. All material deforms somewhat but the boundaries between individual elements do not allow any movement. This is what is called the elastic response of a homogeneous structure. However, at the same time the loose connections, such as the stitches in the sewn Dover boat, due to sliding, straining of the fibres or other may lead to deformations of similar magnitude as the elastic deformations. Analysis of ancient ships must take these effects into account.

LONGITUDINAL BENDING OF THE HULL GIRDER

Most authors tackling the strength of ancient boats and ships did so using the standard longitudinal strength assessment as used for modern ships.
According to Archimedes, the total weight of any ship must equal the weight of the displaced water. Neither weight nor displacement is uniformly distributed along the length of the ship's hull. In some loca-

tions there is an abundance of weight, in others there is more buoyancy. The hull redistributes those vertical forces so that the total system is in equilibrium. This results in bending of the beam and eventually may lead to breaking. Integration of the loads along the hull length leads to the distributed shear force and bending moment, the so-called internal loads. The max. bending moment is found at about half-length. In order to find the shear force and the bending moments, the structural arrangement of the vessel needs not to be known. This becomes important only in the next step when assessing whether the vessel is capable to accommodate the internal loads.

This standard longitudinal bending assessment is performed for the vessel both in a still-water condition as well as in a wave. Any wave will contribute to the unevenness of the buoyancy distribution and thus increase the bending moment. Extreme situations are those where at the ends of the vessel exists an over-supply or shortage in buoyancy and at mid-length the opposite. More buoyancy at mid-length means addi-tional up-bending, the hogging situation, whereas less buoyancy at half-length results in additional down-bending, the sagging situation. This sets the standard wave length for bending as being equal to the ship length. At the same time the wave height is 1/20 of the wave length. This standard wave height is based upon physical considerations, as well as practical observation and experience. This standard wave height is based upon the worst load situation of the vessel and is not related to the worst environmental conditions in more general terms.

The standard longitudinal strength assessment of ships is based upon application to ships much longer than ancient ships. It may be wondered whether the method is as valid for ancient boats. However, without further study no better alternative is available. The method may be used at least for comparative analyses. However, the possibility of non-relevant results should never be forgotten.

LONGITUDINAL BENDING OF THE DOVER BOAT

Roberts (2004) made a valuable attempt to use the standard longitudinal bending analysis in interpretation of the remains of the Dover boat found in 1993. He did so by establishing hull shape characteristics with a standard computer programme for the hydrostatic properties of ship hulls. The hull shape he used was the reconstructed form of the Dover boat remains lengthened as little as possible leading to an overall length of 11.7 m. He estimated the weight of the hull with 20 paddlers and 2 tons of cargo resulting in a draft of 0.5 m or 0.3 m remaining freeboard for the established 0.8 m hull depth. The cargo was distributed over half of the total hull length (from 0.3 to 0.8). Manually the weight and buoyancy distributions were established for still water as well as with either a hogging or a sagging wave. The wave height used was taken as 1/20 of the hull length in accordance with present day standard. Integration of the load led to shear forces and bending moments distributed over the length of the vessel. The remaining freeboard with the wave must have been about zero based on the assumption that the vessel could be quasi/statically balanced on this wave. Subsequently Roberts investigated a 14.3 m long hull where the transom is replaced by an aft body identical to the (reconstructed) fore-ship. He continued this process with a vessel similar to the previous, however with a still longer midship section bringing the total length up to 18.0 m. For the latter two versions Roberts did not repeat the bending moment calculations, but assumed that they would increase with a constant ratio in relation to the product of hull length and vessel displacement. In this way Roberts arrived at bending moments which increased considerably with the vessel length, albeit that the hogging moment always remained smaller than the sagging moment. This approach is used for modern ships where all dimensions and cargo capacity increase in relation with the displacement whereas the wave height in-creases in direct relation to the vessel length. In the Dover reconstruction several of these conditions do not

Version	loading	Displ. ton	sea state	max. BM tonm	max SF ton	Displ ton	draft m	trim m	max BM tonm	max SF ton
		Owain Roberts				Hydromax				
Dover 1	light	2.3	calm	0.14	0.05	2.375	0.152	-0.113	0.388	0.095
Dover 1	20 crew	3.5	calm	0.14	0.06	3.575	0.208	-0.015	0.209	0.088
Dover 1	20 crew and cargo	5.5	calm	1.2	0.50	5.575	0.299	-0.141	-0.814	0.386
Dover 1	20 crew and cargo	5.5	hogging	1.8	0.55	5.575	0.239	-0.437	1.977	0.624
Dover 1	20 crew and cargo	5.5	sagging	3.9	1.40	5.575	0.33	0.102	-3.909	1.375
Dover 2	20 crew and cargo	6.4	calm			6.392	0.327	0	0.103	0.104
		6.4	hogging	2.7	0.76	6.392	0.227	0	3.118	0.891
		6.4	sagging	5.4	1.80	6.392	0.383	0	-4.273	1.061
Dover 3	20 crew and cargo	8.7	calm			8.713	0.323	0	-0.229	0.204
		8.7	hogging	4.6	1.02	8.713	0.238	0	5.290	1.157
		8.7	sagging	9.2	2.04	8.713	0.369	0	-7.701	1.473

Table 1 Comparison between bending moments from Roberts and those using Hydromax.

apply. Length only is considered variable because depth and breadth are known from the excavation remains. Neither can draught increase because depth remains the same, and freeboard cannot decrease in view of the risk of shipping water into the vessel. Cargo capacity will increase, possibly relatively more than length in order to get to the same draught. In view of all these considerations it may be disputed how realistic extrapolation is when using the constant ratio to the length displacement product.

Modern computer programmes, like Hydromax, allow the determining of the real bending moment in a simple way. Van Rietbergen (2006) did such analysis for the various variants of the Dover boat. Roberts reconstructions are used as input. In addition to the shear forces and bending moments an estimate of the hull weight based upon shape and plank thickness is calculated. For Dover 1 the results are similar to those of Roberts. For the bending moment a cargo distributed as in Roberts' original version is taken. A comparison between the present results and those of Roberts is given in **Table 1**. Where Roberts used the words »hogging« and »sagging« to indicate the direction of the bending moment, the present results use the plus and minus sign for the hogging and sagging conditions respectively.

The bending moments for the two longer Dover reconstructions differ from those calculated by Roberts by about 20%. Considering the comments given about the applicability of extrapolating the bending moment for a longer vessel this is surprisingly good. The discrepancy in max. shear forces is somewhat larger, but this for the present discussion is of less interest.

The max. sagging moment calculated for Dover 2 is only slightly larger than the bending moment for Dover 1 as calculated by Roberts. The latter was considered »just acceptable« by him, thus it may be concluded that with the new calculations Dover 2 should be considered nearly as acceptable as Dover 1.

In the laden situation Roberts concentrated the 2 tons of cargo over the middle part of the vessel length. Therewith he introduced a sagging moment already in the calm water situation. Using the computer program it is easy to investigate the effect of different cargo distributions. **Table 2** shows that concentration at mid length (a distribution from 0.25 L to 0.75 L) leads to higher sagging moments. If, however, the cargo is distributed over two parts of the vessel, i.e. from 0.2 L to 0.4 L and from 0.6 L to 0.8 L, the sagging moment reduces, in particular for the longer versions. Actually the max. sagging moment for Dover 2 now is lower than that in Roberts' calculations for Dover 1. Such cargo distribution in two parts of the vessel certainly is not something unrealistic.

Case	Distribution Crew	Cargo	Sea state	Max BM		
				Dover 1	Dover 2	Dover 3
a)	0.1 - 0.9 L	0.2 - 0.8 L	calm	-0.814	0.103	-0.229
			hogging	1.977	3.118	5.290
			sagging	-3.909	-4.273	-7.701
b)	0.2 - 0.8L	0.25 - 0.75 L	calm	-1.443	-0.782	-1.669
			hogging	1.304	2.233	3.85
			sagging	-4.581	-5.157	-9.141
c)	0.2 - 0.8 L	0.2 - 0.4 L 0.6 - 0.8 L	calm	-0.772	0.585	1.032
			hogging	2.227	3.601	6.552
			sagging	-3.727	-3.79	-6.44

Table 2 The effect of different cargo distributions.

The bending moment as established by Roberts for the various Dover boat reconstructions are not unrealistic, although somewhat conservative for his longer reconstructions. Improvement by redistributing the cargo is possible. The optimised max. bending moment for Dover 2 in this way is smaller than the max. sagging moment originally established for Dover 1. His bending moment was just acceptable, so it must be concluded that a more optimal cargo distribution makes Dover 2 just as acceptable.

BENDING STRENGTH OF THE MIDSHIP SECTION

Until now only the bending moment has been established as a result of hull shape and weight distribution only. Now must be assessed whether the hull is strong enough to accept this load.

In evaluating the strength of the hull deformations play a role. When bending a homogeneous beam, cross-sections that originally were plane remain plane. In **Figure 1** the cross-sections are indicated by thin lines and AA remains plane.

It is clear that bending of a beam in hogging results in tensile stresses and elongations at the top of the beam (or hull girder) and in compressive stresses and shortening at the bottom. When sagging, this is *vice-versa*. At half-height there is a level with no strain and bending stresses. This level is called the neutral plane. In case of sliding between members (**Fig. 2**) each member will show its own neutral plane and experience tensile and compressive stresses at its extreme fibres. The common way to express the stresses acting in a beam is through the formula:

$$\sigma = \frac{Mz}{I}$$

where σ represents the local bending stress, M is the bending moment acting on the cross-section under consideration, z is the local vertical distance to the neutral plane and I is the moment of inertia of the cross-section. The way to calculate I was illustrated by Roberts (2004) in his table 10.4. In this way he finds a total moment of inertia for the Dover boat when acting as one homogeneous beam of 1,380,000 cm⁴.

From the bending stress formula above results that the largest stresses occur at the top and bottom of the hull. The quotient I/z_{max} is called the section modulus Z. As calculated by Roberts Z_{keel} = 57,500 cm³ and Z_{sheer} = 21,563 cm³. The section modulus is often used when only the max. stress is of interest: $\sigma_{max} = M/Z$. The max. bending moment is 39,000 Nm for the Dover 1 version in sagging. This then leads to max. bend-

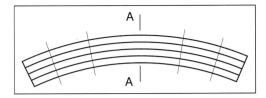

Fig. 1   Bending of a homogeneous beam.

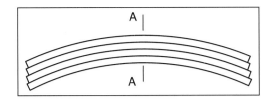

Fig. 2   Bending of a non-homogeneous beam with sliding layers.

ing stress of 1.5 MN/m² in the top of the sheer strake. The failure strength of oak as mentioned by Roberts is 92 MN/m². This is a factor 60 larger than the max. bending stress found. This safety factor is larger than the safety factor of 40 suggested by Coates (1985) for stitches of a sewn boat. Similarly the bending stresses for the longest Dover version in sagging results in a safety factor of around 30. Although this is smaller than the factor suggested by Coates, authors are of the opinion that this still is large enough to consider even the longest Dover version feasible.

The bending assessment until now assumed that all parts of the boat will act together and that the hull may be considered to act as one homogeneous beam. As mentioned by Coates (1985) in cases where more than one layer (plank) is stacked upon each other, sliding may take place as illustrated in **Figure 2**. In this case the originally plane cross-section at both ends of the beam, no longer remains plane. Instead this cross-section takes on a stepwise shape caused by the sliding of the individual layers. At mid length (A-A) the cross-section remains plane.

Sufficient shear strength between the individual layers would cause the assembly to act as one beam as shown in **Figure 1**.

When sliding between individual members is possible the effective moment of inertia of the assembly consists of the sum of the moments of inertia of the individual beams. In Roberts' table 10.4 this is two times 1/12 of his column 10, or 74,300 cm⁴. This value is about 18.5 times smaller than when acting as one beam. Fortunately the extreme fibre-neutral plane distance now also must be taken as half the height of the highest individual member instead of that of the total hull, meaning 15 instead of 60 cm. The max. bending stress of an assembly of perfectly sliding components thus increases the max. bending stress with a factor of around 4.5, and the safety factors decrease with the same factor. They become 13.3 for the shortest and 6.7 for the longest Dover version. These values are much below those suggested by Coates. But it is not absolutely impossible. It illustrates, however, the importance of building vessels in such way that they act as one beam as far as possible. The present authors feel that the homogeneous beam theory in case of the Dover boat may be over-optimistic, but that the fully sliding theory is overly pessimistic. It should however be noted that sliding is almost certain to damage caulking or stopping in seams, leading to leakage.

SHEAR STRESSES AND LONGITUDINAL DEFORMATION

Until now the bending stresses in the hull have been considered. Nevertheless deflections of the hull also may shed some light on the behaviour of the ship.

With the hull acting as a homogeneous beam Roberts calculated the radius of hull curvature as R = 8,000 m. In a wave, when sliding is fully possible, the curvature will be much different. Using the formula given by Roberts and the bending moments from **Table 1**, the radius becomes R = 200 m, 181 m and 101 m short-

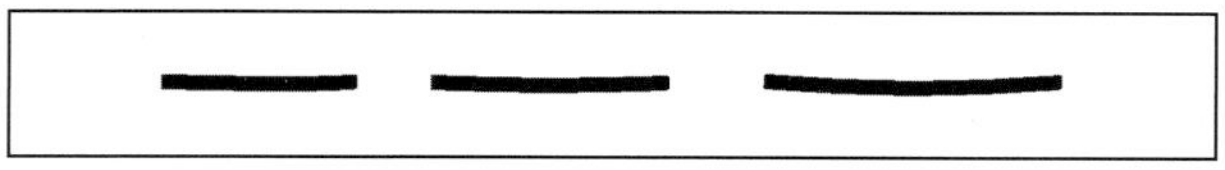

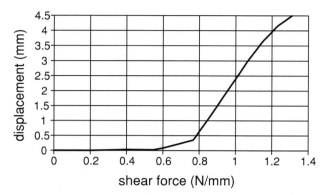

Fig. 3 Deformation in sagging of various Dover boat lengths when full sliding exists.

est, medium and longest Dover boat version. **Figure 3** illustrates the combined effects in sagging on, from left to right, the 11.7, the 14.3 and the 18.0 m vessel. The lengths and amount of sagging are shown to the same scale! Purely visually this shows that a fully sliding structure certainly is not likely for the longest vessel with the bending moments as calculated by Roberts.

In conclusion, even if such an assembly of sliding components were strong enough (see the comments above) the corresponding curvature looks rather big, certainly for the longer vessel. However, modern feeling is based upon boats without sliding; the feeling of Bronze Age people could be quite different.

Individual planks slide relative to each other over a total distance $a * l / R$, where a is the distance between the neutral axes of the two adjacent planks (being 30 cm in the Dover reconstruction), l is the plank length (vessel length) and R is the radius of curvature. Equal distribution forward and aft leads to sliding distances at the plank ends of 9 mm, 12 mm and 27 mm respectively for the shortest, the medium and the longest hull version. These sliding distances are quite large. Certainly luting of the seams would quickly become in service ineffective. The sliding tests performed when rebuilding the Hjortspring vessel resulted in displacements less than 0.5 mm (see below). Thus the vessel cannot be assumed to act in this fully sliding way. As a consequence analysis of the strength of the stitches following the approach of Coates (1985) is of limited value because this is not the way in which the vessel behaves.

Without sliding a max. shear stress is found as calculated by Roberts of 1.698 MN/m² or with a plank thickness of 6 cm this becomes 50,000 N/m per side. How realistic it is to assume that such shear load can be transferred by the stitches may be assessed by the test performed when rebuilding the Hjortspring boat (Fenger & Valbjørn 2003). Sliding started after reaching a shear force of about 0.6 N/mm or 600 N/m (**Fig. 4**), obviously much and much (a factor 80) below the shear stress transfer needed according to Roberts' calculations which result in a max. hog-sag stress difference of 8.6 N/mm, nearly 15 times as much. But of course the Dover boat stress of about 50 N/mm (in sagging direction only from still water; the hog-sag difference is higher still) is even more above this value. Whether the stitches would be capable of transferring such loads, remains to be investigated. Nonetheless, this consideration suggests that sliding between the planks is likely to have occurred. Roberts (2004) considers that such sliding would have been unacceptable in view of keeping the vessel watertight, but Crumlin-Pedersen (2006) reports that wear marks have been found on the Dover boat indicating that such sliding did take place in reality.

The amount of sliding in the Dover boat may be estimated from the radius of curvature as shown above. Using the radius as determined by Roberts of 8,000 m and a max. vertical distance of 30 cm between two vertically adjacent planks, sliding could be as much as 0.3/8,000 m per meter plank length, or taking 4 m as a typical plank length for the vessel half length, this would amount to 0.15 mm. The real radius of curvature probably lies between the 8,000 m from Roberts and the 200 m for completely sliding planks (Dover 1). Assuming that the real radius would be 800 m, sliding between two planks over 4 m length could amount

Fig. 4 Displacement force relation for stitches (After Fenger & Valbjørn 2003).

to 1.5 mm. Such value following the Hjortspring tests would be large but not impossible. The Hjortspring sewing is quite different from the Dover stitching. Further research is necessary.

In conclusion, full sliding of the planks is unlikely. Notwithstanding, homogeneous beam behaviour is not very realistic either. Probably an intermediate behaviour will be the case. Further investigations, including possibly full-scale replicas and tests, are necessary for more final considerations.

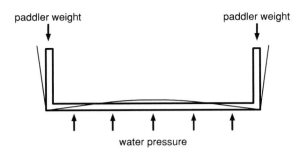

Fig. 5 Loads on the cross-section of a dug-out.

TRANSVERSE STRENGTH OF A DUGOUT

The transverse strength in modern ships is often assessed within one transverse slice of the hull with the length of only a few meters between two web frames. This is different from the assessment of the longitudinal strength where the complete hull is taken into account. In such a transverse slice deck beams, frames and floors provide »transverse strength of the ship«. This structure is needed to transfer cargo weight on decks to water pressure on the bottom and to transfer water pressure from one shell to the opposite one.

Similar functions may be discussed for dug-outs: vertical loads result in bending of a vessel cross-section as shown in **Figure 5**. The weight of paddlers assumed to be sitting on the boat sides or on thwarts resting on the sides is compensated by the water pressure acting on the bottom. As a result the bottom tends to bend upwards and obviously has to be strong enough to withstand such bending. This already is the case for a simple dugout.

Such transverse bending may be a major strength aspect for logboats in addition to longitudinal bending. As is clear from the illustration such bending due to vertical forces is restricted to the bottom. No bending needs to be transferred from the sides to the bottom. This latter aspect is different when horizontal forces such as stemming from static or dynamic water pressure on the sides is considered. For the type of vessel now being discussed, this effect probably is small compared to that from vertical forces. The load situation as sketched through the sides is the most onerous one and likely to be governing the transverse strength. This involves bending in a direction transversely to the grain of the wood. The strength of wood in that direction is substantially less than for a direction parallel to the grain. The bottom thickness will take this into account. Is this a reason why dugouts often have more thickness in the bottom than in the sides?

Transverse bending may be one of the limiting factors for reduction of the bottom thickness. In this respect the ribs on the bottom of dugouts may well lay a beneficial role. As an example the transverse bottom strength of the Scey-sur-Saône dugout (Rieth 1998) is considered as shown in **Figure 6**. Leaving aside the material of stem and stern and concentrating on the bottom, its longitudinal section in a simplified way is characterised by the following dimensions: length 780 cm, thickness 10 cm. The moment of inertia of this section amounts to 65,000 cm^4 and the section modulus is 13,000 cm^3. In this dugout two transverse ribs exist located near mid-length with cross-section dimensions of 15 by 15 cm (above the bottom thickness). Now the moment of inertia amounts to 140,000 cm^4 of this section and the section modulus to 7,250 cm^3. The moment of inertia, accordingly the stiffness, of the bottom doubles by adding the transverse ribs. This means that the deformations will reduce to about half. The section modulus, however, reduces by nearly half, meaning that the bending stresses increase by about a factor of 2. In common terms (as generally used

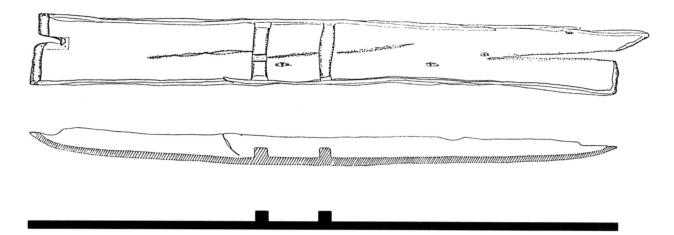

Fig. 6 Scey-sur-Saône dugout (Rieth 1998) and its calculation model.

for modern steel ships) this suggests that the strength decreases rather than increases due to the addition of the transverse ribs. If, however, deformations rather than stresses would dictate failure of the wood (and this may quite well be the case) the structure would have become more reliable. Possibly even more important is that the max. stresses and deformations under the given loads, are localised at he top of the ribs rather than equally distributed over the full length of the bottom, as would be the case without the ribs. Cracks at that location might easily be detected, possibly be less likely to propagate and more easily to be repaired. In other words it may well be that the ribs although not contributing to the transverse strength in the traditional sense, do actually contribute considerably to the reliability of the wooden dugout structure.

The longitudinal »cross-section« as shown in **Figure 6** does not take into account the contribution of the transverse material in bow and stern. The example was chosen because the ribs are located near mid-length of the boat making these observations somewhat less relevant. Many dugouts have ribs near the forward and aft ends of the vessel making the 3-D-effects more important. Yet authors feel that the simple analysis given above may serve to illustrate the speculation (at present it certainly is no more than that; the word hypothesis already would be too much) given for the existence of ribs in dugouts.

RELEVANCE OF REPLICA BUILDING AND CONCLUSION

The two examples above illustrate how ship structural analysis may help to answer questions that arise from studying archaeological remains. The Dover boat length is unknown because part of the vessel could not be excavated (changing circumstances may possibly allow further archaeological investigations of the Dover boat remains in the future). Structural analysis may not be as decisive as suggested earlier but certainly sheds some light on what is feasible and what not. The often seen ridges in dugouts have seen a variety of explanations. Structural analysis may add further suggestions for the possible function of such ridges.

Structural analysis is based upon physical laws that are timeless. Modern analysis therefore is as relevant to ancient ships as it is to modern ships. However, the materials used and the structural concepts and details are completely different from those in modern ships. Aspects are of prime importance for ancient ships that do not play a similar role in modern steel ships. An example is the non-homogeneity of the hull structure consisting of many different components that are more or less loosely connected through stitches, treenails etc. Another is degeneration of materials which for wood is much more intense than even the most corroding type of steel. A third is that deformations may be far more critical than stresses, which require a different way of thinking by a modern ship structural analyst.

This means that a lot must still be learned before ship strength theory can be used to suit archaeological purposes. This involves further development of the basic structural knowledge and philosophies. Applying modern numerical analysis techniques may be relevant in some cases. In any event above everything else, validation of these theories is essential. Small scale testing, such as performed by the Hjortspring boat builders, is very useful. Laboratory experiments may offer more detailed and accurate results but would soon be unacceptably expensive. However, many replicas of ancient boats and ships are being built and sailed. Some of them are as authentic as possible. Observation of structural aspects always takes place. However, the scope of such seems to be limited. Authors are of the opinion that validation of various aspects could be relatively easy obtained during sailing experiments with replicas, in particular when constructed in an authentic way. They plead that replica builders consult with structural analysts to investigate what is possible and desirable. Much new information may be gained at relatively very little additional cost. The experiments performed with the replica of the Hjortspring canoe (Fenger & Valbjørn 2003), or by Gifford (2004) with the half-scale model of the Ferriby boat, are good examples of what is possible. Adding this sort of scientific objectives to replica sailing greatly increases the value of such experiments. The design of the replica of the Dover boat, now under consideration, would benefit from structural analysis. Yet dedicated observation of the structural behaviour of any replica when being sailed, may very much add to the structural knowledge about ancient ships. If ship archaeologists and modern naval architects come to cooperate in such way both will benefit.

REFERENCES

Coates, J., 1985, Some structural models for sewn boats. In: S. McGrail & E. Kentley (eds), *Sewn plank boats*. BAR, Internat. Series, no. 276. Oxford, 9-18.

Crumlin-Pedersen, O., 2006, The Dover Boat – A Reconstruction Case Study. *IJNA*, 35, 58-71.

Fenger, N. P. & Valbjørn, K. V., 2003, Stress and Strain. In: O. Crumlin-Pedersen & A. Trakadas (eds), *Hjortspring, a pre-Roman iron-age warship in context*. Ships and Boats of the North, vol. 5. Roskilde, 95-100.

Gifford, E. & J., 2004, The use of half-scale model ships in archaeological research with particular reference to the Graveney, Sutton Hoo and Ferriby ships. In: P. Clark (ed.), *The Dover boat in context: Society and water transport in prehistoric Europe*. Oxford, 67-81.

Hausen, J., 1979, *Schiffbau in der Antike*. Herford.

Jensen, K., 1999, *Documentation and analysis of ancient ships*.

PhD dissertation Technical University of Denmark, Lyngby (www.mt.mek.dtu.dk/reports/PHDthesis/abs/kj.htm).

John, W. G., 1874, On the strength of iron ships. *Transactions of the Institute of Naval Architects*, 15, 74-94.

Morrison, J., Coates, J. & Rankov, N. B., 2000, *The Athenian trireme. The History and Reconstruction of an Ancient Greek warship*. Cambridge (2nd ed.).

Rietbergen, E. van, 2006, *Study of the Dover Bronze Age boat*. Spaarnwater, Report R&D-RP01. Haarlem.

Rieth, É., 1998, *Des bateaux et des fleuves. Archéologie de la battellerie du Neolithique aux Temps modernes en France*. Paris, 66-67.

Roberts, O., 2004, Reconstruction and Performance. In: P. Clark (ed.), *The Dover Bronze Age Boat*. Swindon, 189-210.

Wright, E., 1990, *The Ferriby boats. Sea craft of the Bronze Age*. London.

OLE CRUMLIN-PEDERSEN

PLANK BOAT – A PROBLEMATIC TERM
FOR PREHISTORIC VESSELS?

ARCHAEOLOGICAL EVIDENCE FOR THE IMPACT OF LOGBOAT TECHNIQUES
ON THE CONCEPTS OF EARLY BUILT BOATS

The subject of this paper is the role of different woodworking technologies in the formation of the constructional principles, and cognitive templates of prehistoric and medieval boats and ships of Europe N. of the Alps.

There are several problems to take into account when dealing with this subject, such as large *lacunae* in the finds record and in several cases inadequate publication, as well as the lack of a distinct terminology. For instance, the term »clinker« is derived from a type of riveted iron fastening which is not used in all »clinker-built« boats since some of these were fastened with stitches or treenails. In addition, modern man is strongly influenced by a lack of knowledge of production processes and terms different from those used today, and seldom possesses the practical experience needed to evaluate different options. However, this may be partly compensated for by being involved in archaeological experiments.

ANCIENT WOODWORKING TECHNOLOGIES

The term »plank boat« is generally used for early as well as later boats, but it is problematic when used in relation to early boats. This is because it indicates that the concepts of early multiple-part boats implicitly are seen in relation to planks as construction elements. Modern man is so used to working from flat, sawn boards that he often forgets that wooden elements were produced by means of other woodworking technologies in the past. Therefore, there is a need to focus first on the various woodworking technologies, known to us today as hewing, carving, expanding, cleaving, and sawing, which have been used for processing the main elements of watercraft up to ca. A.D. 1500:

- *Hewing*: Various types of axes and adzes are needed in order to produce flat surfaces on elements of a log, as well as to cut directly across the grain.
- *Carving*: Axes and adzes are also used for carving sculptured elements of any shape out of logs or parts of logs. The technique is normally associated with logboats but carving is also the basic procedure for making expanded boats as well as individual elements of lashed and sewn boats built up from several parts.
- *Expanding*: Expansion of logs which have been carved to slender half-cylindrical or »bellow«-shaped elements is an efficient way to create a broader and more seaworthy hull than provided by the log itself. Until recently, this technology has been practised over a large part of the globe, likely indicating that it was known to early migrating men. Recent studies have shown that boats based on expanded elements were common in the Scandinavian Iron Age.
- *Simple cleaving*: Plank-like elements may be produced from cleft logs which are hewn by axe or adze to form major parts of the hull, primarily as tangentially-oriented elements of a specific shape needed in the structure.

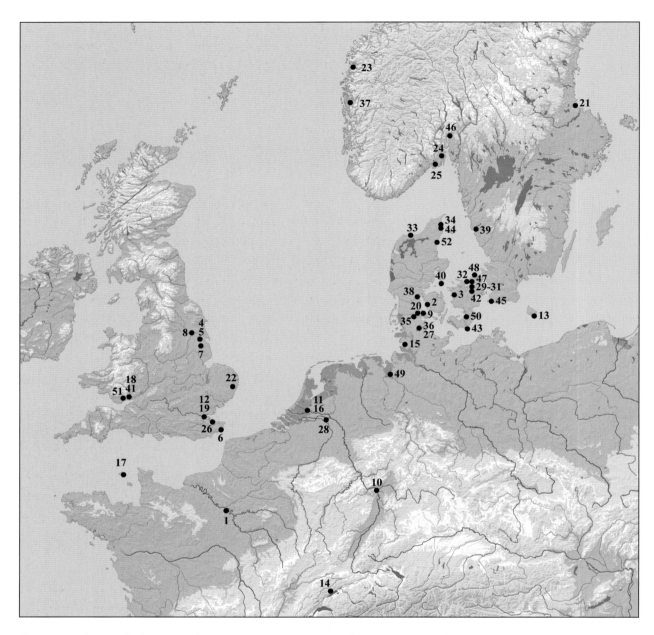

Fig. 1 Map showing the locations, where the 52 boat and ship finds of tables 1 to 7 were found.

– *Radial cleaving*: Logs cleft into halves, quarters, eights etc., to produce radially-oriented elements of triangular cross-section which may be hewn by axe into planks of varying cross-sections. This technique, based
on a continuous halving of the sectors of a log, was practised on moderately sized pieces of timber since
the Neolithic, and it was in use until recently for barrel staves and roof shingles. This technique leaves the
wood fibres intact and not cut across, as is often the case with sawn planks. Therefore, the cleft planks,
and especially the radially-oriented planks, can be made slim and still take large stresses without cracking
or breaking.

– *Sawing*: For producing parallel-sided planks, cut lengthwise from logs, large saws are needed. Such
planks are primarily tangentially oriented. The use of saws for cutting planks was widespread around the
Mediterranean at a very early stage and also during the Roman period in C. Europe and Britain. For badly

preserved planks of tangential orientation it is sometimes difficult to distinguish between those cleft and sawn. Apart from distinctive saw-marks, the fibre structure may reveal use of a saw: if the grain is diverging considerably from the direction of the plank, and if large knots have been cut right through, a saw has been used.

ANCIENT BOATS STUDIED IN THE LIGHT OF THEIR WOODWORKING TECHNOLOGIES

In **Tables 1 to 3**, 52 N.- and C.-European boat and ship finds (**Fig. 1**) have been grouped, sampled, and analysed in order to study the general pattern of use of these woodworking technologies[1] in different types of vessels up to around A.D. 1500. It has been the aim to ensure that each group was represented by one or more characteristic finds. Carvel-built ships have not been included.

The central questions are: When and where were boats and ships built from sawn planks – rather than from radially-cleft planks – or from single-cleft and hewn »planks« – or from carved-out elements? And what are the implications of these distinctions?

Logboats (Table 1, top)

Logboats are all »dug-outs«, carved to shape from logs, whether heavy models or carved elegantly, lightweight ones. The huge Hasholme boat was carved out of a log, but it was also fitted with a number of smaller elements of cleft and hewn wood to close the hull at both ends.

There are several finds of expanded logboats that date to the 1st millennium A.D. There are also reasons to believe that some of the earlier boats with very thin sides were probably expanded and pre-stressed with internal frames, thwarts or simple stretchers in order to expand the sides and thereby achieve an element of structural stability in the hull.

British Bronze-Age boat technology (Table 1, middle)

British Bronze Age boat technology is represented here with the Ferriby, Dover and Brigg vessels, none of which has sawn elements. All major parts of the Ferriby and Dover boats should be characterized as having been carved individually from whole logs or single-cleft logs, whereas the bottom of Brigg 2 was made up from relatively identical plank-like elements, carved out of halved oak logs.

Roman and Romano-Celtic ship and barge technology (Table 1, bottom)

For these vessels (and others from the same group), the planking consists entirely of sawn boards. The County Hall ship from London was evidently built from local timber but mortise-and-tenon joints were used between the planks, indicating the work of a shipwright working in Britain to Mediterranean standards, no doubt using sawn planks as well.

Medieval barges (Table 2, top)

Flat-bottomed, keel-less barges with constructional links to the barges of the Roman period are known from the medieval and later periods. The mid-14th-c. Falsterbo barge was built locally in S.W. Sweden but

Table 1

no.	find	timber origin	timber date	primary wood species	primary technology for producing the major shell elements						references
					carved	expanded	single cleft	radially cleft	hewn	sawn	
1	Paris-Bercy 6	France	4810-4360 BC	oak	X	?					Arnold 1995, 1: 45; 2003: 48-53
2	Tybrind Vig 1	(Denmark)	4330-3810 BC	lime	X	?					Andersen 1987; Arnold 1995
3	Verup 1	(Denmark)	3020-2510 BC	alder	X						Arnold 1995, 1: 43
8	Hasholme	(N. England)	c. 300 BC	oak	X		X	X	X		Millet & McGrail 1987
13	Slusegård 1072	(C. Baltic)	c. 150	oak	X	X	X				Crumlin-P. 1991
15	Vale	(N. Germany)	80-380	oak	X	X	X				Hirte 1989
4	Ferriby 3	(N. England)	2030-1780 BC	oak			X				Wright 1990
5	Ferriby 1	(N. England)	1880-1680 BC	oak			X				Wright 1990
6	Dover	S. England	c. 1550 BC	oak	X		X				Clarke. 2004; Crumlin-P. 2006a
7	Brigg 2	(N. England)	c. 600 BC	oak			X				McGrail 1981; Roberts 1992
10	Mainz 6	(Rhine region)	81	oak						X	Bockius 2006
11	Zwammerdam 4	(Rhine region)	c. 100	oak						X	Weerd 1988
12	Blackfriars 1	(E. England?)	c. 150	oak						X(?)	Marsden 1994
14	Bevaix	(W. Switzerland)	182	oak						X	Arnold 1992
16	Zwammerdam 3	(Rhine region)	c. 200	oak, pine	X				?	X	Weerd 1988
17	St. Peters Port 1	(Channel region?)	250-300	oak						X	Rule 1990
18	Barlands Farm	(Wales)	c. 300	oak			x			X	Nayling & McGrail 2004
19	County Hall	(England)	c. 300	oak	x					X	Marsden 1994

Table 1 Top: logboats. – Middle: British Bronze-Age boat technology. – Bottom: Roman and Romano-Celtic ship and barge technology.

Table 2

no.	find	timber origin	timber date	primary wood species	primary technology for producing the major shell elements						references
					carved	expanded	single cleft	radially cleft	hewn	sawn	
35	Egernsund	S. Jutland	1150-1200	oak			X?			X?	Crumlin-P. 1997: 300-303
36	Haithabu 4	S. Jutland	c. 1184	oak			X?			X?	Kühn 2004
45	Falsterbo 6	Gdansk region	1345-50	oak			X?			X?	Nilsson et al. 2004
33	Kollerup	S. Jutland	c. 1150	oak			X		X		Andersen 1983
38	Kolding	S. Jutland	1189	oak			X		X		Hansen 1944; Hocker 2000
47	Ll. Kregme	Pomerania	1358	oak						X	Rieck 1996; Wessman 2005
48	Vejby	Poland	1372	oak						X	Bonde & Jensen 1995
49	Bremen	W. Germany	1380	oak						X	Lahn 1992

Table 2 Top: medieval barges. – Bottom: seagoing cogs.

no.	find	timber origin	timber date	primary wood species	primary technology for producing the major shell elements						references
					carved	expanded	single cleft	radially cleft	hewn	sawn	
9	Hjortspring	(W. Baltic)	300-350 BC	lime	X	X	X		X		Crumlin-P. & Trakadaseds 2003
21	Björke	(E. Sweden)	c. 400	lime, pine	X	X	X		X		Humbla 1950
28	Utrecht 1	W. Holland	1000-1050	oak	X	X	X		X		Vleck 1987; Van de Moortel 2006
20	Nydam 2	(W. Baltic)	c. 320	oak	X		X		X		Engelhardt 1865; Rieck 1998
22	Sutton Hoo 2	(E. England?)	c. 600	oak?	?		?		X		Bruce-Mitford 1975
23	Kvalsund 2	(W. Norway)	c. 700	oak, pine	?		?		X		Shetelig & Johannessen 1929
24	Oseberg	(S. Norway)	c. 820	oak	X			X	X		Shetelig 1917; Bonde 1994
25	Gokstad	(S. Norway)	c. 900	oak	X			X	X		Nicolaysen 1882; Bonde 1994
26	Graveney	(E. England)	927	oak	X			X	X		Fenwicked. 1978
27	Hedeby 1	W. Baltic	c. 985	oak	X			X	X		Crumlin-P. 1997
29	Skuldelev 1	W. Norway	c. 1030	pine			X		X		Crumlin-P. & Olseneds 2002
30	Skuldelev 3	W. Denmark	c. 1030	oak			x	X	X		Crumlin-P. & Olseneds 2002
31	Skuldelev 2	W. Ireland	1042	oak			x	X	X		Crumlin-P. & Olseneds 2002
32	Lynæs 1	S.W. Sweden	c. 1140	oak				X	X		Crumlin-P. 1979; Englert 2001a
34	Ellingå	S. Norway/ S.W. Sweden	1163	oak				X	X		Crumlin-P. 1981
37	Bergen	W. Norway	1188	pine			X		X		Christensen 1985; Englert 2001b
39	Galtabäck 1	(W. Sweden)	c. 1195	oak				X	X		Humbla 1937; Åkerlund 1942
40	Kyholm	DK/S.W. Sweden	c. 1217	oak				X	X		Crumlin-P. et al. 1980
41	MagorPill	S.W. Britain	1239	oak			x	X	X		Nayling 1998
42	Roskilde 1	(Denmark?)	c. 1336	oak				X	X		Bill et al. 2000
43	Gedesby	(W. Baltic)	c. 1320	oak				X	X	X	Crumlin-P. 1989; Bill 1999, forthc.
44	Nordstrand	Poland	c. 1346	oak, pine			x	X	X		Billforthc.; NMU j. nr. 355
46	Sørenga 2	S.W. Sweden	c. 1355	oak				X	X		Paasche & Rytter 1998
50	Vedby Hage	E. Denmark	1436	oak				X	X		Gøthche & Myrhøj 1996
51	Newport	W. France?	c. 1450	oak				X	X	X	Roberts 2004
52	Vejdyb	Pomerania	1475	oak				X	X		Billforthc.; NMU j. nr. 73

Table 3 Top: expansion-based boats with strakes. – Bottom: lapstrake vessels of »traditional clinker« construction.

from Polish timber, demonstrating the use of imported timber in the Late Middle Ages. It has not been possible on the basis of the publications of these barges to determine how the planks had been cut from the logs.

Seagoing cogs (Table 2, bottom)

This group of seagoing vessels with distinct cog characteristics (Crumlin-Pedersen 2000) includes two early cogs of the late 12th c. which were built from hewn planks without the use of saws, and three cogs of the 14th c. which were all constructed with sawn planks. They are all dated by dendrochronology. The cog from Bremen was built in 1380 with a planking of broad, sawn planks of remarkably poor quality with large diagonal cracks that had been mended even before the ship was launched. This is in contrast to the much better wood quality of the sawn planks of the contemporary Vejby cog, built in the Gdańsk/Elbląg region from local oak.

Expansion-based boats with strakes (Table 3, top)

An entirely different wood technology is found among vessels based on the expanded boat's principles. Here it is represented by three very different vessels from the Iron Age and medieval periods that all combine an expanded bottom element with a few strakes. The 4th-c. B.C., Iron-Age Hjortspring boat was made entirely of lime with an expanded bottom element, and two wide, long and extremely thin hewn panels were used as strakes on each side.

Recent investigations have revealed 28 finds of expanded boats, dating between the 1st and the 16th c. A.D. and spread from Scandinavia over the Netherlands to England, and from Germany and Poland into Russia and Ukraine (Crumlin-Pedersen 2006b). Several species of wood have been used for the expanded parts of these boats but oak was the preferred material wherever it was available at a suitable size and quality for the intricate process of carving and shaping the boat.

In Scandinavia, the production process of expanded boats established an ideal of a light and subtle structure, a basic set of lines, and a framing system that was kept alive as an imaginary »master plan« for all builders of clinker boats until recently. However, the technique itself of expanding logs was evidently given up in S. Scandinavia during the Viking Age, as the boats were then built with overlapping clinker strakes of cleft and hewn planks and with keel, stem and stern as separate elements.

In the Netherlands, the Utrecht type was also developed on the basis of expanded large logs, but these logs were probably soon in short supply and had to be replaced by planks assembled to produce vessels of the same shape, known by the name of hulk (Van de Moortel 2006). After the 12th c., the expansion technology for logboats was largely forgotten in the W. However, the technique survived for inland boats in Finland, Estonia, Russia and Ukraine well into the 20th c.

Lapstrake vessels of »traditional clinker« construction (Table 3, bottom)

The 23 sampled vessels of the 4th to 15th c., built in the »traditional Nordic clinker manner« are found in Scandinavia, as well as in Britain. It is interesting to note the total absence of sawn planks except for a few elements in ships from the 14th and 15th c. Otherwise, all oak vessels were built from radially-cleft oak boards, including such large and late vessels as the mid-15th-c. Newport ship (Roberts 2004).

The Roman and Romano-Celtic practise of using relatively uniform planks in shipbuilding may have inspired contemporary and later boat builders outside of the regions of direct Roman influence, e.g. in Scandinavia, to work from stocks of ready-made planks, although cleft and not sawn. This would allow the master boat builders to have plank-cutters to cleave out and prepare most of the elements before the specialized know-how was applied, building up the keel and stems and undertaking the shaping, bending and fitting together of the planks into the complex shape of the boat or ship.

In the light of these observations, the »genesis« of the traditional Nordic clinker boat may be seen as the result of the transfer of the expanded boat's basic shape, framing system and structural lightness into a new technological phase when the new larger clinker-built ships and boats were based on a keel-stem backbone and iron-fastened boards (primarily of oak or pine).

The earliest Scandinavian example of a vessel of this kind among the 23 finds discussed here is the Nydam 2 ship from the 4th c. A.D., built from tangentially-cleft planks. The earliest recorded evidence for radially-oriented long planks in clinker-built ships is from the early 9th c. (Oseberg), although they may have been in use for some c. by then. Up to the 15th c., all recorded clinker-built ships from these regions had their oak planks radially cleft, and this may be considered a »fingerprint« of the medieval clinker tradition, although some of the largest oak planks and all pine planks in these ships were tangentially oriented.

The Danish ship finds present important evidence on variations in the availability of such planks for the shipbuilders. A rapid decrease in the average length and width of the planks from the 11th through to the 13th c. has been demonstrated, indicating that domestic resources were being exploited and partly exhausted during this period, except for ships built to a royal standard (Crumlin-Pedersen 1986). Some of the late finds were built from planks imported from Poland. This commodity was found in the »Copper Wreck« from ca. A.D. 1400 in the Bay of Gdańsk where such boards were part of the cargo (Smolarek 1983). They may have been traded under the name of *cloveboards,* known from medieval English sources (Sandahl 1951).

TRADITIONAL CLINKER VESSELS – A WIDE RANGE OF SHAPES AND SIZES

Once the traditional clinker technology had been established for building double-ended boats with a keel, almost identical stems as the basis for a plank shell of overlapped, iron-fastened planks fitted with symmetrical frames, then this construction concept could be used with variations for more than a millennium for everything from small boats to longships and large cargo carriers.

Numerous Scandinavian Bronze-Age rock carvings indicate that large boats or ships had an important role in the local culture, but no substantial remains of these vessels have been found to date. However, the striking similarity of the profile of the Hjortspring boat with several of the late ships on the rock carvings is a strong argument in favour of taking the building principles of the Hjortspring boat as a likely pattern for these large and prestigious Scandinavian vessels during the Late Bronze Age.

From Hjortspring to Nydam ca. 300 B.C. to A.D. 300

For the centuries between the Hjortspring and Nydam vessels one can trace a number of changes that greatly affected boat building in the North:
– design principles from expanded boats were maintained;
– a transition from carving to hewing cleft planks;
– a change-over from softer woods to oak and pine (since species like lime are ideal for carving but hard to cleave and less durable than oak);
– introduction of keel, stem and sternposts (probably inspired by Mediterranean or Romano-Celtic practice);

- iron fastenings replacing sewn fastenings (with variations such as pegged planking on the S. coast of the Baltic);
- propulsion changing from paddling to rowing (first rowing vessels in Scandinavia on rock carvings of the 3rd to 2nd c. B.C. [Østmo 2006]).

From Nydam to the Vikings (4th to 11th c.)

The next major steps had to be taken in order for ships to assume the long voyages of assault, exploration and colonisation across the North Sea and the N. Atlantic which characterize these centuries. These steps were:
- preference for radially-cleft oak planks (Oseberg again. However, some ship types maintained, or returned to, carved and stepped stems, such as the Skuldelev ships);
- introduction of rig and sail (the earliest direct evidence being Oseberg, ca. A.D. 800);
- specialisation in ship types (specialised cargo ships in the 10th c., fully developed in the 11th-c. Skuldelev ships [Crumlin-Pedersen & Olsen 2002]).

These changes were not a matter of technological modification alone, and they should be understood in the broader political and cultural context, which is not discussed here, however.

BRITISH BRONZE-AGE BOATS

There is a strong difference between the early Scandinavian light-weight vessels and the solidly-built boats that sailed on the rivers of Britain and along its coasts during the Bronze and Iron Ages. Here ship images are not known but parts of several vessels have been found and recorded in detail.

Most of the elements of the British boats are carved or hewn to shape from heavy timbers of oak. This may explain their survival over millennia until the moment of discovery. However, in some cases the degradation of the wood structure by biological activity and the pressure from the overburden of soil have caused changes to the overall shape as well as to the scantlings of these timbers.

The vessels themselves have some common traits but there are also marked differences between them showing that they should be classified within at least four different categories:
1. logboats with additional fittings (Hasholme);
2. boats of carved and hewn timbers constructed from one or more central longitudinal elements (Ferriby 1 and 2; Caldicot);
3. boats made by integrating two boats of category 2 into one vessel (Dover);
4. boats made from almost identical plank-like elements, assembled and possibly bent to shape (Brigg 2).

When comparing these finds to recent parallels among local boat types, it is easy to imagine the process leading from the single logboat to a vessel composed of several carved elements fastened to one or more central longitudinal core elements and to each other to form a broader hull than a single log could provide. This principle is found in the remains of the boats 1 and 2 from Ferriby, as well as in the Caldicot fragment. Carving the elements to their near-final shape is the most important factor within this group, although some bending may have occurred.

As a contrast to this, the Dover boat seems to represent the double-boat type, although the 2004 reconstruction of the boat (Roberts 2004b) was based on the assumption that construction originally started with the fitting of two plane bottom planks together with wedges along the centreline. However, this interpretation has been questioned (Crumlin-Pedersen 2006a) for a number of reasons: it does not fully take into account the serious post-depositional deformations of the original timbers as they were compressed by several metres of sediments and topsoil overburden. The recorded wear pattern on the outside of the bottom boards indicates that the bottom originally was not flat but hollow underneath along the centre-line. The wedges locking the two parts and the bow-panel together represent an entirely different system to the yew stitches used between the chine elements and the planks on both sides of these.

The conceptual origin of the Dover boat can be understood as developing from vessels constructed by joining together side-by-side two extended logboats to achieve a seaworthy and beamy craft. Such double-boats are known from archaeological finds as well as among recent types of vessels from various parts of Europe and Asia. In the Dover case, each of the two parts of the double-boat has been modified in shape to match one another as parts of the resulting vessel, and at this stage the two parts would not have been able to function individually if taken apart. Further studies and experiments with models will be required to find the most likely original shape of each of these units and of the resulting vessel, and to establish the original building sequence of the Dover boat.

The consequences of this observation reach beyond the Dover boat itself, since similar principles are used in the construction of many later barge types with carved chine elements forming the transition between bottom and sides. This is the case, for instance, in the 2nd-c. A.D. Bevaix barge from Lake Neuchâtel in Switzerland (Arnold 1992). Here, the bottom planking is filled in with a mosaic of irregularly shaped sawn timbers between the chines that were positioned on the stocks as the first step of the process.

An entirely different concept is the so-called Brigg »raft«, ca. 800 B.C., consisting of a panel of five almost identical hewn planks and an edge plank. By no means originally a proper raft, two very different interpretations have been presented as reconstructions of the original vessel: a box-shaped version (McGrail 1981) and another with the bottom boards bent to form a crescent-shaped hull, curved both longitudinally and transversely (Roberts 1992). It will be interesting in future studies to investigate these two options.

However, in relation to wood technology, the important point is that the Brigg 2 vessel may be the earliest N.-European representative of a new trend in boatbuilding, replacing the older tradition for British Bronze Age boats. That is, instead of using elements carved to match the individual shape of the relevant part of the boat, a plank-oriented concept with bent planks of relatively uniform shape was implemented as part of the creation of the hull shape.

CONCLUSIONS

The aim of this paper has been to note the importance of taking early woodworking technologies into consideration as opposed to proscribing modern ideas of plane boards and straight lines when reconstructing prehistoric vessels from N.W. and N. Europe. It has also been intended to caution against the uncritical use of the term plank-built boats for prehistoric boats.

Instead, early boat types grew more organically from the trunks of trees, carved out and hewn to shape by boat builders who were sculptors rather than shipwrights. For their conditions, they created marvellous vessels by building up the craft from carefully shaped individual elements cut from logs – stout and heavy vessels in Britain, slender and light ones in Scandinavia. At a certain stage, the idea of building the vessels from more or less standardised plank-like elements, as well as the bending of planks and the use of keels and stem posts, was adopted, probably from Mediterranean shipwrightry. In Scandinavia the expanded logboat provided a »master plan« for the lines and internal structure for early clinker-built and iron-fastened ships, primarily made from radially-cleft oak planks. This influence culminated in the elegant and epoch-making Viking ships, and continued throughout the entire medieval period for large and small vessels.

NOTE

1) In the tables of the primary wood technology the numbering of the finds is chosen to give the chronological sequence of these. The markings by X refer to major structural parts and x to supplementary elements, while the question mark refers to uncertainty about the technology involved. Timber origin shown in brackets is based on the location of the find site, without brackets as established by dendrochronology.

REFERENCES

Åkerlund, H., 1942, Galtabäcksbåtens ålder och härstamning. *Göteborgs och Bohuslän fornminnesförenings tidskrift 1942*, 24-49.

Andersen, P. K., 1983, *Kollerupkoggen*. Museet for Thy og Vester Hanherred. Thisted.

Andersen, S. H., 1987, Mesolithic dug-outs and paddles from Tybrind Vig, Denmark. *Acta Arch.*, 57, 87-106.

Arnold, B., 1992, *Batellerie gallo-romaine sur le lac de Neuchâtel* 1-2. Archéologie Neuchâteloise, vols 12-13. Saint-Blaise.

1995-1996, *Pirogues monoxyles d'Europe centrale – construction, typologie, evolution* 1-2. Archéologie Neuchâteloise, vols 20-21. Saint-Blaise.

2003, Les pirogue néolithiques de Bercy. In: *Aux origines de Paris*. Exhibition catalogue Laténium. Neuchâtel, 48-53.

Bill, J., 1999, Fra vikingeskib til bondeskude. Middelalderens almuesøfart under lup. *Nationalmuseets Arbejdsmark*, 1999, 171-185.

in press: *From Nordic to North European. Coastal seafaring and changes in Danish shipbuilding A.D. 900-1600*. Ships & Boats of the North. Roskilde.

Bill, J., Gøthche, M. & Myrhøj, H. M., 2000, Roskildeskibene. In: T. Christensen & M. Andersen (eds), *Civitas Roscald – fra byens begyndelse*. Roskilde, 211-260.

Bockius, R., 2000, Antike Prähme. *Jahrb. RGZM*, 47, 439-493.

2006, *Die spätrömischen Schiffswracks aus Mainz*. Monographien des Römisch-Germanischen Zentralmuseums, no. 67. Mainz.

Bonde, N. & Jensen, J. S., 1995, The dating of a Hanseatic cog-find in Denmark. In: O. Olsen *et al.* (eds), *Shipshape. Essays for Ole Crumlin-Pedersen*, Roskilde, 103-121.

Bonde, N., 1994, De norske vikingeskibsgraves alder. *Nationalmuseets Arbejdsmark* 1994, 128-148.

Bruce-Mitford, R., 1975, *The Sutton Hoo Ship-Burial*, vol. 1. London.

Christensen, A. E., 1985, Boat Finds from Bergen. *The Bryggen Papers*, Main Series, no. 1. Bergen, 47-278.

Clark, P., (ed.) 2004, *The Dover Boat in Context: Society and water transport in prehistoric Europe*. Oxford.

Crumlin-Pedersen, O., 1979, Danish Cog-finds. In: S. McGrail (ed.), *The Archaeology of Medieval Ships and Harbours in Northern Europe*. BAR, Internat. Series, no. 66. Oxford, 17-34.

1981, Skibe på havbunden. Vragfund i danske farvande fra perioden 600-1400. *Handels- og Søfartsmuseet, Årbog 1981*, 28-65.

1986, Aspects of Viking-Age Shipbuilding in the Light of the Construction and Trials of the Skuldelev Ship-Replicas Saga Siglar and Roar Ege. *Journal of Danish Archaeology*, 5, 209-228.

1989, Skibet i Bøtøminde – en falstersk middelalderskude. In: J. Skamby Madsen & O. Crumlin-Pedersen, *To skibsfund fra Falster*. Roskilde, 33-44.

1991, Bådgrave og gravbåde på Slusegård. In: *Slusegård-gravpladsen, vol. III*. Jysk Arkæologisk Selskabs Skrifter, no. XIV, 3. Århus, 93-266.

1997, *Viking-Age Ships and Shipbuilding in Hedeby/Haithabu and Schleswig*. Ships & Boats of the North, no. 2. Roskilde, Schleswig.

2000, To be or not to be a cog. The Bremen cog in perspective. *IJNA*, 29.2, 230-246.

2004, Nordic clinker construction. In: F. M. Hocker & C. A. Ward (eds), *The philosophy of shipbuilding. Conceptual approaches to the study of wooden ships*. College Station/Texas, 37-63.

2006a, The Dover boat – a reconstruction case-study. *IJNA*, 35.1, 58-71.

2006b, Den nordiske klinkbåds grundform – en totusindårig tradition og dens rødder. In: Arisholm *et al.*, *Klink og seil*, 33-56.

Crumlin-Pedersen, O., Nymark, L. & Christiansen, C., 1980, Kyholm 1978. A joint archaeological-geological investigation around a 13th c. wreck at Kyholm, Samsø, Denmark. *IJNA*, 9.3, 193-216.

Crumlin-Pedersen, O. & Olsen, O., (eds) 2002, *The Skuldelev Ships I. Topography, Archaeology, History, Conservation and Display*. Ships & Boats of the North, vol. 4.1. Roskilde.

Crumlin-Pedersen, O. & Trakadas, A., (eds) 2003, *Hjortspring. A Pre-Roman Iron-Age Warship in Context*. Ships and Boats of the North, vol. 5. Roskilde.

Engelhardt, C., 1865, *Nydam Mosefund 1859-1863*. København.

Englert, A., 2001a, Große Lastschiffe in dänischen Gewässern von 1000 bis 1250. *Archäologisches Nachrichtenblatt*, 6, 354-357.

Englert, A., 2001b, The Dating and Origin of the »Big Ship« from Bergen. In: I. Øye *et al.* (eds), *Ships and Commodities*. The Bryggen Papers. Supplementary Series, no. 7. Bergen, 43-50.

Fenwick, V. (ed.), 1978, *The Graveney Boat*. BAR, British Series, no. 53. Oxford.

Gøthche, M. & Myrhøj, H. M., 1996, The wreck from Vedby Hage – a late medieval wreck from Storstrømmen. *MAN Roskilde*, 7, 12-15.

Hansen, K. E., 1944, Kolding Skibet. Foreløbig Meddelelse om Fund af et Middelalderskib. *Handels- og Søfartsmuseet paa Kronborg, Aarbog 1944*, 119-129.

Hirte, C., 1989, Bemerkungen zu Befund und Funktion der kaiserzeitlichen Stammboote von Vaale und Leck. *Offa*, 46, 111-136.

Hocker, F., 2000, Relocating the Kolding cog. *MAN Roskilde*, 14, 50-55.

Humbla, P., 1937, *Galtabäcksbåten och tidigt båtbyggeri i Norden*. Göteborg.

1950, Björke-båten från Hille. *Från Gästrikland*, 1949, 5-38.

Kühn, H. J., 2004, Ein hochmittelalterlicher Fährprahm im Haddebyer Noor (Haithabu Wrack IV). In: Brandt & Kühn, *Haithabu*, 9-16.

Lahn, W. 1992, *Die Kogge von Bremen*. Band I: Bauteile und Bauablauf. Bremen.

Marsden, P., 1994, *Ships of the Port of London first to eleventh centuries A.D.* English Heritage, Archaeological Report, vol. 3. London.

2004, Description of the boat. In: Clark 2004, 32-95.

McGrail, S., 1981, *The Brigg »Raft« and her Prehistoric Environment*. BAR, British Series, no. 89. Oxford.

Millet, M. & McGrail, S., 1987, The Archaeology of the Hasholme Logboat. *The Archaeological Journal*, 144, 69-155.

Nayling, N. & McGrail, S., 2004, *The Barland's Farm Romano-Celtic Boat*. CBA, Res. Report, no. 138. York.

Nayling, N., 1998, *The Magor Pill medieval wreck*. CBA, Res. Report, no. 115. York.

Nicolaysen, N., 1882, *The Viking-ship discovered at Gokstad in Norway. Langskibet fra Gokstad ved Sandefjord*. Kristiania.

Nilsson, M., Krąpiec, M. & Ossowski, W., 2004, Medieval Barges from Falsterbo, Sweden. In: K. Brandt & H. J. Kühn, *Der Prahm aus dem Hafen von Haithabu. Beiträge zu antiken und mittelalterlichen Flachbodenschiffen. Schriften des Archäologischen Landesmuseums*. Neumünster, 71-82.

NMU: Archive of the Institute for Maritime Archaeology at the Viking Ship Museum, Roskilde.

Østmo, E., 2006, Skipsmotivet på helleristninger fra jernalderen på Østlandet. In: Arisholm *et al*., *Klink og seil*, 57-72.

Paasche, K. & Rytter, J., 1998, Fra skip til skute. Forudsetninger for, og utvikling av middelalderske skip av nordisk type. *Universitetets Oldsaksamling Årbog* 1997/1998, 155-178.

Rieck, F., 1996, Ll. Kregme-koggen. Et middelalderligt skibsforlis i Roskilde Fjord. In: *Søfart, politik, identitet – tilegnet Ole Feldbæk*. København, 17-25.

1998, Die Schiffsfunde aus dem Nydammoor. Alte Funde und Neue Untersuchungen. In: G. Bemmann & J. Bemmann (eds), *Der Opferplatz von Nydam 1. Die Funde aus den älteren Grabungen: Nydam I und Nydam II. Schriften des Archäologischen Landesmuseums*, no. 4. Neumünster, 267-292.

Roberts, O. T. P., 1992, The Brigg »raft« reassessed as a round bilge Bronze Age boat. *IJNA*, 21.3, 245-258.

2004a, Llong Casnewydd: the Newport Ship – a Personal View. *IJNA*, 33.1, 158-163.

2004b, Reconstruction and performance. In: Clark 2004, 189-210.

Rule, M., 1990, The Romano-Celtic ship excavated at St Peter Port, Guernsey. In: S. McGrail (ed.), *Maritime Celts, Frisians and Saxons*. CBA, Res. Report, no. 71. London, 49-56.

Sandahl, B., 1951, *Middle English Sea Terms* I. Essays and Studies on English Language and Literature, vol. VIII. Uppsala.

Shetelig, H. & Johannessen, F., 1929, *Kvalsundfundet og andre norske myrfund av fartøier*. Bergens Museums Skrifter ny rekke, no. II.2. Bergen.

Shetelig, H., 1917, Skibet. In: A. W. Brøgger (ed.), *Osebergfundet* I. Kristiania, 283-366.

Smolarek, P., 1983, The genesis, present state and prospects of Polish underwater archaeological investigations in the Baltic. *Acta Universitatis Nicolai Copernici, Archeologia*, IX, 5-38.

Van de Moortel, A., 2003, A New Look at the Utrecht Ship. In: *ISBSA 9*, 183-189.

Vlek, R., 1987, *The Mediaeval Utrecht Boat*. BAR, Internat. Series, no. 382. Oxford.

Weerd, M. D. De, 1988, *Schepen voor Zwammerdam*. Academisch Proefschrift Universiteit van Amsterdam. Haarlem.

Wessman, S., 2005, *A 14th c. cog wrecked in Roskilde Fjord*. Unpublished PhD dissertation, Turun Yliopisto.

Wright, E., 1990, *The Ferriby Boats. Seacraft of the Bronze Age*. London, New York.

HANUS JENSEN

FULL-SCALE RECONSTRUCTION
OF EXPANDED BOATS FROM THE IRON AGE

In the summers of 2005 and 2006, the boat yard of the Viking Ship Museum in Roskilde reconstructed three hollowed-out, heat-expanded log boats. The purpose of this work was to examine the transition from boats hollowed out from a single log to boats with several components, and to determine whether there is a correlation between these boats and the Nordic clinker-built boats. The definition of the term »expanded boats« is as used by Ole Crumlin-Pedersen (Crumlin-Pedersen 2006). Three different boats were built representing the period A.D. 170 to approx. A.D. 800. Apart from a wide time span, these vessels also included many different materials and techniques of craftsmanship. They provide a good basis to research possible development trends in the period leading to the fully developed clinker-building technique in the Viking Age.

The oldest and youngest of these three boats have been chosen to briefly discuss, the boat in excavation trench 1131 from the Slusegård burial site on Bornholm from approx. A.D. 170 (Crumlin-Pedersen 1991: 144-146) and the boat in excavation trench 75 from the burial site Tuna i Badelunda in Sweden from approx. A.D. 800 (Schönbäck 1994). Thereafter it will be focussed in more depth on the third boat, a single find from Bjørke in Sweden from approx. A.D. 380 (Humbla 1950).

The Slusegård boat is an expanded boat, hollowed out from a single oak trunk, possibly strengthened with frames and breasthooks (**Fig. 1**). Tuna i Badelunda has a hollowed and expanded base section of pine. It has an attached strake, similarly of pine, frames of juniper and keel and stem parts of pine. The frame, keel and stem parts are fixed with juniper treenails, whilst the strake is sewn to the expanded base section with roots of spruce trees (**Fig. 2**). The Bjørke boat comprises an expanded base of lime wood and an attached strake of pine. The stem parts are similarly of pine, although the frames are of spruce. The frames are lashed with juniper withies to clamps in the bottom and on the planks. The stem parts are riveted to the ends of the base section with iron rivets and the strake is riveted to the base and both stems, similarly with iron rivets.

The first problem that arises in connection with the reconstruction of an expanded boat is to determine how the boat appeared before the expansion. This has implications for determining the thickness of the trunk from which the boat was hollowed out. This problem was solved by overlaying the drawing with thin metal wire thread to create a framework (**Fig. 3**). Afterwards the wire threads could be bent together to form a series of circles and thereby gain an impression of the trunk's diameter. Together with the curvature of the bottom the appearance of the upper edge of the trunk prior to hollowing could be calculated. This problem was not experienced with the Slusegård boat, since it was collapsed when found. In this case the opposite problem occurred, as the starting point was known, but not the final form (Crumlin-Pedersen 1991: 183-185). In order not to work completely blind with large trees, it was first experimented with smaller models. A 1:10 model gave a good indication of the shape but the model was too small to confirm how the wood would react to heating and expansion. In order to understand this technique which was unknown, and therefore unpredictable, a 1:2 scale model was built and heated over an open fire, before the full-scale project using a very costly lime wood trunk began.

The experiments with 1:10 scale models of the three boats demonstrated that they did not open in an even and smooth arc. Instead the sides had a tendency to pull inwards approx. halfway down. Thereby the boat

Fig. 1   The Slusegård boat afloat (Photo W. Karrasch).

Fig. 2   The finished Tuna boat (Photo W. Karrasch).

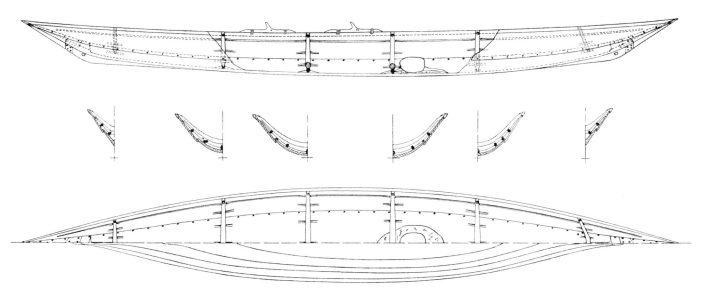

Fig. 3 Reconstruction of an expanded boat (Drawing A. Sundstrand, after Humbla 1950).

acquired a slightly triangular cross-section (**Fig. 4**). Since the same thing happened with the 1:2 scale model, it seemed that this was not caused by an incorrect working method but might be a law of physics, which the author has not yet found a method to counteract. It is also in this region of the boat that the majority of the cracks occur during expansion, so it is important that this region is under control.

When working started on the full scale boat, it was chosen to leave the sides slightly thicker in this region, thinking that they would cope better with the pull when expanded. During the attempt it quickly became apparent that the tendency to pull inwards was the same as with the model experiments. In this case, however, it split even more extensively due to the greater thickness of the material. The boat split so badly that all of the work seemed to be wasted. It was a disastrous day since the entire summer project seemed about to be ruined.

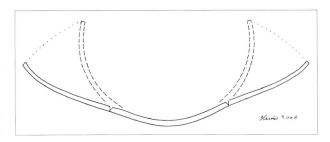

Fig. 4 Diagram showing where the boat pulls inwards and splits.

In the original boat there are repair patches in the same region as the area where the experimental boat had split so fatally. The patches are under the frames which were interpreted to mean that they were applied during the construction and are not repairs due to damage caused later by use. There is a possibility that the patches were already applied during expansion. If this were the case, perhaps the test boat could also be rescued.

The cracked boat was pared down in the split area after which the repair patches over the cracks were riveted before the dugout was heated up again. This time the expansion occurred without a problem, and a boat of the desired shape has been achieved, without further incident (**Fig. 5**). It is highly likely that this method was used originally, since a lot of work and materials are wasted if the boat is scrapped at this stage. When building the Tuna boat the same problems were experienced. Therefore the procedure was repeated with the same good result.

Fig. 5 Expansion of the logboat by fire (Photo W. Karrasch).

The next step in the construction was the Bjørke boat's well preserved and unusual fore and after ends. They are composed of two pieces each, made from pine: an upper triangular and hollow part, which makes it possible to rivet a plank on to it, and a lower part that locks and strengthens the upper part. Both parts are riveted to a scarf in the ends of the base section (**Fig. 6**). The pieces are joined by eleven nails. It is worth noting that the nails in the Bjørke boat are square, whereas the nails in the Nordic boats from the Viking period were round. The nails in the Slavic boats from Ralswiek, found on Rügen in N. Germany, dated to shortly after A.D. 977 (Englert *et al.* 1999: 172; Fircks 1999: 11), are also square.

Once the stem parts are fixed, the boat is ready to have the strakes attached, which increase its volume by approx. 80 % and thereby definitively distances this boat from the logboats.

The two planks for this strake are manufactured from an approx. 50 cm thick pine trunk. The trunk was cleaved with wooden wedges (Sandvig 1931: 3-27) that are knocked into a preformed cut into each side of the tree. When the tree is cleaved, one is left with two semi-circles, each of which yields a plank of approx. 45 cm width and, in this case, down to 12 mm thickness. This happens by shaving the cut surface smooth where-after a cut is made across the rounded part approx. every metre. These pieces can now be cleaved off without risk of the wood splitting towards the middle, which would ruin the plank. These faces are also shaved to a smooth finish.

A trunk was cleaved in this manner but it proved to be too thin. Although a thicker trunk was obtained, there was not enough time to perform additional chopping experiments. Therefore the trunk used to make the attached strake was cut using a motorised plank cutter.

Even though the planks were cut with a saw, there was still a great deal of work left chopping and surface finishing, since the planks of the Bjørke boat are very complicated. For each of the six frames there is a fastening clamp on the inside of the planks. Close to the top edge there is also a type of recess in which the tops of the frames are caught. On the outside of the top edge, there is also a widening of the plank along the length of the boat that both stiffens the boat and forms a good foundation for lashing the rowlocks (**Fig. 7**).

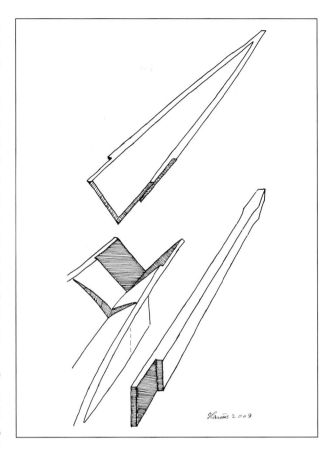

Fig. 6   Construction of the stems.

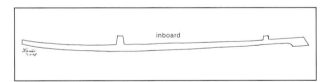

Fig. 7   Cross-section of the planks.

The top of the base has a curved line, making it difficult to bend a plank into, even though the plank is very thin. Therefore, the author cut a special shape into the bottom edge of the planks to ease their bending (**Fig. 8**). This technique, which he used in modern traditional boat-building, makes it possible to bend a plank without building high tension into the boat. However, as the planks were not given sufficient shape, significant strength was still required to fit the planks. The latter was compensated by chopping the planks for the Tuna boat, and this time the planks fitted to the sides of the boat with little difficulty. Once the planks were fitted, the frames had to be inserted. They are formed of spruce roots which have grown in the desired shape and are easy to find with the correct dimensions and shape. The frames are lashed to the clamps in the base section and to the planks with juniper withies. The holes in the clamps have been burned through with a square iron. There was a good reason for burning the holes through, since one

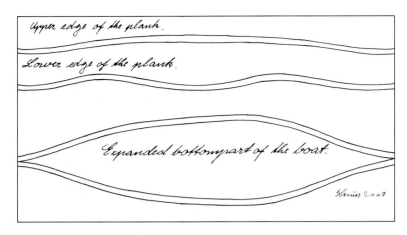

Fig. 8 Diagram showing how the planks were shaped.

Fig. 9 The plank, frame and rowlock on the Bjørke boat (Photo W. Karrasch).

cannot gain access to drill or chisel them out down in the hollowed trunk. It was impossible to force the iron through the clamps simply by warming it in a fire. Therefore there must have been a forge at the construction site and the boat nails could possibly also have been forged on site. The tops of the frames are riveted on to the planks. Here the nail heads fit elegantly into the hollow under the widening of the planks' top edges.

Since the preserved part of the Bjørke boat's rowlock consists only of one end with the lashings, it seemed reasonable to give them the same shape as one of the rowlocks from the Nydam boat (Engelhardt 1865:

Fig. 10 The finished boat on the water (Photo W. Karrasch).

pl. III, fig. 16) (**Fig. 9**). This contemporary rowlock has a similar lashing although the rowlock from Nydam is significantly larger. The rowlock holes do not appear to have been drilled through but rather whittled out with a knife. This also appears to be the case with the holes in the Bjørke boat's stem beards. It was not difficult to whittle the holes instead of drilling them, thereby recreating the appearance of the original holes. The shape of the oars is similarly taken from the Nydam boat (Engelhardt 1865: pl. III, fig. 19). They are short, square towards the blades, and round towards the rowlock and loom.

No caulking was found on the ancient boat. However, the replica was sealed by pouring a resin-tar mixture in all cracks on the boat's external surface (Crumlin-Pedersen 1991: 162-164). The boat is straight but with three men at the oars and one to steer with a paddle it is well balanced and easily attains a speed of six knots (**Fig. 10**).

CONCLUSIONS

The shape of the Bjørke boat's base, the hollowed stem parts, the iron nails, the design of the planks and the lines in the course of the planks that elegantly reach all the way to the tops of the stems, indicate a relationship with the boat complex from the burial site in Gokstad (Damman 1996).

The shape of the Tuna boat's base section, fore and after stems, planks, keel and sewing technique demonstrate a relationship to finds such as Malkijärvi in Lapland (Arbman 1940: 82-85), an imprecisely dated boat, and the boat from Årby in Sweden from approx. A.D. 850 to 950 (Arbman 1940: 93). These two boats both have a broad plank keel and two additional strakes.

It is possible to save a split expanded boat by cutting through the cracked area, keeping the mid-section as a plank keel and then fitting in an extra strake to recapture the lost depth and breadth. Thereby this area, which is problematic and difficult to control, is removed from the construction process. The Malkijärvi boat has a broad bottom plank, the Årby boat has a loose keel nailed to the same kind of broad bottom plank, whereas the Tuna boat has a loose keel nailed on to the expanded bottom part. The Bjørke boat has a stem beard at each end, which can be interpreted as a step towards a T-shaped keel. The keel from the pine boat from Nydam (Engelhardt 1863) could be such an early keel, derived from the Bjørke boat's construction tradition.

It is probably more due to the problems caused by inadequate access to good building materials that new discoveries are made, rather than them being the result of experimental thinking at the drawing table. The problems experienced during the project led to different ideas to achieve the result than otherwise would have been thought of if the project had progressed to plan and without difficulty.

ACKNOWLEDGEMENTS

A great number of people have been involved in this project and have made possible its completion. With their balance of support and challenge, they have been indispensable in the development of ideas and methods. The author wishes to thank his colleagues at the Viking Ship Museum as well as everyone else involved for their significant contributions; all those who took part in actually building the boats; those who assisted with the groundwork by providing the necessary data and materials, and those who have helped with the text, translation and graphics; the forestry people who always afforded the boat builders great understanding, and the museum staff in Gävle and Uppsala for their helpfulness and cooperation.

REFERENCES

Arbman, H., 1940, *Acta Archaelogica,* XI, 43-102. Republished in: C. O. Cederlund (ed.), *The Årbyboat.* The Museum of National Antiquities/Stockholm Monographs, vol. 2. Stockholm 1993.

Crumlin-Pedersen, O., 1991, Bådgrave og gravbåde på Slusegård. In: S. H. Andersen, B. Lind & O. Crumlin-Pedersen (eds), *Sluse-gårdgravpladsen III. Gravformer og gravskikke. Bådgravene.* Århus, 93-263.

2006, Den nordiske klinkbåds grundform – en totusindårig tradition og dens rødder. In: T. Arisholm *et al.,* *Klink og seil. Festskrift til Arne Emil Christensen.* Oslo, 33-56.

Damman, W., 1996, *Das Gokstadschiff und seine Boote.* Brilon-Gudenhagen.

Engelhardt, C., 1865, *Nydam Mosefund 1859-1863.* København.

Englert, A., Indruszewski, G., Jensen, H. & Gülland, T., 1999, *Bialy Kons* Jungfernreise von Ralswiek nach Wollin – Ein marinearchäologisches Experiment mit dem Nachbau des slawischen Bootsfundes Ralswiek 2. *Jahrb. BMV,* 46, 171-200.

Fircks, J. v., 1999, *Der Nachbau eines altslawischen Bootes.* Archäologie in Mecklenburg-Vorpommern, no. 1. Lübstorf.

Humbla, Ph., 1950, Björke-båten från Hille. *Från Gästrikland,* 1949, 5-30.

Sandvig, A, 1931, Om bord og plankehugging før vannsagens tid. *De Sandvigske Samlinger. Årsberetning,* 1928-1930, 3-27.

Schönbäck, B., 1994, Båtgrav 75. In: E. Nylén & B. Schönbäck (eds), *Tuna i Badelunda 1. Guld, kvinnor, båtar.* Västerås, 44-73.

RONALD BOCKIUS

MARKINGS AND PEGS:
CLUES TO ANCIENT SHIP ARCHITECTURE?

The late-Roman Mainz wrecks are remnants of oared inland vessels, a category of ancient ship finds from which only a small number survived in Italy and in the Roman provinces along the rivers Rhine and Danube. Although their functional character is not in all cases clear, the wrecks from Vechten/NL, Oberstimm/D and Mainz reveal a military background. But different from the former the Mainz ships share features with the Romano-Celtic shipbuilding tradition as reflected by seagoing and inland vessels from Central and NW. Europe. They also bear some exceptional details which point to influences from the Mediterranean, at least from the Classical sphere of ancient ship building.

Besides evidences for the use of the Roman foot system as part of the ship construction, all the Mainz wrecks comprise not only features related to measuring systems but also clues to a preconceived design: Transverse linear markings and two times symbols cut into the keel planks of wrecks nos 1, 2, 3 and 5 roughly defined the positions, where floor timbers, half frames or other types of ribs had to be attached. Moreover all the wrecks bear lots of pegs driven into planking an keels underneath the ribs but not into the frames. Obviously the remains of temporarily used treenails, their distribution within a wreck reflects a scheme. Under certain frames, as it seems, planking had been fastened by each one to three pegs per strake to wooden objects which were arranged exactly athwardship on the keels. Particulary because such »ghosts« are indicated in longitudinal distances of 1.6 to 2.3 m, they are interpreted as templates or moulds used to control the ship's form.

The paper discusses the subject by comparisons with similar features known from Mediterranean and Romano-Celtic shipbuilding. The findings are understood as rare examples of a ship architecture under official supervision.

The paper has been published as an extended version under the title »Markings and Pegs: Clues to Geometrical Procedures of Roman Naval Architecture?«. In: H. Nowacki & W. Lefèvre (eds), 2009, *Creating Shapes in Civil and Naval Architecture. A Cross-Disciplinary Comparison*. History of Science and Medicine Library, vol. 11, Leiden, in press.

GEORGE INDRUSZEWSKI

THE ORIGIN OF THE CLINKER HULL CONSTRUCTION

A TECHNOLOGICAL INTERCOURSE OF EUROPEAN DIMENSION

Ever since the use of the »clinker-built« term in the nautical terminology of the 18th and 19th c., the point was expressly made that it denotes a specific method of hull strakes assemblage where one strake is fastened to the adjacent one through overlapping. During the 20th c., the term was elevated even to a higher theoretical ground, by being presented as a method of boatbuilding practiced within a defined region of the world, namely N. Europe. Lately, the term was even attached to a certain »philosophy« emanating from a perceived continuity in N.-European boatbuilding practices for more than two millennia. All this, led to the actual widespread belief that the »clinker-built« method, from its inception, is tantamount to the Scandinavian cultural element throughout its history. In a nutshell, a method of hull timber joining is regarded as a theoretical boatbuilding concept tied to a certain ethnic group. No answers are provided, however, about how this boatbuilding method was born, how it reflects the previous boatbuilding traditions that precedes it, and not least, why the archaeological record about this technological transition is so poor precisely in Scandinavia?

These questions related to the appearance and development of this boatbuilding method are answered in the following pages with a focus on the archaeological and ethnographic evidence that may illuminate the origin of the clinker method in boatbuilding[1].

CLINKER CONSTRUCTION ENVISAGED AS A BOATBUILDING CONCEPT

The specialist literature abounds with clinker terminology, although its usage can be strictly classified in two categories: the first usage is related to the term understood to define a conceptual approach in historical boatbuilding, while the second regards it as a method of plank joining in a hull. As for the first usage, the term is tied to the building process related to the construction of a hull. To paraphrase the words of O. Crumlin-Pedersen (pers. comm., Roskilde 2004), the clinker method of construction »must have started with a process that in itself created the double-pointed hull with its sweeping lines and curved bottom contour, and which demanded internal support by symmetrical and regularly spaced elements across«. According to this theoretical inference, the diagnostic features of the clinker boatbuilding concept are:
– double-ended hull shape with a rockered keel, visible sheer, and incurved stems;
– backbone of keel and curved stems and overlapped strakes (fastened with iron rivets);
– light framing system with floors regularly spaced and placed symmetrical against the keel;
– light, resilient hull structure.

These features are seen as »Nordic clinker construction«, meaning that the clinker method is a Scandinavian invention, where the concept is characterized by the existence of symmetry in both longitudinal and transverse planes (implicitly also in the vertical plane) of a four-timber structure (keel, posts, planking, and framing). Lightness and resiliency are properties derived from the previous characteristics, and as such, they do not play a primary definitional role.

After setting these benchmarks for the »Nordic ship«, O. Crumlin-Pedersen (2004: 56) tries to pinpoint the origin of the concept, but is forced to recognize that the origin of the »Nordic clinker tradition« is a difficult issue, particularly because of the missing archaeological evidence before the Roman Iron Age in Scandinavia: »Except for the fourth-century B.C. Hjortspring boat, there is hardly any evidence of Nordic boatbuilding in the pre-Roman Iron Age. Therefore, it is fair to focus on the boats of the Roman Iron Age and later, to see if they can supply us with a clue to the establishing of such a strong and persistent complex of features«. Implicitly, the author states the fact that up to this moment, the clinker tradition seems to have started without any transitional period, just »out of the blue«. In order to avoid this situation, which would strongly suggest technological import into N. Europe, the author turns to the modified logboat, expanded and extended, as the key to explaining the origin of clinker tradition.

P. Humbla had outlined this theoretical construct already in 1937, when he considered the modified logboat as the origin and the primary link of the »evolutionary technological chain« of the Nordic clinker tradition as a response to A. W. Brøgger's skin-boat theory. This methodological construct has nonetheless its shortcomings. The available archaeological evidence of expanded logboats appears too thin and/or too late at the moment to permit such an »evolutionary«, chronological ranking not to mention its use to support a theoretical construct. On the other hand, this theory bears a fundamental contradiction by amalgamating the Roman Iron Age logboat finds from Scandinavia with the Finnish *haapio/esping*, since the latter represents not only another boatbuilding tradition, but is also located outside the Nordic region (Denmark, Sweden, and Norway).

The ethnic geography becomes even more complicated, because the Nordic tradition ought to have spread »in those areas where Angles, Saxons, Jutes, Vikings, and Normans settled«, but the technique »[…] was also practiced by the W. Slavs […] the Sami (Lapps) and Finns […]«, and in modern times it is also found on the Iberian Peninsula (Crumlin-Pedersen 2004: 43).

The archaeological evidence from the British Isles, the Netherlands, France, Germany, Belgium, Russia, Finland, Poland, and other countries shows a far more complex archaeological situation than implied in the aforementioned sentence. In summing up this theory, one arrives inadvertently to two basic assumptions employed in its construct:

1. The sum of all four traits is perceived as the main characteristics of vessels from N. Europe over a longer period of time, hence the tradition. There is a perceived homogeneity in hull shape and construction method.

2. The sum of all these traits originate from a singular source: the expanded logboat, since its shape and construction resemble a »Nordic clinker boat« in its infantile form.

From a historiography point of view, this view can be seen as an »inside Scandinavia« belief in a continuous and unbroken tradition that first and foremost originated in one of the three »Nordic countries«, and spread afterwards throughout N. Europe through Scandinavian migratory movements. Although this theoretical construct draws its robustness from its straightforwardness and a logical developmental sequence (expanded logboat-planked boat), it does not provide the answer to several crucial questions such as:

– Why is the archaeological record so poor (in such »primary Nordic clinker vessels«) in the supposed core area, that is Scandinavia?

– Why does the main Nordic fastener, the rivet, appear in N. European shipbuilding around A.D. 200 (Roman period) with no preceding phases?

– Why and how do hulls with overlapping planks appear in N. European contexts about the same time?

– How do these hulls with a riveted strake overlapping reflect the boatbuilding tradition that preceded them?

– Why is there no conceptual evolution behind both the »root« – the expanded logboat – and its developed version – the »Nordic« planked boat – for at least two millennia? Both the »root« and the developed version have hulls whose stability is given by the hull shape.

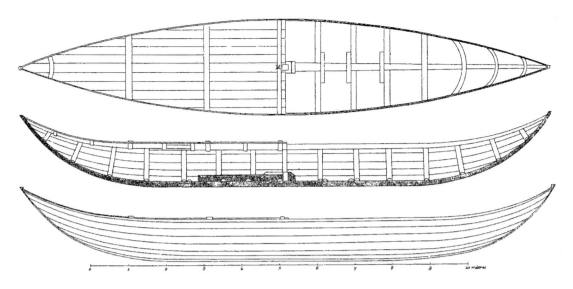

Fig. 1 The double-ended hull and incurving stems of Golo shipwreck, Corsica (After Nucci & Orsini 2003).

In addition, there is the issue of geographic representativity. The strength of the Nordic origin theory of the clinker concept is drawn mostly from the archaeological evidence unearthed in Scandinavia. However, the defining characteristics of »clinker-built construction« (double-ended hull, regularly-spaced framing, sheer line, incurving stems) are not topical to N. Europe, as they are shown by the Roman Period[2] shipwreck from Golo, Corsica (**Fig. 1**). This find is unusual because it shows mortice-and-tenon joinery that resembles the hypothetical evenly spaced mortice-and-tenon joints from the Bronze Age Uluburun shipwreck in a hull that displays features regarded characteristic to the Nordic clinker construction, such as the regular spacing between the frames at ca. 1 m interval[3], feature claimed to be proper only for the »clinker built« hulls. Important to note also is that the positioning of the end framing follows the curvature of the posts, this resulting in the skewed position of the framing from the perpendicular, feature characteristic to Viking Age (Oseberg, Gokstad) and medieval ships (Skuldelev 1, Ellingå) from N. Europe. Without its keelson, and with an oar propulsion, the hull e.g. of the Golo vessel resembles the Nydam-type craft built and sailed, nonetheless, far away from the Nordic clinker construction area. In spite of its uniqueness, this find can be scarcely regarded as a singular event, and although it could have been built in some »exotic« parts of the Graeco-Roman world, the vessel is not the only one showing a double-ended hull concept. On the basis of its resemblance with the textually-mentioned *camara*[4], L. Basch suggested it could originate from the Black Sea (Basch 1973: 331).

One other vessel, exhibiting a double-ended hull with elegant up-curving posts is the small freighter from Barland's Farm, displaying similar joints between keel and posts, a double-ended hull profile, a regular framing interval, and skewed framing in the hull ends (Nayling & McGrail 2004: 85).

If one wishes to look through a more global perspective, there is also the evidence from the Pacific, where the ethnographically documented Kiribati canoe from the Solomon Islands displays the same features thought particular only to Nordic shipbuilding (double-ended hull, elegant up-curving stems, regular framing etc.).

The evidence of all of the above leads to the conclusive remark that, with the notable exception of the overlapped planking, all the other »diagnostic« traits of the Nordic clinker construction, are present in earlier vessels not originating in the N. countries and moreover, being part of other »non-clinker« traditions:

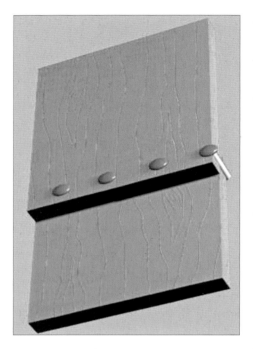

Fig. 2   Diagnostic features of clinker construction: overlapping secured by rivets.

– the double-ended hull registered in the Romano-Celtic and the Mediterranean shipbuilding tradition[5];
– framing spaced at regular intervals was also practiced in the Romano-Celtic and Graeco-Roman tradition;
– backbone made of keel and stems is also present in the Graeco-Roman tradition.

On this basis, these traits cannot be considered as diagnostic for the »clinker construction«, therefore one needs here to turn to the issue of overlapping and plank joining as the main technological playground for defining clinker construction. This area was already explored in the specialist literature, and is referred to here as the second usage of the term clinker, whereas »clinker« means specifically a method of joining planks within a coherent hull. Its definition is illustriously contained in O. Hasslöf's words about clinker construction (1970: 65), who regarded it more »strake-oriented« than »boat-oriented«: »The strakes are assembled overlapped […] with nails clenched over roves from inside the hull. […] This assembly method is called to clinker/clinch. This working stage is thought to have given the whole process the name of clinker construction method«.

His definition lays the basic ground for most modern encyclopaedic definitions of clinker construction in boatbuilding, as shown in the following passage: »Clinker building is a method of constructing hulls of boats and ships by fixing wooden planks, and in the early nineteenth century, iron plates to each other so that theplanks overlap along their edges. The overlapping joint is called a land. In any but a very small boat, the individual planks will also be joined end to end; the whole length of one of these composite planks is a strake. The technique developed in northern Europe and was successfully used by the Vikings. The Tang (7th century AD) and Song (9-11th century AD) Chinese developed the technique independently. The construction method is known in some places as lapstrake«[6].

THE DIAGNOSTIC FEATURES OF »CLINKER CONSTRUCTION«

Summing up these and other definitions, the clinker construction as a boatbuilding method is defined by the presence of two important features (**Fig. 2**):
1. the overlapping of the edges of two adjacent strakes/planks and
2. the rivets driven through that overlap.

As in the case with the other diagnostic features, these are also met in other regions and shipbuilding traditions throughout Europe. The overlapping is documented in preroman and Roman European and Mediterranean shipbuilding, and it occurs in hulls at the
– keel joint with the post,
– floor timber joint with the keel,
– keelson joint to floor timber and the keel, and at the
– strake joints.

Overlapping was documented in continental European shipbuilding dated to the Roman Period, specifically in the pram-type vessel from Zwammerdam (Zwammerdam 2 dated to ca. A.D. 200, Zwammerdam 3 to A.D. 200, Zwammerdam 4 to A.D. 97, and Zwammerdam 6 dated to A.D. 200) and Woerden (Woerden 1 [A.D. 175], Woerden 3 [A.D. 200], Woerden 7 [A.D. 155]). Another barge from Belgium, Pommeroeul 1 (A.D. 100), shows a strong rail construction and a stern cabin with a roof made of overlapped oaken boards.

Extension with an overlapped side strake is met also in logboats (e.g. the extended logboat Pommeroeul 3, around A.D. 100) and in barge-type vessels, both belonging to inland continental craft. Overlapping, as a convenient joining method, was also used in building up the sides of the interesting barge from Xanten-Lüttingen (A.D. 275). All these finds point to the Lower Rhine region as the earliest region in Europe where joining through overlapping was preferred in building up the upper sides of the hull. To these finds, one can add the most important find from Mainz Kappelhof (Mainz 6) where the hull is shown to have an irregularly-shaped sheer strake overlapped to the main side-strake on each side of the hull. Dendrodated to or after A.D. 81, this find is the earliest from continental Europe that exhibits an overlapped sheer strake. Its place of discovery, also on the Rhine middle course, seems to be the best indication so far, that the imperial borders were in fact places of technological exchanges between the advanced technologies of the Romans and those of the »barbarians« inhabiting Non-Roman Europe.

For comparison purposes, one should remember here, that overlapping as a method of timber joining appears in N.-European contexts apparently around A.D. 200 (the Nydam A broken vessel) and certainly around A.D. 320 (Nydam B oaken vessel). Afterwards, the method is met increasingly in N.-European shipbuilding in
– keel scarfs (Vendel period),
– floor joint with planking, and in
– strake joints and scarfs.

The second diagnostic attribute of the clinker construction method is the use of rivets in shipbuilding. While not physically preserved, the rivets were claimed to have been the strake joint fasteners for Nydam B and other later finds in N. Europe. However, the rivet as a timber fastener appears for the first time in S. Europe, most specifically in the Mediterranean realm. The rivets were documented as fasteners between keel and floor timbers in the Dramont E shipwreck (A.D. 423; Santamaria 1995), Dramont F (ca. A.D. 400), the Merovingian shipwreck from St. Gervais B (A.D. 612; 17 out of a total of 27 floor timbers). Large rivets (bolts) were also used in fastening the keel-floor timbers-keelson bolted together (Jezegou 1983). The Heliopolis A (A.D. 350) shipwreck showed even bolted scarfs (Joncheray 1997). Copper rivets were found securing principal floors to the backbone of La Bourse de Marseille hull dated to ca. A.D. 200 (Cuomo & Gassend 1983). The most representative example, however, comes from the impressive shipwreck from Madrague de Giens (dated ca. 60 B.C.) showing interesting framing sections with bolts with square roves that fasten them to the keel below. There is no contact between the two joining elements, suggesting that the fastening occurred after the floor was inserted into the pre-assembled hull (**Fig. 3**).

Nevertheless, the most interesting find comes not from the seawaters of the Mediterranean but from Continental Europe, more precisely from the Bordeaux estuary. The Bordeaux artefact no. 1017-1018[7] represents reused plank fragments dendrodated to after A.D. 174 (**Fig. 4**)[8]. The two strakes (strake width ca. 45 to 47 cm, max. preserved length: 3.74 m, plank thickness: ca. 5 cm) are joined through an overlap of ca. 8 to 9 cm secured by ca. 12 cm-long rivets with a shaft diameter of ca. 0.7 to 1 cm and with an average fastening interval of ca. 21 cm. The almost round, deformed head together with the hammered free end of the shaft locked each rivet in its place. The hammered end and the head have similar diameters, and this clearly

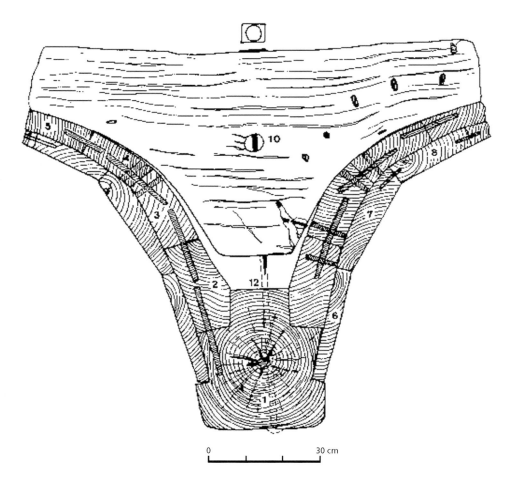

Fig. 3 Floors secured by large rivets in the 1st c. B.C. Madrague de Giens shipwreck (After Tchernia 1978).

shows that the boatbuilder took every precaution to prevent the worst nightmare of a boat builder, which is the opening of the seams under high dynamic stress. The shafts were square in section. No watertight material was observed in the seam at the time of the excavation, a characteristic of watertight techniques employed by the Mediterranean shipwrights. What is most interesting, though, is the combination of rivets and overlapping found in the heart of Roman Gaul, far away even from the Imperial borders with *Germania Libera*. In addition, the find antedates the earliest find from N. Europe claimed to exhibit overlapping and riveting (Nydam A, dated to around A.D. 200). This shows indubitably that the two features diagnostic to clinker construction appear together first in the Roman Europe, and then afterwards in the »Barbarian North«. However, the tracks of these two diagnostic features have to be related to earlier finds of Mediterranean shipwrecks exhibiting large rivets used to fasten two or three-element joints in their structure. These finds seem to cluster mostly in the W. part of the sea, specifically at the mouth of the river Rhône and around the Thyrenian Sea, and it is not precluded that the technique reached somehow the Mediterranean shores via the Rhône or other continental tributaries. Double-clenched nails, a feature considered diagnostic of the Gallo-Roman shipbuilding tradition are also present in Mediterranean shipwrecks, as well as those from Roman Britain. If these two types of fasteners are geo-referenced together with the continental finds exhibiting overlapped strakes, one can visualize the geographical distribution area of these finds all located within the imperial boundaries of the Roman Empire. This gives an idea of the spatial spread of

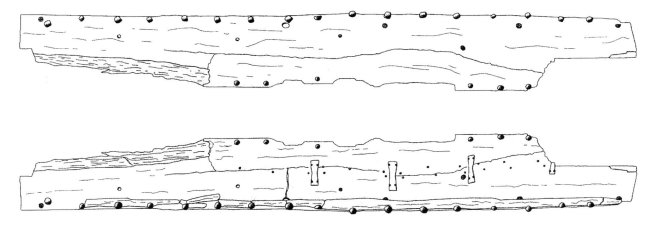

Fig. 4   The »clinkered« plank fragments from Bordeaux (After Sibella *et al.* 2006).

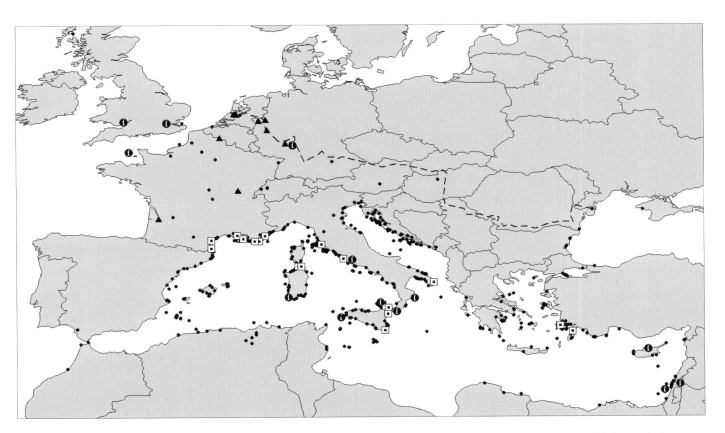

Fig. 5   Distribution of vessels displaying rivets (dotted squares), double-clenched nails (i dots), and overlapped strakes (black triangles) within the boundaries of the Roman Empire (USG DEM background).

these fastening technologies within the imperial boundaries, and also their spatial relationship to those finds exhibiting hulls with overlapped strakes (**Fig. 5**).

This situation leads inevitably to the issue of the origin of clinker construction, more precisely the roots of such boatbuilding technique. In view of the spread of the aforementioned archaeological evidence, one needs to question not only the interpretative aspects of existing archaeological evidence from N. Europe,

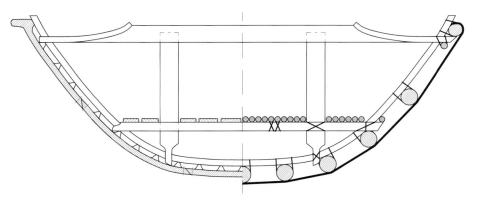

Fig. 6   Hjortspring section with a combined wood and hide skin (Drawing U. Kessel).

but also the theoretical basis of Humbla's opinion about the locality of clinker construction, since it seems quite clear that the roots of the clinker construction method are more diversified and older than the »genealogical theory« he had envisaged.

ROOTS OF *CLINKER CONSTRUCTION*

The existence of identical technological solutions of plank joining and fastening methods in N., Central and S. Europe, coupled with the absence of clear evidence about the beginnings and the origin of the clinker construction in N. Europe, indicate that this technological method of hull construction may be the result of a more complex process than previously thought.

The skin and bark component

All of the features claimed by the Humbla/Crumlin-Pedersen theory to be diagnostic of the clinker construction, such as the double-ended hull shape, the light framing system with floors regularly spaced and placed symmetrical in the hull, and the light, resilient hull structure, are in fact major characteristics of hulls built from lighter materials such as skin and bark. With few notable archaeological exceptions that have not yet been fully investigated, N. Europe has to date nothing major to present in the domain of skin and bark boatbuilding, with the notable exception of rock-art representations and the wooden hull of Iron Age boat from Hjortspring, Denmark (ca. 320 B.C.). Ironically, but not unexpectedly, this Iron Age hull enshrines not the future »clinker construction« method still to come in N. Europe, but all the characteristics inherited from a skin/bark boatbuilding tradition, and for this reason is to be regarded as a »backward reflecting mirror« in the genealogical process of the clinker construction method. As the skin/bark hulls before it, this hull is double-ended, with high, incurving ends, has a very light framing system placed regularly in the hull, and most important, it is a technological hybrid showing how older boatbuilding technology transited towards the use of new building materials, such as wood. It shows how the role of the bottom and side stringers in skin/bark hulls were taken by the cleats carved in the inner faces of the large wooden strakes (**Fig. 6**), and also how the »blind« method of sewing hides in a hull translated into the looped stitching of beveled lap joints between limetree strakes and between planking and the massive hull ends (**Fig. 7**).

In spite of the change in building material and of the appearances, the wooden hull of the Hjortspring vessel was not a genuine shell-first construction, and its assembly sequence must have started with some form of moulding that gave and held the initial shape of the mounted lime-tree strakes. Again, one meets here the same principle and construction sequence employed in the skin/bark boat-building.

This is the most direct and unique evidence of the transformation processes that made the Iron Age wooden hulls to contain some of the »seeds« and the technological premises of the future clinker construction, and it may be that this skin and bark component is the most local of all the technological components of the aforesaid construction.

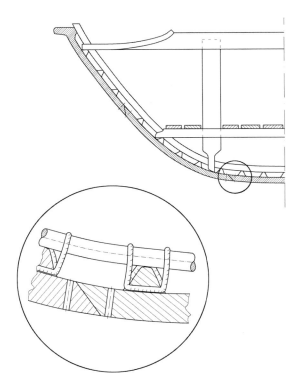

Fig. 7 Hjortspring seam reconstructed after Rosenberg and Alsie project (Drawing U. Kessel).

The modified logboat component

Originally used by the Finno-Ugric groups in the large forested regions of Siberia, the expanded logboat »arrived« sometime during the final Bronze Age on the E. Baltic shores becoming very popular with the proto-Finns, the proto-Eastern Balts, and the proto-Eastern Slavic groups. Its main characteristic was an incredible lightness much appreciated by these semi-nomad people. In its most simple form, the expanded logboat has no added strakes, nor framing. It simply resembles a »wooden sheath« and this can still be seen today among the Ostjak group populating the banks of the Middle and Lower Obi River in N. Siberia (**Fig. 8**). Its elegant, double-ended hull is sufficiently light for one person to carry it and one can envisage that hulls of the Hjortspring type were the result of the »meeting« between the skin/boat skeleton and the light, resilient wooden hull of such logboats.

Fig. 8 An expanded Khanti/Ostjak logboat in the Middle Obi region (Photo A. Y. Filtchenko).

The fastener component

Lorica segmentata appeared in the 1st c. A.D. in response to the increased warfare experienced by the Roman legions on the European fronts and by the need to increase body protection in face of more lethal weaponry. Together with it, the rivets as main fasteners appear in the defensive apparel of the Roman soldier, these being used to connect straps and fittings to the body armour. The best earliest examples are

Fig. 9 Closing a rivet's free end over a rove in Skuldelev 2 reconstruction (Photo W. Karrasch).

the Kalkriese fragment in Germany, and the Corbridge *lorica* in England. Besides body armour, the rivets were used also in weaponry, more specifically in swords, with imitations of Roman *gladii* from the later part of Roman B2 period (first half of the 2nd c. A.D.) being manufactured in Germanic metal workshops. In Denmark itself, the Møllerup *gladius* (Roman Early Iron Age B2; 70 to 150 A.D.) is a Germanic imitation featuring rivets on the scabbard strap.

Round-headed rivets with profiled roves used in the construction of Early Roman period shields are typical grave finds in Denmark and N. Germany during the B1 period (1st c. A.D.). Riveted shield bosses and straps were also unearthed in Torstedlund (Ålborg County) and Brøndum (Viborg County), Denmark, while the riveted shield-boss from Erritsø displayed copper rivets as principal fasteners. These and other finds all over the Barbaricum suggest that round-headed copper or silver rivets became signs of varied and prestigious weapon offerings in graves during the later part of the Early Roman Age (60 to 220 A.D.), and that the rivet, as preferred fastener, has a long use-history going back to the ceremonial wagon fragments found at Sesto Calende (ca. 600 B.C.), on the Italian peninsula. Here one can notice, the thin metal foil used to secure the outer shape of the finial. The foil was fastened to the wood with round-headed rivets, the free end of these rivets being hammered over the foil, a technique seen in the later ship-related find from Bordeaux.

Hammering the cut end over a rove is the final step in the process of riveting two strakes in a hull as the experimental riveting of the Skuldelev 2 replica in Roskilde shows (**Fig. 9**). However, the use of low-grade iron alloys permitted also the hammering in place of the free end of the shaft without the use of a rove. The appearance of the rivet technology can be pushed even further back in time, when it was used in weapon manufacture in the Greek Bronze Age LM IIIA (ca. 1400 B.C.). The swords manufactured at that time display tang nuts in form of rivets with hammered ends. The rivets have therefore an established past in the technological know-how of both the Roman-influenced and Non-Roman Europe, and it may be assumed that the technological resemblance of iron fasteners used in vessels from Roman and Non-Roman Europe, such as the similarity of nail morphology (head, shaft, length, nailing interval) between Woerden 7 (A.D. 155) and Nydam B (ca. A.D. 320) can be ascribed to a kind of cultural mimesis that started with the heavy use of iron fasteners by the Gallo-Roman boat builders in inland shipbuilding. In the course of the process of technological transfer, the Legion camps located along the N. Frontier must have been main centres where this transaction was negotiated (**Plate 4, 1**).

The review of the published material related to rivets and overlapping indicates, so far, that both diagnostic features of the clinker construction – strake overlapping and rivets – appear for the first time in continental Europe. Rivets seem to occur in relationship to all structural parts of a hull, and also in all instances related to the hull construction phases. The earliest rivets used in shipbuilding are those used to fasten internal skeleton timbers to the keel, and the evidence up to now comes, paradoxically, not from N., but from S. Europe, specifically W. Mediterranean. The earliest overlapped strake construction comes also from continental Europe, namely from Mainz, Germany and Pommeroeul, Belgium. It is safe, therefore, to assume on this basis, that the rivets, as main fasteners, »returned« to the Barbarian Europe, and in the last instance to N. Europe as the last component that brought to fulfillment the clinker construction method (**Plate 4, 2**).

THE TECHNO-GENESIS OF CLINKER CONSTRUCTION

In chronological terms, one can construct a traceable path from the first use of rivets in 110 B.C. in the Mediterranean shipbuilding and ending with the Nydam B vessels dated largely to the 3rd c. A.D. Throughout this time span the two diagnostic features of clinker construction »travelled« their way northwards through the inland shipbuilding and the rivers of continental Europe. What is of more interest here, however, is the process reflected by this kind of »travelling«, process that may explain the genesis of the clinker construction in N. Europe. One can also adapt to this issue, cultural transfer models, such as the periphery influential model of P. Brun, which sets the Centre (Roman World) and the Periphery (Non-Roman Europe) in a clear cultural relationship. The Centre would have acculturated the Periphery, represented by the Central-European Celtic cultures in the centuries preceding our era. Afterwards, this acculturated periphery would have bridged, in cultural terms, the Roman and Non-Roman Europe. In shipbuilding terms, this would have been translated into the adoption of rivets and the perfection of an otherwise local form of overlapping as the culminant traits of the clinker construction method that was to become so pervasive in N. Europe for the centuries to come.

The genesis of the clinker construction method of boatbuilding in N. Europe, thus, seems to have been a technological syncretism of hugely temporal dimensions, involving sometimes a straight transition from softer to harder materials, and sometimes a more complex transmission of technical traits through technological intermediaries (**Plate 4, 3**). The main »ingredients« of this method of boatbuilding are:

1. the symmetrical framing inherited from the »soft« boatbuilding (hide, bark etc.) coupled with a form of element joining in the hull (bevelled lap),
2. the hull lightness from the continental expanded logboat, and
3. the full overlap and the use of iron fasteners as main strake fasteners from the continental European cultural agents.

NOTES

1) The work presented herein was the result of a joint research project between the Römisch-Germanisches Zentralmuseum in Mainz and the Viking Ship Museum in Roskilde carried out in 2005 at both locations.

2) The boat from Golo (Mariana) is thought as being built in B.C., but until a more secure dating is offered, the boat is here treated as an early Roman Period vestige. For pre-Roman dating cf. Dell'Amico 2008.

3) Measured centre-to-centre. Nucci & Orsini (2003: 20) give an approximate value of 0.8m between frames.

4) Tacitus, hist., 3, 47; Strabo, geogr., XI 2, 12

5) Cf. Nayling & McGrail 2004: 52-58 on the reconstruction of the Barland's Farm boat (ca. A.D. 300).

6) http://en.wikipedia.org/wiki/Clinker_(boat_building).

7) The find and its context was presented by P. Sibella and J. Atkins at the previous ISBSA 10 conference in Roskilde, 2003. Cf. Sibella *et al.* 2006.

8) The dendrochronological analysis was carried out at the Bordeaux Dendrochronology Laboratory by B. Szepertyski.

REFERENCES

Basch, L., 1973, The Golo wreck and sidelights on other ancient ships culled from Admiral Paris' Souvenirs de marine conserves. *IJNA*, 2.2, 329-344.

Crumlin-Pedersen, O., 2004, Nordic Clinker Construction. In: F. M. Hocker & C. A. Ward (eds), *The Philosophy of Shipbuilding. Conceptual approaches to the study of wooden ships*. College Station/Texas, 37-63.

Dell'Amico, P., 2008, Rivistazione del relitto di Golo ed alcune considerazioni in merito. *Archaeologia Maritima Mediterranea*, 5, 13-22.

Hasslöf, O., 1970, Huvudlinjer i skeppsbyggnadskonstens teknologi. In: O. Hasslöf *et al.* (eds), *Sømand, Fisker, Skib og Værft – Introduktion til Maritim Etnologi*. København, 28-73.

Humbla, P. & von Post, L., 1937, Galtabäcksbåten och tidigt båtbygger i Norden. *Göteborgs Kungl. Vetenskaps- och Vitterhetssamhälles Handlingar*, vol. A 6.1. Göteborg.

Nayling, N. & McGrail, S., 2004, *The Barland's Farm Romano-Celtic Boat*. CBA, Res. Report, no. *138*. York.

Nucci, F. & Orsini, S., 2003, *Les fouilles de Mariana (XII) – Informations nouvelles sur l'épave antique retrouvée près de Mariana*. Cahiers Corsica, no. 209-210.

Sibella, P., Atkins, J. & Szepertyski, B., 2006, Contributions of maritime archaeology to the study of an Atlantic port: Bordeaux and its reused boat timbers. In: *ISBSA*, *10*, 290-294.

Tchernia, A, *et al.*, 1978, *L'épave romaine de la Madrague de Giens, Fouilles de l'Institut d'archéologie méditerranéenne*. XXXIVe supplément à *GALLIA*. Paris.

IWONA POMIAN · JERZY LITWIN

ATTEMPT AT EVALUATING THE SCIENTIFIC VALUE
OF THE P-2 BOAT
ORIGINATING FROM THE EARLY MIDDLE AGES

The coming 30th anniversary of the discovery of an underwater archaeological site in the Puck Bay is an opportunity to take a closer look at the results of scientific works that have been written about this discovery. It all started with a group of divers who recognized an ancient structure of oak beams, fascine strengthening and the wreck of a wooden boat on a nearshore shoal near Puck. The regional Museum of Puck was informed about the discovery, and in 1978 it initiated exploration works supervised by Wiesław Stępień. The first articles regarding the progress of work appeared within a few years (Stępień 1983; 1984; 1987). They contained a description of the vastness of this nearly 12 ha underwater archaeological site identified as the remains of an early mediaeval port. Furthermore, information appeared concerning a discovery of a concentration of artefacts, from ceramic elements to bones on the wrecks of boats near the outlet of the Płutnica River into Puck Bay (**Fig. 1**). The uniqueness of the archaeological site constituted the identification of shore elements, three boat wrecks, a log boat and of scattered parts of wreck structures coming from other boats from the period between the 9th and the 13th c. A.D. The publishing of the information about the P-2 boat wreck attracted the attention of research circles, including those from abroad. The wreck intrigued Wiesław Stępień from the very moment of the discovery. He published the dating of the boat and also a few drawings of its structure – the boat was equipped with a technologically advanced mast housing. There was slight consternation caused by the dating, undertaken using ^{14}C carbon dating, which determined the time of hull construction to the year A.D. 555 (Stępień 1984: 319). It should be

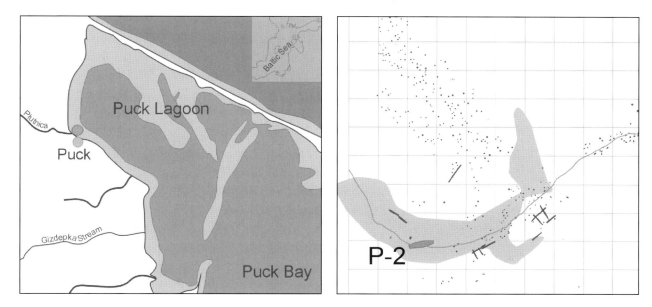

Fig. 1   Outlet of the Płutnica River into the Puck Bay and the Baltic Sea.

mentioned here that, according to a common view, sails appeared on Baltic boats not before the 9th c. Moreover, the P-2 boat mast was seated in a housing of a type developed in the form of a keelson that was used in Scandinavia between the 10th and 12th c. Doubtless, the wrong dating resulted from the carbon-dating method used at that time. The method was not precise enough when used on relatively »young« artefacts. Comments passed to Wiesław Stępień concerning the controversial dating led to another examination using the ^{14}C method, performed on another sample taken from the same ceiling plank but sent to a different laboratory (Stępień 1987: 153). The new results gave the year A.D. 810 as the time of the boat's construction, but this was also met with certain reservations (Litwin 2007: 98-99). Similarly to the P-2 wreck, Stępień also uncovered a large part of the P-3 wreck. The works were facilitated by the fact that some of the planks from the hull midship section were protruding from a shallow area of the Puck Bay. This wreck was also published (Stępień: 1984; 1987).

In 1985, by virtue of the decision by the Voivodship Officer for Historic Monuments in Gdańsk, the underwater exploration works at Puck Bay were interrupted (Litwin 1995: 138-139). However, the works were resumed thanks to letters sent by the Museum of the Puck Region to the Voivodship Officer for Historic Monuments over the next few years. These letters regarded the matter of securing two objects: a log boat and the already partly uncovered P-3 wreck. The objects were particularly at risk as a result of the interruption of underwater investigations.

The P-3 boat issue was put off for a time due to the fact that there was no financial means and no finalized concept for raise the wreck from the sea bed. The endangered P-4 logboat was raised in February 1989 by order of the authority. As well as the logboat, a large floor, stem and a bailer were recovered; the objects could have been lost since they were not bound to other elements of the boat's structure and equipment, and could have moved along the sea bed as a result of movement in the bay's waters. All the elements were transported to the Polish Maritime Museum conservation labs. After treatment, the logboat found its place at the Museum of the Puck Region. The date of its construction was determined as approx. A.D. 1190±70 (Ossowski 1999: 188-189).

In 1990, P. Smolarek, previously director of the Polish Maritime Museum in Gdańsk, took over the supervision of the underwater exploration works in Puck. The first activity undertaken was to raise the P-3 wreck. After having prepared the preliminary underwater documentation, the disassembled wreck was transported to the CMM workshops where it underwent further tests and the usal PEG treatment.

The preparation of the P-3 wreck for recovery, i.e. excavating it, led to the discovery of another artefact, later known as the P-5 wreck. It was the remains of a boat over 12 m long, laying 1.50 to 2.65 m under the surface. Only about 35 % of the artefact's length was identified; nevertheless, it turned out that the boat was built by using a method typical for early mediaeval Slavic shipbuilding; and the samples taken enabled dendrochronological tests to be made. The tests showed that the structure detail was consistent with a tree felled in A.D. 1248. (Ważny 1991: 3). Soon after the sudden death of P. Smolarek in June 1991, the employees of CMM intended to raise the partially uncovered P-2 wreck; however, they eventually only secured the remains of the boat against damage (Litwin 1995: 142).

Starting from 1992, the new Central Maritime Museum authorities included the continuation of works in the waters of Puck Bay as part of their long-term plan for exploration, with Iwona Pomian being appointed to be in charge of the works. The researchers familiarized themselves with the results of works carried out in the previous years, and it was found that the greatest interpretation difficulties were connected with the vastness of the discovery. An additional difficulty was that there were no written sources to help understand the role of Puck in the early Middle Ages. The earliest piece of information dates from the 13th c. and defines Puck as a »castellan's town« – one of 14 such towns to attain that position out of approx. 125 towns existing at that time within the area of Pomorze Gdańskie-Słowieńskie (Grot: 1998)

Puck is located within a territory that during the Middle Ages was owned by the Sobiesławic family. In A.D. 1116, Boleslaus the Wry-Mouthed sent the family to Pomorze Gdańskie in order to act as governors, and they were supposed to strengthen its relations with Poland. Locating some of the Sobiesławic family's oldest estates is possible thanks to the Oliwa Monastery foundation charter, the oldest written document in Pomorze Gdańskie. However, it is thought that this is a copy, made in the 1340s, of an original document which came from 1186 but which has not survived. The name »Village of Puck« appears for the first time in a charter given to the Cistercians by Świętopełk, the Duke of Gdańsk, in A.D. 1220. It originates from an earlier charter that the village had been given to the monastery under Duke Sambor I; however, within a short period of time it was exchanged for the village of Starzyno. The eldest information about the foundation of a *kasztelania* (a mediaeval administrative unit) in Puck comes from A.D. 1271 and is contained in a charter given to the Cistercian Monastery in Oliwa by Mściwoj II (Grot: 1998).

While inventorying archaeological structures visible on the surface, scholars came to the conclusion that the vastness of the site could be connected with the movements of the Puck Bay shoreline during the early Middle Ages, and to the gradual flooding of coastal areas. These changes would have required constructing new shore protection and changing the location of the fishing and shipbuilding base. In order to establish this hypothesis, dendrochronological analyses were carried out for selected elements of the wooden structures and wrecks, and a preliminary geological and palynological analysis was also carried out (Pomian *et al.* 2000).

However, the location of the P-3 boat wreck shows that it was ready for repair works. Another supporting feature was the fact that there were large amounts of wood shavings around the wrecks and inside their hulls. A similar situation was met while examining the P-2 wreck. Its documentation, carried out between 2003 and 2005, proved it to be a plank boat with a specific structure combining both Scandinavian and Slavic construction features. The wreck lay on a S.-E./N.-E.-axis, at a depth of approx. 1.9 m. The fore-ship at the starboard side was protruding from the sediment whereas the midship section was buried ca. 80 cm deep, and the damaged stern part remained uncovered. While inventorying the hull components, the vessel's bottom in the bow and within the midship section was found to be lined with flax. The keelson bore traces of burning, and in the proximity there were traces of a hearth. Analysing the layout of the wreck, the condition in which it was preserved and its contents, it can be assumed that it rested within the shoreline area of that time, partly submerged in water and used secondarily for flax soaking before further processing. In order to secure the boat from sliding down into the water, it was fixed to the bottom by means of wooden posts with diameters of 5 to 7 cm. The stern part of the vessel, sitting on the shore, was used to house a fireplace which was protected from the sea breeze by the remains of side planking (Pomian 2003).

DESCRIPTION OF RESEARCH METHODS AND WRECK RETRIEVAL

The wreck was uncovered by means of a lift operated by a water ejector pump, and was inventoried during the 2003 and 2005 summer seasons. Moreover, in October 2003, the CMM research team, using a Pressler drill, took two core samples from the keel of the P-2 boat located in Puck Bay. After having been secured in a helium atmosphere, the samples were sent to the Chemical Department of the Swedish University of Agricultural Sciences in Uppsala. There, under the supervision of I. Persson, tests for sulphur and iron content were carried out with regard to the possibility of forming destructive inorganic sulphur compounds. The microchemical tests showed a 0.5% sulphur content within one whole sample length; and the tests of

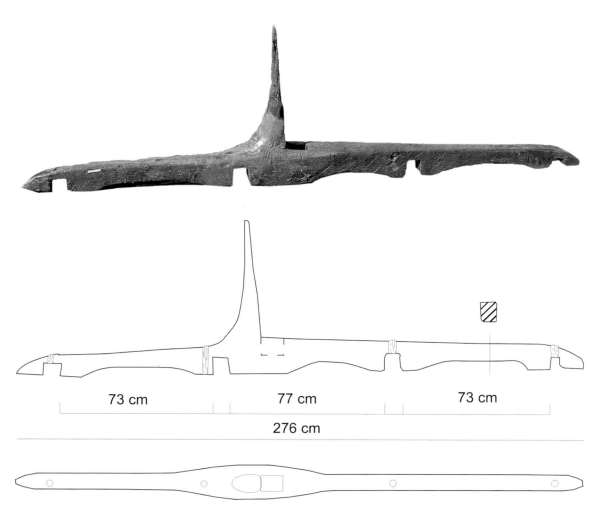

Fig. 2 P-2 wreck, keelson.

the second sample, carried out in Japan with the use of X-ray-spectroscopy, showed that almost all the sulphur was in the form of elemental and reduced sulphur, and only a small part in the form of sulphates. A small quantity of iron compounds was also detected; iron compounds are catalysts for the oxidation of sulphur compounds into dangerous sulphuric acid. The sulphur content in the P-2 boat was not alarming; it was comparable to that of the *Mary Rose* wreck, much smaller than the ratio found in the *Vasa* after her treatment. The destructive sulphur compounds deposited on the *Vasa* was a very well known issue around the world (Jagielska 2004).

The underwater documentation, prepared for the P-2 site, consists of a horizontal photographic projection and twelve cross-sections performed on the floor line and within immediate proximity. A series of pictures was taken, and a video was made presenting construction details and generally the preservation of the wreck. During those activities, it has been decided not to raise the vessel in a single piece but to disassemble its remains because of the poor condition of the wood, namely of the starboard planking, the transverse structure elements, and the soft wood stringer.

Individual planks were marked with plastic markers with the symbols PP1, PP2, PP3 etc. (i.e. the right first strake – garboard plank – numbered from the keel upwards); and similarly LP1, LP2, LP3 etc. (i.e. the left garboard plank nos 1, 2, 3 etc). Moreover, individual planks constituting strakes were marked with consecutive letters of the alphabet. Starting from the vessel's bow, ribs and floors were numbered subsequently W1, W2, W3 etc. (Pomian 2005a).

Several thwarts, which were no longer fixed to the wreck's structure, were lifted in 2003; they were localised each near ribs or floors. Detailed measurements and photographic documentation was undertaken after the elements had been removed. Before placing them in a tank with polyethylene glycol, drawings of elements were made at a scale of 1:1. The drawings were digitalized and were used together with other documentation to draw the theoretical lines for the hull and to prepare a 3D-reconstruction based on Auto CAD type software (**Fig. 2**).

element	number
keel	1
keelson	1
floors and ribs	47
beam knee	8
rowing thwarts	5
thwart supports	5
oarlock	2
unknown elements	2
oar elements	2

Table 1 P-2 wreck, hull components removed during documentation.

DESCRIPTION OF WRECK COMPONENTS

During disassembling the wreck the following elements were salvaged (**Table 1**):

Keel

The keel consisted of the main part (dimensions 1117 by 20 by 15 cm), with a T-shape cross-section, whereas its forward extension shows the form of a trapezoid-like beam (dimensions 157 by 14.5 by 9 cm), and a rectangular cross-section. The garboards strakes were fastened to the keel by means of wooden pegs of diameter 1.6 to 1.8 cm, the pegs being placed every 6 cm. The keel extension bears traces left by rivets. On its top surface two rectangular grooves similar to those found on the P-3 wreck were visible. On the port side there are remains of the garboard strake preserved along the whole keel.

Despite many dendrochronological attempts, it has not yet been possible to determine the felling date of the tree used to shape the keel.

Keelson

One of the most interesting elements of wrack P-2 is a keelson showing a mast step (**Fig. 3**) to which close parallels exist in the Viking Age wrecks Skuldelev 3, Hedeby and Schleswig (Crumlin-Pedersen 1997: 119). The frame distance is slightly larger – 0.73 to 0.77 m. Whether the keelson was secondly used or its type adapted by shipbuilders from Puck remains to be answered.

Planking

The vessel was clinker built with planks made of oak wood. Seven well preserved strakes and the relics of a severely damaged strake no. eight were preserved on starboard (**Table 2**). On port side there were found fragments of six strakes. The planking was joined lengthwise with the use of oaken pegs with diameters of 1.5 to 1.8 cm; pegs were wedged from inside the hull with triangular wedges. The planks showed a straight transverse type of seam. All transverse joints were made with the use of the same technique consisting in using two rivets and a wooden peg. Luting material was identified as animal hair without further specification.

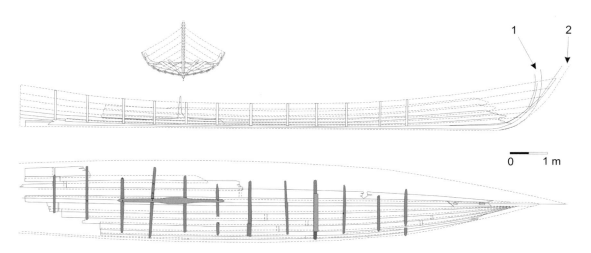

Fig. 3 P-2 wreck, reconstruction **1** according to Stępień, **2** according to Litwin.

strake	length (cm)	thickness (cm)	strake	length (cm)	thickness (cm)
right			left		
garboard	1185	1.7	garboard	1223	1.7
2	1153	1.7	2	1270	1.7
3	1108	1.7	3	1260	1.7
4	1058	1.7	4	1260	1.7
5	1027	1.7	5	1142	1.7
6	875	1.6	6	1140	1.7
7	295	1.6			
8		1.6			

Table 2 P-2 wreck, strake dimensions numbered from the keel.

CHRONOLOGY

In the light of the most recent research, special attention should be given to the latest attempt at dating the find, which verifies earlier results. During the surveys carried out at the site in the 1980s, wood samples were taken from the P-2 wreck planking and the fascines. The samples were sent for radiocarbon analysis to the Laboratory of the Institute of Physics at the Silesian University of Technology in Glivice, and to the Radiochemical Laboratory at the Archaeological and Ethnographic Museum in Łódź. M. Pazdur dated the wreck to the first half of the 9th c. W. Stępień, who was conducting archaeological research at that time, estimated that result as being too recent and claimed for a dating to the second half of the 8th c.

The fascine samples were dated by 14C to the second half of the 10th c. (Stępień 1987). Most recent results of the dendrochronological analysis of samples taken from planking in 1999, shift the date of boat construction to the first half of the 10th c. (**Fig. 4**), which is in accordance with the dating of the oldest bridges located in the N. part of the site (Ważny 2001).

It should be emphasized, however, that from the seven analysed starboard planks, two (no. 5 and 9) were older. M. Pazdur suggested they belong to the first half of the 9th c. The oldest plank (no. 9) was made of wood grown in the area of modern Denmark, contrary to other planks which were made of material obtained from the Gdańsk region of Pomerania. By now, it has not been possible to dendrologically date

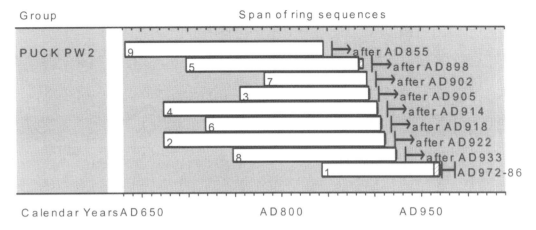

Fig. 4 P-2 wreck, dendrodating.

the keel and keelson. The latter was made very carefully – in contrast other hull elements. The origin of the keelson and the felling date of the tree from which it was made still have to be determined. This would answer the question whether the P-2 vessel was constructed on the basis of local Slavic skill; or whether an attempt was made at copying Scandinavian shipbuilding techniques, related to Danish activity in this region during the 9th to 11th c. (Pomian 2003).

Radiocarbon dating of the flax found inside the wreck gave as a result the 11th c. The flax was located inside the hull and covered with tree branches, thus indicating the secondary usage of a boat which sailed still in the first half of the 11th c. This assumption is also confirmed by the fact that the wreck's structure was fixed to the sea bed by wooden posts (Pomian 2002; 2003).

ATTEMPT AT INTERPRETING THE CONSTRUCTIONAL FEATURES OF THE WRECK FOUND AT THE SITE OF A MEDIAEVAL PORT IN THE LIGHT OF CURRENT RESULTS

Only the interior of the P-2 wreck, described by Stępień, was documented; and as a result the studies seemed to be misleading. Despite the incorrect datings made before the raise and careful examination of the wreck, possible inaccuracies were noted (Litwin 1998). There were in particular reservations concerning the quality of drawings, and especially with regard to the cross-section of the keel which was given a T-form with an offset – a groove for the edge of garboard plank – by Stępień (1987: 145-147). Doubts concern the cross-section drawing of the P-2 boat's keel showing this offset (Litwin 1995: 143). After raising the wreck, the doubts were finally dispersed and the keel was found to have a typical T-shape also observed in other wrecks of contemporary plank boats.

There were also question marks concerning the number of strakes, only seven in the midship section, and the top plank showing no rowlocks, but instead numerous traces of studding as a kind of preparation for an eighth strake. It can be assumed, therefore, that the rowlocks were located in the lacking upper strakes where they possibly have been broken off. This was confirmed by two rowlocks found with holes for pegs that were supposed to fix them to the top edge of the sheer strake.

The wreck under discussion appears extremely interesting also for another reason. It combines features characteristic of two separate shipbuilding traditions connected with Scandinavia and the Slavic territories. The Scandinavian features include using iron rivets, luting with animal hair, and of course the typical keelson. On the other hand, Slavic features include joining the strakes of planking with wedged pegs and luting transverse seams with moss. The results of wood analysis so far prove that the significant majority of wood came from the area of Gdańsk Pomerania, and only one of the nine examined planks was of Danish provenance. Worth to be reflected is also the type of wood used for the boat's construction. The majority of planks, floors and ribs were made of oak wood. However, some of them consist of a soft, diffuse porous wood. With regard to the poor condition of the wood, sample taking has been rescheduled until the first conservation stage is completed, which will reinforce the structure of particular elements.

The spindle-like shape of the vessel, and its 1:9 length-beam-ratio, point to a warship usage. This function is also confirmed by the remains of battens fixed from outside to the top strake. These battens were used to mount the warriors' shields. The clearance for a shield was about 30cm. It was definitely not enough in order to place the Scandinavian type of shields there, but it was enough for the leaf-like Slavic shields that may be found on images from the *Gniezno Door*. This could be one more proof for the local provenance of the find. However, the authors refrain from final conclusions until the full results of wood analysis have been obtained. In the meantime, this report should be treated as a preliminary study that gives an account of the first impressions after the raise of the wreck.

REFERENCES

Crumlin-Pedersen, O., 1997, *Viking-Age Ships and Shipbuilding in Hedeby/Haithabu and Schleswig*. Ships and Boats of the North, vol. 2. Schleswig, Roskilde.

Grot, A. (ed.), 1998, *Historia Pucka*. Gdańsk.

Jagielska, I., 2004, Zawartość siarki w łodzi P-2. Opracowanie wyników badań [Sulphur Content in P-2 Boat. Analysis of Tests Results], (CMM own materials).

Litwin, J., 1995, The Puck Bay wrecks – an opportunity for a »Polish Skuldelev«. In: O. Olsen, J. Skamby Madsen & F. Rieck (eds), *Shipshape. Essays for Ole Crumlin-Pedersen*. Roskilde, 135-160.

1998, Stanowisko archeologiczne w Zatoce Puckiej szansą na nowe Muzeum Morskie. *Nautologia*, 33.3-4, 9-20.

2007, Slav Boatbuilding Centres on the southern Baltic shore (8th-13th centuries). In: F. Biermann & T. Kersting (eds), *Siedlung, Kommunikation und Wirtschaft im westslawischen Raum*. Beiträge zur Ur- und Frühgeschichte Mitteleuropas, no. 46. Langenweissbach, 91-105.

Ossowski, W., 1999, *Studia nad łodziami jednopiennymi z obszaru Polski*. Gdańsk.

Pomian, I., 2002, Prace Centralnego Muzeum Morskiego w Gdańsku na stanowisku portu średniowiecznego w Pucku. In: *Zapiski Puckie*, 1, 127-132.

2003, Changes to the coastline in the neighbourhood of the Medieval port in Puck in the light of the research done so far by the Central Maritime Museum in Gdańsk. In: Sz. Uścinowicz, B. Anagniotis, R. Kramarska & J. Zachowicz (eds), *Rapid Transgressions Into Semi-enclosed Basins. Proceedings of the Conference*. Polish Geological Institut Special Papers, no. 11. Gdańsk, 31-36.

2005a, Archeologia morska w Polsce stan obecny i perspektywy. In: B. Wieżbicka & J. Czaj-Walus (eds), *Ochrona Zabytków*, vol. 2, 309-317.

2005b, Ostatnie prace Centralnego Muzeum Morskiego – archeologia morska. In: H. Paner & M. Fudziński (eds), XIV Sesja Pomorzoznawcza. Od wczesnego średniowiecza do czasów nowożytnych, vol. 2. Gdańsk, 309-317.

Pomian, I., Latałowa, M., Łęczyński, L. & Badura, M., 2000, Preliminary results and interdisciplinary project of palaeoenvironmental reconstruction at the site of the medieval harbour in Puck (N. Poland). In: *ISBSA*, 8, 27-36.

Stępień, W., 1983, Puck przed Gdańskiem. *Z Otchłani Wieków*, 49, 139-154.

1984, Archaeological Excavations in Puck Harbour, Gdańsk District, Poland. *IJNA*, 4, 311-321.

1987, Wczesnośredniowieczny wrak łodzi klepkowej W-2 z Zatoki Puckiej. *Prace i materiały Muzeum Archeologicznego i Etnograficznego w Łodzi, Seria Archeologiczna*, 34, 139-154.

Ważny, T., 1991, *Dendrochronologiczna analiza drewna z wraków W-24 (Tolkmicko) i P-5 (Puck)*. Manuscript in the PMM.

2001, *Analiza dendrochronologiczna wraka łodzi PW (Zatoka Pucka)*. CMM own materials.

JAN BILL

FROM NORDIC TO NORTH EUROPEAN

APPLICATION OF MULTIPLE CORRESPONDENCE ANALYSIS
IN THE STUDY OF CHANGES IN DANISH SHIPBUILDING A.D. 900 TO 1600

During the last fifty years, the number of medieval ship-finds in Northern Europe has been increasing, and so have the quality and the quantity of the archaeological data collected from them. As the amount of information available for the study of the history of shipbuilding grows, its complexity becomes ever clearer. Designs and building techniques appears to have been highly adopt- and adaptable, and subject to frequent modification and transfer between various shipbuilding environments. Consequently, the explanation power of archaeologically defined shipbuilding traditions is reduced as the number of finds combining features from different traditions grows. Some ship archaeologists have reacted to this with an intensified discussion of the definitions and nomenclature of the supposed shipbuilding traditions, as exemplified by the debate about the cog (Weski 1999; Crumlin-Pedersen 2000). It may be questioned if such an effort would actually help us to understand more about medieval shipbuilding. Applying the concept of tradition on an archaeological material requires a balance between the continuity in the handicraft production that has formed the material, and the number and quality of the examples studied. In a dynamic, but archaeologically poorly represented environment like the medieval shipbuilding scene, the risk is that traditions can only be identified on a superficial level. An elaborate nomenclature of ship types and building traditions, based on an imperfect archaeological material, may hide rather than expose relations between the individual ship finds and groups of finds.

It is possible, however, to analyse shipbuilding traditions and their interaction without defining them as such a priori. One tool, which is frequently used for similar tasks in other fields within archaeology, is multiple correspondence analysis (MCA) (cf. e.g. Madsen 1988; Baxter 2003). It analyses correspondence between qualitative features present in series of finds. In combination with absolute or relative dating, it can be used to identify traditions, but it can also be used to investigate relationships between clearly differing groups of finds.

SHIP ARCHAEOLOGICAL DATA FOR MCA

The nature of the observations that we can make on ship remains is defining for, what relationships between them that MCA analyses can establish. The construction of a ship involves knowledge and techniques on many different levels, from organisation and planning skills over design techniques and the selection of raw materials to the mastering of tools and materials. The final product is formed by combining those. For the individual shipbuilder, this combination process is guided by demand and environment – what technical, economical and social requirements should the ship meet and what resources could be invested – but also of practice, the way he is using his experience in his trade. The same demand may be responded to in different ways, and it is the decision of the individual shipbuilder – based on his experience – which one to chose. Some shipbuilders may work from the same rural workshop during a lifetime, others may travel and have experiences from shipbuilding in different countries and towns, in commercial and in royal yards. Their experiences and practices are at the same time both individual, and reflections of the societies in which they live. It is the application of practice on the materials of the ship – on the wood, the iron, the caulking etc. – that provides the ship-archaeological remains with most of their qualitative properties. Only if practice is passed on from generation to generation, it becomes tradition and may be inferred from comparison of the archaeological finds.

What MCA provides us with, are maps of the correspondence between examples of practice. Such a map of the entire ship archaeological material will thus be a map of where related knowledge was applied – and so also of the exchange of knowledge within shipbuilding. Tradition can be regarded as one pattern of knowledge exchange, and would reveal itself as closely corresponding expressions of practice from adjacent points in time, indicating transfer of knowledge between generations of shipbuilders. Other patterns, like an increase in correspondence between clearly differentiated groups of ships may reflect knowledge transfer between different groups of shipbuilders. What MCA does not provide us with, is explanations – it can only show us where the changes take place, not how or why.

THE FIND CORPUS

The following is an attempt to use MCA on a corpus of ship-finds from the area of medieval Denmark, from A.D. 900 to 1600. The analysis are made in preparation for a forthcoming book, and background information will be presented there (Bill in press).

The MCA is based on a total of 105 finds, found and/or constructed in present day Denmark, Scania, Halland, Blekinge or S. Schleswig. The finds have been dated by dendrochronology or context, not by typology. Many finds were foreign and had sunk or been broken up and reused while in Danish waters. The provenance could be established for 64 finds – either by dendrochronology, or by interpreting a limited seaworthiness of the vessel as an indication of regional origin (**Fig. 1**). The vast majority of provenanced finds dating to or before ca. 1355, namely 35 of a total of 42 finds, come from medieval Denmark or the parts of present day Sweden and Norway facing Kattegat and Skagerrak. Of these five are cogs and four barges, the rest lapstrake vessels. Further three lapstrake vessels may originate on either side of the W. Baltic, while one, from 1346, appears to be from the area of present day Poland. Two 11th-c. ships were built in W. Norway, one in Ireland. Turning to the period after ca. 1355, eleven of 22 provenanced vessels, including three cogs, are made of wood from the shores of the Baltic from Holstein to Estonia. One carvel-built ship is known historically to be Danish-built, and four lapstrake vessels were made of S. Scandinavian wood. Five further ships, all carvel-built, were constructed on the southern shores of the North Sea, and one as far away as – possibly – in the Basque country. The provenanced finds indicate that the record of ship-finds until ca. 1355 is dominated by ships from medieval Denmark or adjacent Scandinavian waters, while it for the remaining two and half century is more internationally composed, although timber trade may obscure the picture.

All the finds have been systematically described, with emphasis on features observable even on fragmentarily preserved ship remains, and representing the practices of the individual shipbuilders. These included: conversion method for the planking, type of fasteners, plank scarf types, choice of caulking material, the absence or presence of decorations, framing design and distance between frames, keel and keelson design, joint types for joints in keel, stems, keelson and stringers (the main longitudinal elements in the ships) and fastening methods for the keelson. Furthermore wood species have been recorded, together with date and, if available, vessel size and provenance. These data, however, have not been included in the MCA, as little as the typological identification of the finds as »lapstrake vessels«, »cogs«, »barges« and »carvel-built

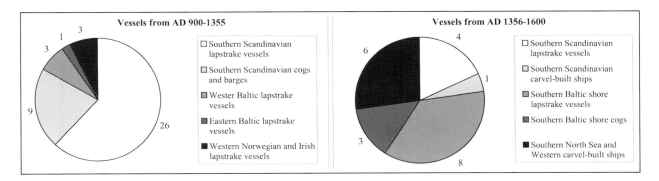

Fig. 1 Comparison between provenances attributed to older and younger vessels in the find corpus. The numbers refer to the number of finds from each region.

vessels« has. Thus the MCA focus entirely on the individual »imprints« of the shipbuilder's practice on the preserved ship remains.

THE MCA ANALYSIS

For the analysis, the recorded features were reformulated as 49 qualitative variables, and the data arranged as an indicator matrix. Only positive observations were included as is not possible to know what features were present in missing parts of the finds. The statistical package XL Stat 2006 from Addinsoft was used, as it allows making MCAs on incomplete data sets by creating new categories for missing data. XL Stat is an add-in to Microsoft Excel, and the data were transferred from Excel via Notepad to Rhinoceros 3 to visualize them in 3D.

The MCA calculates a multidimensional space with 49 axis to contain the entire corpus of information. In **Figure 2** the observations or finds are depicted along F1 and F2, the two axis representing most of the information, in total 45.60 %. The distribution of the observations roughly forms a parable, showing that a gradual change in the composition of variables in the finds can be established. The size of the dots is scaled to reflect the number of observed variables for each find – the actually number is found to the left of each dot. The average number of observed variables per find is slightly above 9. As it appears, finds with few observed variables tends to position themselves near the bottom of the parable, close to the figure's centre. Those with more observed variables are distributed along the parable, and the distribution indicates that the position of finds with less than 5 to 6 observed variables should not be regarded significant.

The diagrams in **Plate 5,1** show plots of the observations, as they are distributed along the three most important axis, together representing 52.24 % of the information. In order to facilitate the discussion of the result, the observations according to the construction date (per century) and type (lapstrake, cog, barge, carvel) have been colour-coded. A clear and gradual change over time can be observed for the lapstrake vessels, as the older vessels clearly are placed in the left side of both plots and the younger ones in the right side. It can further be observed that the early and later cogs in both plots are found together with the some of the youngest lapstrake vessels, dating to the 14th to 16th c. This is interesting, because the cogs themselves date to the 12th to 14th c. The analysis thus indicates that some of the techniques used in cog building found its way into lapstrake building at a time when the cog was actually leaving the scene, but also

find	dating	length	provenance	comment
traditionally built lapstrake vessels				
1 Roskilde 1b	ca. 1336 (dendro)	ca. 9 m	E. Denmark (size)	–
2 Copenhagen Dokøen 2	ca. 1405 (dendro)	>10 m (medium)	Polish (dendro)	(Gøthche & Høst-Madsen 2001)
3 Copenhagen Dokøen 3	1420-25 (dendro)	>11.5 m (medium)	Polish/Kattegat (dendro)	the bulk of the planking was Polish, but a few planks from the construction phase came from the Kattegat region (Gøthche & Høst-Madsen 2001)
4 Flatvarp, Småland. SE Sweden	ca. 1542 (dendro)	ca. 22 m	Scania/Blekinge (dendro)	(Rönnby & Adams 1994: 32-41; Bill in press, cat. no. 11)
5 Copenhagen Havnegade	after 1564 (dendro)	(large)	S. Sweden or Poland (dendro)	included because of split planking (Gøthche 1996)
6 Amager Strand, E Zealand	after 1580	ca. 10 m	Zealand/Scania/Blekinge (dendro)	included because of split planking (Gøthche & Bill 2006)
modern built lapstrake vessels				
7 Galtabäck 2, Halland, W Sweden	ca. 1100 (^{14}C)	ca. 14.5 m	–	the dating interval allows for a date later in the 12th c.; thus the »modern« status is uncertain (Björck 1998)
8 Gislinge Lamme-fjord, NW Zealand	after 1130 (dendro)	7.5 m	N. W. Zealand (size)	four samples without sapwood produced very similar dates, making it likely that the vessel was not much younger than 1150 (Gøthche 1995)
9 Haderslev Mølle strømmen 2, SE Jutland	ca. 1220 (dendro)	12-21 m	W. Baltic region (dendro)	(Kristensen 1997)
10 Gedesby 1, Falster, SE Denmark	1320-50 (dendro)	12.5 m	S. E. Denmark (dendro)	(Bill 1991)
11 Gedesby 2, Falster, SE Denmark	1330-31 (dendro)	(small)	Zealand, S. W. Scania (dendro)	(Bill in press, cat. no. 15.2)
12 Vejdyb, NE Jutland	1475 (dendro)	(medium)	Poland (dendro)	combination of pegs and clenched nails may indicate Dutch provenance and imported materials (Bill in press, cat. no. 57)
13 Knudsgrund, SE Jutland	ca. 1537 (dendro)	ca. 10 m	S. E. Jutland (size)	included because of sawn planking (Dencker 1998)
14 Copenhagen Nationalbanken	after 1580 (dendro)	ca. 13 m	–	included because of sawn planking (Bill in press, cat. no. 33.2)
15 Bredfjed	ca. 1600 (dendro)	13.4 m	Lübeck region, Holstein (dendro)	included because of sawn planking (Bill 1999)
Early Danish cogs and barges (12th to 13th centuries)				
16 Kollerup cog, NW Jutland	1149-1166 (dendro)	ca. 21 m	S. E. Jutland (dendro)	(Daly et al. 2000; Kohrtz Andersen 1983)
17 Hedeby 4 barge, Schleswig	ca. 1184 (dendro)	14.5 m	E. Schleswig (size)	(Kühn 2004)
18 Kolding Fjord cog,	1189 (dendro)	ca. 19.2 m	S. E. Jutland (dendro)	(Hocker & Dokkedal 2001)
19 Skagen cog, N Jutland	1193 (dendro)	> 17.5 m	present-day Denmark (dendro)	(Bill in press, cat. no. 49)
20 Egernsund barge, SE Jutland	ca. 1200 (dendro, ^{14}C)	7 m	S. E. Jutland (size)	(Bill & Hocker 2004)
21 Kuggmaren cog, E Sweden	1215 (dendro)	ca. 19 m	present-day Denmark (dendro)	(Adams & Rönnby 2002; Daly 2007)
22 Bossholmen cog, Småland, SE Sweden	after 1270	15-17 m	E. Scania (dendro)	(Adams 1990; Daly 2007)

Table 1   Summary information on Danish »traditional« and »modern« lapstrake vessels, cogs and barges.

provenance, Roskilde 1b, was only ca 9 m long, and it may be argued that a vessel of this size probably is a local product.

Turning to the »modern built vessels« the picture is quite different. Chronologically the finds spread over a longer period, from the 12th to the 15th c., and the finding sites are spread over most of medieval Denmark – only the west coast of Jutland, which is poor in archaeologically excavated wrecks, is not represented. The vessels are all small or of medium size – even as lapstrake vessels. The dendroprovenance is only known for five of the nine finds, but two more may tentatively be provenanced on basis of their small size. When compared to the distribution of the »traditionally built vessels«, both in terms of finding sites and of provenance (**Plate 5, 2**), it appears that the »modern built vessels« rather tend to have a S.-W. distribution, while the former is more oriented towards the E. A likely explanation is that lapstrake shipbuilding within medieval Denmark and the surrounding area was not changing simultaneously, but that new techniques and materials were taken into use earlier in the S. and W. parts of the region, while the eastern and perhaps N. parts retained traditional ways of building longer.

This tendency is further enhanced, if the finds of early cogs and barges built within medieval Denmark are included. Both cogs and barges are constructed in »bottom first« technique, with carvel-built bottoms and lapstrake sides, and also share other constructional characteristics differing from those of clinker-built vessels (Hocker 2004). As appears from the table, four of the seven »bottom first« vessels originate from S. E. Jutland. Two more can only be attributed a provenance within present day Denmark, and only one – the youngest of them – have been built in the E. part of medieval Denmark. The »bottom first« technique has its roots in the Rhine estuary and the Wadden Sea region, and the Danish finds of cogs and barges are the oldest evidence for its use in the Baltic area. Thus the distribution of these finds supports the impression of S. W. Denmark as the entry-way for new impulses into Danish shipbuilding, especially in the 12th c. (Bill & Hocker 2004). The three better-preserved, later cog-finds found within medieval Denmark – the Vejby, the Lille Kregme and the Skanör cogs – all are made from Polish or E. Baltic oak and dates from the second half of the 14th c. Being used, but not built at the Danish coasts, they represent another and less direct influence on Danish shipbuilding from the Hanseatic towns and their shipbuilders. The same kind of influence may be observed in the carvel-built vessels from N. W. Germany and the Netherlands which are found in Denmark in the 16th c.

CONCLUSIONS AND DISCUSSION

Details in this picture may be discussed, but the overall trends are clear and may be summarized as:
1. a continuous change of lapstrake shipbuilding, accelerating from the 13th c. onwards,
2. an increasing similarity between lapstrake vessels and cogs, including, in the 16th c., the carvel-built vessels, and
3. a more innovative shipbuilding in the S. and S. W. parts of medieval Denmark, and a more traditional one in the E.

It may also be noted that although both cogs and carvel-built vessels stood clearly out as separate groups, it was not possible to discern separate lapstrake traditions in the material, although it contained both »Nordic« and »Slavic« vessels. The latter being few and early – only three, all from the 10th c. – and in part very sparsely preserved, they were not well enough represented in the analyses to stand out as separate. The same is true for the barges, which could not be adequately described by the chosen variables.

These results may be relevant for several different discussions, two of which shall be touched upon here. The first one is hinted at in the title of the paper. The Scandinavian lapstrake tradition is often referred to as being »Nordic«, and is defined by a number of features, including the double-pointed hull, the lapstrake building method, clench nails and animal hair as inlaid caulking. It is hence seen as in opposition to other lapstrake traditions, like the »Slavic« with treenails and caulking of moss (cf. Westerdahl 1989: 32-44). The idea about the existence of a Nordic or Scandinavian shipbuilding tradition can be traced back to the mid-19th c., when early excavations of prehistoric ship-finds demonstrated their similarity to traditional N. Norwegian fishing boats (Nicolaysen 1854; Engelhardt 1866). The excavation of the younger Skuldelev ships, confirmed this picture (Crumlin-Pedersen *et al.* 2002). The MCA analysis has shown, however, that lapstrake building did change over time in S. Scandinavia, and that it took up influences from fundamentally different traditions like cogs and carvel-building. During this process it incorporated features, which can also be found in the lapstrake building as it was exercised in many other places in N. Europe, and it may be considered if it did not at some point become N. European rather than Nordic? As an experiment, a traditional Norwegian *ottring* from Misvær, built between 1750 and 1800, was included in the analysis with 15 recorded variables (Eldjarn & Godal 1990: 132). The ten-oared boat, which was equipped for sailing as well, placed itself among the 12th-c. Danish lapstrake vessels. This may be an indication that it was in the following centuries that lapstrake shipbuilding in S. Scandinavia started to deviate from that further N., and that shipbuilding in parts of N. Scandinavia had reached an equilibrium which was not to be changed seriously for centuries to follow.

The second discussion to be mentioned is that of the reason for the changes. The influences from the S. and W. appear clear, but the pattern of change may be insufficiently explained as gradual adaption of techniques present in adjacent areas, since this process over time failed to replaced the tradition in N. Norway. It may have been urbanisation that gave the ship- and boat-builders in S. Scandinavia the impetus to change their ways, as it spatially and chronologically coincides with the picture of change that we see in shipbuilding (Andrén 1985). Before ca. 1130, urbanisation in Denmark included only about a dozen settlements and seems mostly directed by administrative needs. A few towns apparently were strongly oriented towards trade, and among these Schleswig and Ribe were the most important ones. Together these two towns made the S. W. part of the country its most important commercial region, and linked it up with the more developed urban landscape along the Wadden Sea. This was the region, in which the medieval variances of bottom-based shipbuilding were developed, and the early appearance of cogs and bottom-first built barges in S. E. Jutland may be an attempt to transplant a successful concept from this region into the Baltic.

Danish dominance in the Baltic culminated with the rule over Lübeck from 1201 to the early 1220s. As this dominance collapsed, the developing German towns on the S. shore of the Baltic almost eliminated the Danish role in the E.-W. trade. At the same time, however, they provided a new market for the country's agricultural production. Through the 13th and early 14th c. a dense net of coastal market towns were established. The development encompassed most of the country but was especially marked in its S. parts, where the towns would often lie few kilometres apart (**Fig. 3**). The thorough urbanization is likely to have had a large impact on shipping, as most of the goods shipped now would be directed through a market town. The development coincides with changes in the ship-archaeological record. Large, Danish-built ships (longer than 20 m) became rare, and small and medium-sized ones dominant. Accelerating changes in shipbuilding from the 13th c. on can be observed to represent a more economical approach to shipbuilding, with simpler ways of construction and more efficient use of space.

Turning to the N. parts of Scandinavia, urbanisation in Sweden and Norway took another course (Ersgård 1992). Initially the pattern was similar, with the establishing of only a handful of urban settlements before 1200, some as trading centres like Hedeby, many of them primarily being administrative centres. Most were to be found to the S. of a line from Bergen in W. Norway to Sigtuna N. of Mälaren in Central Sweden

(**Fig. 3**). Urbanisation after 1200 also generally took place S. of this line, although no further towns were founded in Norway during the Middle Ages. In 1294 Bergen achieved the right of staple for foreign trade with N. Norway, and around 1350 Stockholm got similar rights for the N. parts of Sweden. Thereby the possibilities for further urbanisation in the N. were severely hampered, and so was the exposure of the ship-building in these areas to continental ships and seafarers. In the end it was perhaps this that allowed high medieval boat building practices to continue to exist in there until they were linked with archaeological finds in the 19th and 20th c., to create the idea about the »Nordic« tradition.

BIBLIOGRAPHY

Adams, J., 1990: The Oscarshamn cog. Part II: excavation, underwater recording and salvage. *IJNA* 19, 207-219.

Adams, J. & Rönnby, J., 2002: Kuggmaren 1: the first cog find in the Stockholm archipelago, Sweden. *IJNA* 31, 172-181.

Andrén, A., 1985: *Den urbana scenen. Städer och samhälle i det medeltida Danmark.* Acta Archaeologica Lundensia. Series in 8°. No. 13 Liber Förlag, Malmö.

Baxter, M., 2003: *Statistics in archaeology*, Oxford

Bill, J., 1991: Gedesbyskibet. Middelalderlig skude- og færgefart fra Falster. Nationalmuseets Arbejdsmark 1991, 188-198.

1999: Fra vikingeskib til bondeskude. Middelalderens almuesøfart under lup. Nationalmuseets Arbejdsmark 1999, 171-185.

in press: *From Nordic to North European. Coastal seafaring and changes in Danish shipbuilding AD 900-1600.* Ships and Boats of the North, the Viking Ship Museum, Roskilde.

Bill, J. & Hocker, F. M., 2004: Haithabu 4 seen in the context of contemporary shipbuilding in Sourthern Scandinavia. In: Brandt & Kühn, Haithabu, 43-53.

Björck, N., 1998: Arkeologisk undersökning av Galtabäck II. *Marinarkeologisk Tidskrift* 1998, 6-7.

Crumlin-Pedersen, O., 2000: To be or not to be a cog: the Bremen Cog in perspective. *IJNA* 29, 230-246.

Crumlin-Pedersen, O. et al., 2002: *The Skuldelev Ships I. Topography, Archaeology, History, Conservation and Display.* Ships and Boats of the North 4.1. The Viking Ship Museum & the National Museum. Roskilde, Copenhagen.

Daly, A., 2007: *Timber, Trade and Tree-rings. A dendrochronological analysis of structural oak timber in Northern Europe, c. AD 1000 to c. AD 1650.* Ph.D.-thesis, University of Southern Denmark, Esbjerg.

Daly, A., Eriksen, O. H., & Englert, A., 2000: New dendro dates for Danish medieval ships from Eltang and Kollerup. *Maritime Archaeology Newsletter from Roskilde, Denmark* 14, 61.

Dencker, J., 1998: A gem of a Wreck. *Maritime Archaeological Newsletter from Roskilde, Denmark* 10, 26-29.

Eldjarn, G. & Godal, J., 1990: *Nordlandsbåten og Åfjordsbåten.* 2. Båtstikka, Rissa.

Engelhardt, C., 1866: Nydambaaden og Nordlandsbaaden. *Aarbøger for Nordisk Oldkyndighed og Historie* 1866, 197-206.

Ersgård, L., 1992: Tidig urbanisering i Danmark och Sverige – en översikt. In: I. Øye, *Våre første byer.* Onsdagskvelder i Bryggens Museum 7, Bergen.

Gøthche, M., 1995: Båden fra Gislinge. *Nationalmuseets Arbejdsmark* 1995, 185-198.

1996: At the edge of Gammelholm. *Maritime Archaeology Newsletter from Roskilde, Denmark* 7, 18-19.

Gøthche, M. & Bill, J., 2006: Renæssance i småskibsbyggeriet – arkæologisk set. *Maritim Kontakt* 28, 43-68.

Gøthche, M. & Høst-Madsen, L., 2001: Medieval wrecks at Dock Island, Copenhagen. *Maritime Archaeological Newsletter from Roskilde, Denmark* 17, 28-34.

Hocker, F. M., 2004: Bottom-Based Shipbuilding in Northwestern Europe. In: F. M. Hocker & C. a: Ward, *The Philosophy of Shipbuilding. Conceptual Approaches to the Study of Wooden Ships.* 65-94. College Station.

Hocker, F. M. & Dokkedal, L., 2001: News from the Kolding cog. *Maritime Archaeology Newsletter from Roskilde, Denmark* 16, 16-17.

Kohrtz Andersen, P., 1983: *Kollerupkoggen.* Museeet for Thy og Vester Hanherred, Thisted.

Kristensen, T. R., 1997: Møllestrømmen – en middelalderudgravning i Haderslev. *Nordslesvigske Museer. Årbog for museerne i Sønderjyllands amt* 22, 31-34.

Kühn, H. J., 2004: Ein hochmittelalterlicher Fährprahm im Haddebyer Noor (Haithabu Wrack IV). In: Brandt & Kühn, Haithabu, 9-16.

Madsen, T. (ed.), 1988: *Multivariate Archaeology. Numerical Approaches in Scandinavian Archaeology.* Jysk Arkæologisk Selskabs Skrifter 21. Århus.

Nicolaysen, N., 1854: Om Borrefundet i 1852. *Aarsberetning. Foreningen til Norske Fortidsmindesmerkers Bevaring* 1852, 25-34.

Rönnby, J. & Adams, J. R., 1994: *Östersjöns sjunkna skepp.* Tidens förlag, Stockholm.

Weski, T., 1999: The Ijsselmeer type: some thoughts on Hanseatic cogs. *IJNA* 28, 360-379.

Westerdahl, C., 1989: *Norrlandsleden I. Källor till det maritima kulturlandskapet.* Arkiv för norrländsk hembygdsforskning, Örnsköldsvik.

SEÁN MCGRAIL

RENAISSANCE AND ROMANO-CELTIC SHIP DESIGN AND SHIPBUILDING METHODS COMPARED

It was the author's original intention that aspects of Renaissance shipbuilding in the Mediterranean and the Atlantic should be compared in this paper with Byzantine and Romano-Celtic shipbuilding of the early centuries A.D.; this has proved to be only partly possible.

In N. Europe the first Romano-Celtic vessel was excavated in the late 1950s and, from the 1970s onwards Renaissance ships were excavated in E. American and W. European waters. The publications resulting from those excavations included discussion of ship design, framing patterns and building sequences. In the Mediterranean, Yak Kahanov (2001; 2003) and Hadas Mor (2006), building on pioneering research by Dick Steffy (1994: 85-91), recently demonstrated that in the late 5th/early 6th c. A.D. E. Mediterranean vessels without plank-to-plank fastenings were built in a frame-first sequence. Furthermore, Rieth (1991; 1996; 1998; 2003) has shown that Mediterranean wrecks of Renaissance date were also built in that sequence. In contrast with the research on Romano-Celtic and Atlantic Renaissance vessels, however, the surviving evidence for Mediterranean vessels has not allowed Kahanov or Rieth to deduce the precise building sequence, nor have they yet been able to comment on the design methods used.

This paper is therefore restricted to a comparison of design and building methods used in Atlantic shipyards during the Renaissance, with those used one thousand years earlier in Celtic N. W. Europe.

RENAISSANCE SHIP DESIGN AND SHIPBUILDING METHODS

At a conference in Lisbon in 1998, Thomas Oertling (2001) up-dated an earlier paper (1989) when he spoke on »The Concept of the Atlantic vessel« and used evidence from 16th-c. wrecks to define an Atlantic shipbuilding tradition. Although the value of such classification schemes has been doubted by some archaeologists, they can be an extremely useful tool, leading to the clarification of ideas and an increase in understanding. A shipbuilding tradition may be defined as: that style of building perceived by the archaeologist/historian as having been generally used in a certain region during a given time range. Such a tradition is a theoretical construct: it is a 21st-c. identification of an ancient style of building, and it may not be what the people of earlier times recognised. As more evidence is gathered, however, such theoretical constructs should become more akin to ancient reality.

Another criticism of Oertling's research has been that several of the twenty or so ships in his study group do not have one or more of the defining attributes of this tradition (Loewen 2006: 170). This criticism is true, but it does not necessarily invalidate Oertling's hypothesis. Such ships may be considered to form a polythetic group in which each member shares with every other member a large number of characteristics in common, but no one characteristic has to be possessed by all members, although it may (Doran & Hodson 1975: 160). Such polythetic groupings reflect an intuitive understanding of the real world and are considered by numerical taxonomists to be »natural« (McGrail 1995). The inclusion of *Mary Rose* and the

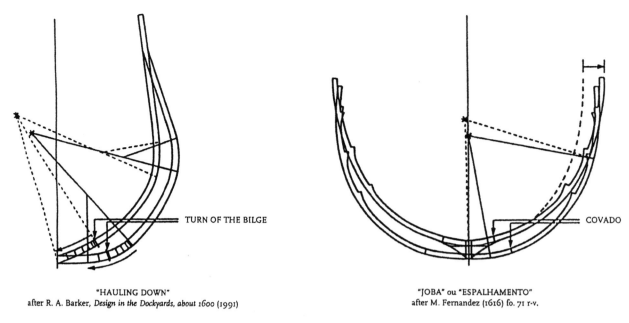

"HAULING DOWN"
after R. A. Barker, *Design in the Dockyards, about 1600* (1991)

"JOBA" ou "ESPALHAMENTO"
after M. Fernandez (1616) fo. 71 r-v.

Fig. 1   Two design methods: Atlantic on the left; Mediterranean on the right (After Loewen 2001: 244 fig.1).

Studland Bay wreck in this group is justifiable, even though neither of them has the dovetail joint between floor and futtock that appears to be a feature of other Atlantic ships.

Oertling's table (2001: table A) of the characteristic features of Atlantic ships needs further changes, not only in the light of recently excavated wrecks, but more fundamentally by the addition of three attributes – design methods, framing patterns and building sequence – to the present twelve characteristics which are mainly fittings (e.g. »buttresses and stringers«) and woodworking techniques (e.g. »carved garboard«).

Design methods

Using Renaissance shipbuilding treatises dating from ca. 1450 to 1600 (Barker 1991; Bellabarba 1993; Rieth 1996), and data from excavated wrecks, Loewen (1997; 2001; 2006), Barker (1997) and Barker *et al*. (in press) have argued that 16th-c. Atlantic and Mediterranean design methods, although similar in many respects, differed in one particular aspect: the way the master frame was used to derive the shape of successive »calculated« frames – »calculated« frames define hull form as the ship's transverse section rises and narrows, and they are grouped both forward and aft of the master frame (McGrail 2001a).

In the Atlantic region (**Fig. 1**, left) a fair curve was constructed on the mould floor between futtock arc and bilge arc by extending the futtock arc downwards as the bilge arc was progressively reduced in length; in the shipyard the futtock mould fashioned from these curves was slid downwards alongside the similarly fashioned bilge mould in a process described in English treatises as »hauling down the futtock«. In the Mediterranean, on the other hand (**Fig. 1**, right), a process was used which generated a non-geometric arc with a kink or knuckle at the turn of the bilge that had to be faired by eye or by a reconciling arc: in the shipyard this involved the progressive rotation of the futtock mould about the end of each floor – a process known as *trébuchement* in French, *ramo* in Venetian, *joba* in Spanish, and *espalhamento* in Portuguese (Rieth 1996; Barker 1997: 173; Loewen 1997: 169-170).

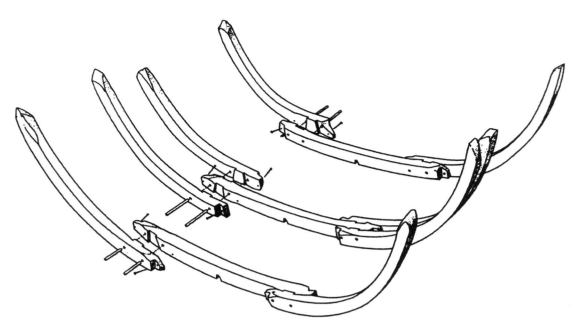

Fig. 2   Exploded view of dovetail joints between floors and futtocks in the 16th-c. Red Bay wreck (After Grenier 2001: fig. 9).

Framing patterns

Which of these two design methods, Atlantic or Mediterranean, was used in a particular wreck may be determined by detailed survey of a vessel's framing. Several such studies have been undertaken and, in their recent research, Loewen and Barker concentrated on wrecks that proved to have been designed and built in the Atlantic fashion: for example, the Basque ship *San Juan* from Red Bay in Canada (Grenier 1988; 1994; 2001), *Mary Rose* from the Solent off Portsmouth (Barker *et al.* in press), and the wreck excavated off Cavalaire-sur-Mer, S. France (Loewen & Delahaye 2006). These ships had a mixed framing pattern: the futtocks of each of the central group of frames had been fashioned using the process of »hauling down the futtock«, and each futtock was fastened to its associated floor, sometimes by a dovetail joint (**Fig. 2**). The other framing timbers in these 16th-c. ships were »floating«: they were not fastened to any other framing element but to planking or other longitudinal timbers.

Building sequence

Furthermore, these 16th-c. Atlantic ships had been built in an »alternating« or »stepwise« sequence: first the lower framing was fastened to the keel, and planking was then fastened to that framing; then higher framing, followed by more planking; and so on. These vessels had thus been built »framing-first«. »Framing-first« is not the same as that sequence used in Europe from the 18th c. when the hull framework might be entirely assembled before any planking began (**Fig. 3**). Rather, »framing-first« is a stepwise process in which the lower framing is first erected, followed by its planking; then the upper framing, followed by its planking (McGrail 1995: 141; 1997; 2004a: 200).

Fig. 3   A late 18th-c. depiction of the framework of a French ship.

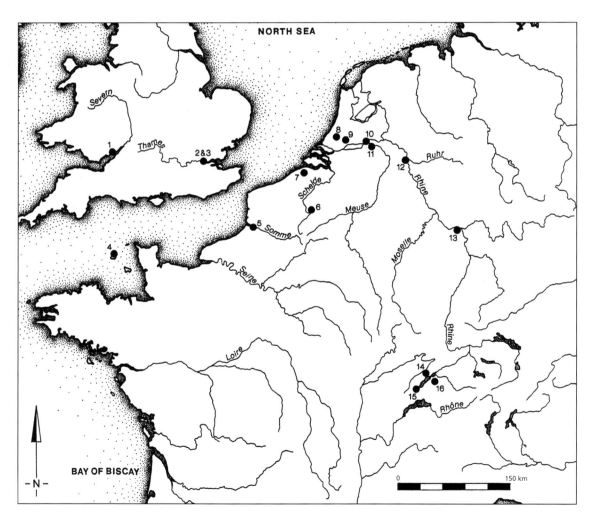

Fig. 4   Map showing the distribution of excavated Romano-Celtic boats and ships: **1** Barland's Farm. – **2** Blackfriars. – **3** New Guy's House. – **4** St. Peter Port. – **5** Abbeville. – **6** Pommeroeul. – **7** Bruges. – **8** Zwammerdam. – **9** Woerden. – **10** Kapel Avezaath. – **11** Druten. – **12** Xanten. – **13** Mainz. – **14** Bevaix. – **15** Yverdon. – **16** Avenches (Glamorgan-Gwent Archaeological Trust).

In summary, one may say that in 16th-c. Atlantic yards ships were designed by a process generally similar to but distinguishable from that used in Mediterranean shipyards, and they were built »stepwise, framing-first with floating timbers«.

ROMANO-CELTIC SHIP DESIGN AND BUILDING METHODS

The Romano-Celtic shipbuilding tradition was first recognised by Peter Marsden (1967) in his publication of Blackfriars ship 1. Subsequently, Detlev Ellmers (1969) set this vessel and the boat from New Guy's House, London (Marsden 1965) into their historical and archaeological context. Some of the structural characteristics of these vessels echo aspects of Julius Caesar's description of the ships of the *Veneti*, a Celtic people of S. W. Brittany (Marsden 1967: 34-35; McGrail 2004b).

Figure 4 shows the distribution of the excavated boats and ships of the Romano-Celtic tradition (known in France as »Gallo-Romaine«). Some of the dots denote more than one find, and recent finds in the River Rhône, near Lyon (Guyon & Rieth, this volume pp. 157-165), have not been included. These vessels are dated between the 1st and 5th c. A.D. and may be divided into two main groups (McGrail 2001b; 2004a: 197):

A 23 or so river »barges«;

B three seagoing, sailing vessels.

Techniques considered to be Celtic had been used when building the boats in Group A, but other techniques appear to have been Roman in origin. Furthermore, the building of these »barges« seems to have been dominated by the specific requirements of a flat-bottomed boat (McGrail 2001b). Further work is needed on this large group of vessels to determine its full range of characteristics.

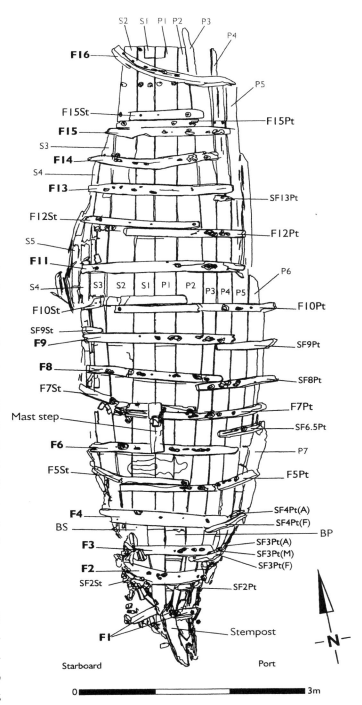

Fig. 5 Plan of the Barland's Farm boat *in situ* (Glamorgan-Gwent Archaeological Trust).

Group B is smaller and technologically more homogenous than Group A. It consists of: Blackfriars 1 of the mid-2nd c. A.D. excavated in1965 by Peter Marsden (1994: 33-96) from the River Thames in London, the late 3rd-c. Guernsey ship St. Peter Port 1 excavated in 1985 by Margaret Rule (Rule & Monaghan 1993), and the Barland's Farm boat of ca. A.D. 300 excavated in 1993 from the margins of the river Severn in S. E. Wales (McGrail & Roberts 1999; Barker 2003: 47-48; Nayling & McGrail 2004). It is this group of three seagoing crafts that is relevant to the present paper.

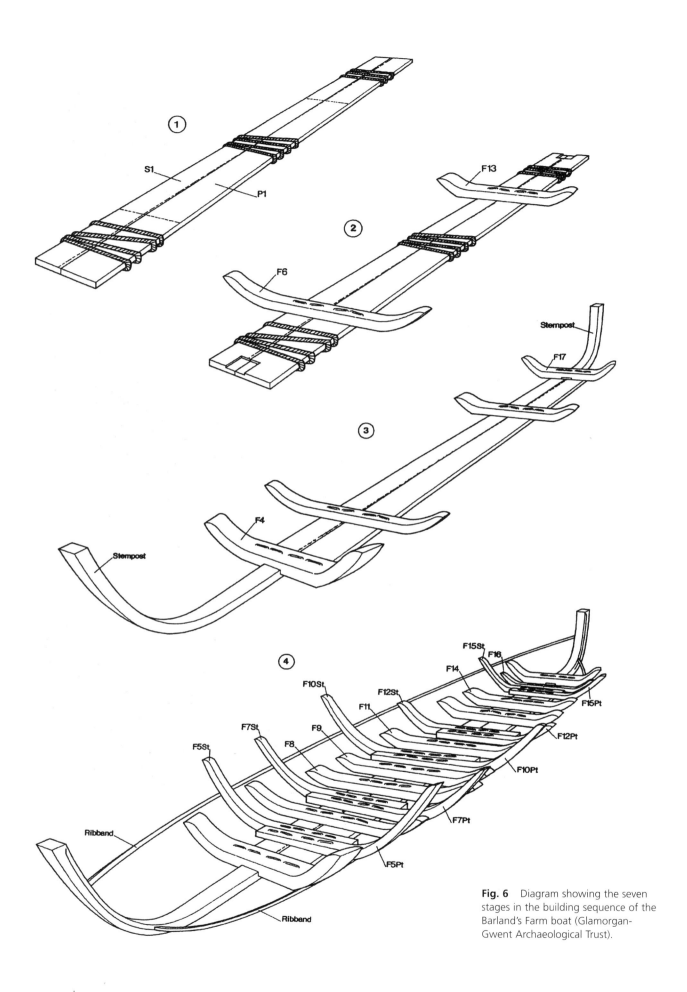

Fig. 6 Diagram showing the seven stages in the building sequence of the Barland's Farm boat (Glamorgan-Gwent Archaeological Trust).

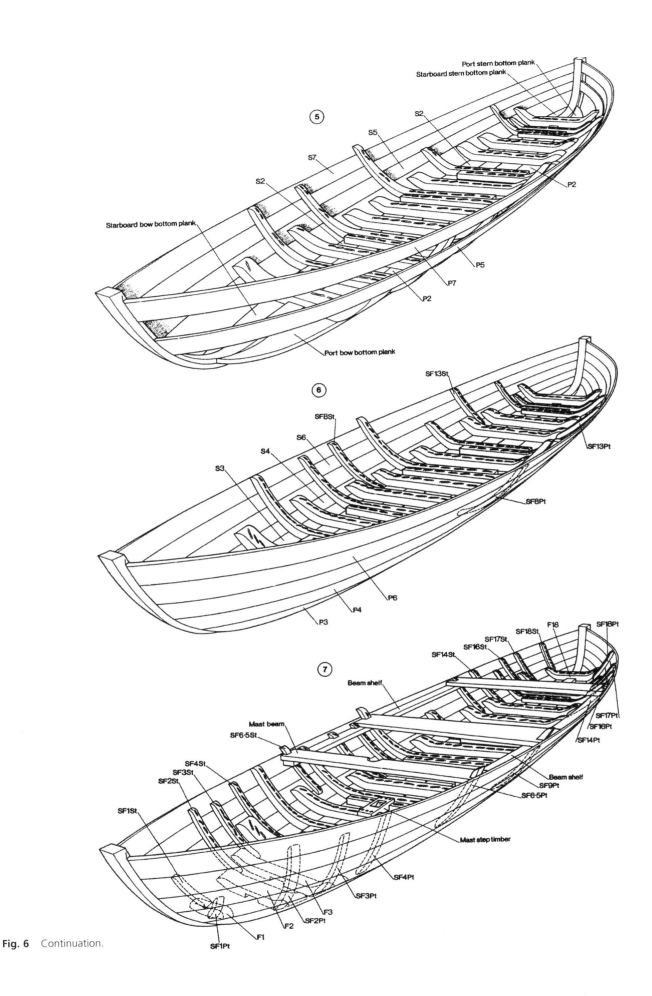

Port stern bottom plank
Starboard stern bottom plank

(5)

S2

S2

S5

S7

S2

Starboard bow bottom plank

P2

P5

P7

P2

Port bow bottom plank

(6)

SF13St

SF8St

SF13Pt

S6

S4

S3

SF8Pt

P6

P4

P3

F18

SF18Pt

SF18St

SF17St

SF16St

SF14St

SF17Pt

SF16Pt

SF14Pt

(7)

Beam shelf

Mast beam

SF6-5St

SF4St

SF3St

SF2St

SF1St

Beam shelf

SF9Pt

SF6-5Pt

Mast step timber

SF4Pt

SF3Pt

SF2Pt

F3

F2

SF1Pt

F1

Fig. 6 Continuation.

Framing pattern

The plank-keels of the three Romano-Celtic seagoing craft project below their outer-bottom planking. Their bottom and side planking is not fastened together; rather it is fastened to the framing timbers by large iron nails clenched by hooking the point back into the frame. A caulking of macerated wood mixed with tar or resin was nailed by tacks, or possibly glued, to plank edges before each plank was offered up. The two ships, St. Peter Port and Blackfriars, have relatively massive floors, closely spaced and fastened to the plank-keel, and their side timbers generally alternate with these floors. The Barland boat's framing, on the other hand, is of two types: thirteen floors with associated side timbers (futtocks) to port and to starboard; and five pairs of L-shaped half-frames interspersed among the floors and extending (almost) to the boat's sheerline (**Fig. 5**). In all three vessels, timbers within groups overlap and lie close to, and even alongside, each other, but they are not fastened together: floors are fastened to the plank-keel, but side timbers are »floating«.

Building sequence

The building sequence of all three vessels was »stepwise, framing first with floating timbers« (**Fig. 6**). As in Atlantic-designed Renaissance ships, planking in a lower side strake of these seagoing Romano-Celtic vessels had to be fastened in position so that further framing timbers could be fastened to it. Nevertheless, as the hull was built up, framing timbers always preceded planking – in other words, the framing was active, hull shape was determined by the framing (together with the plank-keel and posts, and possibly ribbands). A few framing timbers towards the vessel's ends may, however, have been passive, that is, their shape was determined by the planking.

Design methods

A unit of measurement of ca. 55 to 56 cm (possibly equivalent to two human feet) had been used in the frame spacing of both the St. Peter Port ship and the Barland's Farm boat, and also possibly in the curvature of Barland's lower post and the upward-curving ends of her framing timbers. The ratio of maximum beam, to length of plank-keel, and to overall length may have been approx. 1:2:3. Other aspects of the design process are not yet fully understood (Barker 2003: 48; Nayling & McGrail 2004: 197-199): it may be that a simple way of moulding the framing timbers was used, involving the builder's eye and »rules of thumb« rather than standardised gauges. More may be learned when the timbers of the Barland's boat are re-assembled for display in Newport Museum in S. E. Wales.

DISCUSSION

Romano-Celtic and Atlantic ship design and building methods

As Richard Barker (2003: 48) has pointed out, framing-first construction pre-supposes the ability to mould (»design«) the shape of at least some critical parts of a vessel, before building begins. Although the design methods used by the builders of the three seagoing Romano-Celtic vessels are not yet fully understood, a building sequence and other constructional characteristics have been deduced. These Celtic vessels were built »stepwise, framing first with floating timbers«: similar in this respect to the methods used by the

Fig. 7 Building a *currach* in the W. of Ireland in the mid-20th c. The framework was first assembled; then the »skin« was added and subsequently tarred (After P. Johnstone).

builders of 16th-c. Atlantic ships. Some of the distinguishing features of 16th-c. Atlantic ships were fore-shadowed, if not had their origin, in Celtic shipbuilding methods used in the early centuries A.D. It was a long haul of a thousand years and more, from the stepwise, planking-first sequences used in the Classical Mediterranean, and in the early-Nordic tradition of the Baltic, to the frame-first sequence of the 18th c. Nevertheless, it seems possible to suggest that a »stepwise framing-first« sequence of building was the link between »plank-first« and »frame-first«. This is a tentative hypothesis: more excavation-based research is clearly needed.

Origins of framing-first?

The Romano-Celtic seagoing ship building tradition is clearly distinguishable from other known contemporary traditions by the absence of plank-to-plank fastenings, and by its use of the framing-first sequence – the earliest known. The building techniques of this tradition are fundamentally different from those used to build prehistoric logboats and sewn plank boats, the only wooden boats known to have preceded Romano-Celtic vessels in Atlantic Europe. Nevertheless, the origins of the framing-first sequence may well lie within N. W. Europe. Pre-Roman, seagoing boats were built there using frame-first techniques, skin upon frame (**Fig. 7**; McGrail 1990: 36-39). It is possible that this aspect of hide-boat building was transferred to plank boats during the 1st millennium B.C. (Nayling & McGrail 2004: 228-9). It is also not difficult to visualise the framing-first approach to plank boat-and-ship building continuing in use in coastal N. W. Europe after Roman times, despite the increasing intrusion of the Nordic tradition, to be taken up by the Renaissance designers of the ocean-going Atlantic ships, but further excavation-based research is needed before such conjecture can become hypothesis.

DAMIAN GOODBURN

A NEWLY DISCOVERED LOST TRADITION OF RIVER BARGE BUILDING ON THE THAMES (16TH TO 18TH CENTURIES)

BACKGROUND: THE HISTORIC PORT OF LONDON

Archaeological work in waterfront zones of the historic port of London has been extensive and systematically carried out since the 1970s, revealing much evidence of the Roman and Medieval ports (Milne & Milne 1982; Milne 1985). More recently the post-medieval waterfront zones have received systematic archaeological attention and a number of publications have been produced or are being prepared (e.g. Saxby & Goodburn 1998; Divers 2002; Heard & Goodburn 2003). Some earlier investigations had already revealed a small number of relatively intact, wrecked or abandoned vessel finds from the post-medieval period (Marsden 1996). Later work has revealed a much larger number of reused nautical elements, most commonly sections of vessels reused in foreshore structures (Goodburn 1991; Marsden 1996; Saxby & Goodburn 1998; Divers 2002; Heard & Goodburn 2003).

Apart from archaeological material, some information on the vessels used in the region can be extracted from historical sources (Wilson 1987: 35) and the great series of Thames panoramas from the 16th c. onward. However, these sources provide only very general information about the cargoes carried and the general hull shape and rig of the vessels with which this paper deals: the river barges. The 1647 Thames view by Hollar provides perhaps the earliest intelligible images of river craft (**Fig. 1**). This paper is focused on distinctive features of hull construction only recently discovered which both contrast with material found earlier and show some surprising ancient parallels.

Post-Medieval planked boat and ship building styles in the Thames region known up to 1999

For the early post-medieval period, prior to 1999 three main styles of planked vessel construction were known of, clinker keel-type building for boats, barges and small ships (**Fig. 2, 1**) and both frame-first and frames afterwards forms of carvel construction for small and larger ships (Goodburn 1991; Marsden 1996). The keel type barges were slowly developed from medieval forms incorporating new materials such as

1   2

Fig. 1   Images taken from Hollar's 1647 Thames panorama showing upriver »western barge« with pram type hull forms. – **1** Unladen craft alongside wharves with canvass covered shelters or tilts shown. – **2** Laden western barges under way with large square sails.

Fig. 2 Two very different types of 16th c. Thames river barge construction. – **1** Round hulled, clinker keel type construction with lower hull planking of wide sawn elm planks and sides of narrow cleft oak boards. – **2** Western barge hard-chined construction with flush laid planking edge fastened with tenons. Planking, mainly of sawn oak with elm at the chines.

wide, pit-sawn elm planks for the bottoms combined with archaic, narrow cleft oak boards for the sides. By the late 16th-c. pictorial evidence clearly shows that flat bottomed punt or »pram« shaped river sailing barges had also been developed. It seems that these craft were developed further with the impetus of the industrial revolution into the Thames lighters and distinctive Thames sailing barges of the late 19th and early 20th c. About 30 of the latter are still to be found in sailing trim and their construction has been subject to some detailed archaeological investigation (Milne, McKewan & Goodburn 1998).

New finds shed light on a previously undocumented fourth tradition of building river craft with some very ancient characteristics

From 1999 there is evidence of a fourth style of construction for flat bottomed swim ended river barges (pram type vessels; **Fig. 2, 2**). These were probably what were referred to as western barges in historic sources because they went W. of London well up the River Thames (Wilson 1987: 35). All the relevant finds were sections of articulated barge hull planking up to 6.5m long with occasional fragments of framing attached. They occurred on two sites on the Thames in late 1999: the Millennium Bridge S. site (**Figs 3-4**), and Adlards Wharf in central London; and in 2003 on the river Lea at Crown Wharf in E. London (Goodburn 2002; Divers 2002; Goodburn in prep). On the two former sites the remains of at least two separate vessels were found and small fragments of one at Crown Wharf. This brings the total number of craft

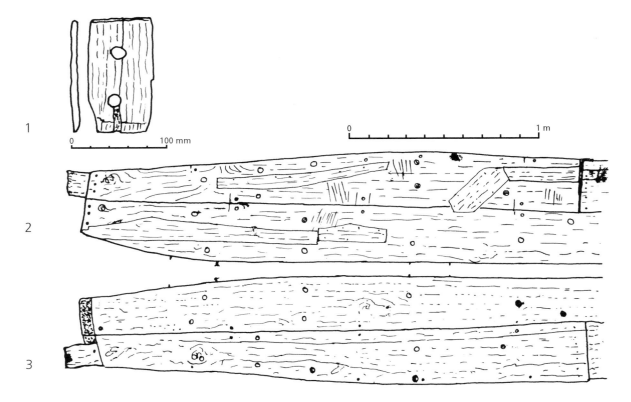

Fig. 3 Millennium Bridge site, London. – A section of the bottom of a western barge of ca. 1580. – **1** Detail of oak plank seam tenon. – **2** port side towards the bow, inboard, with stop splayed scarves for the sloping swim head planking, tarred hair and »Dutchmen« (patches) shown over seasoning shakes. – **3** Outboard; an aborted scribed line for fitting the bottom planking, tenon pegs, and floor timber fastening holes.

represented to at least five. Dating by tree-ring and finds dating of associated foreshore structures runs from ca. 1580 to the later 18th c.

All the remains clearly came from hard-chined, flat bottomed craft and all shared one surprising and very distinctive feature, the flush laid planking was closely fitted and edge fastened with pegged oak tenons. This was quite unexpected, and has clear parallels with classical Mediterranean styles of planked vessel construction, even though the tenons are fairly widely spaced. So much so that a sample of »western barge« planking taken to the ISBSA 10 at Roskilde was frequently identified as of the Roman period by those attending! Some of the tenons lay underneath frame stations marked by staggered lines of treenails and occasional clench bolt holes. This clearly shows that bottoms and even sides, were closely scribed to fit (cf. erroneous scribe mark on planking in **Figure 4**) and then tenoned together before the framing was added. The tenons used were of cleft oak and varied a little in size from ca. 120 to 130 mm long by 70 to 80 mm wide by 8 to 10 mm thick. The spacing of the tenons varied in the 16th-c. example, which are mainly dealt with here, they were set on centres of ca. 650 to 800 mm, whereas the 18th-c. material shows tenons spaced much further apart at ca. 1.3 m. The seams were water proofed with hair applied over pine tar (Walton Rogers 2000) prior to fastening the tenons (called »setwork« on the Thames).

The obvious question is where does this tradition of barge building come from? Was it a local innovation in the 16th c., or was it a rare survival of some form of classical river vessel construction? Despite a trawl of the archives no relevant medieval London evidence has come to light. However, evidence of the use of edge

Fig. 4 Millenium Bridge site, London. – A roughly midships section of the articulated bottom planking of a western barge of ca. 1580. – **1** A partial vessel cross-section with part of an oak floor timber and an oak side plank *in situ*. – **2** Inboard; bottom plank scarf, attached floor timber, and the knotty grain of the lower, elm, chine plank. Also shown, frequent »Dutchmen« covering defects in the planks existent before fitting the floor timbers. – **3** Outboard; edge tenon *in situ* in a broken mortice, and sinuous lines of the plank edges.

tenoning applied to the planking of hard chine river barges has recently been found not very far from the Thames estuary in a silted Rhine channel near Utrecht in the Netherlands.

A recently found evidence for an ancient tradition of edge tenoned planking in pram-type river barges, De Meern 4

In 2003 archaeologists from NISA (Nederlands Instituut voor Scheeps- en onderwater Archeologie, Lely-stad), excavating ahead of building development found a spectacularly preserved pram-type river barge of the 2nd c. A.D. The find was made at De Meern near Utrecht and termed De Meern 1 (Bazelmans & Jansma 2005; Van Holk 2006). The remains of other craft were also found and one, De Meern 4, was just partially exposed. In summer 2005 a combined team, including NISA staff and British TV Archaeologists (Time Team, Channel 4 with this writer) carried out a trial trenching of this vessel which proved to be of later 1st c. A.D. date. During the extraction of timber for tree-ring dating it was discovered that the flush laid bottom and side planking and L-shaped *île* timber were all edge joined with tenons. This is currently atypical for the finds of Roman period prams in the Netherlands, where combinations of flush set and overlapping plank-ing are better known as in De Meern 1.

During ISBSA 11 evidence presented from excavations in central France also showed the Roman use of tenon joining of planking in pram type river barges (Guyon & Rieth, this volume pp. 162-163, fig. 7, 2). Thus, some Roman river barges of pram form had hulls edge joined with tenons as well as classical round hulled craft. Indeed, one may possibly see the survival of a simplified form of edge tenoning in the rough pegs of timber used in the bottom plank seams of some French river barges of recent times (Beaduoin 1985:137). Such a practice on French rivers might also be a source for the adoption of the technique on the Thames.

SOME OTHER CONSTRUCTIONAL FEATURES OF THESE CRAFT

Space does not permit a full summary of all features of the newly found archaeological evidence for this tradition of barge building but several features that contrast with those associated with the clinker keel type barges are outlined below. Readers might also consult the following reference for more information (Goodburn 2002).

Hull form

The pram or punt-shaped hull form seems to dominate in the pictorial evidence, but in the later 18th c. some hard chined vessels are indicated with one end punt shaped (a swim-head) and the other a sharp bow. Where the archaeological evidence is complete enough swim ends are indicated (**Fig. 3**). The hull cross-section was box like with slightly flared sides (**Fig. 4**). The lowest side planks were simply spiked to the edges of the bottom at the chine whilst all other plank seams included edge tenons locked with pegs. The pictorial and archaeological evidence indicate that some degree of sheer was built in to some craft but not all. The craft appear to have generally been fairly narrow with beam to length ratios of ca. 6 to 7:1 (Wilson 1987: 40).

Planking raw materials

The excavated remains of these craft show a mix of timber species were used. The majority of the planking was oak which was often of modest size and rather knotty requiring the use of many small patches or »Dutchmen« (**Figs 3-4**). It is clear that the tangentially faced (pit-sawn) planking was seasoned to a large extent before use resulting in many drying shakes requiring patching. Elm was also used as main hull planking as well as for some sheathing. Imported softwoods including larch, *larix decidua* (Gray Rees 2000) were used for cross-wise sheathing of the worn bottoms of the 18th-c. craft. No sheathing was found on the 16th-c. barge bottom section which was clearly less than five years old. In the 16th-c. bottom section the planking was only ca. 35mm thick, although it thickened at the chines to ca. 45 to 50mm thick. The overall impression is of relatively cheap raw material made good by extensive use of »Dutchmen«.

Fragmentary evidence for framing and fastenings

The patterns of fastenings show that frame elements were spaced on ca. 0.5m centres. In the case of the 16th-c. barge bottom from Millennium Bridge S. a section of an oak floor timber was found still attached by oak treenails (**Fig. 4**). This timber was sided 160mm and moulded 90mm. It had been sawn from a rather waney and knotty oak trunk and trimmed with an axe or adze. A simple bridle joint, locked with an oak peg, was used to locate the end of the side frame. Patterns of widely spaced clench bolt holes suggest to this author that the barge probably also had grown knee type frames set at intervals amongst the jointed examples.

Cargoes, capacity and use

The »western barges« were the multi-purpose cargo carriers, taking cargoes such as firewood, timber and agricultural produce to London and mixed transhiped cargoes from silks to imported boards and food stuff back up river. The documented capacity of western barges varied greatly from small craft carrying just a few tons as far up river as possible, to huge craft carrying as much as 200 tons cargo as far as Reading when water conditions were right (Wilson 1987: 37). Propulsion was by means of the tides and river flow, square sail in fair winds, »shoving« with poles, the use of large oars or »sweeps« and by haulage against the stream mainly by gangs of men rather than animals. Copious pictorial evidence shows that many vessels had small cabins or canvas covered »tilts« for crew and passenger accommodation (**Fig. 1**). Interestingly the clinker keel type vessels are not shown with any clear accommodation indicating shorter haul use perhaps as day boats in the central port area only. Western barge journeys varied in time but could take weeks in low water conditions.

Postscript: Very new evidence for other systems of river vessel planking on the Post Medieval Thames

Very recent excavations on the London waterfront at Bridges Wharf, Wandsworth have produced slabs of reused barge hull planking initially dated to ca. 1700. The oak and elm planking show yet another method of making plank seams strong and watertight. Rebates or »rabbets« were carefully planed into the butting edges and smeared with tarred hair before fastening with small iron nails. Small fragments of planking with rabbeted seams have also been found elsewhere in London and will now repay more considered attention. It is important to note here that by the late 19th c. rabbeted planking was very common in Thames sailing barges but it was not then used with edge fastening. The introduction of cross-planked bottoms on narrow canal boats (»narrow boats«) was also an innovation which may have been used for a variety of Thames river vessels by the 19th c. if not earlier as a recent find at Binsey in Oxford shows (C. Mckewan, pers. comm). Many of the details of developments in the styles of building method used in the local river and estuary cargo vessels from the late-medieval period remain to be discovered although some broad trends are clear and noted in this paper.

SOME CONCLUSIONS

The basic features of the western barge style of construction of hard-chined, flat bottomed hulls with edge tenoned planking were known in the W. and N. W. part of the Roman Empire but, as yet, there is no medieval evidence of the use of the technique in England. However, in Switzerland the remains of a small 16th-c. lake boat bore traces of the technique of edge fastening (Arnold 1992: 103), and some French river barge builders also used a similar technique in recent times. So the use of the technique may have been a post-medieval borrowing from the continent. The borrowing of the edge tenoning used in the construction of tables and some building carpentry may also have been an independent route by which barge builders on the Thames adopted the technique Although adding labour costs it would clearly have strengthened the relatively weak flat bottoms subject to frequent groundings in the shallow upper Thames. It is clear that the expansion of trade on the upper river in the 16th c. was in part a response to the wider explosion of European trade at this time. Some barge builders clearly worked within traditions of considerable antiquity such as in the keel tradition but at times builders also appear to have been able to innovate, developing or adopting new constructional systems. All these systems involved turning cheap materials into practical craft. The varied unglamorous river craft of which fragments have been uncovered, were able to feed the demands of the growing city for country products and return with city and foreign products. They became part of the infrastructure of the largest port in the world by the early 19th c., but before 1900 they were already only a distant memory escaping the earliest photographer's lenses.

ACKNOWLEDGEMENTS

This writer would like to thank field excavation staff of the Museum of London Archaeology Service, AOC Archaeology England, and Pre-Construct Archaeology for their co-operation with the *in-situ* recording of the barge remains discussed here. The detailed recording, and study were the responsibility of the author as were this text and figures. Thanks are also due to J. Minkin for assistance with recording the Millenium Bridge barge elements and other specialists such as L. Gray and P. Walton Rogers for their cited reports. The author is indebted to Time Team and NISA for making it possible for him to examine part of the De Meern 4 vessel.

REFERENCES

Arnold, B., 1992, *Battellerie gallo-romaine sur le lac de Neuchatel*, vols. 1-2. Archéologie Neuchâteloise 12-13. Saint-Blaise.

Bazelmans, J. & Jansma, E., 2005, Das Leben an Bord. Im Schiffsfund von De Meern (Niederlande) ist der Alltag auf einem römischen Frachter konserviert. *Antike Welt*, 36.1, 23-29.

Beaduoin, F., 1985, *Batteaux de fleuves de France*. Douarnenez.

Divers, D., 2002, The Post-medieval waterfront development at Adlards Wharf, Bermondsey, London. *Post-Medieval Archaeology*, 36, 39-117.

Goodburn, D., 1991, New light on early ship and boatbuilding in the London area. In: G. Good, R. Jones & M. Ponsford (eds), *Waterfront Archaeology*. Proceedings of the 3rd International Conference, Bristol 1988. CBA, Res. Report, no. 74. London, 105-111.

2002, Analysis of ship timbers from the south bank excavation. In: J. Ayre & R. Wroe-Brown, *The London Millennium Bridge*. Museum of London Archaeology Service, Archaeology Studies Series, no. 6. London, 84-89.

in prep., *Analysis of the Woodwork Found at Crown Wharf, Wandsworth, SW London. With AOC Archaeology*.

Gray Rees, L., 2000, *Wood Sp. Id report for Millennium Bridge site MFB 98*. Museum of London Specialist Services, unpublished report.

Heard, K. & Goodburn, D., 2003, *Investigating the Maritime History of Rotherhithe*. Museum of London Archaeology Service, Archaeology Studies Series, no. 11. London.

Marsden, P., 1996, *Ships of the port of London: twelfth to seventeenth centuries AD*. English Heritage, Archaeological Reports, no. 5. London.

Milne, G., 1985, *The Port of Roman London*. London.

Milne, G. & Milne, C., 1982, *Medieval waterfront development at Trig Lane, London*. London and Middlesex Archaeological Society, Special Paper, no. 5. London.

Milne, G., McKewan, C. & Goodburn, D., 1998, *Nautical Archaeology on the Foreshore*. London.

Saxby, D. & Goodburn, D., 1998, Seventeenth-Century ships'. Timbers and a Dock on the Thames Waterfront at Bellamy's Wharf, Rotherhithe, London SE16. *MM*, 84.2, 173-192.

Van Holk, A., 2006, A Roman barge with an artefactual inventory from De Meern (the Netherlands). In: *ISBSA 10*, 295-299.

Walton Rogers, P., 2000, *Tarred fibres in association with barge timbers, at the Millennium Footbridge, Bankside Southwark, London*. Unpublished report.

Wilson, D., 1987, *The Thames; record of a working waterway*. London.

PAUL BLOESCH

A GLIMPSE OF THE SHIPWRIGHT'S SECRET:
SOME EVIDENCE FROM THE *BARQUE DU LÉMAN*

The *Barque du Léman*, the two-masted, lateen-rigged cargo ship of Lake Geneva evolved from a particular type of *galiote* or half-galley introduced on the lake in 1689 by a shipwright from Nice, Laurent Dental, on the orders of the duke of Savoy, Victor-Emmanuel II (Bloesch 2001). At the end of its evolution, around the year 1900, the *Barque du Léman* was a highly specialized stone carrier plying between the Savoyan quarries and the rapidly growing urban centres like Geneva, Lausanne, and others. This evolution did not affect the Mediterranean design and building method, that remained in use right down to the last unit built in 1931.

This method, characterized mainly by the geometrical and progressive variation of the midship section along the ship's longitudinal axis, can be studied for the last century of its use on Lake Geneva on the base of a very happy source constellation. There are three historic sources at disposal which might be called the technical archives of three shipwrights or shipwrights' families, covering the period between about 1800 and 1931:

1. A collection of eight sets of *barque* dimensions from about 1800, compiled by the shipwright Pierre-Joseph Portier of Thonon (Haute-Savoie, France) in an almanac which he used as a notebook.

2. A manuscript kept by three generations of the shipwrights' family Derivaz of Saint-Gingolph (Valais, Switzerland), and containing the building specifications of twenty-two *barques* as well as of some flat-bottomed craft built between 1813 and 1863. Both the Portier almanac and the Derivaz manuscript are kept in the Musée du Léman at Nyon (Vaud, Switzerland).

3. A collection of moulds and their associated objects like rising boards and bevel boards, gathered by the shipwrights François Jacquier and his son Louis of Le Locum (Haute-Savoie, France), and covering 15 vessels built between 1891 and 1931. The greater part of them are still in the hands of the Jacquier family; some pieces have been deposited in local museums or given to the proprietors of the last two surviving barques, *Neptune*, at Geneva, and *Vaudoise*, at Ouchy (Bloesch 2003).

The Jacquier collection of moulds has to be considered as the true continuation of the Derivaz manuscript, François Jacquier having learnt his trade at the Derivaz shipyard at Saint-Gingolph. The manuscript and the moulds constitute, if considered as a whole, a most homogeneous serial source material representing the professional knowledge of five generations of shipwrights, all of them working within the same shipbuilding tradition.

The *Barque du Léman* was built skeleton-first according to the classical Mediterranean method which can be traced back to the Middle Ages. The shipwright erected all the framework before beginning to fasten any planking. Each frame consists of a floor timber (*courbe*) and two futtocks (*montants*). The frames to be set in the middle part of the vessel, from about two thirds to three quarters of the total number, were shaped and assembled before erecting them on the keel. This set of pre-determined and pre-erected frames was called the first set of frames (*première monture, première carcasse*) (**Fig. 1**). The frames that terminate the first set forward and aft do not seem to have had a particular name (as *cavo de sesto* in Venetian) – at least it is not to be found in the available sources. The remaining frames at both ends of the vessel are called the second set of frames (*seconde monture, seconde carcasse*). They take their shapes from a few ribbands fitted between the last frames of the first set and the stem or the fashion pieces.

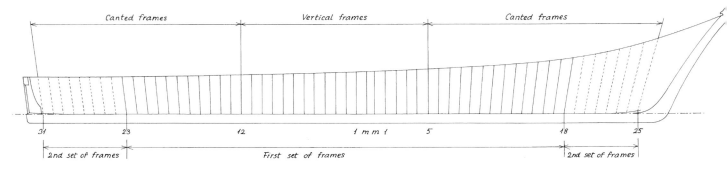

Fig. 1 Typical framing of *Lorraine*, built in 1903 (Drawing P. Bloesch).

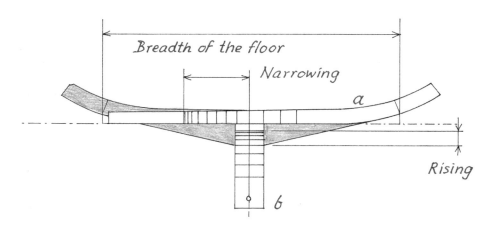

Fig. 2 Moulding a floor timber by means of a floor mould *a* and a rising board *b* (Drawing P. Bloesch).

Figure 2 illustrates the principle of moulding a floor timber (shaded) by means of two patterns: a floor mould *a* and a rising board *b*. Both these patterns are marked with scales of steadily increasing intervals, each point of these scales corresponding to one of the floors of the first set of frames, from the master floors amidships to those at its limits forward and aft. Each two correspondig points of the narrowing and rising scales serve to exactly align the floor mould and the rising board in their proper position for tracing the outline of each of the floor timbers. This is done directly on the slab of wood from which the timber is then cut with its proper bevel as taken from the bevel board. For more details and illustrations cf. Bloesch 2003.

It is the scales marked on the patterns, and in particular the narrowing scales (called »diminution«), the present article is dealing with.

Figure 3 is a graphic translation of the building specification of a *brigantin* (small *barque*) built in 1813 by Jean Derivaz. This specification from the Derivaz manuscript is the earliest one to include some informations about the narrowing of the floor. The first set of frames consists of 28 frames distributed symmetrically forward and aft of the middle of the keel, and extending over a little less than two thirds of the keel's length. The narrowing is given as 15 inches 6 lines (twelfths of a French inch) or about 42cm at the floors terminating the first set of frames (numbered 14). The intermediate narrowings are not included in the building specification, but this is not really a shortcoming as the shipwright should have been able to re-

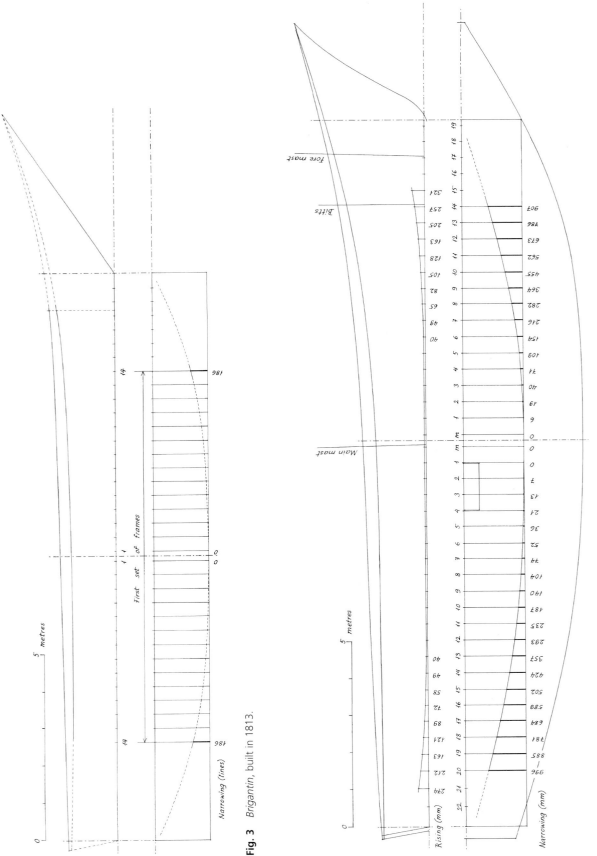

Fig. 3 *Brigantin*, built in 1813.

Fig. 4 Brick *Amiral Courbet*, built in 1896 (Drawing P. Bloesch, based on surveys made by G. Cornaz from the still existing ship in 1950 to 1952 and 1958; Cornaz' plans and records in a private collection, Pratteln, Switzerland).

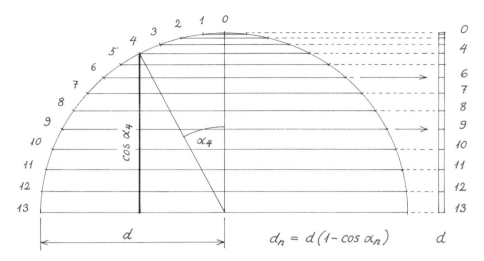

$$d_n = d\,(1 - \cos\alpha_n)$$

Fig. 5 Halfmoon diagram used to produce the narrowing scale *d* (Drawing P. Bloesch).

calculate the missing values. The evolution of the narrowing between the master frames (numbered 1) and the frames no. 14 was probably the same forward and aft, as in other specifications of a slightly later date. After about 1825 this symmetry was gradually reduced, first by introducing different narrowing scales forward and aft of the master frames, and later by moving the master frames forward. **Figure 4** shows the typical configuration of the narrowing at the end of the 19th c. By this time the notion of an exact limit between the first and second sets of frames had also disappeared. For *Amiral Courbet* (**Fig. 4**), the rising has been calculated for one more floor forward and aft than the narrowing, but it appears from the crosses marked on the divisional points of the scales on the floor moulds and on the rising board, that in the actual building of the vessel the last pre-erected frames were those numbered 12 forward and 19 aft.

Of course one would like to know how the shipwright produced his narrowing and other scales. The two devices most commonly used in the Mediterranean area to produce scales of regularly increasing intervals are the so-called halfmoon and the triangle diagrams (Rieth 1996; 1998: 159-165). They are in fact recipes for producing the desired scales by a graphic and purely mechanical process without any mathematics. If this writer is going to use here some mathematical concepts, it is only to understand better the properties of the different scales under examination.

Figure 5 illustrates the application of the halfmoon diagram to produce a narrowing scale *d* for a set of 14 frames, a small but realistic number as in the *brigantin* of 1813 (**Fig. 3**). In this case the narrowing of the floors is a trigonometric function of their stations along the longitudinal axis of the vessel. These positions appear in the diagram as the dividing points on the periphery of the two quadrants, but for the sake of easier calculating their numbering begins with 0 instead of with 1 as in the *barques* built in the Derivaz shipyard at Saint-Gingolph. The narrowing (*diminution*) of a floor at a particular station *n* can thus be written as

$$d_n = d\,(1 - \cos\alpha_n)$$

d denoting the total amount of narrowing at the end of the set of frames to which the narrowing has to be applied.

The diagram shown in **Figure 6** is one of several devices all of which produce the same sequence of regularly increasing intervals making up the required narrowing scale. Here the narrowing is a quadratic func-

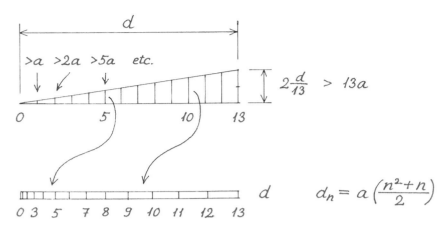

Fig. 6 Triangle diagram used to produce the narrowing scale *d* (Drawing P. Bloesch).

tion of the floors' stations along the longitudinal axis of the vessel. The narrowing of any particular floor at station *n* is given by the formula

$$d_n = a \left(\frac{n^2 + n}{2} \right)$$

the parameter *a* denoting the first and smallest interval of the scale.

There is a minor problem in that the diagram presented here is not mathematically precise: the narrowing scale intervals produced with it (the verticals in the triangle) are all a trifle too big, and their sum is greater than the total amount of narrowing *d*, the excess being equal to

d / n.

In spite of this drawback this type of triangle diagram has the advantage of being very simple and easy to apply, and the problem of inaccuracy can be overcome cheating a little when transferring the intervals from the triangle to the narrowing scale *d* by means of a pair of dividers.

Both diagrams, the halfmoon and the triangle, produce similar sequences of narrowing (**Fig. 7**). The narrowing scale made with the triangle gives the hull of the vessel a little more volume than that made with the halfmoon. The curves in **Figure 7** can be considered mathematically as graphs of the respective functions of narrowing, but they can also be seen, with the eyes of a shipbuilder, as a projection of a section of the ribband connecting the ends of the floor timbers and ending on the stem and on the fashion pieces, thus delineating the outline of the floor in the sense of hull form conception. Yet in **Figure 7** the longitudinal dimension (the distances between the floor timbers) is much reduced in comparison with the transverse dimension (the values of narrowing). **Figures 3** and **4** show this projection of the floor ribband with its true proportions.

Supposing that the shipwrights of Lake Geneva used one of these two devices – halfmoon or triangle – or both of them, it has to be verified. This could be done by visual comparison of the curves obtained by offsets taken from the sources, with others derived from the two diagrams. But visual inspection might well prove to be inconclusive, as can be seen in **Figure 7** where both curves appear nearly identical for about one third of their extent. They even cross each other at the point marked *x*. So one has to look more closely

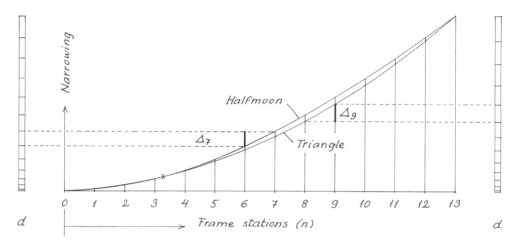

Fig. 7 Narrowing scales made with the halfmoon diagram (left) and with the triangle diagram (right) (Drawing P. Bloesch).

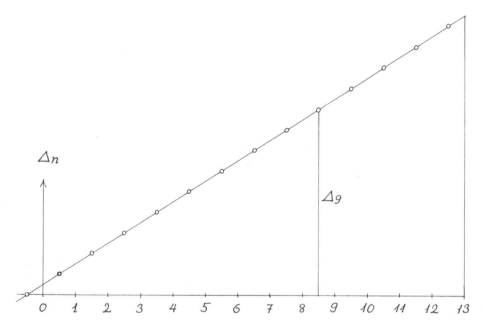

Fig. 8 Intervals of the scale made with the triangle diagram. The units on the y axis are ten times as big as those in figure 7 (Drawing P. Bloesch).

at the properties of these narrowings or floor ribband curvatures. One could look at them through a magnifying glass, but taking them as a sequence of values or numbers, they may be treated in a mathematical way.

The author calculates the differences of consecutive narrowing values (Δ_1, Δ_2, Δ_3 etc.) which are nothing else but the intervals of the narrowing scale **(Fig. 7)** and plots them in another graph **(Figs 8-9)**, taking care to choose the scales of the units on the x and the y axes in order to produce an easily readable result. In the **Figures 8** and **9** the units on the x axis are the same as in **Figure 7**, whereas the units on the y axis are ten times as big as those in **Figure 7**. The result is what might be called a »mathematical image of the narrowings«, and it seems perfectly clear.

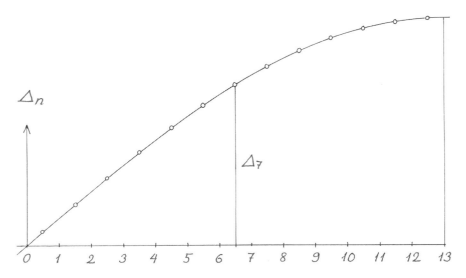

Fig. 9 Intervals of the scale made with the halfmoon diagram. The units on the y axis are ten times as big as those in figure 7 (Drawing P. Bloesch).

The differences of the narrowings derived from the triangle lie all on a straight line and form a linear function of *n* (**Fig. 8**). The second differences (the differences of the differences) remain constant (not plotted in the figure). It can be shown – and this is important in the present context – that this is a rule valid for any quadratic function: for a quadratic polynomial, the first differences form a linear function, and the second differences remain constant (Batschelet 1975: 99-101).

The differences of the narrowing derived from the halfmoon, on the other hand, lie on a sine curve (**Fig. 9**). If the narrowing and rising scales known from the Derivaz manuscript and from the Jacquier moulds (the Portier specifications do not include narrowings and risings) are analysed using the method defined above, it becomes immediately apparent that all of them are of the type produced with the triangle diagram. There is no evidence of the halfmoon diagram having been employed in any of these scales.

Figure 10 represents the analysis of the narrowing of the floors in the after part of *Andalouse* built in 1901. This example has been selected for two reasons: Firstly because the plot of its narrowing differences is among the most regular ones available from the existing evidence, and secondly because the half-breadth of floor values of *Andalouse* are, according to Cornaz (1976: 70-71; 187), nearest to those which could be derived from a halfmoon diagram. Yet **Figure 10** demonstrates that at the origin of this narrowing scale there was not a halfmoon diagram, but a least three different triangles.

Analysing more examples, which it is not possible to include in this short article, it can be concluded that the shipwrights of Lake Geneva did not derive the narrowing of all floor timbers situated between the master frames and the ends of the first set of frames (or tail frames) from one geometrical device as all known shipbuilding treatises would suggest. Every set of narrowings is obviously composed of several different scale sections. According to Gérard Cornaz, who in the 1950s had the opportunity to interview regularly the last shipbuilder of the lake, Louis Jacquier, at least the last generations of Lake Geneva shipbuilders never calculated their narrowings anew, but copied them from existing ones (Cornaz 1976: 70). But how?

By comparing every one of the known narrowing scales with every other, it becomes obvious that none is a direct copy of another one. Partial coincidence, on the other hand, can be observed quite frequently. This leads to the following hypothesis: The shipwright probably had among his tools a set of several different scales, perhaps marked on rather thin laths or sticks, and when he had to prepare the narrowing scales for

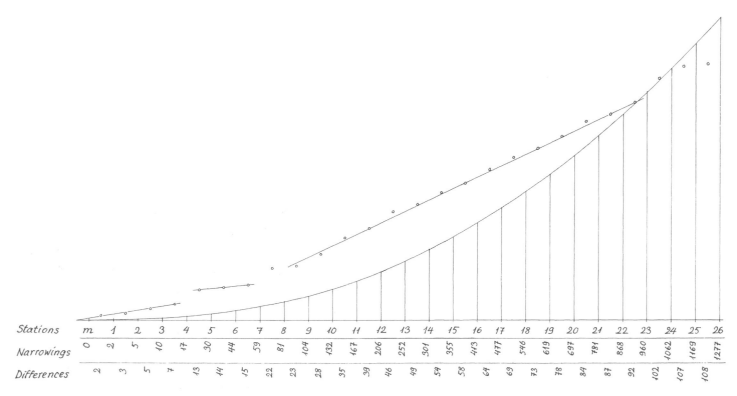

Stations	m	1	2	3	4	5	6	7	8	9	10	11	12	13	14	15	16	17	18	19	20	21	22	23	24	25	26
Narrowings	0	2	5	10	17	30	44	59	81	104	132	167	206	252	301	355	413	477	546	619	697	781	868	960	1062	1169	1277
Differences	2	3	5	7	13	14	15	22	23	28	35	39	46	49	54	58	64	69	73	78	84	87	92	102	107	108	

Fig. 10 Narrowing in the after part of *Andalouse*, 1901, and its differences plotted against it. On the *y* axis, the units of the differences are ten times as big as those of the narrowing. The values of narrowings and their differences are given in millimetres (Drawing P. Bloesch).

a new ship, he could do this combining the appropriate sections chosen from his set of model scales. He normally made the narrowing rather flat for a certain distance from the midship frame, and then definitely steeper until the ends of the first set of frames. This implies that there were up to five key stations along the keel to guide the design process: one amidships, two at the ends of the first set of frames, and two about halfway in-between. Whereas the narrowing scales were doubtless composed of several different sections, all belonging to the same geometrical type, the existence of a set of different model scales in the hands of the shipwright can only be supposed, although with good reasons. Concerning the rules which might have guided the shipwright when he had to decide about the position of the key stations and the choice of the different degrees of narrowing at these places, nothing is known.

REFERENCES

Batschelet, E., 1975, *Introduction to Mathematics for Life Scientists*. 2nd ed., Berlin, Heidelberg, New York.

Bloesch, P., 2001, Die Erfindung der Genferseebarke 1691. Ein Beispiel technischer Innovation aus dem 17. Jahrhundert. In: H.-J. Gilomen, R. Jaun, M. Müller & B. Veyrassat (eds), *Innovationen. Voraussetzungen und Folgen – Antriebskräfte und Widerstände*. Schweizerische Gesellschaft für Wirtschafts- und Sozialgeschichte, no. 17. Zürich, 47-66.

2003, Moulds, Rising Boards and Bevel Boards. The Wooden Memory of the Shipyard of Le Locum, Lake Geneva. In: *ISBSA 9*, 144-151.

Cornaz, G., 1976, *Les barques du Léman*. Grenoble (new edition, corrected: Genève 1998).

Rieth, É., 1996, *Le maître gabarit, la tablette et le trébuchet. Essai sur la conception non-graphique des carènes du moyen-âge au XX*e *siècle*. Mémoires de la section d'histoire des sciences et des techniques, no. 9. Paris.

1998, Les éléments transversaux de la charpente. In: X. Nieto & X. Raurich (eds), *Culip VI. Excavacions arqueologiques subaquàtiques a Cala Culip*, vol. 2. Girona, 137-189.

DANIELA GRÄF

BOAT MILLS IN EUROPE
FROM EARLY MEDIEVAL TO MODERN TIMES

In her thesis the present writer gathered archaeological finds as well as technical and historical data on boat mills over the entire period of their existence. Boat mills largely contributed to the supply of the European population with milled products from the early Middle Ages into modern times. The geographical scope is the whole of Europe. In her catalogue the author included almost 700 locations, as many as could be taken from the sources.

To the study of boat mills three different sorts of source material were available dating from the first appearance to their abandonment in the 20th c.: substantial remains, iconography and written sources. With representations of boat mills as parts of town views and plans a distinction between constructional precise and symbolic images had to be made by comparison of many contemporaneous illustrations. For this reason every available representation was considered. Technical drawings and descriptions from machine books were examined in relation to their period and time of origin. The analysis of historical sources served as the basis for the interpretation of archaeological finds, which were recorded by investigation of finds in museums and other locations around Europe.

Time and place of the invention of boat mills remain obscure. They were first mentioned by Procopius in his account of the siege of Rome by the Goths in A.D. 537. Boat mills were common on all large rivers and many tributaries in Europe with the exception of Scandinavia. 695 places on different large rivers and their tributaries could have been identified in particular at which occasionally or over long times one or more boat mills were situated (**Fig. 1**).

Boat mill technology might be brought to N. and W. Europe by Roman engineers. The first documentary evidence for boat mills N. of the Alps goes back the 6th c. A.D. As early as 563 there would seem to have been boat mills working at Geneva, and the archaeological remains found at Gimbsheim near Mainz are dated to ca. 760. References to mills at Mainz between 780 and 802 which almost certainly refer to boat

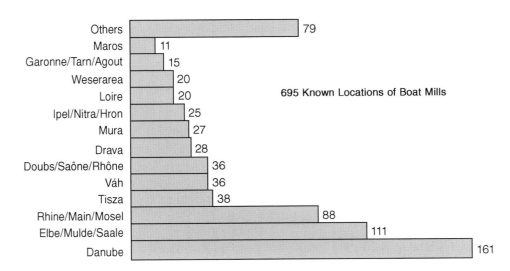

Fig. 1 Quantities of boat mills along European rivers and river systems. Inventory based on archaeological, historical and pictorial evidence.

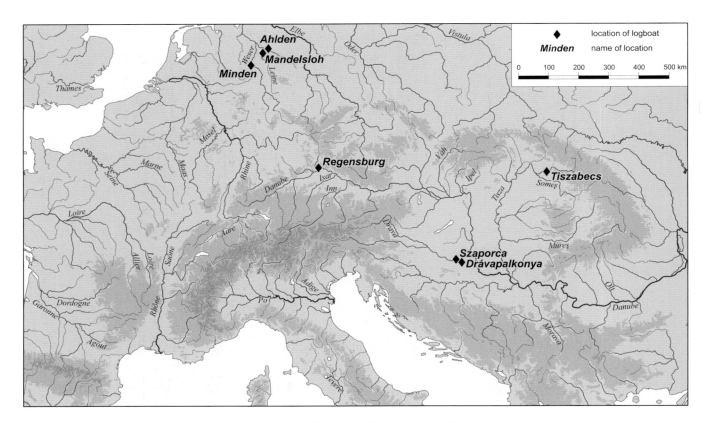

Fig. 2 Dugouts as constructional components of boat mills. The distribution map considers archaeological finds, historical texts or images of mill-dugouts, and also rivers where dugouts were used as boat mill hulls.

mills, to a boat mill at Strasbourg in 850, as well as to another boat mill on the Rhine around 840, confirm the knowledge of this milling technology N. of the Alps for the early Middle Ages. According to a notice referred to the village of Böllberg near Halle boat mills were known on the Saale River at the latest in ca. 950.

Boat mills existed on the Seine at Paris in the 9th c. and at Cologne no later than the 10th c. (**Plate 6**). From the 11th c. there is evidence of boat mills on the river Mosel at Trier, on the Garonne at Toulouse, on the Loire at Angers, Ponts-de-Cé, Souzay-Champigny and Montsoreau, as well as on the river Nisava near Niš in present-day Serbia. On the Saône at Chazelle, the Inn at Passau and the Rhine near Bingen there were boat mills from at the latest the 12th c.

By the 12th-c. boat mills were spread across Europe in certain numbers and at the latest in the 13th c. boat mills were established on all large European rivers (**Figs 4-5**). After a time of continuous increase up to the 17th c. (on the lower Danube up to the 19th c.), the gradual decline of the number of ship mills began (**Figs 3-8**). Almost all Rhône mills fell into disuse by the middle, or the end, of the 18th c. already. At the same time on the Rhine and Elbe the slow fall of this kind of mill began. By the end of the 19th c. almost all mills on the Rhine, Elbe and upper Danube disappeared, whereas on the middle and lower Danube a quantitative reduction of boat mills starts in the middle of the 19th c. By the middle of the 20th c. they also disappeared there (**Figs 10-12**). After a peak of using water power by boat mills in the 16th and 17th c. they were gradually displaced by innovative plant, new sources of driving power and increasing navigation on the rivers.

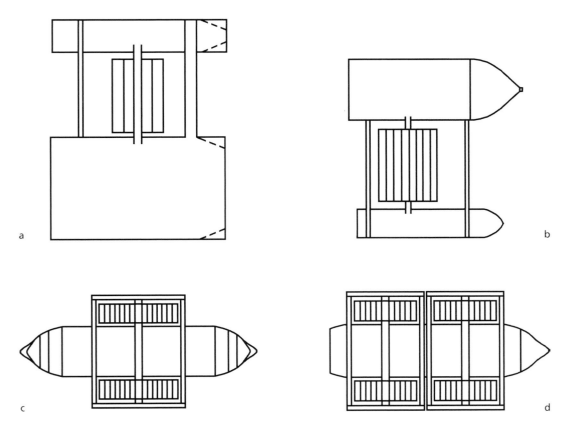

Fig. 3 Construction types: **a** type 1. – **b** Type 2. – **c** Type 3. – **d** Type 3, Nied 1650 and Mainz 1565 variant.

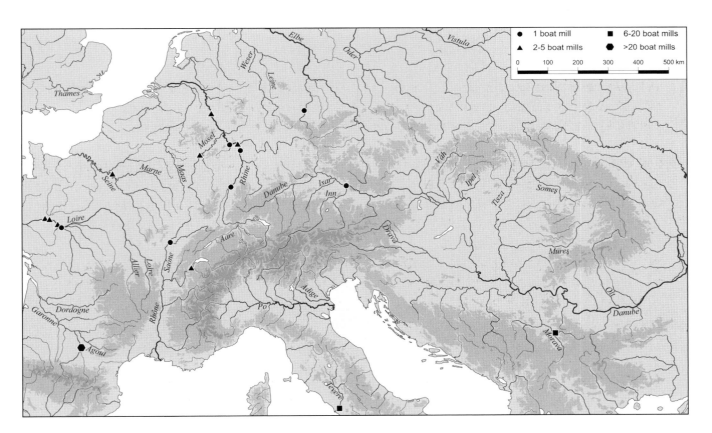

Fig. 4 Distribution of boat mills in Europe in the 12th c.

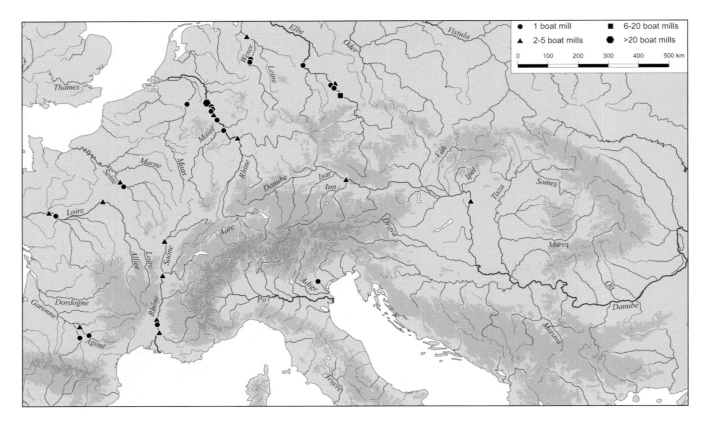

Fig. 5 Distribution of boat mills in Europe in the 13th c.

The reasons which led to the introduction of floating mills were changing water levels of rivers, which constantly changed their beds, along with the emergence of large settlements with a concentration of handicraft, which urgently needed flour, barley and other food as well as power to run early machines.

Boat mills had the big advantage of being able to work reliably at every water level, apart from extremes, as they would rise and fall with the river. Big rivers as Danube, Rhine and Elbe regularly rise to high water levels, and additionally they often changed their beds in the past. Therefore it was virtually impossible to operate land-based watermills. This problem is very well illustrated by the example of the Rhine: In 1818 first steps were made to carrying out river corrections. By making shortcuts, larger bends were cut off and the riverbed was straightened. By 1860 the Rhine between Basel and the mouth of the small river Lauter had been shortened by 14%.

In W. Central Europe, increasingly different functions of boat mills developed, e.g. malt, sawing or sharpening mills, whilst in E. Europe boat mills exclusively served as meal mills.

From the analysis of available pictures and written sources and their geographical and chronological spreading three different building types of European boat mills could be traced back. Numerous regional designs and variations were determined likewise.

TYPE 1

Floating mills consisting of two ship bodies, one of which bore the grinding mechanism and the other supported the main axle and waterwheel. The hulls have a box shaped appearance with transom and

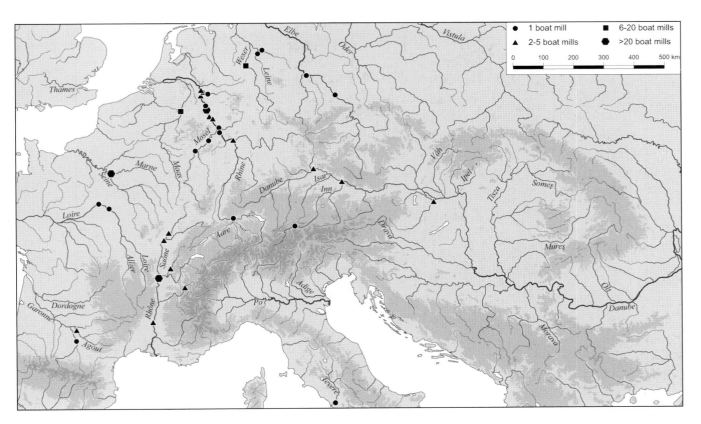

Fig. 6 Distribution of boat mills in Europe in the 14th c.

usually a slight sheer rising up to the square bow (**Fig. 3a**). This construction type with high probability was almost without exception used for boat mills on the rivers Elbe, Mulde, Weser, Maas, Rhine (except central and upper Rhine between Bonn and Breisach), Aare, Reuss, Loire, Adige and the city of Rome on the Tiber. At other rivers, as Morava and Alt, only boat mills of type 1 construction existed in the 19th and 20th c.

It was from these early type 1 mills, which on the Elbe, Rhine and Danube can be separated by the different diameters of the waterwheels, shipbuilders at Cologne (at the Rhine) developed the typical Cologne design of boat mills based on three ship bodies of identical size, at the latest at the beginning of the 15th c. Two of the hulls carried the grinding mill and mill house, the third one served to support the main axle. This form was transferred, e.g. to the town of Bonn in 1754/1756. A design of the type 1 floating mill on three equal ships was also common on the river Adige in Italy. This characteristic design arose probably exclusively in areas in which many boat mills were concentrated on a river or its section.

TYPE 2

Boat mills based on two hulls, one with the grinding mechanism and house, the other one carrying the axle, with hulls ending at a point at the bow with or without a stempost (**Fig. 3b**).

To be found on the rivers Danube (except the lower Danube in Bulgaria), Inn, Tisza, Garonne, Saône and Rhône, this type of construction was built probably over the entire period of their existence, almost exclusively. On other rivers, like Váh, Someș, Mura, Doubs, Sava and Po, exclusively boat mills of type 2 construction were present still in the 19th and 20th c.

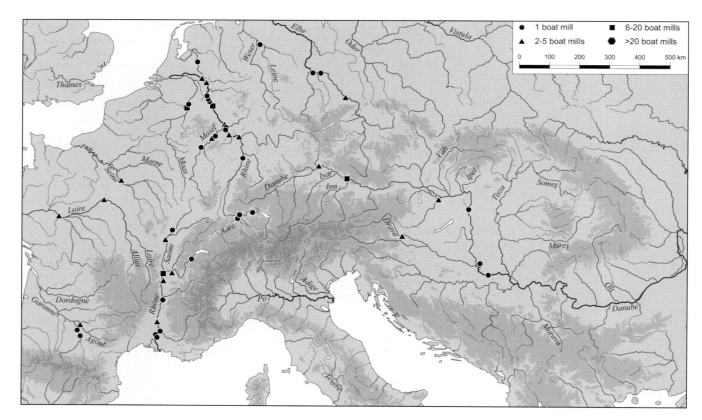

Fig. 7 Distribution of boat mills in Europe in the 15th c.

The building method on three equal ships of the type of building 2 is known unfortunately only from two photographs referring to the places Sered' at the river Váh and Bosanska Gradiška at the river Sava.

The distinction of boat mills with an axle-bearing vessel (outrigger) as to two building types on the basis of the square-bow (type 1) or pointed-bow (type 2) helps to overview the abundant material. However, the regional spread of these two types shows that the preference for sharp or straight and wide bow constructions can, despite occasional structural similarity of both types, serve as distinctive feature of boat mills of different river basins.

TYPE 3

Floating mills which consisted of only one ship body with two mill wheels turning in the river left and right of the hull, independently of the shape of the ship (**Fig. 3c**). The hulls of those mills were built in different shapes: sharp-ended with a sternpost, or stem and sternpost, or with straight stern or straight bow and stern.

Type 3 mills were prevailing in three river basins: Seine river (1), the rivers Main and middle Rhine in the W. part of Central Europe (2) as well as the lowest section of the Danube in E. Europe. It is to be stated that at Rhine and Main a design with blunt tail was preferred (an exception being Bingen in 1856), whilst boat mills on the Seine predominantly showed pointed ends.

In the 19th c. changes in the type of floating mill and/or of displacement can be determined by examples of unusual designs in all three regions where the spread of single-hull mills (type 3) was usual: the dis-

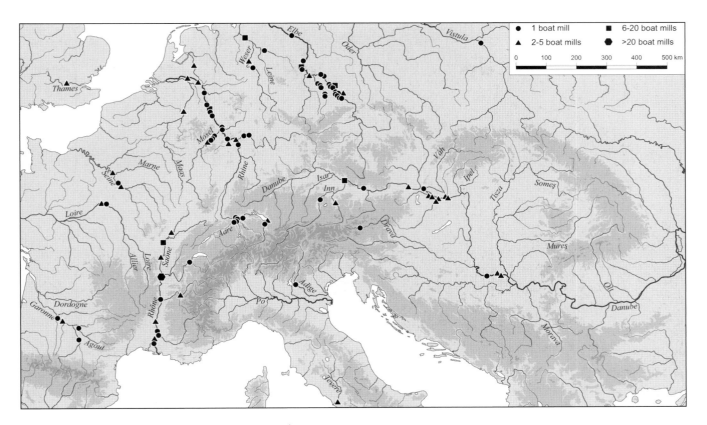

Fig. 8 Distribution of boat mills in Europe in the 16th c.

tribution areas of type 1 and 2 boat mills show the employment of individual type 3, particularly in the 19th c.

VARIANTS WITH MORE THAN ONE WATERWHEEL

To increase the performance, the main axle of floating mills on the river Rhône (building type 2) was extended occasionally to bear a second water wheel outside the second axle-bearing ship's body. This construction was common on the Rhône in the 19th and 20th c. only, where to type 1 and 2 mills two water wheels could be attached, one behind the other, between the individual hulls. Sources which confirm the presence of such boat mills with two or more wheels following on one side are known also from the upper Rhine and upper Danube in large numbers. Floating mills with more than one water wheel also seem to have existed on the river Elbe. Also were type 3 mills on the river Main occasionally provided with two pairs of water wheels, one behind the another, as it is shown by depictions of the villages Nied and Segnitz (**Fig. 3d**).

GENERAL OBSERVATIONS

The structure of boat mills is described in detail in the thesis, whereby special attention was paid to regional characteristics of design and technical details of floating mills. Hulls in all regions were carvel-planked with

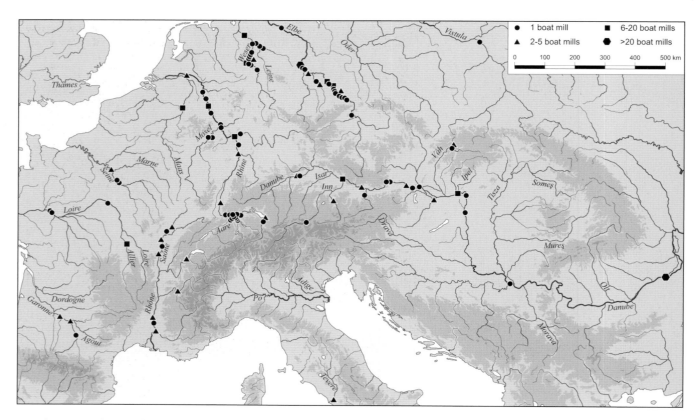

Fig. 9 Distribution of boat mills in Europe in the 17th c.

a flat bottom and without keel. The design differed regionally, but it always resembled locally used cargo vessels. Nevertheless, boat mills were built for their specific function, and they never completely corresponded to the construction of inland vessels.

In some areas dugouts were used bearing the mechanism and/or supporting the axle, and it seems most plausible that dugouts were common in many regions as means to carry milling devices before the development of dockyards (**Fig. 2**): the dugout from Mandelsloh (cf. below) belongs to a find complex of the 14th c. A representation of the 19th c. might show a boat mill at Minden with an outrigger consisting of a dugout, and the same seems to be true for a dugout found at Ahlden S.E. of Bremen (Erler & Matthiesen 1989: 26). Logboats were used in such a way evidently in the Hungarian Danube area, on the rivers Drava and Szamos/Someş in the 18th c., and on the river Tisza up to the 19th c. One account points to the use of dugouts as floats of boat mills in the town Regensburg (Upper Danube) during the 14th c.

A relation between the velocity of flow of the river and the building type of boat mills did not exist. Their design was dominated mainly by the ship building tradition of the area in which the mill was built and operated.

Building types characteristic for a river or river section hardly changed during long periods. The choice of construction and design and the adjustment of the specific form of boat mills to local natural and river-conditions in most regions probably emerged before the first figurative sources arose, and in close reciprocal effect with existing designs of riverboats. So far no region is known, in which the building type found on a tributary differed from that of the related main stream. This observation clearly indicates the influence of tradition which finally dominated over the natural conditions.

The geographical setting of regions with similar traditions of boat mill building was an essential basis for the interpretation of archaeological remains (**Plate 6**).

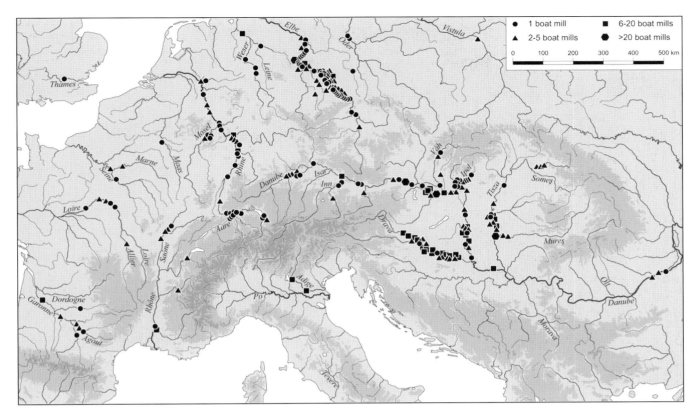

Fig. 10 Distribution of boat mills in Europe in the 18th c.

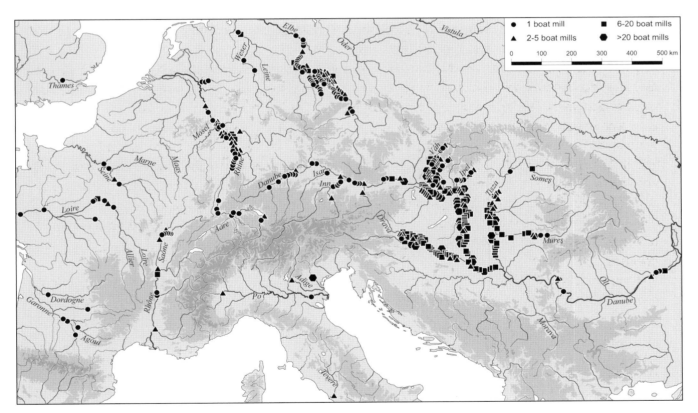

Fig. 11 Distribution of boat mills in Europe in the 19th c.

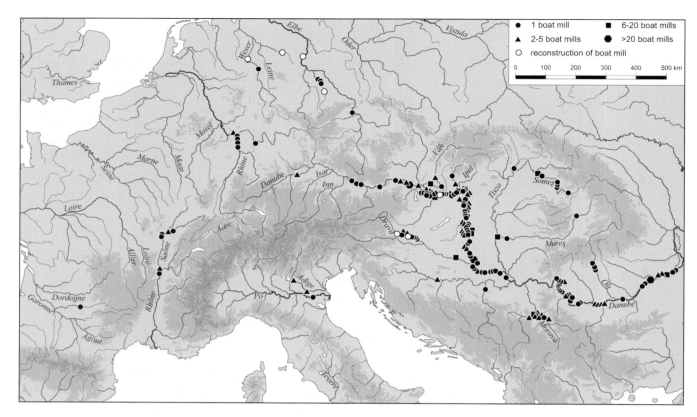

Fig. 12   Distribution of boat mills in Europe in the 20th c.

FINDS FROM GIMBSHEIM NEAR MAINZ

During gravel dredging at Gimbsheim (Lkr. Alzey-Worms), some planks and frames, a stone spindle, three lantern-wheel disks and two millstones were discovered in summer 1989. O. Höckmann (1994a; 1994b) identified the most artefacts as components of a Carolingian boat mill which according to dendrochronological and radiocarbon analyses was build around 760. His reconstruction includes a double-hulled vessel; two pairs of stones placed on the hulls were driven by a wide water-wheel turning in between (Höckmann 1994a: 209, fig. 71; 1994b: 114, fig. 10).

The suggestion of a different reconstruction is based on the realisation that no reference points for the occurrence of double mills (tandem mills) could be found in the historical sources. The representation of a double mill in a machine book of the early baroque is no sound proof for the existence of this kind of mill. Publications of the late Renaissance and early Baroque periods (17th-18th c.) which play an important role in mill research can only be consulted with reservation regarding interpretation, since they contain many fantasy constructions.

The past interpretation of the early floating mills on the river Tiber in Rome as double mills with broad water wheel has to be changed due to the data given in Procopius' account (cf. above) to a form with two ship's bodies and two water-wheels turning behind one another in the current. In contrast, examples of working mills with more than one water-wheel show, that this technique did work. Thus, Höckmann's reconstruction of the Gimbsheim boat mill seems doubtful. Moreover, Gimbsheim lies in an area in which in later time exclusively single-hull type 3 mills were used. The continuity of type 3 construction is proven in the area, e.g. in Mainz by sources from the 16th c. up to the abandonment of boat mills. The roots of this tradition may go back well to the 8th c. A.D.

FINDS FROM MANDELSLOH NEAR HANNOVER

The relics found at Mandelsloh (Lkr. Region Hannover) belong to a complex of the 14th c., as it followed by the dendrochronological analysis of the dugout (Doll 1983; Ellmers 1985), and by the type of caulking clamps found in the logboat. The disk of a lantern-gear, which also was found in the dugout, has two central perforations, since it was obviously screwed onto an axle. This lantern-wheel apparently was part of an early multi-level transmission. All objects of the find complex can be identified as remains of a boat mill, and accessories for milling. This interpretation can be based on historical sources which prove the presence of ship mills in Minden, Bremen and other towns of the region starting from the 13th c. The design with two ship's bodies, one carrying the mill and house and the other supporting the axle of the water-wheel was a feature typical for this region. On the other hand, evidences of boat mills with dugout-outriggers on the rivers Weser, Aller and Leine are missing so far, though a representation from Minden of the 19th c. seems to show such a construction which is well-known from S.E. Europe, especially the Danube area, and from the medieval town of Regensburg (cf. above).

CONCLUSIONS

Analyses of archaeological relics, historic depictions and written sources under the perspective of technical considerations shed new light on the history of boat mills. Though of most different quality, comprehensive data about constructional details, function and efficiency of such floating devices not only proved their widespread use on European rivers but also peculiarities of design typical for certain geographical areas. Attempts to reconstruct boat mills which were based on comparisons of substantial remains and iconography, retrieved the traditional appearance of boat mills including the aspect of their function. As artificial parts of medieval to modern fluvial landscapes, boat mills on the one hand competed with inland vessels, on the other hand their architecture was influenced from local shipbuilding.

NOTE

This paper represents an abstract of the author's dissertation which was published in English language with German and French summaries as a joined project by The Archaeological Heritage Service Saxony in two series (Gräf 2006).

REFERENCES

Doll, E., 1983, Der Einbaum von Mandelsloh. Schwimmkörper einer Wassermühle. *Heimatbuch Menschen und Landschaft um Hannover*, 1, 60-64.

Erler, G. & Matthiesen, H., 1989, *Erfahrungen am Wasserlauf – dem Wind entgegen. Mühlen der alten Heide – Erbschaft und Erlebnis*. Fallingbostel.

Ellmers, D., 1985, Die Schiffsmühle von Mandelsloh. In: Komitee »1000 Jahre Mandelsloh« (ed.), *Mandelsloh 985-1985. Beiträge zur älteren Geschichte des Dorfes und seiner Umgebung* Neustadt am Rübenberge, 32-37.

Gräf, D., 2006, *Boat Mills in Europe from Medieval to Modern Times*. Veröffentlichungen des Landesamtes für Archäologie Sachsen, vol. 51, and Bibliotheca Molinologica, vol. 19. Dresden.

Höckmann, O., 1994a, Eine Schiffsmühle aus den Jahren um 760 n.Chr. in Gimbsheim, Kr. Alzey-Worms. *Mainzer Archäologische Zeitschrift* 1, 191-209.

1994b, Post-Roman Boat Timbers and a Floating Mill from the Upper Rhine. In: *ISBSA* 6, 105-116.

COLIN PALMER · LUCY BLUE

THE COUNTRY BOATS OF THE GANGES DELTA –
AN ETHNOGRAPHIC STUDY OF INLAND NAVIGATION

One of the striking sights for a visitor to the Ganges Delta region (**Fig. 1**) is the large numbers of traditional boats that operate on the rivers and the great diversity of their size and shape. Up until the late 1980s, it was sometimes possible to see hundreds of boats in one spot, ranging in size from small, one or two person boats to massive cargo vessels capable of carrying 100 tons or more. The boats came in many different shapes that were given a bewildering range of names by their owners and operators. At that time they relied largely on human power or the wind and currents for propulsion and were central to the movements of goods and people.

Outside observers (e.g. Hornell 1946) have speculated about the reasons for, and origins of, this diversity but no comprehensive view has been presented. This paper describes the diversity of the boat types and offers insight into change over time and the reasons for the variety and change. In so doing, it also describes a unique (and fast disappearing) water borne culture. In addition to its intrinsic value as an historical record, it has by analogy the potential to provide insights into the development and operation of inland water transport in earlier times.

PHYSICAL ENVIRONMENT

Bangladesh and the E. regions of the Indian states of West Bengal and Bihar contain one of the world's great deltas. It is here that three mighty rivers come to the sea – the Ganges, the Brahmaputra-Jamuna and the Meghna. In the N. of the region the main river, the Jamuna is heavily braided and shallow for most of the year. Currents can be locally fierce even in the dry season.

The Ganges, although now dammed by the Farakka Barrage, has a substantial flow that makes its way through the W. of Bangladesh. In roughly the centre of Bangladesh the Ganges is joined by the larger Jamuna/Brahmaputra and they flow S. E. as the Padma before being joined from the N. E. by the Meghna, the river which drains the Sylhet region of Bangladesh.

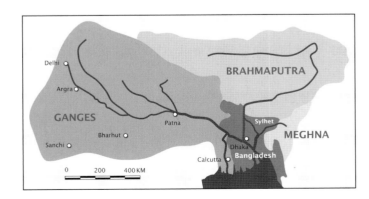

Fig. 1 Map showing the geographical context of the Ganges Delta and the river basins which it drains.

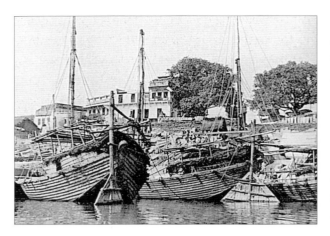

Fig. 3 Photograph from Hornells' book Water Transport, showing reverse clinker boats (which he called *Patella*) on the mid reaches of the Ganges river (Hornell 1946: pl. XXIX B).

all the others. It has clinker topsides and is of hard chine construction. A unique photograph is contained in Hornell (1946) and reproduced here (**Fig. 3**).

Greenhill lived and worked in Bangladesh (then East Pakistan) in the 1950s, and in »Boats and Boatmen of Pakistan« (Greenhill 1971) and other works (Greenhill 1957; 1966) he provides the first attempt at not only a description of the boats but also a system of analysis through which to understand the observed features. Recognising the inconsistencies in the boat names used by the boatmen, he adopted a feature based approach to classification.

Recent sources

Jansen undertook extensive fieldwork in Bangladesh in the mid to late 1980s (Jansen *et al.* 1989). The objective was to understand the operations of the boats so that their »contribution [to development] can be safeguarded and enhanced«. As such it was not an explicit ethnographic study, but did record details of boats observed on just one river, the Lakhya River near Dhaka. The authors noted (Jansen *et al.* 1989: 74-75): »One type of boat may, however, have different names in different localities. Different names can also be given to the same boat to give expression to the purpose for which it is used«. They also found that the boatmen mainly used colloquial words which relate more to the size and function of the boat than any specific morphological features.

Jansen *et al.* (1989) determined that the presence or absence and the shape of a *goloi* (a structure used to terminate the planking at the bow and stern of many, but not all boats) were perceived by the boatmen as important aids to classification and identification of their boats. They consequently proposed a typology based upon the presence or absence of goloi as an aid to classification. They also commissioned a professional photographer to photograph the boats. The photographs were collected in the book »Sailing Against the Wind« (Bolstad & Jansen 1992), and the captions were prepared with advice from Nazibor Rahman.

A subsequent study was undertaken between 1988 and 1992 (reported in BIWTA 1994). Palmer was engaged as the naval architect and was able to photograph and study a number of boats in detail. Finally, in 1997, Blue and McGrail (McGrail *et al.* 2003: 25-66) studied the reverse clinker boats of N. E. Bangladesh. This filled the gap in the data obtained by Jansen and Palmer. Taken together, the records of Jansen, Bolstad, Palmer, McGrail and Blue allow a very detailed definition of 15 boats types that were in operation in Bangladesh in the late 1980s to the late 1990s.

THE PROBLEMS OF NAMES

As noted above, attempts to classify the boats based on the names given to them by the boatmen have proved to be ineffective since the names they use are not consistently linked to specific hull forms. Rather, it appears that the role for which a boat is used is of more importance to the boatmen than its shape.

However, it is also clear that there are consistent differences between the boats, even if these do not appear to be of great significance to the boatmen. Therefore, the approach that will be adopted in this paper is to use names that the authors know to have been applied to a specific type in at least one location. These are in effect code names, but this approach seems preferable to allocating anonymous code numbers or letters to the boats. Thus the names that are used in what follows are not claimed to be universal, but wherever possible they have been chosen as the name most often associated with a particular type.

REASONS FOR BOAT SHAPES

Some authors suggest that the shapes of the boats are adapted to the uses to which they are put or the environments in which they operate, e.g. Deloche (1980: 16): »In the category of barges, carriers of heavy cargoes, one might distinguish the boats of Hindusthan with bulging convex hulls which were well-adapted to the rivers of the mid-valley of the Ganga, encumbered with sand banks; and the boats of Bengal with slender tapered hulls suited to the strong currents of the deltaic arms«. Similarly, Hornell (1920: 69) notes: »All the larger boats, whether small fishing boats or large rice carriers, with the frequent need to row against the current are characteristically low forward [in order to facilitate rowing]«. More generally, Green-hill and Mannering (1997) were of the opinion that »[a] working boat's shape, as McKee has so clearly shown, is governed by her purpose, the circumstances in which she will operate, and the materials and resources available for her construction«.

There are a number of examples from the Ganges Delta datasets that challenge this view. A very common type in the far S., in the deep tidal rivers of the Sundarbans, is the beamy, flat bottomed *podi* whereas Deloche's model would predict slender tapered hulls in this region, and by extension of his argument, deeper draft to take advantage of the available water depth. Conversely, the *malar*, which has a relatively flat bottom, is common in the S. E. of the country (an area of relatively deep water) and travels widely on the big, deep rivers. Thus, while shallow water may favour flat-bottomed boats, there is no indication that when deep water is the norm, the flat bottom is abandoned. Also contrary to the view that flat bottomed types are always associated with shallow waters, the round bottom, relatively deep draft *patam* type is common not only in the rivers around Dhaka, but specialises in the boulder carrying trade from the shallow waters around Sylhet. Lastly, contrary to Hornell's observation that the boats have low bows to facilitate rowing, the *patam* type is higher at the bow, yet is rowed from this position.

While these examples question the functional explanations of earlier writers, it may be no coincidence that today the most common type in the N. W. of the country, where the rivers are shallow, braided and often very fast flowing, is the shallow draft, mechanised *kosha*. The conditions here, especially in the dry season, are now so extreme that no other type can possibly operate. In the more benign conditions of the rest of the region, it is apparent that a much wider range of boats types can be found operating side by side. We therefore conclude that the operating environment can be an influence on form, but only in circumstances where the conditions are extreme.

A photograph in Bolstad and Jansen (1992: 29) illustrates this point. It was taken at Barmi, a town about 20 km N. of Dhaka. At least eight, if not ten different types of boat can be seen in the same place, many of them apparently carrying the same cargoes. This diversity is also apparent from Jansen *et al.* (1989) where they describe 54 different types seen on the Lakhya River, a relatively minor river in central Bangladesh. Generally it is clear that the operators find it quite acceptable to use their boats in a range of different locations and for a range of tasks, and that therefore there is, at best, only weak evidence of one type being favoured over another in particular operating environments.

Despite this, certain types are widely known to be »from« a specific area or region, although they will regularly travel far away from these home locations. *Malars* are from Noakali, *ghashis* are very common around Dhaka and the *bachari* is most common in Barisal and Swarapkuti. It seems likely that this is a reflection of the owners personal preferences and sense of identity rather than a reflection of specific physical conditions.

If environment and function do not have strong influences on the form of the boats, how then have these distinct types come to be linked to specific localities? The most likely explanations probably lie in complex cultural influences. The boats are a central part of the identities of the peoples who use them and they are artefacts that are deeply embedded in the history and culture of the societies. Quite simply, the local shape constitutes a »proper boat« in the eyes of the local people. As such, it is also what the resident builders will make for the owner when he asks for a boat. In view of the »hands-off« relationship between the builder and the owner (Glassie 1997) and the suppression of innovation in the apprenticeship systems by which boatbuilding is passed from generation to generation (Simpson 2006), there are conservative forces at work that will tend to support the persistence of specific types in particular locations.

At a more general level, the work of Darwinian cultural evolutionists can shed some light on this matter. The work of Richerson and Boyd (2005: 162) predicts that what they define as »conformist bias« will »tend to reduce the amount of variation within groups and increase and preserve variation between groups«. By »conformist bias« they mean a form of social learning in which people tend to imitate the most common behaviour they see around them. Richerson and Boyd show that this form of learning is favoured in circumstances where the environment changes slowly and the information available to individuals is poor or »noisy«. By the latter they mean the feed back of information available to people concerning the effects of specific actions they may take; such as making changes to the shape of a boat in the context of this paper. These circumstances largely pertain to rural societies of the Ganges Delta, so may explain circumstances in which there is overall variety amongst boats, but a tendency for the major diversity to be geographically zoned and for more limited diversity to be exhibited within the zones.

CHANGE OVER TIME

The datasets described above provide a somewhat variable record of the types of boats found in the Ganges Delta region from the early centuries B.C./A.D. until the mid- to the late 1990s. Assuming that the early records do reflect the limited range of boat types in existence at the time, there was a great increase in the range of boat types in the period from the earliest records until some time before the 18th c., but then perhaps little further change.

Cluster analysis

In order to test the hypothesis that change had not been very great in the period over which the detailed European records are available, a statistical cluster analysis approach was adopted. The analysis was undertaken using a Raup-Crick clustering algorithm (Raup and Crick 1979) available in a statistical package developed for palaeontology called PAST (http://folk.uio.no/ohammer/past). The algorithm is preferred because of its suitability for use with data in the form of an absence/presence matrix. Some 47 morphological boat characteristics were selected.

The analysis was applied to a selection of the recent boats and to the boats from Solvyns' records. In total 43 boats were considered, and the groupings were compared. **Figure 4** shows the result obtained for the recent dataset. The result identifies a number of types that are clearly very different from the general population. The *chhataki nauka* and *sylheti nauka* are slender, reverse clinker types found exclusively in the N. E. of the Meghna Basin (modern-day Sylhet). The *balam* is an extended logboat and the *patalia* is a large »European« clinker built boat with a flat bottom, and the *kosha* a flat bottomed, hard chine form.

The one apparent anomaly is that the large reverse clinker type described by Greenhill, the *sylheti nauka*, which, considering its unusual construction technique, does not stand out as a distinctive form, but is shown to be very similar to a *saronga* (but otherwise rather different from others in the group at the bottom of the diagram). This is in part because the method was used without weighting the characters, so while the presence of reverse clinker is a very clear identifying feature to the human eye, it is to the statistics simply one feature amongst many. However, the statistical similarity between the reverse clinker *sylhet nauka* and the *saronga* may

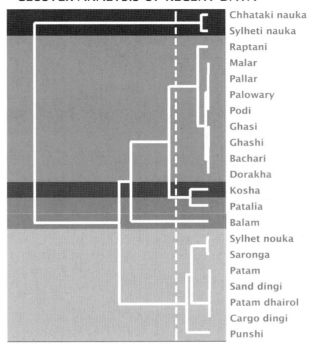

CLUSTER ANALYSIS OF RECENT DATA

Chhataki nauka
Sylheti nauka
Raptani
Malar
Pallar
Palowary
Podi
Ghasi
Ghashi
Bachari
Dorakha
Kosha
Patalia
Balam
Sylhet nouka
Saronga
Patam
Sand dingi
Patam dhairol
Cargo dingi
Punshi

Fig. 4 Typical dendrogram output obtained from cluster analysis, in this case showing the boats types described by Solvyns (1799).

reflect a real similarity between the types. Greenhill (1971: 111-113) describes the *saronga* as a logboat. If the *sylhet nauka* is very similar in form to the *saronga*, a boat that retains the form of its logboat ancestry, perhaps the same applies to the *sylhet nauka*? Greenhill (1971: 121-122) stated that »The Sylhet *digkata* boats show beyond doubt that a clinker or lapstrake form of construction can come into existence quite spontaneously from the desire to extend a hollowed out log«.

The result of the analysis of the Solvyns dataset is presented in **Figure 5**. It seems that there had been no large-scale changes in the boat types. The most consistent group is the smooth skinned, medium to large sized cargo boats and it is appears that this type has become more numerous since Solvyns' time. While these results have not been subject to rigorous statistical analysis, it does appear that the recent boats and Solvyns boats do share substantial similarities, which supports the view that change was not very rapid over the last two hundred years.

RAPID CHANGE AND THE PERSISTENCE OF FEATURES

While the overall impression from this study is that many boat types changed little in the 300 years since Bowrey's time, there has actually been some very rapid change in the last 20 years. This has coincided with a steep rise in the cost of wood (and a commensurate reduction in its availability and quality), reductions in water levels, increasing competition from other transport modes, the use of engines in the boats and more general socio-economic changes in the country such as urbanisation and the rise of a cash based economy.

In parallel with, and perhaps in response to these very strong forces, the boats have changed. Most noticeably the large, bulky load carriers such as the *pallar* have almost disappeared, and operation under sail is now rare, while the flat bottomed *koshas* have boomed. Despite this, certain features and combinations of

SOLVYNS

L	Donga
H	Magarcehra
B	Morpankhi
A	Filchera
M	Bangles
S	Palwar
Q	Ulak
U	Bhur
R	Kosa
T	Hola
N	Pateli
O	Katra
P	Balam
I	Jaliya Dingi
K	Ektha
J	Saranga
C	Bajra
D	Bhauliya
F	Khela_Dingi
G	Dingi
E	Pansi
V	Ita Dingi

RECENT

MM	Chhataki nauka
QQ	Sylheti nauka
FF	Raptani
JJ	Malar
X	Pallar
GG	Palowary
OO	Podi
KK	Ghasi
W	Ghashi
NN	Bachari
PP	Dorakha
LL	Kosha
Y	Patalia
BB	Balam
Z	Sylhet nouka
HH	Saronga
AA	Patam
DD	SandDingi
II	Patam dhairol
CC	CargoDingi
EE	Punshi

Fig. 5 Comparison of the groupings obtained from cluster analysis of Solvyns' types and those described by more recent authors.

features persist. Many mechanised *koshas* continue to use a steering oar even though rudders set in rudder posts are well known. Staples are used for the edge joining of planks on the *koshas* even though the framing is constructed first and thus an edge joined construction technique is functionally redundant.

The construction of the *koshas* is much less complex than for the other boat types, and this has enabled house carpenters and others to start building boats. They bring new ways of working and new ideas, which when coupled with the process of mechanisation have facilitated rapid change that continues to this day. One very striking example of this innovation is the so-called »tin« *kosha* – a boat that is »planked« with thin metal roofing sheet instead of wood. Engine installations also show great ingenuity, with a wide variety of flexible coupling systems and lifting mechanisms that enable the boats to operate under power in very shallow water.

It appears therefore that the techniques used by the builders (*mistris*) have recently become »hybridised« and that if there ever was one single method it has now been selectively adapted and modified in response to changing times.

DISCUSSION AND CONCLUSIONS

The available information provides only a very limited insight into the early history of the boats. It appears however that the use of externally visible edge joining has a very long history, as does the use of a steering oar and single square sail. From 1700 onwards, the large triangular rudder was established, as was the use of a framework to support a large steering oar. Many of the boats had the now common low bow, high stern shape and one type was shown to have nailed plank fastenings and possibly clinker planking. Later records show that specific types are associated with specific localities and social groups. However, it is also clear that many of the boats travel far and wide and thus come into regular contact with each other, and indeed engage in similar trades in the same environments, so it generally proved impossible to link specific types to specific operating environments.

A number of functional explanations of specific features of the boats that have been proposed by other authors have been examined and shown not to be universally applicable, which throws further doubt on the explanatory power of this model.

The most likely explanation of the diversity is that it reflects the diversity amongst the peoples and social groups who build, own and operate the boats. Cultural conservatism and »conformist bias« besides suppressing change and innovation can also result in new forms being preserved when they do occur, regardless of their adaptive value. Over time, a multitude of small changes, each perhaps the result of the whim of an individual or possibly imperfect transmission of knowledge and techniques, resulted in the emergence of a large number of distinctly different boat types.

Overlaid on this model of slow, »non-adaptive« change, there are also clear examples of where change has occurred in response to powerful forces. Recently, the flat bottomed *kosha*, mentioned by Solvyns (Hardgrave 2001: 103) and by Greenhill (1971: 110), has become the dominant type. This coincided with, and was in all probability driven by, a number of powerful, externally influenced changes in both society and the operating environment. The result was that between 1988 and 1992 almost all the boats were mechanised, and as the old boats became uneconomic, they were replaced by new *koshas*, often built not by the traditional carpenters, but by house builders and other semiskilled people.

Innovation blossomed and new ideas flowed. The country boats, after a long period of almost compete stasis, were changing quickly and forever. We will never know which of these influences was the most important, or if this change would have happened if some of them had not existed, but we do know that taken together, the huge upheavals in society combined with rapid environmental change most likely precipitated this transformation.

Lessons for the nautical archaeologist

- Forms persist for long periods and operate alongside each other. They do not appear to »learn« from one another in order to evolve progressively into a functionally optimised hybrid.
- Change tends to be as a result of extinction rather than introduction of new forms.
- The rise of a new form is more likely to be associated with major social changes than with environmental or functional changes.
- Form has more to do with community/culture than with function/environment.
- Names are an unreliable indicator of form, but a better indicator of function. Boats of the same form can have different names, boats of different form can have the same name, often dependent upon how the owners use them.
- Change when it happens may be very sudden and not directly related to any one influence.
- Some features survive change. The reasons relate to what matters to the users, what for them is the essence or core of a boat. It is more a matter of tradition, familiarity and cultural identity than functional performance.

NOTE

1) Solvyns does not describe the construction method and his illustrations show smooth sides, which might reflect either that they were homogeneous logboats or simply that they were painted, which obscured the plank joins.

REFERENCES

BIWTA 1994, *Experimental project for improving the efficiency and profitability of country boat operation*. Dhaka.

Bolstad, T. & Jansen, E. G., 1992, *Sailing against the Wind – the Boats and Boatmen of Bangladesh*. Dhaka.

Bowrey, T., 1669-1679, *A Geographical Account of the Countries round the Bay of Bengal*, ed. R. Temple. London, 1905.

Deloche, J., 1994, *Transport and Communications in India prior to Steam Locomotion*, vol. II: Water Transport. Delhi.

Glassie, H., 1997, *Art and life in Bangladesh*. Indiana.

Greenhill, B. & Mannering, J. (eds), 1997, *Inshore Craft: Traditional working vessels of the British Isles*. London.

Greenhill, B., 1957, Boats of East Pakistan, *MM* 43, 106-34; 203-15.

1966, *Boats of East Pakistan*. London.

1971, *Boats and Boatmen of Pakistan*. Newton Abbot.

1995, *The Archaeology of Boats and Ships*. London.

2000, The Mysterious Hulc. *MM* 86.1, 3-18.

Hardgrave, R. L., 2001, *Boats of Bengal*. New Delhi.

Hornell, J., 1920, Origins and ethnographical significance of Indian boat design. *Memoirs of the Asiatic Society of Bengal*, 7, 139-256. Reissued by SIFFS, Trivandrum. www.siffs.org.

1922, Boats of the Ganges. *Memoirs of the Asiatic Society of Bengal*, 8, 185-94.

1946, *Water Transport*. Cambridge.

Jansen, E. G., Dolman, A. J., Jerve, A. M., Rahman, N., 1989, *The Country Boats of Bangladesh*. Dhaka.

Keay, J., 2000, *India – a history*. London.

McGrail, S., 2001, *Boats of the World*. Oxford.

McGrail, S., Blue, L. & Kentley, E., 1999, Reverse clinker boats of Bangladesh and their planking pattern. *South Asian Studies*, 17, 221-223.

McGrail, S., Blue, L., Kentley, E. & Palmer, C., 2003, *Boats of South Asia*. London, New York.

Mookerji, R., 1912, *Indian Shipping*. Bombay; repr. 1999. New Delhi.

Raup, D. M. & Crick, R., E., 1979, Measurement of Faunal Similarity in Paleontology. *Journal of Paleontology*, 53/5, 1213-1227.

Richerson, P. J. & Boyd, R., 2005, *Not by genes alone: how culture transformed human evolution*. Chicago.

Simpson, E., 2006, Apprenticeship in western India. *Journal of the Royal Anthropological Institute*, 12, 152-171.

Solvyns, F. B., 1799, *Les Hindous*. Calcutta.

JULIAN WHITEWRIGHT

TRACING TECHNOLOGY

THE MATERIAL CULTURE OF MARITIME TECHNOLOGY IN THE ANCIENT MEDITERRANEAN AND CONTEMPORARY INDIAN OCEAN

The study of ancient ships has drawn the attention of scholars for at least 100 years (e.g. Torr 1895). During this time the study of the rigging and sails of these vessels has generally received less attention than the hulls upon which they were set. The advent of organised, systematic shipwreck archaeology in the last 50 years has perhaps exacerbated this trend. Archaeologists have naturally tended to focus on the classes of evidence which they have found in most abundance; hull remains and the cargoes contained within them. Although rigging components (blocks, sails, masts, brails, cordage, etc) have survived in the archaeological record, they have often been overlooked within the context of individual sites (some recent exceptions include Beltrame & Gaddi 2005; Brusic & Domjan 1985; Fitzgerald 1994; Hesnard *et al.* 1988; Mathews 2004; Riccardi 2002; Santamaria 1996; Wild & Wild 2001). Our understanding of ancient hull construction has developed in conjunction with archaeological discoveries and has been reassessed in the light of fresh excavation (e.g. Kahanov & Royal 2001; Kahanov *et al.* 2004; Mor & Kahanov 2006; Steffy 1994). However, an understanding of the rigging of ancient ships and the technological change which they underwent has been based largely on iconographic and textual evidence (e.g. Basch 1987; Casson 1995).

Within the limited body of literature devoted to the discussion of the ancient sailing rig, much of the focus has been devoted to the study and discussion of technology and technological change. Within this field the subject of the transition from square-sail to fore and aft sail has witnessed continued, albeit sporadic study, the principal subject of which has been the development and introduction of the lateen sail into the Mediterranean (Basch 1989; 1991; 2001; Brindley 1926; Casson 1956; Friedman & Zoroglu 2006; La Roerie 1956; Le Baron-Bowen 1956; 1957; Pomey 2006; Pryor 1994; Sottas 1939). This paper sets out to characterise the square-rig and the lateen rig of the ancient Mediterranean from the perspective of their rigging components. Such an approach aims to elucidate the technological change which occurs to the sail-plans of Mediterranean vessels during late-antiquity by highlighting technical continuity and disparity between the square and lateen sailing rigs.

BACKGROUND AND APPROACHES TO THE SUBJECT

The traditional explanation for the development of the lateen sail-plan has been based on its placement within a unilinear, evolutionary progression from the ancient square-sail to the modern Bermudan rig (**Fig. 1**). The existence of the square-sail in the earliest sources of evidence has lead to its position at the beginning of the unilinear progression. Subsequent developments have been viewed as deriving from early forms of the square-sail. The assumption which has underpinned this technological development is that each example of change indicates an »improvement« in the technology available to ancient mariners. This »improvement« is usually expressed as an increase in a sailing vessel's ability to sail to windward (e.g.

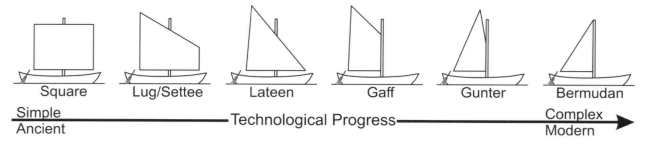

Fig. 1 Generic unilinear evolution of sailing rigs based on sail-plan.

Greene 1986: 27; Kingsley 2004: 78; Pryor 1994: 67-68), which in turn implies that there was a »need« for such an improvement to be made. Such progression has been founded on the shape, in plan-form, of sails throughout history as a means to document change and explain their technological characteristics. Little attempt has been made to acknowledge their wider context; cultural, economic, environmental, functional or otherwise. Maritime archaeologists and scholars have generally addressed the development of the lateen sail in accordance with this approach and have focused upon the relevant section of the progression which sees the first evolution from a square sail-plan to a triangular one (e.g. Le Baron-Bowen 1953: fig. 18).

The extensive use of iconography as a primary source of evidence has further facilitated the emphasis on the study of plan-form alone. Ancient artists have generally depicted sailing vessels from the side while showing a plan-view of the sail which makes identifying the general shape of the sail relatively simple. This has led to a cyclical situation as a theoretical progression which continues to rely on the study of sail-plan naturally turns to iconographic sources for its main form of evidence. Much of the resulting focus has therefore been directed at analysis of the shape of sails depicted in mosaics, frescoes, reliefs, graffitos and the like. In many cases this has included attempts to catalogue detailed areas of the rig on the basis of the iconography. Examples drawn from the iconographic record are seen as representing certain stages of the development of the sail which correspond with stages assumed to exist within the unilinear progression (e.g. Basch 1989). The availability of seemingly accurate iconographic information has ensured that the interpretation of sail development has remained confined to an analysis of sail shape alone.

The processes and rationale which underpin maritime technological change cannot be fully understood if analysis continues to be based on broad observations restricted mainly to the sail-plan of ancient vessels as seen in the iconography. Iconographic evidence has been invaluable to maritime archaeologists as a means of tracing general patterns and technical development. However, the acknowledged problems of ambiguity associated with its interpretation mean that in many cases it should not be relied upon for detailed interpretation (cf. Basch 1987; Lambrou-Phillipson 1996; Turner 2006: 1; Tzalas 1990; Villain-Gandosi 1994). Only occasionally are iconographic examples obviously unambiguous in the ancient artist's portrayal of a maritime scene. Therefore, recourse must be made to the more detailed evidence available through archaeological and even ethnographic study and analysis. In conjunction with this, an attempt must be made to fully understand and characterise every area of the ancient sailing rig over and above the shape of the sail itself. Such an approach will allow maritime technological change to be addressed from the perspective of all the elements which comprise a sailing rig and which are equally important to its successful operation, rather than the sail-plan alone.

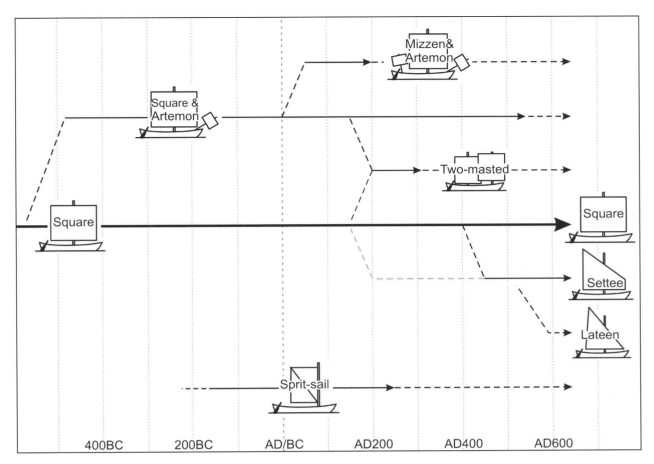

Fig. 2 Multi-linear reality of ancient Mediterranean sailing rig development based upon sail-plan. Where unequivocal evidence occurs, paths of development are represented by solid lines. Conjectural paths are represented by dashed lines.

THE ORIGINS OF THE LATEEN SAIL

The origin of the lateen sail has traditionally been attributed by scholars to the Indian Ocean and its introduction into Mediterranean waters ascribed to the Arab expansion of the early 7th c. (e.g. Hourani 1951: 103). The latter was due mainly to the only iconographic depictions of lateen rigged ships from the Mediterranean post-dating the Islamic expansion into the Mediterranean basin (Frost 1995: 154; Kingsley 2004: 78). It follows that the Indian Ocean origin of the lateen is founded on the predominance of the lateen amongst the sails of the Indian Ocean in recent times. It was assumed that the Arab peoples who invaded the Mediterranean basin in the 7th c. carried with them the sailing rig with which they were familiar. However, these depictions and their accompanying theories have been superseded by clear depictions of lateen sails which predate the Arab expansion (cf. Basch 1991: fig. 1; Friedman & Zoroglu 2006: fig. 2; Pomey 2006: figs 1 & 3; in press). There can be no doubt that the lateen sail was in use in the Mediterranean during the Late Roman period and possibly before that.

These depictions of lateen sails from the Mediterranean are also the earliest examples of the lateen sail in either the Indian Ocean or the Mediterranean. Early depictions of sails in the Indian Ocean show vessels rigged with square sails (e.g. Nicolle 1989: 175, fig. 14a-b; Sridhar 2005: 67-73, fig. 24). It is obviously too simplistic to ascribe a geographic origin founded on the location of the earliest currently known example.

There is now little or no evidence to back up the traditional belief that the first example of the lateen sail developed in the Indian Ocean before spreading to the Mediterranean. Overall, the evidence currently available is probably too limited at the present time to be able to ascribe a specific geographical origin, Mediterranean, Indian Ocean or otherwise to the lateen sail at this time. Although this has not prevented some recent general commentaries from giving the lateen sail a S.-E. Mediterranean origin (Bennett 2005: 89; Kingsley 2004: 79). Furthermore, as maritime archaeologists are now following the trend previously set within general archaeological theory in rejecting an evolutionary linear progression of technology, an alternative approach to the study of sail and rig development needs to be developed. At the very least this should acknowledge the multi-linear progression which the currently available evidence allows us to observe in the sail-plans of the ancient Mediterranean (**Fig. 2**) (cf. Whitewright in press).

RIG CHARACTERISATION

Studies conducted thus far have relied upon characterising sails based on an observation of sail-plan. However, sailing rigs consist of far more than just a sail. They consist of interconnecting components which can be said to comprise a particular rig when taken as a whole. By addressing the nature and relationship of these components within the context of a single rig it is possible to develop a fuller understanding of the characteristics of a given rig. There are several important differences between the square-sail and lateen sail, over and above the obvious difference in sail-plan. By focusing upon the components of which the square-sail and lateen sail are comprised, it is possible to characterise each rig more fully than simply by looking at sail plan alone. The suitability of sailing ships for this kind of component based, theoretical approach has been observed by Law (1989) and Roland (1992), who have noted that the sailing ship consists of an almost endless list of interlocking parts.

The Roman square rig

The most characteristic aspect of the Roman square-sail rig is probably the system of brails used for shortening sail and this component of the rig has been commented on by academics (e.g. Casson 1995: 70, 234). Brails appear in many iconographic depictions and are also mentioned in some textual sources. From an archaeological perspective the system of brails is visible in the archaeological record via remains of brail rings used to provide a fair lead for the brails. Examples have been excavated in the context of individual wreck sites such as the Kyrenia ship and also from wider contexts at the Roman Red Sea port of Myos Hormos (Whitewright in press). As well as wood, brail rings can be made from lead and animal horn. The Mediterranean system of shortening sail by using brails in this way is unique to this region in the classical and pre-classical periods. As such, this component of the rig should be considered as one of its principle and defining characteristics.

The square-sail rig of the Roman period also relies upon a system of standing rigging, comprising shrouds and stays which is still utilised by sailing vessels of European tradition in the present day. In this system a vessel's mast is supported at four points; with stays fore and aft and with one or more shrouds set to either side. While it is unclear how visible stays may be in the archaeological record, the *deadeyes* used to rig a vessel with shrouds are well-documented (e.g. Beltrame & Gaddi 2005; Brusic & Domjan 1985; Ximénès & Moerman 1990). Furthermore, the physical form and function of the deadeyes of a sailing vessel have changed little since their use in the Roman period. Examples appear in the iconographic record and have also been excavated from wrecks and harbour sites dating to the Roman period.

The square-rig of the Roman world can therefore be partly characterised by its widespread, systematic use of standing rigging, in conjunction with a system of brails utilised for shortening sail. Both of these are particularly visible in the archaeological record via the excavated presence of deadeyes and brail rings. It is possible to note differences in the small detail of manufacture of these components from different contemporary sites in the ancient world. However, their arrangement and integration in the overall system of rigging on ancient square-rigged sailing vessels seems to have been fairly uniform. The aggregation of components in the Roman square-rig is illustrated diagrammatically in **Figure 3**. The general homogeneity of these components is reinforced by the iconographic evidence which consistently depicts the key elements which characterise the Roman square-sail rig. In this instance the iconography provides a general overview while archaeology can provide the material detail.

The lateen rig

The rigging and use of the lateen sail in the ancient world provides a direct contrast to this. The lateen rig is far less uniform in its makeup than the Roman square-rig. There is no easily definable standing rigging present on a lateen rigged vessel and the formalised system of shrouds present on ancient square-rigged vessels is absent (c.f. Dimmock 1946; Johnstone & Muir 1964; Villiers 1940). In their place is a rigging system which can best be described as »mobile standing rigging«. The mast is supported by ropes which fulfil the function of shrouds, but which are not permanently rigged for this purpose and which fulfil other functions at different times and on different points of sailing. Similarly the Indian Ocean lateen rig rarely has a permanently rigged forestay because of the fashion in which the ship is brought about onto a new tack and it never has a dedicated backstay. Standing rigging in the W. definition of the word is entirely absent.

The lateen rig also lacks a dedicated rigging system for shortening sail. Certainly there is no current evidence which points to a similar system to the use of brails being present on lateen rigged vessels. The most common practice on Indian Ocean lateeners is to carry a variety of sails, ranging from very large to small, which can be set according to the wind strength encountered. Mediterranean lateen rigged vessels from the medieval period utilised reef points near the head and foot of the sail in order to reduce the overall size of the sail and such reef points appear on the earliest unambiguous iconographic example of a settee/lateen sail from Kelenderis in S. Turkey (Pomey 2006: 329). Neither system is likely to leave a recognisable, meaningful trace in the archaeological record.

It is therefore possible to view the two rigs being comprised of generally different rigging components over and above the difference in sail-plan. The Roman square-sail (**Fig. 3**) is perhaps more formal and consistent in its physical makeup; certain components always fulfilling the same specific task. This contrasts with the lateen (**Fig. 4**) where components are fewer, but far more flexible in their function. Furthermore, where the brailed square-sail rig of the ancient world has become extinct, the lateen is still in widespread use on traditional craft in the Indian Ocean and the Mediterranean.

Technological continuity

The most characteristic piece of rigging on an Indian Ocean lateener is the halyard system, used to raise the yard and also providing a secondary function as the vessel's backstay. This rigging component is consistently present in the same form on the great majority of Indian Ocean lateen rigged vessels discussed and recorded in the literature.

The halyard system consists of two, large, multi-sheaved blocks providing the purchase with which to raise the heavy, often unwieldy yard. The lower block is set into the deck, while the upper block is mobile and

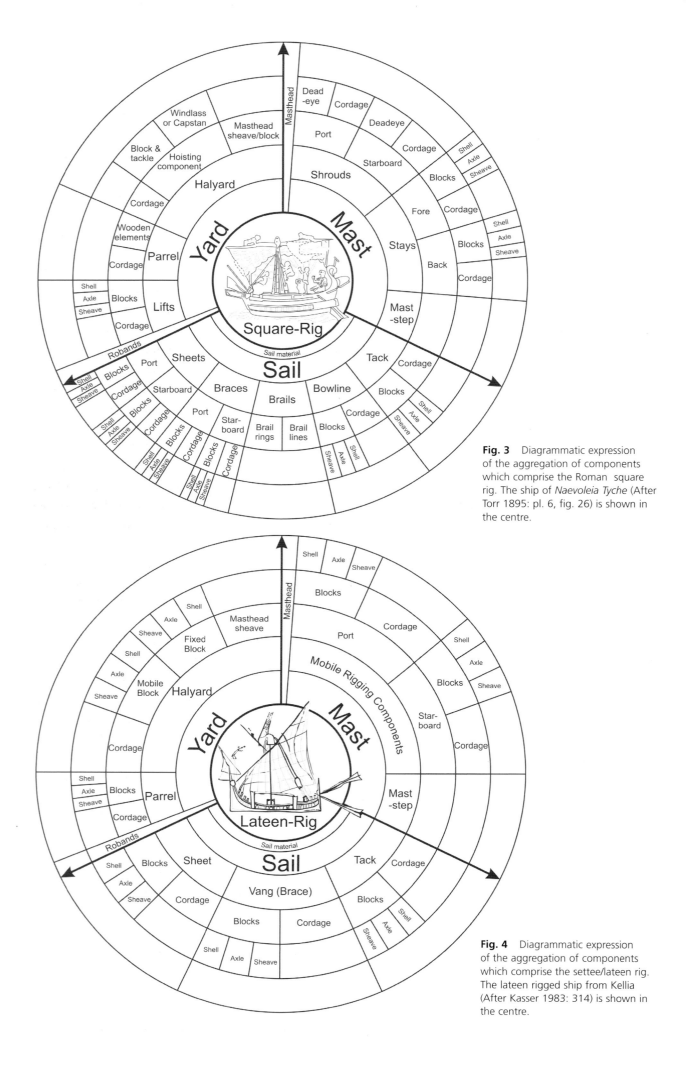

Fig. 3 Diagrammatic expression of the aggregation of components which comprise the Roman square rig. The ship of *Naevoleia Tyche* (After Torr 1895: pl. 6, fig. 26) is shown in the centre.

Fig. 4 Diagrammatic expression of the aggregation of components which comprise the settee/lateen rig. The lateen rigged ship from Kellia (After Kasser 1983: 314) is shown in the centre.

is made off through the masthead to the yard. When the yard is down, the upper block is near the masthead and as the yard is raised the upper block is hauled downwards and nearer to the deck of the vessel. When the yard is at its highest point the upper block is at its lowest.

The use of this item of rigging in the modern period is well-documented, but it would also seem to have considerable antiquity. The remains of such a rigging block have been recovered from the 11th c. Serçe Limani shipwreck, excavated by the Texas Institute of Nautical Archaeology off the Turkish coast (Mathews 2004: figs 11-14). A possible example has also been recovered during the excavation of the Port-Vendres 1 wreck of the S. French coast and dates to ca. A.D. 400 (Parker 1992: no. 874). Significantly, the halyard system also appears on the earliest iconographic depictions of lateen rigged vessels from the Mediterranean including depictions from Kellia and Kelenderis. In these instances it seems clear that the artist is depicting a lateen rigged craft, with a yard hoisted in a similar fashion to the Serçe Limani vessel and modern day, Indian Ocean lateeners. The characteristic halyard system is clearly visible running from masthead to deck. In both the examples from Kelenderis and Kellia the halyard system is associated with the hook-shaped mastheads which come to characterise lateen/settee rigged ships in the early-medieval iconography of the Mediterranean (c.f. Adam & Villain-Gandossi 1991: 21; Basch 1991: 5; Mathews 2004: 179). There has been a long held assumption that the ancient form of the lateen sail is similar to its modern counterpart. The continuity over time of the rigging element, the halyard system and associated masthead fitting, which best characterises the lateen rig serves to confirm this.

At this stage it would seem simple to track occurrences of the two rigs in question in the archaeological record by addressing what type of rigging component is excavated from ancient shipwrecks. While this might be theoretically possible, there are two problems. Firstly, and most obvious are the vagaries of the archaeological record in producing, through excavation, a complete dataset. Archaeologists have no way of knowing what rigging components a vessel may have carried unless they appear in the archaeological record. There is no guarantee that such elements will be excavated; an excavation which does not produce the remains of deadeyes or brail rings may still represent a square-rigged vessel. It can merely be stated that only where such elements are definitely present can they indicate a component which may be representative of a certain type or class of sailing rig. The absence of such an element in the archaeological record is not evidence of its absence in the ancient world.

The second problem clouds the issue far more significantly. It has been noted above that the primary rigging component in a lateen rig is the halyard system. This halyard system has a long and visible usage on lateen rigged vessels since at least the Late Roman period. However, further analysis of the iconographic record shows that such a system is visible in at least two examples of Roman square-rigged ships from the 1st c. A.D. One occurs on a tombstone from Pompeii (cf. Casson 1995: fig. 151), another possible example is depicted on a sarcophagus from Sidon in the Levant (cf. Casson 1995: fig. 156). The carving from Pompeii, on the tombstone of *Naevoleia Tyche*, seems very clear in the artist's depiction of a halyard system which is very similar to those pictured, excavated and observed on lateen rigged craft from the following centuries to the present day. A rigging block excavated from the Grand Ribaud D (end of 1st c. B.C.) shipwreck shares a form similar to that of the halyard block in the Pompeii depiction (Hesnard *et al.* 1988: 115). The block from Grand Ribaud D was significantly larger than other blocks (of characteristically Roman style) from the same vessel suggesting it was intended to resist considerable strain (perhaps in raising a yard and sail). Fragments of wooden brail rings were also found in association with the other rigging components (Hesnar *et al.* 1988: 115), suggesting that the vessel (about 18m in length) was rigged with a typical Mediterranean square-rig. The evidence from archaeological and iconographic sources suggests that it is possible to observe a degree of technical continuity between the halyard systems of ancient Mediterranean square-rigged vessels and those used on lateen rigged vessels from the late antiquity onwards.

CONCLUSIONS

A rigging component strongly associated with the lateen/settee sail from the late antiquity onwards is present on a depiction of a Mediterranean square-sail vessel from the 1st c. A.D. Another possible example may be preserved in the archaeological remains of a shipwreck from the late 1st c. B.C. This has several implications for the understanding of maritime technological change in the ancient world. Firstly it highlights the importance of addressing technological change from the perspective of a detailed understanding of the technology in question. Without such an understanding important details may be misinterpreted, or indeed simply missed. More significantly is that the example outlined above should have repercussions for the way in which changes to rigging technology are observed and interpreted. The traditional reliance on documenting sails in plan-form is inadequate as it overlooks other, equally important areas of the rig. The presence of the same complex rigging component, fulfilling the same function on two rigs which require a fundamentally different method of operation is significant in this regard. Rigs which may appear to be different when analysed by their sail-form alone, may in fact share certain technical traits. Consequently, to fully understand the processes of change which are taking place in the maritime technology of the ancient world one must document the ropes, blocks and tackles with which sails are set, as well as recording the shapes of the sails themselves.

Sailing rigs comprise a series of components which are all equally important to the successful operation of the rig. Therefore to focus on one component, such as sail-plan, at the expense of the others will bias the interpretation and understanding of the rig. Increasing the number of components under study increases the number of external factors, such as cultural traditions, physical materials etc. which may potentially be influencing overall rig-form. By increasing the quantity of the ancient sailing rig under detailed study, an understanding of the factors which affect its long-term change is more likely to be observed.

Ancient sailing rigs should therefore not be viewed as distinct, technically separated entities. Neither should they be observed simply from the perspective of their sail-plan. The importance of addressing all the components of a particular rig, not just their sails, is highlighted by the technical continuity which can be identified between different sailing rigs in the ancient world – a feature which would be overlooked otherwise. The lateen rig, although of superficially different form, shares component parts with other contemporary rigs from the ancient world. Recognising this fact opens up new avenues of investigation and interpretation regarding maritime technological change over and above those currently utilised by maritime archaeologists. By identifying which of these components is abandoned, altered, or retained over time it may be easier to identify the processes and underlying causes by which the lateen sail is developed and adopted in the ancient Mediterranean. Consequently it is time to move away from an observation and understanding of rig technology derived simply from the perspective of sail-plan. Equal attention should be given to all of the components of which any rig is comprised. Documenting and understanding their interaction may better serve the attempts to understand technological change in an ancient maritime context.

REFERENCES

Adam, P. & Villain-Gandossi, C., 1991, Byzantine Ships: Iconography and Archaeological sources. In: C. Villain-Gandossi, P. Adam & S. Busuttil (eds), *Medieval ships and the birth of technological societies*, vol. II: *The Mediterranean area and European integration*. Valletta, 17-38.

Basch, L., 1987, *Le Musée imaginaire de la marine antique*. Athens.

1989, The way to the Lateen Sail. *MM*, 75.4, 328-32.

1991, La Felouque des Kellia. *Neptunia*, 183, 3-12.

2001, La voile latine, son origine, son évolution et parentés arabes. In: *TROPIS VI*, 55-86.

Beltrame, C. & Gaddi, D., 2005, The Rigging and the »Hydraulic System« of the Roman Wreck at Grado, Gorizia, Italy. *IJNA* 34.1, 79-87.

Bennett, J. 2005, *Sailing Rigs – an illustrated guide*. London.

Brindley, H. H., 1926, Early Pictures of Lateen Sails. *MM* 12.1, 9-22.

Brusic, Z. & Domjan, M., 1985, Liburnian Boats – Their Construction and Form. In: S. McGrail & E. Kentley (eds.), *Sewn Plank Boats*. BAR, Internat. Series, no. 276. Oxford, 67-85.

Casson, L., 1956, Fore and Aft Sails in the Ancient World. *MM*, 42.1, 3-5.

1995, *Ships and Seamanship in the Ancient World*. London.

Dimmock, L., 1946, The Lateen Rig. *MM* , 32.1, 35-41.

Fitzgerald, M. A. 1994, The Ship. In: J. P. Oleson (ed.), *The Harbours of Casearea Maritima*, vol. II: *The Finds and the Ship*. BAR, Internat. Series, no. 594. Oxford, 163-223.

Friedman, Z. & Zoroglu, L., 2006, Kelenderis Ship – Square or Lateen Sail? *IJNA*, 35.1, 108-116.

Frost, H., 1995, Masts & Sails, Notes on Chapter 3. In: G. F. Hourani & J. Carswell (eds.), *Arab Seafaring in the Indian Ocean in Ancient and Early Medieval Times*. Princeton/New Jersey.

Greene, K., 1986, *The Archaeology of the Roman Economy*. London.

Hesnard, A., Carre, M.-B., Rival, M. & Dangréaux, B., 1988, L'épave romaine Grand Ribaud D (Hyères, Var). *Archaeonautica*, no. 8. Paris.

Hourani, G. F., 1951, *Arab Seafaring in the Indian Ocean in Ancient and Early Medieval Times*. Princeton/New Jersey (reprint 1995).

Johnstone, T. M. & Muir, J., 1964, Some Nautical Terms in the Kuwaiti Dialect of Arabic. *Bulletin of the School of Oriental and African Studies*, 27.2, 299-332.

Kahanov, Y. & Royal, J. G., 2001, Analysis of hull remains of the Dor D Vessel, Tantura Lagoon, Israel. *IJNA*, 30.2, 257-265.

Kahanov, Y., Royal, J. G. & Hall, J., 2004, The Tantura Wrecks and Ancient Mediterranean Shipbuilding. In: F. Hocker & C. Ward (eds), *The Philosophy of Shipbuilding*: *Conceptual Approaches to the Study of Wooden Ships*. College Station/Texas, 113-128.

Kasser, R., 1983, *Survey Archéologique des Kellia (Basse-Égypte)*. *Rapport de la Campagne 1981*. Louvain.

Kingsley, S. A. (ed.), 2004, *Barbarian Seas – Late Rome to Islam*. London.

La Roerie, G. L., 1956, Fore and Aft sails in the ancient world. *MM*, 42.3, 238-239.

Lambrou-Phillipson, C., 1996, The reliability of ships' iconography: The Theran miniature marine fresco as an example. In: *TROPIS VI*, 351-366.

Law, J., 1989, Technology and Heterogeneous Engineering: The case of Portuguese expansion. In: W. E. Bijker, T. P. Hughes & T. J. Pinch (eds), *The Social Constructioin of Technological Systems*. *New directions in the Sociology and History of Technology*. London, 111-134.

Le Baron-Bowen, R., 1953, Eastern Sail Affinities – Part Two. *American Neptune*, 13, 185-211.

1956, The earliest lateen sail. *MM* 42.3, 239-242.

1957, Fore and Aft sails in the ancient world. *MM*, 43.2, 160-164.

Mathews, S., 2004. Evidence for the rig of the Serçe Limani ship. In: G. F. Bass, S. Mathews, J. R. Steffy & F. H. Van Doorninck Jr (eds), *Serçe Limani. An eleventh-century shipwreck*, vol. I: *The Ship and Its Anchorage, Crew and Passengers*. College Station/Texas, 171-188.

Mor, H. & Kahanov, Y., 2006, The Dor 2001/1 Shipwreck, Israel – a summary of the excavation. *IJNA*, 35.2, 274-289.

Nicolle, D., 1989, Shipping in Islamic Art: seventh through sixteenth century AD. *American Neptune*, 49, 168-197.

Parker, A. J., 1992, *Ancient Shipwrecks of the Mediterranean and the Roman Provinces*. BAR, Internat. Series, no. 580. Oxford.

Pomey, P., 2006, The Kelenderis Ship: A Lateen Sail. *IJNA*, 35.2, 326-329.

in press, Un nouveau témoignage sur la voile latine: la mosaique de Kelenderis (v. 500 ap. J.-C.; Turquie). In:*TROPIS IX*.

Pryor, J. H., 1994, The Mediterranean Round Ship. In: R. W. Unger (ed.), *Cogs, Caravels & Galleons. The Sailing Ship 1000-1650*. London, 59-76.

Riccardi, E., 2002, A ship's mast discovered during excavation of the Roman port at Olbia, Sardinia. *IJNA*, 31.2, 268-269.

Roland, A., 1992, Theories and Models of Technological Change: Semantics and Substance. *Science, Technology & Human Values*, 17.1, 79-100.

Santamaria, C. L., 1996, L'épave Dramont »E« a Saint-Raphael (V[e] siecle apres J-C). *Archaeonautica*, 13, 1-197.

Sottas, J., 1939, An Early Lateen Sail in the Mediterranean. *MM* 25.2, 229-230.

Sridhar, T. S., 2005, *Alagankulam*: *An ancient Roman Port City of Tamil Nadu*. Chennai/Tamil Nadu.

Steffy, J. R., 1994, *Wooden Ship Building and the Interpretation of Shipwrecks*. College Station/Texas.

Torr, C., 1895, *Ancient Ships*. Cambridge.

Turner, G., 2006, Bahamian Ship Graffiti. *IJNA*, 35.2, 253-273.

Tzalas, H., 1990, Kyrenia II in the fresco of Pedoula church, Cyprus. A comparison with ancient ship iconography. In: *TROPIS II*, 323-327.

Villain-Gandosi, C., 1994, Illustrations of ships: Iconography and Interpretation. In: R. W. Unger (ed.), *Cogs, Caravels & Galleons. The Sailing Ship 1000-1650*. London, 169-174.

Villiers, A., 1940, *Sons of Sinbad*. New York.

Whitewright, J., 2007, Roman rigging material from the Red Sea port of Myos Hormos. *IJNA*, 36.2, 282-292.

in press, From Square to Where? Deconstructing the mythology surrounding the transition from square-sail to lateen sail. In: *TROPIS* IX.

Wild, F. C. & Wild, J. P., 2001, Sails from the Roman Port of Berenice. *IJNA*, 30.2, 211-220.

Ximénès, S. & Moerman, M., 1990, Port romain des Laurons (Martigues): éléments d'accastillage antiques. *Cahiers d'Archéologie Subaquatique*, 9, 5-25.

HENRIK POHL

FROM THE *KATTUMARAM* TO THE FIBRE-*TEPPA*

CHANGES IN BOATBUILDING TRADITIONS ON INDIA´S EAST COAST

Up to the present day the major part of India's east coast fishery is carried out with traditional fishing craft. Of all these vessels the *kattumaram* is the most widely used type. These rafts are predominantly sailed at India's east coast between Puri (federal state Orissa) and Kanyakumari (federal state Tamil Nadu). Of around 60,000 vessels at this coastal area of ca. 2,000 km are alone 40,000 *kattumarams*.

The goal of this study is to describe the traditional water-craft of the Indian east coast, i.e. the *kattumaram*. The focus lies on the description of constructional change and usage of this fishing raft. Moreover two other more modern raft types shall be presented here, which are closely related to the *kattumaram*.

Coincidentally this expedition took place in the weeks just before the tsunami of the 26th of December 2004. Henceforth it represents unique inventory just before the partial destruction of the fishing fleet at India's east coast.

In the following it will be attempted to describe three different types of fishing craft. All three types are definable as rafts due to the inherent buoyant nature of the hull components:

– Type A: It represents the oldest type of a wooden raft used along the Indian East coast – the *kattumaram*. The term *kattumaram* applies to a traditionally built vessel, which mainly consists of 3 to 7 tree trunks that are lashed together. Repeated untying and refastening in a new combination of the trunks are characteristic for this type. Thus it is a type of water craft without a permanent identity.

– Type B: The wooden-*teppa* is a raft-construction, which is composed of a boat-shaped hull which is shaped by side planks and filled with polystyrene blocks.

– Type C: The fibre-*teppa* is a modern raft in the shape of a boat. The hull's skin and the deck is made of fibre-reinforced plastic (FRP). The cavities are filled with expanded polystyrene.

The underlying question of the assessment was: In how far has traditional boat-building changed along India's east coast in the last 25 years? The research papers of the Bay of Bengal Programme, which were released in the early 1980s, served as reference point. Did new materials encourage the development of new boat types or were proven types preferred? Are there local types, and if so, did they change individually? Does a survival of the fittest boat type take place?

This paper has been published under the same title in: *IJNA*, 36.2, 2007, 382-408.

PLATES 1-6

PLATE 1

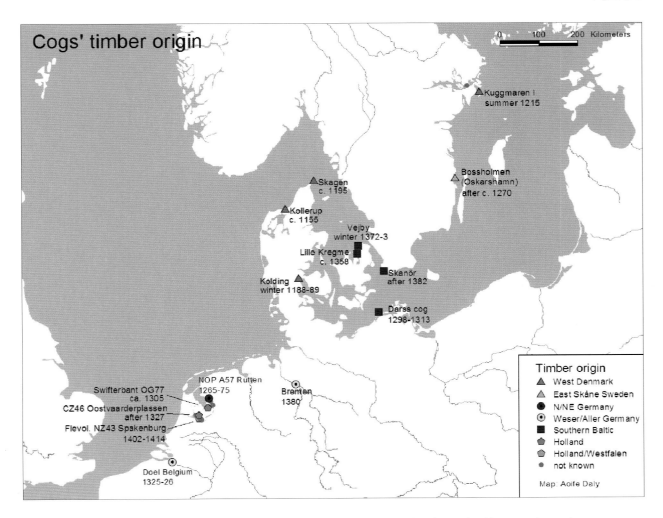

Plate 1 A. Daly: Map showing the distribution of the cogs examined or mentioned in this study with name, date and provenance (After Crumlin-Pedersen 2000: 238, with later finds included and with dating and provenance illustrated).

Plate 2

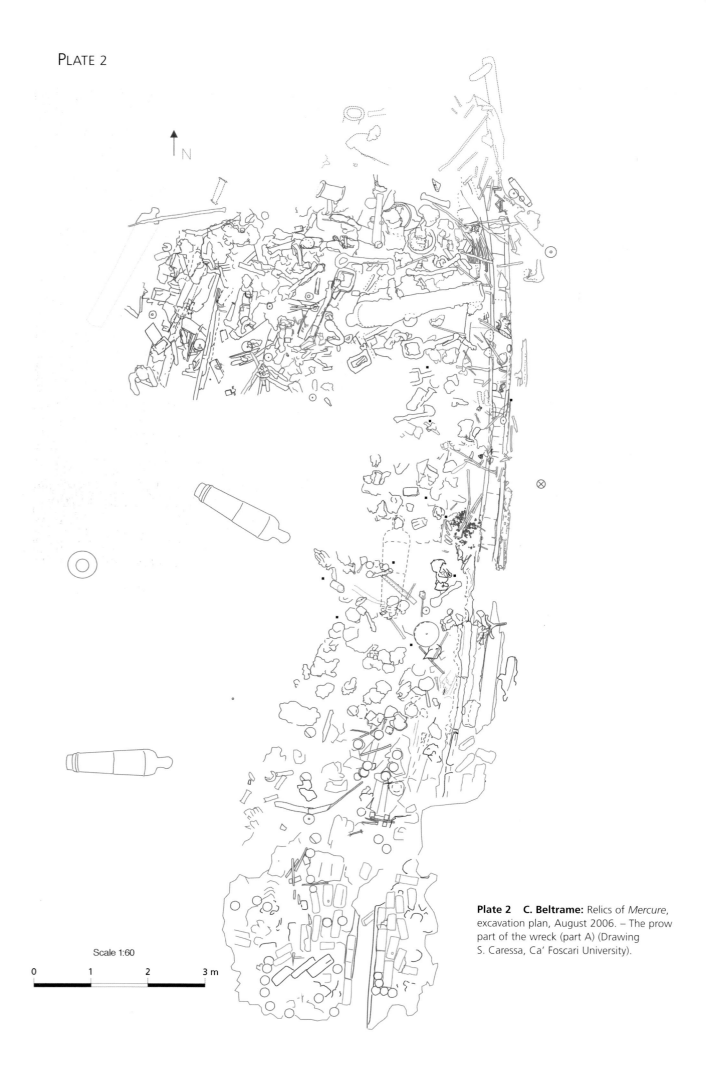

N

Scale 1:60

0   1   2   3 m

Plate 2   C. Beltrame: Relics of *Mercure*,
excavation plan, August 2006. – The prow
part of the wreck (part A) (Drawing
S. Caressa, Ca' Foscari University).

PLATE 3

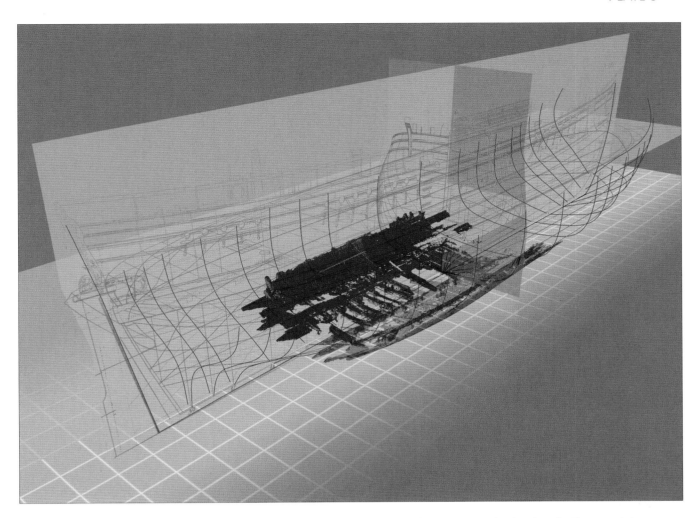

Plate 3 T. Förster: Insertion of the scanned wreck fragment of the Darss Carvel from 1679 into the drawing of a Fleute made by Frederik Chapman in 1768 (Fraunhofer Institut, Rostock; Olaf Hofmann, Hamburg).

PLATE 4

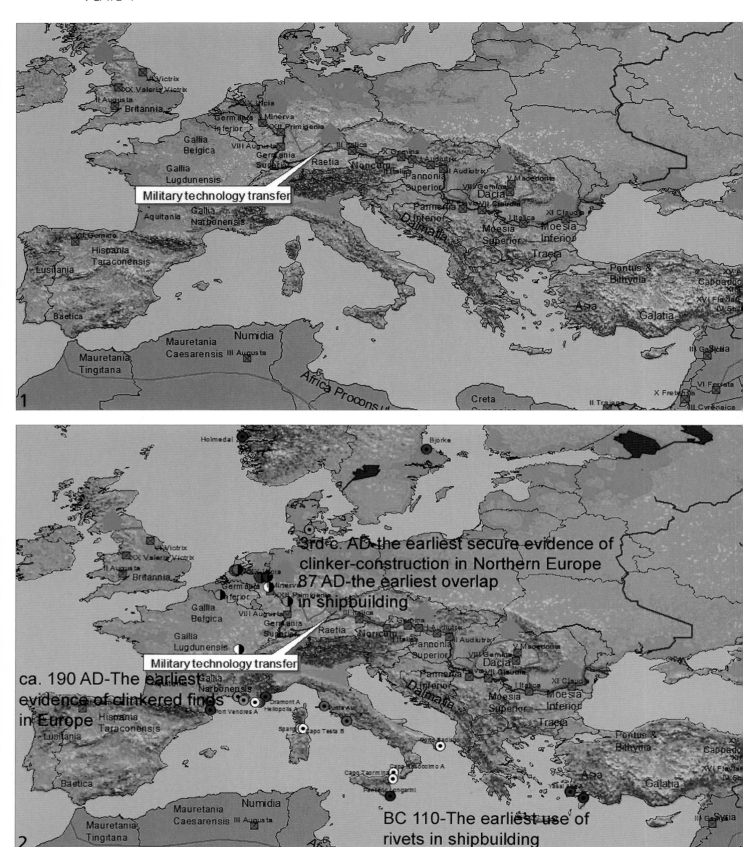

Plate 4   G. Indruszewski: 1 Legion camps along the N. Frontier as transfer centers of military equipment and know-how to Non-Roman Europe (red squares denote castra locations) (USG DEM background). – **2** The chrono-spatial components explaining the genesis of the clinker-built method (dotted white circles denote riveted finds in the Mediterranean) (USG DEM background). – **3** Spatially-referenced finds that display clinker construction method features (USG DEM background).

PLATE 4

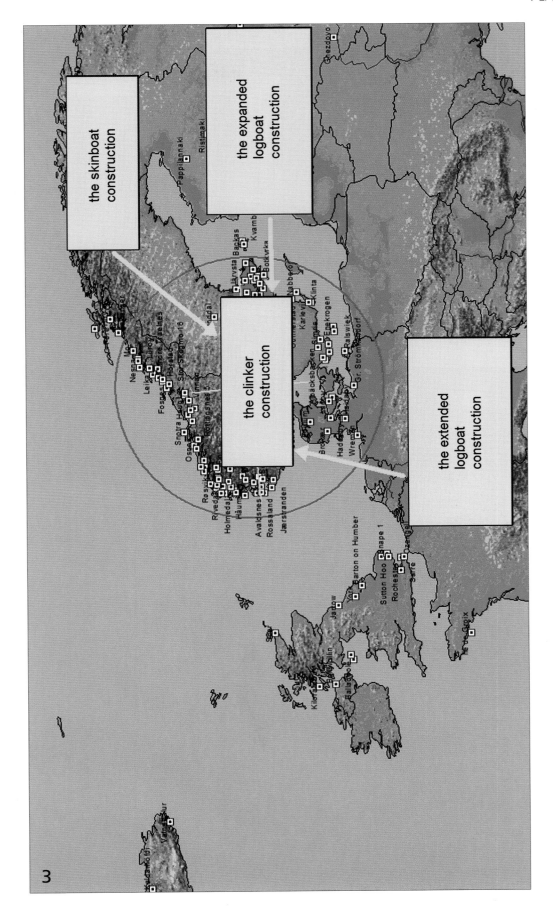

PLATE 5

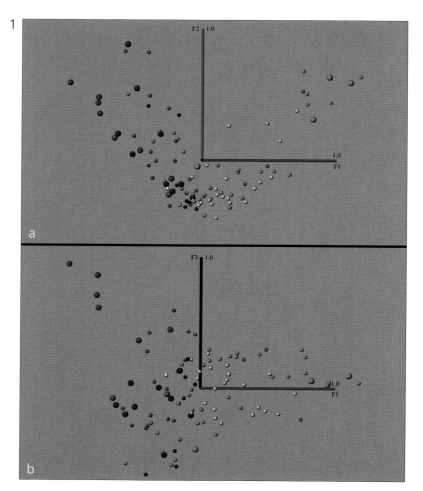

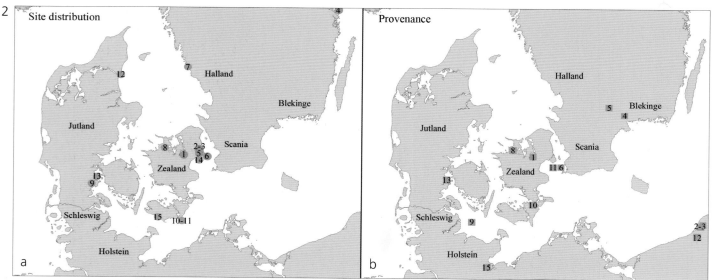

Plate 5   J. Bill: 1 MCA plot of observations along axis F1 and F2 (**a**) and F1 and F3 (**b**). The colour code represents ship type and construction date. Red dots are lapstrake vessels from the 10th c., orange 11th c., yellow 12th c., green 13th c., cyan 14th c., blue 15th c. and purple 16th c. Cogs from the 12th/13th c. are shown with sea green dots, cogs from the 14th c. with dark green ones. Barges from the 12th/13th c. are shown with white dots, those from the 14th c. with black ones. An early and a late barge have achieved the same coordinates in the analysis, resulting in the dappled dot. Brown dots represent carvel-built vessels, which in this material all dates to the 16th c. Dots representing vessels made of wood with known provenance outside S. Scandinavia have been enlarged. The units on the axis are percent of total information. – **2** Distribution maps for the find sites (**a**) and the provenances (**b**) of the traditionally built vessels (red) and the modern built vessels (green).

PLATE 6

European construction types

Legend:

Construction Type 1
Triple-hulled shape
Construction Type 2

Construction Type 2
Hungarian shape
Construction Type 2
Garonne shape
Construction Type 3

single boat mills / individual unusual shapes

0   100   200   300   400   500 km

Plate 6 D. Gräf: Distribution of construction types.